READING MODERN FICTION

REVISED EDITION

READING

MODERN

FICTION REVISED EDITION

29 STORIES WITH STUDY AIDS

SELECTED AND EDITED BY

WINIFRED LYNSKEY

DEPARTMENT OF ENGLISH
PURDUE UNIVERSITY

CHARLES SCRIBNER'S SONS

NEW YORK

LIBRARY OF CONGRESS CATALOG CARD NUMBER 57-7588

A-4.57[H]

ACKNOWLEDGMENTS

Specific acknowledgment for the use of stories in copyright is given on the first page of each story.

To Harcourt, Brace and Company for the quotation on page 208 from the story "The Machine Stops" by E. M. Forster in *The Eternal Moment*, copyright 1928.

To New Directions for the quotation on page 321 from the essay "Escape from Father" by F. J. Hoffman, and the quotation on page 321 from the essay "The Objective Depiction of Absurdity" by Claude-Edmonde Magny, both essays appearing in *The Kafka Problem*, edited by Angel Flores, copyright 1946.

To the Oxford University Press for the quotation on page 321 from *Kafka: His Mind and Art* by Charles Neider, copyright 1949.

To Professor Albert Guérard and *College English* for the quotation on page 320.

To Alfred A. Knopf, Inc., for the quotations on pages 370, 371 and 372 from the essay "Schopenhauer" by Thomas Mann in *Essays of Three Decades*, translated by H. T. Lowe-Porter, copyright 1947 and for the quotations from the preface by Miss Elizabeth Bowen in *Ivy Gripped the Steps*, copyright 1948.

The quotation on page 239 from "Daniel Boone" is from *A Book of Americans*, published by Rinehart & Company, Inc. Copyright, 1933, by Rosemary and Stephen Vincent Benét.

TO MY MOTHER AND FATHER

PREFACE

THE AIM of this book is threefold: to assemble a group of stories varying widely in theme and in form; to present the best modern writers of short fiction, both American and foreign; to give students stories they can enjoy. If we wish students to read good fiction outside the classroom, it seems witless to choose for their introduction to fiction stories which merely repel or bewilder them. The principle of enjoyment has been active, therefore, in the selection.

In the organization of this book, schematization has been avoided. Schematization is essentially artificial; it erects a barrier between the student and the story; and it works harm to the stories it rigidly classifies. Henry James protested long ago against setting up artificial frontiers in the technique of fiction. Any good passage of description, he remarked, is narrative in its intention, and any good passage of dialogue is descriptive. Does not character determine action or incident? Does not action or incident illustrate character?

James asked these questions about the novel, but his comments have value for all fiction. They are especially pertinent today because of the many existing schemes for classifying short stories. How, indeed, does one separate character, action, symbol, and theme in a short story in order to classify? James contended that the only classification he could understand was the division of stories into those which had life and those which had not. It is hoped that the stories in this book can be classified as living.

The study aids which accompany the book are not to be regarded as dogmatic interpretations of the stories. They are intended primarily to serve the student by directing his attention to details whose significance he might otherwise miss. When a student has learned, in Browning's phrase, that in good fiction a detail "means intensely," he is on his way to becoming a good reader. The study aids combine clue and question, as in a natural classroom discussion, and are specifically designed not to give the story away in advance of the reading. For nine of the more complex stories, the study aids have been developed in some detail. The book also contains three analyses: one, long and philosophical; two, short and simple.

The revised edition of this anthology has sought to preserve the spirit and purpose of the original edition. The simplicity of the organization, retained in the revised edition, gives the teacher freedom. It permits him to group the stories according to the purposes and abilities of a given class. He may wish to present first the function of plot through "The Outstation" and "The Hands of Mr. Ottermole." He may then undertake to show how the theme of a story is revealed through character in "The Valiant Woman," "Paul's Case," and "First Confession;" through symbol in "First Love," and "The Man Who Missed the Bus." He may wish to group "Mario and the Magician," "The Secret Sharer," and "The Bench of Desolation," and teach these stories as modern allegories. Or he may prefer to teach "Mario and the Magician," as an indictment of dictatorship when he presents some of the stories dealing with social problems: "Dry September," "Paul's Case," "The New Villa," and "The Passion of Lance Corporal Hawkins." He may wish to illustrate the function and power of irony through "They Weren't Going to Die" and "The Blue Hotel" or compare "The Snows of Kilimanjaro" and "The Second Death" as naturalistic and mystical studies of death. The teacher may thus organize his course according to his own plan.

I have received a good deal of counsel and assistance in the preparation of this book. I am indebted to many people: to Professor Joe Lee Davis of the University of Michigan for his criticism and advice; to many members of the Department of English of Purdue University for their suggestions, encouragement, and wisdom; to the Purdue Library staff: John Moriarty, director, and his assistants: Esther Schlundt, Margaret Sullivan, Eleanore Cammack, Mrs. Richard Crowder, and others; to Mrs. Ethel M. Hancock and Mrs. Jennie Bishop, who prepared the manuscript; to Mrs. Virgil Lokke, Mrs. Harold H. Watts, and Mrs. Bessie Mason, who read proof; and to Mr. T. J. B. Walsh of Charles Scribner's Sons for his unfailing kindliness and assistance.

My thanks are due also to the authors and publishers who generously gave me permission to reproduce copyrighted stories. Individual acknowledgments are made in the footnotes accompanying each story.

W. L.

CONTENTS

A TOOTH FOR PAUL REVERE

BY STEPHEN VINCENT BENÉT

STEPHEN VINCENT BENÉT (1898–1943), a distinguished novelist, poet, and writer of short stories, was born in Pennsylvania. He graduated from Yale in 1919 and received a Guggenheim award in 1926. *John Brown's Body*, a long narrative poem, won the Pulitzer Prize in 1929. Many of his short stories are contained in *Selected Works*, published in 1942.

SOME say it all happened because of Hancock and Adams (said the old man, pulling at his pipe), and some put it back to the Stamp Act and before. Then there's some hold out for Paul Revere and his little silver box. But the way I heard it, it broke loose because of Lige Butterwick and his tooth.

What's that? Why, the American Revolution, of course. What else would I be talking about? Well, your story about the land down South that they had to plough with alligators reminded me.

No, this is a true story—or at least that's how I heard it told. My great-aunt was a Butterwick and I heard it from her. And, every now and then, she'd write it out and want to get it put in the history books. But they'd always put her off with some trifling sort of excuse. Till, finally, she got her dander up and wrote direct to the President of the United States. Well, no, he didn't answer himself exactly—the President's apt to be a pretty busy man. But the letter said he'd received her interesting communication and thanked her for it, so that shows you. We've got it framed, in the trailer—the ink's a little faded, but you can make out the man's name who signed it. It's either Bowers or Thorpe and he wrote a very nice hand.

A TOOTH FOR PAUL REVERE   From *Selected Works of Stephen Vincent Benét*, published by Rinehart & Company, Inc. Copyright, 1937, by Stephen Vincent Benét.

You see, my great-aunt, she wasn't very respectful to the kind of history that does get into the books. What she liked was the queer corners of it and the tales that get handed down in families. Take Paul Revere, for instance—all most folks think about, with him, is his riding a horse. But when she talked about Paul Revere—why, you could just see him in his shop, brewing the American Revolution in a silver teapot and waiting for it to settle. Oh yes, he was a silversmith by trade—but she claimed he was something more. She claimed there was a kind of magic in that quick, skillful hand of his—and that he was one of the kind of folks that can see just a little bit farther into a millstone than most. But it was when she got to Lige Butterwick that she really turned herself loose.

For she claimed that it took all sorts to make a country—and that meant the dumb ones, too. I don't mean ijits or nincompoops—just the ordinary folks that live along from day to day. And that day may be a notable day in history—but it's just Tuesday to them, till they read all about it in the papers. Oh, the heroes and the great men—they can plan and contrive and see ahead. But it isn't till the Lige Butterwicks get stirred up that things really start to happen. Or so she claimed. And the way that they do get stirred up is often curious, as she'd tell this story to prove.

For, now you take Lige Butterwick—and, before his tooth started aching, he was just like you and me. He lived on a farm about eight miles from Lexington, Massachusetts, and he was a peaceable man. It was troubled times in the American colonies, what with British warships in Boston Harbor and British soldiers in Boston and Sons of Liberty hooting the British soldiers—not to speak of Boston tea parties and such. But Lige Butterwick, he worked his farm and didn't pay much attention. There's lots of people like that, even in troubled times.

When he went into town, to be sure, there was high talk at the tavern. But he bought his goods and came home again—he had ideas about politics, but he didn't talk about them much. He had a good farm and it kept him busy—he had a wife and five children and they kept him humping. The young folks could argue about King George and Sam Adams—he wondered how the corn was going to stand that year. Now and then, if somebody said that this and that was a burning shame, he'd allow as how it might be, just to be neighborly. But, inside, he was wondering whether next year he mightn't make an experiment and plant the west field in rye.

Well, everything went along for him the way that it does for most folks with good years and bad years, till one April morning, in 1775, he woke up with a toothache. Being the kind of man he was, he didn't pay much attention to it at first. But he mentioned it that evening, at supper, and his wife got a bag of hot salt for him. He held it to his face and it seemed to ease him, but he couldn't hold it there all night, and, next morning, the tooth hurt worse than ever.

Well, he stood it the next day and the next, but it didn't improve any.

He tried tansy tea and other remedies—he tried tying a string to it and having his wife slam the door. But, when it came to the pinch, he couldn't quite do it. So, finally, he took the horse and rode into Lexington town to have it seen to. Mrs. Butterwick made him—she said it might be an expense, but anything was better than having him act as if he wanted to kick the cat across the room every time she put her feet down hard.

When he got into Lexington, he noticed that folks there seemed kind of excited. There was a lot of talk about muskets and powder and a couple of men called Hancock and Adams who were staying at Parson Clarke's. But Lige Butterwick had his own business to attend to—and, besides, his tooth was jumping so he wasn't in any mood for conversation. He set off for the local barber's, as being the likeliest man he knew to pull a tooth.

The barber took one look at it and shook his head.

"I can pull her, Lige," he said. "Oh, I can pull her, all right. But she's got long roots and strong roots and she's going to leave an awful gap when she's gone. Now, what you really need," he said, kind of excited, for he was one of those perky little men who's always interested in the latest notion, "what you really need—though it's taking away my business —is one of these-here artificial teeth to go in the hole."

"Artificial teeth!" said Lige. "It's flying in the face of Nature!"

The barber shook his head. "No, Lige," he said, "that's where you're wrong. Artificial teeth is all the go these days, and Lexington ought to keep up with the times. It would do me good to see you with an artificial tooth—it would so."

"Well, it might do *you* good," said Lige, rather crossly, for his tooth was jumping, "but, supposing I did want one—how in tunket will I get one in Lexington?"

"Now you just leave that to me," said the barber, all excited, and he started to rummage around. "You'll have to go to Boston for it, but I know just the man." He was one of those men who can always tell you where to go and it's usually wrong. "See here," he went on. "There's a fellow called Revere in Boston that fixes them and they say he's a boss workman. Just take a look at this prospectus"—and he started to read from a paper: " 'Whereas many persons are so unfortunate as to lose their fore-teeth'— that's you, Lige—'to their great detriment, not only in looks but in speaking, both in public and private, this is to inform all such that they may have them replaced by artificial ones'—see?—'that look as well as the natural and answer the end of speaking to all intents'—and then he's got his name—Paul Revere, goldsmith, near the head of Dr. Clarke's wharf, Boston."

"Sounds well enough," said Lige, "but what's it going to cost?"

"Oh, I know Revere," said the barber, swelling up like a robin. "Comes

through here pretty often, as a matter of fact. And he's a decent fellow,
if he is a pretty big bug in the Sons of Liberty. You just mention my
name."

"Well, it's something I hadn't thought of," said Lige, as his tooth gave
another red-hot jounce, "but in for a penny, in for a pound. I've missed a
day's work already and that tooth's got to come out before I go stark,
staring mad. But what sort of man is this Revere, anyway?"

"Oh, he's a regular wizard!" said the barber. "A regular wizard with
his tools."

"Wizard!" said Lige. "Well, I don't know about wizards. But if he can
fix my tooth I'll call him one."

"You'll never regret it," said the barber—and that's the way folks always
talk when they're sending someone else to the dentist. So Lige Butterwick
got on his horse again and started out for Boston. A couple of people
shouted at him as he rode down the street, but he didn't pay any attention. And, going by Parson Clarke's, he caught a glimpse of two men
talking in the Parson's front room. One was a tallish, handsomish man in
pretty fine clothes and the other was shorter and untidy, with a kind of
bulldog face. But they were strangers to him and he didn't really notice
them—just rode ahead.

II

But as soon as he got into Boston he started to feel queer—and it wasn't
only his tooth. He hadn't been there in four years and he'd expected to
find it changed, but it wasn't that. It was a clear enough day and yet he
kept feeling there was thunder in the air. There'd be knots of people,
talking and arguing, on street corners, and then, when you got closer to
them, they'd kind of melt away. Or, if they stayed, they'd look at you,
out of the corners of their eyes. And there, in the Port of Boston, were
the British warships, black and grim. He'd known they'd be there, of
course, but it was different, seeing them. It made him feel queer to see
their guns pointed at the town. He'd known there was trouble and dispute,
in Boston, but the knowledge had passed over him like rain and hail. But
now here he was in the middle of it—and it smelt like earthquake weather.
He couldn't make head or tail of it, but he wanted to be home.

All the same, he'd come to get his tooth fixed, and, being New England,
he was bound to do it. But first he stopped at a tavern for a bite and a
sup, for it was long past his dinnertime. And there, it seemed to him,
things got even more curious.

"Nice weather we're having, these days," he said, in a friendly way,
to the barkeep.

"It's bitter weather for Boston," said the barkeep, in an unfriendly
voice, and a sort of low growl went up from the boys at the back of the
room and every eye fixed on Lige.

Well, that didn't help the toothache any, but, being a sociable person, Lige kept on.

"May be, for Boston," he said, "but out in the country we'd call it good planting weather."

The barkeep stared at him hard.

"I guess I was mistaken in you," he said. "It *is* good planting weather— for some kinds of trees."

"And what kind of trees were you thinking of?" said a sharp-faced man at Lige's left and squeezed his shoulder.

"There's trees and trees, you know," said a red-faced man at Lige's right, and gave him a dig in the ribs.

"Well, now that you ask me—" said Lige, but he couldn't even finish before the red-faced man dug him hard in the ribs again.

"The liberty tree!" said the red-faced man. "And may it soon be watered in the blood of tyrants!"

"The royal oak of England!" said the sharp-faced man. "And God save King George and loyalty!"

Well, with that it seemed to Lige Butterwick as if the whole tavern kind of riz up at him. He was kicked and pummeled and mauled and thrown into a corner and yanked out of it again, with the red-faced man and the sharp-faced man and all the rest of them dancing quadrilles over his prostrate form. Till, finally, he found himself out in the street with half his coat gone galley-west.

"Well," said Lige to himself, "I always heard city folks were crazy. But politics must be getting serious in these American colonies when they start fighting about trees!"

Then he saw the sharp-faced man was beside him, trying to shake his hand. He noticed with some pleasure that the sharp-faced man had the beginnings of a beautiful black eye.

"Nobly done, friend," said the sharp-faced man, "and I'm glad to find another true-hearted loyalist in this pestilent, rebellious city."

"Well, I don't know as I quite agree with you about that," said Lige. "But I came here to get my tooth fixed, not to talk politics. And as long as you've spoken so pleasant, I wonder if you could help me out. You see, I'm from Lexington way—and I'm looking for a fellow named Paul Revere—"

"Paul Revere!" said the sharp-faced man, as if the name hit him like a bullet. Then he began to smile again—not a pleasant smile.

"Oh, it's Paul Revere you want, my worthy and ingenuous friend from the country," he said. "Well, I'll tell you how to find him. You go up to the first British soldier you see and ask the way. But you better give the password first."

"Password?" said Lige Butterwick, scratching his ear.

"Yes," said the sharp-faced man, and his smile got wider. "You say to that British soldier, 'Any lobsters for sale today?' Then you ask about Revere."

"But why do I talk about lobsters first?" said Lige Butterwick, kind of stubborn.

"Well, you see," said the sharp-faced man, "the British soldiers wear red coats. So they like being asked about lobsters. Try it and see." And he went away, with his shoulders shaking.

Well, that seemed queer to Lige Butterwick, but no queerer than the other things that had happened that day. All the same, he didn't quite trust the sharp-faced man, so he took care not to come too close to the British patrol when he asked them about the lobsters. And it was lucky he did, for no sooner were the words out of his mouth than the British soldiers took after him and chased him clear down to the wharves before he could get away. At that, he only managed it by hiding in an empty tar-barrel, and when he got out he was certainly a sight for sore eyes.

"Well, I guess that couldn't have been the right password," he said to himself, kind of grimly, as he tried to rub off some of the tar. "All the same, I don't think soldiers ought to act like that when you ask them a civil question. But, city folks or soldiers, they can't make a fool out of me. I came here to get my tooth fixed and get it fixed I will, if I have to surprise the whole British Empire to do it."

And just then he saw a sign on a shop at the end of the wharf. And, according to my great-aunt, this was what was on the sign. It said "PAUL REVERE, SILVERSMITH" at the top, and then, under it, in smaller letters, "Large and small bells cast to order, engraving and printing done in job lots, artificial teeth sculptured and copper boilers mended, all branches of goldsmith and silversmith work and revolutions put up to take out. Express Service, Tuesdays and Fridays, to Lexington, Concord and Points West."

"Well," said Lige Butterwick, "kind of a Jack-of-all-trades. Now maybe I can get my tooth fixed." And he marched up to the door.

III

Paul Revere was behind the counter when Lige came in, turning a silver bowl over and over in his hands. A man of forty-odd he was, with a quick, keen face and snapping eyes. He was wearing Boston clothes, but there was a French look about him—for his father was Apollos Rivoire from the island of Guernsey, and good French Huguenot stock. They'd changed the name to Revere when they crossed the water.

It wasn't such a big shop, but it had silver pieces in it that people have paid thousands for, since. And the silver pieces weren't all. There were prints and engravings of the Port of Boston and caricatures of the British and all sorts of goldsmith work, more than you could put a name to. It was a crowded place, but shipshape. And Paul Revere moved about it, quick and keen, with his eyes full of life and hot temper—the kind of man who knows what he wants to do and does it the next minute.

There were quite a few customers there when Lige Butterwick first came in—so he sort of scrooged back in a corner and waited his chance. For one thing, after the queer sign and the barber's calling him a wizard, he wanted to be sure about this fellow, Revere, and see what kind of customers came to his shop.

Well, there was a woman who wanted a christening mug for a baby and a man who wanted a print of the Boston Massacre. And then there was a fellow who passed Revere some sort of message, under cover—Lige caught the whisper, "powder" and "Sons of Liberty," though he couldn't make out the rest. And, finally, there was a very fine silk-dressed lady who seemed to be giving Revere considerable trouble. Lige peeked at her round the corner of his chair, and, somehow or other, she reminded him of a turkey-gobbler, especially the strut.

She was complaining about some silver that Paul Revere had made for her—expensive silver it must have been. And "Oh, Master Revere, I'm so disappointed!" she was saying. "When I took the things from the box, I could just have cried!"

Revere drew himself up a little at that, Lige noticed, but his voice was pleasant.

"It is I who am disappointed, madam," he said, with a little bow. "But what was the trouble? It must have been carelessly packed. Was it badly dented? I'll speak to my boy."

"Oh no, it wasn't dented," said the turkey-gobbler lady. "But I wanted a really impressive silver service—something I can use when the Governor comes to dinner with us. I certainly *paid* for the best. And what have you given me?"

Lige waited to hear what Paul Revere would say. When he spoke, his voice was stiff.

"I have given you the best work of which I am capable, madam," he said. "It was in my hands for six months—and I think they are skillful hands."

"Oh," said the woman, and rustled her skirts. "I know you're a competent artisan, Master Revere—"

"Silversmith, if you please—" said Paul Revere, and the woman rustled again.

"Well, I don't care what you call it," she said, and then you could see her fine accent was put on like her fine clothes. "But I know I wanted a real service—something I could show my friends. And what have you given me? Oh, it's silver, if you choose. But it's just as plain and simple as a picket fence!"

Revere looked at her for a moment and Lige Butterwick thought he'd explode.

"Simple?" he said. "And plain? You pay me high compliments, madam!"

"Compliments indeed!" said the woman, and now she was getting furious. "I'm sending it back tomorrow! Why, there isn't as much as a lion or a unicorn on the cream jug. And I told you I wanted the sugar bowl covered with silver grapes! But you've given me something as bare as the hills of New England! And I won't stand it, I tell you! I'll send to England instead."

Revere puffed his cheeks and blew, but his eyes were dangerous.

"Send away, madam," he said. "We're making new things in this country—new men—new silver—perhaps, who knows, a new nation. Plain, simple, bare as the hills and rocks of New England—graceful as the boughs of her elm trees—if my silver were only like that indeed! But that is what I wish to make it. And, as for you, madam,"—he stepped toward her like a cat,—"with your lions and unicorns and grape leaves and your nonsense of bad ornament done by bad silversmiths—your imported bad taste and your imported British manners—puff!" And he blew at her, just the way you blow at a turkey-gobbler, till she fairly picked up her fine silk skirts and ran. Revere watched her out of the door and turned back, shaking his head.

"William!" he called to the boy who helped him in the shop. "Put up the shutters—we're closing for the day. And William—no word yet from Dr. Warren?"

"Not yet, sir," said the boy, and started to put up the shutters. Then Lige Butterwick thought it was about time to make his presence known.

So he coughed, and Paul Revere whirled and Lige Butterwick felt those quick, keen eyes boring into his. He wasn't exactly afraid of them, for he was stubborn himself, but he knew this was an unexpected kind of man.

"Well, my friend," said Revere, impatiently, "and who in the world are you?"

"Well, Mr. Revere," said Lige Butterwick. "It is Mr. Revere, isn't it? It's kind of a long story. But, closing or not, you've got to listen to me. The barber told me so."

"The barber!" said Revere, kind of dumbfounded.

"Uh-huh," said Lige, and opened his mouth. "You see, it's my tooth."

"Tooth!" said Revere, and stared at him as if they were both crazy. "You'd better begin at the beginning. But wait a minute. You don't talk like a Boston man. Where do you come from?"

"Oh, around Lexington way," said Lige. "And, you see—"

But the mention of Lexington seemed to throw Revere into a regular excitement. He fairly shook Lige by the shoulders.

"Lexington!" he said. "Were you there this morning?"

"Of course I was," said Lige. "That's where the barber I told you about—"

"Never mind the barber!" said Revere. "Were Mr. Hancock and Mr. Adams still at Parson Clarke's?"

"Well, they might have been, for all I know," said Lige. "But I couldn't say."

"Great heaven!" said Revere. "Is there a man in the American colonies who doesn't know Mr. Hancock and Mr. Adams?"

"There seems to be me," said Lige. "But, speaking of strangers—there *was* two of them staying at the parsonage, when I rode past. One was a handsomish man and the other looked more like a bulldog—"

"Hancock and Adams!" said Revere. "So they are still there." He took a turn or two up and down the room. "And the British ready to march!" he muttered to himself. "Did you see many soldiers as you came to my shop, Mr. Butterwick?"

"See them?" said Lige. "They chased me into a tar-barrel. And there was a whole passel of them up by the Common with guns and flags. Looked as if they meant business."

Revere took his hand and pumped it up and down.

"Thank you, Mr. Butterwick," he said. "You're a shrewd observer. **And** you have done me—and the colonies—an invaluable service."

"Well, that's nice to know," said Lige. "But, speaking about this tooth of mine—"

Revere looked at him and laughed, while his eyes crinkled.

"You're a stubborn man, Mr. Butterwick," he said. "All the better. I like stubborn men. I wish we had more of them. Well, one good turn deserves another—you've helped me and I'll do my best to help you. I've made artificial teeth—but drawing them is hardly my trade. All the same, I'll do what I can for you."

So Lige sat down in a chair and opened his mouth.

"Whew!" said Revere, with his eyes dancing. His voice grew solemn. "Mr. Butterwick," he said, "it seems to be a compound, agglutinated infraction of the upper molar. I'm afraid I can't do anything about it tonight."

"But—" said Lige.

"But here's a draught—that will ease the pain for a while," said Revere, and poured some medicine into a cup. "Drink!" he said, and Lige drank. The draught was red and spicy, with a queer, sleepy taste, but pungent. It wasn't like anything Lige had ever tasted before, but he noticed it eased the pain.

"There," said Revere. "And now you go to a tavern and get a good night's rest. Come back to see me in the morning—I'll find a tooth-drawer for you, if I'm here. And—oh yes—you'd better have some liniment."

He started to rummage in a big cupboard at the back of the shop. It was dark now, with the end of day and the shutters up, and whether it was the tooth, or the tiredness, or the draught Paul Revere had given him, Lige began to feel a little queer. There was a humming in his head and a lightness in his feet. He got up and stood looking over Paul Revere's shoulder, and it seemed to him that things moved and scampered in that cupboard in a curious way, as Revere's quick fingers took down this box and that. And the shop was full of shadows and murmurings.

"It's a queer kind of shop you've got here, Mr. Revere," he said, glad to hear the sound of his own voice.

"Well, some people think so," said Revere—and that time Lige was almost sure he saw something move in the cupboard. He coughed. "Say—what's in that little bottle?" he said, to keep his mind steady.

"That?" said Paul Revere, with a smile, and held the bottle up. "Oh, that's a little chemical experiment of mine. I call it Essence of Boston. But there's a good deal of East Wind in it."

"Essence of Boston," said Lige, with his eyes bulging. "Well, they did say you was a wizard. It's gen-u-wine magic, I suppose?"

"Genuine magic, of course," said Revere, with a chuckle. "And here's the box with your liniment. And here—"

He took down two little boxes—a silver and a pewter one—and placed them on the counter. But Lige's eyes went to the silver one—they were drawn to it, though he couldn't have told you why.

"Pick it up," said Paul Revere, and Lige did so and turned it in his hands. It was a handsome box. He could make out a growing tree and an eagle fighting a lion. "It's mighty pretty work," he said.

"It's my own design," said Paul Revere. "See the stars around the edge—thirteen of them? You could make a very pretty design with stars—for a new country, say—if you wanted to—I've sometimes thought of it."

"But what's in it?" said Lige.

"What's in it?" said Paul Revere, and his voice was light but steely. "Why, what's in the air around us? Gunpowder and war and the making of a new nation. But the time isn't quite ripe yet—not quite ripe."

"You mean," said Lige, and he looked at the box very respectful, "that this-here revolution folks keep talking about—"

"Yes," said Paul Revere, and he was about to go on. But just then his boy ran in, with a letter in his hand.

"Master!" he said. "A message from Dr. Warren!"

IV

Well, with that Revere started moving, and, when he started to move, he moved fast. He was calling for his riding boots in one breath and telling Lige Butterwick to come back tomorrow in another—and, what with all the bustle and confusion, Lige Butterwick nearly went off without his liniment after all. But he grabbed up a box from the counter, just as Revere was practically shoving him out of the door—and it wasn't till he'd got to his tavern and gone to bed for the night that he found out he'd taken the wrong box.

He found it out then because, when he went to bed, he couldn't get to sleep. It wasn't his tooth that bothered him—that had settled to a kind of dull ache and he could have slept through that. But his mind kept going over all the events of the day—the two folks he'd seen at Parson Clarke's and being chased by the British and what Revere had said to the turkey-gobbler woman—till he couldn't get any peace. He could feel something stirring in him, though he didn't know what it was.

" 'Tain't right to have soldiers chase a fellow down the street," he said to himself. "And 'tain't right to have people like that woman run down New England. No, it ain't. Oh me—I better look for that liniment of Mr. Revere's."

So he got up from his bed and went over and found his coat. Then he reached his hand in the pocket and pulled out the silver box.

Well, at first he was so flustrated that he didn't know rightly what to do. For here, as well as he could remember it, was gunpowder and war and the makings of a new nation—the revolution itself, shut up in a silver box by Paul Revere. He mightn't have believed there could be such things before he came to Boston. But now he did.

The draught was still humming in his head, and his legs felt a mite wobbly. But, being human, he was curious. "Now, I wonder what *is* inside that box," he said.

He shook the box and handled it, but that seemed to make it warmer, as if there was something alive inside it, so he stopped that mighty quick. Then he looked all over it for a keyhole, but here wasn't any keyhole, and, if there had been, he didn't have a key.

Then he put his ear to the box and listened hard. And it seemed to him that he heard, very tiny and far away, inside the box, the rolling fire of thousands of tiny muskets and the tiny, far-away cheers of many men. "Hold your fire!" he heard a voice say. "Don't fire till you're fired on—but, if they want a war, let it begin here!" And then there was a rolling of drums and a squeal of fifes. It was small, still, and far away, but it made him shake all over, for he knew he was listening to something in the future—and something that he didn't have a right to hear. He sat down on the edge of his bed, with the box in his hands.

"Now, what am I going to do with this?" he said. "It's too big a job for one man."

Well, he thought, kind of scared, of going down to the river and throwing the box in, but, when he thought of doing it, he knew he couldn't. Then he thought of his farm near Lexington and the peaceful days. Once the revolution was out of the box, there'd be an end to that. But then he remembered what Revere had said when he was talking with the woman about the silver—the thing about building a new country and building it clean and plain. "Why, I'm not a Britisher," he thought. "I'm a New Englander. And maybe there's something beyond that—something people like Hancock and Adams know about. And, if it has to come with a revolution—well, I guess it has to come. We can't stay Britishers forever, here in this country."

He listened to the box again, and now there wasn't any shooting in it—just a queer tune played on a fife. He didn't know the name of the tune, but it lifted his heart.

He got up, sort of slow and heavy. "I guess I'll have to take this back to Paul Revere," he said.

Well, the first place he went was Dr. Warren's, having heard Revere mention it, but he didn't get much satisfaction there. It took quite a while to convince them that he wasn't a spy, and, when he did, all they'd tell him was that Revere had gone over the river to Charlestown. So he went down to the water front to look for a boat. And the first person he met was a very angry woman.

"No," she said, "you don't get any boats from me. There was a crazy man along here an hour ago and he wanted a boat, too, and my husband was crazy enough to take him. And then, do you know what he did?"

"No, mam," said Lige Butterwick.

"He made my husband take my best petticoat to muffle the oars so they wouldn't make a splash when they went past that Britisher ship," she said, pointing out where the man-of-war *Somerset* lay at anchor. "My best petticoat, I tell you! And when my husband comes back he'll get a piece of my mind!"

"Was his name Revere?" said Lige Butterwick. "Was he a man of forty-odd, keen-looking and kind of Frenchy?"

"I don't know what his right name is," said the woman, "but his name's mud with me. My best petticoat tore in strips and swimming in that nasty river!" And that was all he could get out of her.

All the same, he managed to get a boat at last—the story doesn't say how—and row across the river. The tide was at young flood and the moonlight bright on the water, and he passed under the shadow of the *Somerset*, right where Revere had passed. When he got to the Charlestown side, he could see the lanterns in North Church, though he didn't know what they signified. Then he told the folks at Charlestown he had news for Revere and they got him a horse and so he started to ride. And, all the while, the silver box was burning his pocket.

Well, he lost his way more or less, as you well might in the darkness, and it was dawn when he came into Lexington by a side road. The dawn in that country's pretty, with the dew still on the grass. But he wasn't looking at the dawn. He was feeling the box burn his pocket and thinking hard.

Then, all of a sudden, he reined up his tired horse. For there, on the side road, were two men carrying a trunk—and one of them was Paul Revere.

They looked at each other and Lige began to grin. For Revere was just as dirty and mud-splashed as he was—he'd warned Hancock and Adams all right, but then, on his way to Concord, he'd got caught by the British and turned loose again. So he'd gone back to Lexington to see how things were there—and now he and the other fellow were saving a trunk of papers that Hancock had left behind, so they wouldn't fall into the hands of the British.

Lige swung off his horse. "Well, Mr. Revere," he said, "you see, I'm on time for that little appointment about my tooth. And, by the way, I've got something for you." He took the box from his pocket. And then he looked over toward Lexington Green and caught his breath. For, on the Green, there was a little line of Minute Men—neighbors of his, as he knew—and, in front of them, the British regulars. And, even as he looked, there was the sound of a gunshot, and, suddenly, smoke wrapped the front of the British line and he heard them shout as they ran forward.

Lige Butterwick took the silver box and stamped on it with his heel. And with that the box broke open—and there was a dazzle in his eyes for a moment and a noise of men shouting—and then it was gone.

"Do you know what you've done?" said Revere. "You've let out the American Revolution!"

"Well," said Lige Butterwick, "I guess it was about time. And I guess I'd better be going home, now. I've got a gun on the wall there. And I'll need it."

"But what about your tooth?" said Paul Revere.

"Oh, a tooth's a tooth," said Lige Butterwick. "But a country's a country. And, anyhow, it's stopped aching."

All the same, they say Paul Revere made a silver tooth for him, after the war. But my great-aunt wasn't quite sure of it, so I won't vouch for that.

COMMENT AND QUESTION

1. "A Tooth for Paul Revere" is part history, part folk tale, part fantasy. But its theme is unified. The theme is expressed in the sentence: "But it isn't till the Lige Butterwicks get stirred up that things really start to happen." In other words, how does a farmer become an embattled farmer?

2. The background of the American Revolution is laid before the reader. What well-known arguments are expressed in the following episodes?
   a. The fight in the tavern
   b. The encounter with the redcoats
   c. The customers in Revere's shop

3. Paul Revere is given a fairly complete biography in this story. He is accented, however, in his rôle as a revolutionary. Nevertheless, Lige will perform a service for the Revolution better than Revere can. But Revere is aware of the separate rôles.

    a. How does Lige become a revolutionary in his first few words with Revere?

    b. What is the medicine called Essence of Boston?

    c. What is the meaning of the "shadows and murmurings" in Revere's shop?

4. By altering the normal perspective, fantasy gives a sharper meaning to an idea. The silver box is part of the fantasy here. That Revere would leave the box behind seems incredible at first. But what does the box contain? Why must Lige take it *to* Revere?

Why is it significant that Lige follows the precise route taken by Revere on his historic ride? When Lige reaches Charlestown, he announces that he has news for Revere. Since Revere already knows that the British are coming, what can the news be?

What is important about the way in which Lige finally opens the box?

THE MAN WHO MISSED
THE BUS

BY STELLA BENSON

STELLA BENSON (1892–1933) was born in
England but travelled widely in France,
Germany, Switzerland, and America. For a
number of years she lived in China, where
her husband, Mr. O'Gorman Anderson, was
an officer in the Chinese Customs Service. She
has written essays, novels, and poetry. The
best of her short stories may be found in *Collected Short Stories* (1936).

M R. ROBINSON's temper was quite sore by the time he reached St.
Pierre. The two irritations that most surely found the weak places in his
nervous defenses were noise and light in his eyes. And, as he told Monsieur Dupont, the proprietor of Les Trois Moineaux at St. Pierre, "If
there is one thing, monsieur, that is offensive—essentially offensive—that
is to say, a danger in itself—I mean to say noise doesn't have to have a
meaning. . . . What I mean is, monsieur, that noise—"

"*Numéro trente*," said Monsieur Dupont to the chasseur.

Mr. Robinson always had to explain things very thoroughly in order
to make people really appreciate the force of what he had to say; and
even then it was a hard task to get them to acknowledge receipt, so to
speak, of his message. But he was a humble man, and he accounted for
the atmosphere of unanswered and unfinished remarks in which he lived
by admitting that his words were unfortunately always inadequate to
convey to a fellow-mortal the intense interest to be found in the curiosities
of behavior and sensation. His mind was overstocked with by-products of

THE MAN WHO MISSED THE BUS   From *Collected Short Stories* by Stella Benson.
Published by Macmillan & Co., Ltd. of London, 1936. Used with the permission
of Curtis Brown Ltd. of London.

the business of life. He felt that every moment disclosed a new thing worth thinking of among the phenomena that his senses presented to him. Other people, he saw, let these phenomenal moments slip by unanalyzed; but if he had had the words and the courage, he felt, he could have awakened those of his fellow-creatures whom he met from their trance of shallow living. As it was, the relation of his explorations and wonderings sounded, even to his own ears, flat as the telling at breakfast of an ecstatic dream.

What he had meant to say about noise, for instance, had been that noise was *in itself* terrifying and horrible—not as a warning of danger but as a physical assault. Vulgar people treat noise only as a language that *means* something, he would have said, but really noise could not be translated, any more than rape could be translated. There was no such thing as an ugly harmless noise. The noise of an express train approaching and shrieking through a quiet station; the noise of heavy rain sweeping towards one through a forest; the noise of loud concerted laughter at an unheard joke—all benevolent noises if translated into concrete terms, were *in themselves* calamities. All this Mr. Robinson would have thought worth saying to Monsieur Dupont—worth continuing to say until Monsieur Dupont should have confessed to an understanding of his meaning; but as usual the words collapsed as soon as they left Mr. Robinson's lips.

Monsieur Dupont stood in the doorway of Les Trois Moineaux with his back to the light. Mr. Robinson could see the shape of his head set on stooping shoulders, with a little frail fluff of hair beaming round a baldness. He could see the rather crumpled ears with outleaning lobes bulging sharply against the light. But between ear and ear, between bald brow and breast he could see nothing but a black blank against the glare. Mr. Robinson had extremely acute sight—perhaps too acute, as he often wanted to tell people, since this was perhaps why the light in his eyes affected him so painfully.

"If my sight were less acute," he would have said, "I should not mind a glare so much—I mean to say, my eyes are so extremely receptive that they receive too much, or in other words the same cause that makes my eyes so very sensitive is . . ."

But nobody ever leaned forward eagerly and said, "I understand you perfectly, Mr. Robinson, and what you say is most interesting. Your sight includes so much that it cannot exclude excessive light, and this very naturally irritates your nerves, though the same peculiarity accounts for your intense powers of observation." Nobody ever said anything like that, but then, people are so self-engrossed.

Mr. Robinson was not self-engrossed—he was simply extravagantly interested in *things*, not people. For instance, he looked round now, as the chasseur sought in the shadows for his suitcase, and saw the terrace striped by long beams of light—broad flat beams that were strung like yellow sheets from every window and door in the hotel to the trees, tall urns, and tables of the terrace. A murmur of voices enlivened the air, but there were no human creatures in any beam—only blocked dark figures in the shadows—and, in every patch of light, a sleeping dog or cat or two. Dogs and cats lay extended or curled comfortably on the warm uneven paving stones, and Mr. Robinson's perfect sight absorbed the shape of every brown, tortoise-shell, or black marking on their bodies, as a geographer might accept the continents on a new unheard-of globe.

"It's just like geography—the markings on animals," Mr. Robinson had once said to an American who couldn't get away. "What I mean to say is that the markings on a dog or a rabbit have just as much sense as the markings on this world of ours—or in other words the archipelagoes of spots on this pointer puppy are just as importantly isolated from one another as they could be in any Adriatic sea."

But the American had only replied, "Why, no, Mr. Robinson, not half so important; I am taking my wife, with the aid of the American Express Company, to visit the Greek islands this summer; and we shall be sick on the sea and robbed on the land—whereas nobody but a flea ever visits the spots on that puppy, and the flea don't know and don't care a damn what color he bites into." Showing that nobody except Mr. Robinson ever really studied things impersonally.

Mr. Robinson, a very ingenious-minded and sensitive man with plenty of money, was always seeking new places to go to, where he might be a success—or rather, where his unaccountable failures elsewhere might not be known. St. Pierre, he thought, was an excellent venture, although the approach to it had been so trying. As soon as he had heard of it— through reading a short thoughtless sketch by a popular novelist in the *Daily Call*—he had felt hopeful about it. A little Provençal walled town on a hill, looking out over vineyards to the blue Mediterranean; a perfect little hotel—clean and with a wonderful cook—frequented by an interesting few. . . .

"By the time I get downstairs," thought Mr. Robinson as he carefully laid his trousers under the mattress in his room and donned another pair, "the lights will be lighted on the terrace, and I shall be able to see my future friends. I must tell some one about that curious broken reflection in the river Rhone."

He went downstairs and out onto the terrace, where the tinkle of glasses and plates made him feel hungry. He could hear, as he stood in the doorway looking out, one man's voice making a series of jokes in quick succession, each excited pause in his voice being filled by a gust and scrape of general laughter—like waves breaking on a beach with a clatter and then recoiling with a thin, hopeful, lonely sound. "Probably all his jokes are personalities," thought Mr. Robinson, "and, therefore, not essentially

funny. No doubt they are slightly pornographic, at that. When will people
learn how interesting and exciting *things* are? . . ."

A waiter behind him drew out a chair from a table in one of the
squares of light thrown from a window. Mr. Robinson, after sitting down
abstractedly, was just going to call the waiter back to tell him that his
eyes were ultra-sensitive to light and that he could see nothing in that
glare, when a large dog, with the bleached, patched, innocent face of a
circus clown, came and laid its head on his knee. Mr. Robinson could
never bear to disappoint an animal. He attributed to animals all the hot
and cold variations of feeling that he himself habitually experienced,
identifying the complacent fur of the brute with his own thin human
skin. So that when the waiter, coming quietly behind him, put the wine
list into his hand, Mr. Robinson merely said, "Thank you, garçon, but I
never touch alcohol in any form—or, for the matter of that, tobacco either.
In my opinion—" and did not call the rapidly escaping waiter back to
ask him to move his table. The dog's chin was now comfortably pressed
against his knee, and the dog's paw hooked in a pathetically prehensile
way about his ankle.

Mr. Robinson made the best of his position in the dazzle and tried to
look about him. The Trois Moineaux was built just outside the encircling
wall of the tightly corseted little town of St. Pierre and, since St. Pierre
clung to the apex of a conical hill, it followed that the inn terrace jutted
boldly out over a steep, stepped fall of vineyards overhanging the plain.
The plain was very dim now, overlaid by starlit darkness, yet at the edge
of the terrace there was a sense of *view*, and all the occupied tables stood
in a row against the low wall, diluting the food and drink they bore with
starlight and space. The men and women sitting at these tables all had
their faces to the world and their backs to Mr. Robinson. He could not
see a single human face. He had come down too late to secure one of the
outlooking tables, and his place was imprisoned in a web of light under
an olive tree. In the middle of the table, peaches and green grapes were
heaped on a one-legged dish. And on the edge of the dish a caterpillar
waved five-sixths of its length drearily in the air, unable to believe that its
world could really end at this abrupt slippery rim. Mr. Robinson, shading
his eyes from the light, could see every detail of the caterpillar's figure,
and it seemed to him worth many minutes of absorbed attention. Its
color was a pale greenish-fawn, and it had two dark bumps on its brow
by way of eyes.

"How unbearably difficult and lonely its life would seem to us,"
thought Mr. Robinson, leaning intensely over it. "How frightful if by
mistake the merest spark of self-consciousness should get into an insect's
body (an accidental short-circuit in the life current, perhaps), and it should
know itself absolutely alone—appallingly free." He put his finger in the
range of its persistent wavings and watched it crawl with a looping haste

down his fingernail, accepting without question a quite fortuitous salvation from its dilemma. He laid his finger against a leaf, and the caterpillar
disembarked briskly after its journey across alien elements. When it was
gone, Mr. Robinson looked about him, dazed. "My goodness," he thought,
"that caterpillar's face is the only one I have seen tonight!"

The noise of chatter and laughter went up like a kind of smoke from
the flickering creatures at the tables near the edge of the terrace. At each
table the heads and shoulders of men and women leaned together—were
sucked together like flames in a common upward draft. "My dear, she
looked like a . . . Oh, well, if you want to. . . . He's the kind of man
who . . . *No*, my dear, not in my *bedroom*. . . . A rattling good yarn.
. . . Stop me if I've told you this one before. . . ." One man, standing
up a little unsteadily facing the table nearest to Mr. Robinson, made a
speech: ". . . the last time . . . delightful company . . . fair sex . . .
happiest hours of my life . . . mustn't waste your time . . . us mere
men . . . as the Irishman said to the Scotchman when . . . happiest
moments of all my life . . . one minute and I shall be done . . . always
remember the happiest days of all my . . . well, I mustn't keep you . . .
I heard a little story the other day. . . ." And all the time his audience
leaned together round their table, embarrassed, looking away over the
dark plain or murmuring together with bent heads.

The only woman whose face Mr. Robinson might have seen was
shielding her face with her hands and shaking with silent laughter. The
speaker was wavering on his feet very much as the caterpillar had
wavered on its tail, and his wide gestures, clawing the air in search of
the attention of his friends, suggested to Mr. Robinson the caterpillar's
wild gropings for foothold where no foothold was. "Yes," thought Mr.
Robinson, "the caterpillar was *my* host. No other face is turned to me."

However, as he thought this, a man came from a farther table and
stood quite close, under the olive tree, between Mr. Robinson and the
lighted doorway, looking down on him. The man stretched out his hand
to the tree and leaned upon it. A freak of light caught the broad short
hand, walnut-knuckled and brown, crooked over the bough. Mr. Robinson
could not see the man's face at all, but he felt that the visit was friendly.
To conciliate this sympathetic stranger, he would even have talked about
the weather, or made a joke about pretty girls or beer; but he could not
think of anything of that kind to say to a man whose hand, grasping an
olive bough, was all that could be known of him. All that Mr. Robinson
could do for the moment was to wonder what could have sent the man
here. "It could not have been," thought Mr. Robinson humbly, "that he
was attracted by my face, because nobody ever is." And then he began
thinking how one man's loss is nearly always another man's gain, if considered broadly enough. For one to be forsaken, really, means that another
has a new friend.

"This young man," thought Mr. Robinson, gazing at the black outline of the stranger's head, "has probably come here blindly, because of some sudden hurt, some stab, some insult, inflicted by his friends at that table over there—probably by a woman. Perhaps he thinks he has a broken heart (for he has young shoulders). Nothing short of a wound that temporarily robbed him of his social balance could make him do so strange a thing as suddenly to leave his friends and come here to stand silent by me in the shade. Yet if he only could—as some day, I am convinced, we all shall—know that the sum remains the same—that some other lover is the happier for this loss of his—and that if he had gained a smile from her, the pain he now feels would simply have been shifted to another heart—not dispelled . . . We only have to think impersonally enough, and even death—well, we are all either nearly dead or just born, more or less, and the balance of birth and death never appreciably alters. Personal thinking is the curse of existence. Why are we all crushed under the weight of this strangling *me*—this snake in our garden . . . ?"

So he said to the young man, "Isn't it a curious thing, looking round at young people and old people, that it doesn't really matter if they are born or dead—I mean to say, it's all the same whatever happens, if you follow me, and so many people mind when they needn't, if people would only realize—" At this moment there was a burst of clapping from the far table and the young man bounded from Mr. Robinson's side back to his friends, shouting, "Good egg—have you thought of a word already? Animal, vegetable, or mineral—and remember to speak up because I'm rather hard of hearing."

Mr. Robinson suddenly felt like Herbert Robinson, personally affronted. The sum of happiness (which of course remained unaltered by his setback) for a moment did not matter in the least. He pushed back his chair and walked away, leaving his cheese uneaten and the clown-faced dog without support. He went to his bedroom and sat down opposite his mirror, facing the reflection of his outward *me*. There sat the figure in the mirror, smooth, plump, pale, with small pouched eyes and thick, straight, wet-looking hair.

"What is this?" asked Mr. Robinson, studying the reflection of his disappointed face—the only human face he had seen that evening. "Look at me—I *am* alive—I am indeed very acutely alive—more alive, perhaps, than all these men and women half-blind—half-dead in their limitations of greed and sex. . . . It is true I have no personal claim on life; I am a virgin and I have no friends—yet I live intensely—and there are—there *are*—*there are* other forms of life than personal life. The eagle and the artichoke are equally alive; and perhaps my way of life is nearer to the eagle's than the artichoke's. And must I be alone—must I live behind cold shoulders because I see *out* instead of *in*—the most vivid form of life conceivable, if only it could be lived perfectly?"

He tried to see himself in the mirror, as was his habit, as a mere pliable pillar of life, a turret of flesh with a prisoner called *life* inside it. He stared himself out of countenance, trying, as it were, to dissolve his poor body by understanding it—poor white, sweating, rubbery thing that was called Herbert Robinson and had no friends. But tonight the prisoner called *life* clung to his prison—tonight his body tingled with egotism—tonight the oblivion that he called wisdom would not come, and he could not become conscious, as he longed to, of the live sky above the roof, the long winds streaming about the valleys, the billions of contented, wary, or terrified creatures moving about the living dust, weeds, and waters of the world. He remained just Herbert Robinson who had not seen any human face while in the midst of his fellow men.

He began to feel an immediate craving—an almost revengeful lust—to be alone, far from men, books, mirrors, and lights, watching, all his life long, the bodiless, mindless movements of animals—ecstatic living things possessing no *me*. "I should scarcely know I was alive, then, and perhaps never even notice when I died. . . ." He decided he would go away next day, and give no group again the chance to excommunicate him.

He remembered that he had seen a notice at the door of the hotel giving the rare times at which an auto-bus left and arrived at St. Pierre. "I will leave by the early bus, before any one is awake to turn his back on me."

He could not sleep, but lay uneasily on his bed reading the advertisements in a magazine he had brought with him. Advertisements always comforted him a good deal, because advertisers really, he thought, took a broad view; they wrote of—and to—their fellow men cynically and subtly, taking advantage of the vulgar passion for personal address, and yet treating humanity as one intricate mass—an instrument to be played upon. This seemed the ideal standpoint to Mr. Robinson, and yet he was insulted by the isolation such an ideal involved.

He dressed himself early, replaced in his suitcase the few clothes he had taken out, put some notes in an envelope addressed to Monsieur Dupont, and leaned out of the window to watch for the bus. St. Pierre, a sheaf of white-and-pink plaster houses, was woven together on a hill, like a haycock. The town, though compact and crowned by a sharp white bell-tower, seemed to have melted a little, like a thick candle; the centuries and the sun had softened its fortress outlines. The other hills, un-topped by towns, seemed much more definitely constructed; they were austerely built of yellow and green blocks of vineyard, cemented by the dusty green of olive trees. Gleaming, white fluffy clouds peeped over the hills—"like kittens," thought Mr. Robinson, who had a fancy for trying to make cosmic comparisons between the small and the big. On the terrace of the inn half a dozen dogs sprawled in the early sun. Over the valley a hawk balanced and swung in the air, so hungry after its night's fast that it swooped rashly and at random several times, and was caught up irritably into the air again after each dash, as though dangling on a plucked thread. Mr. Robinson leaned long on his sill looking at it, until his elbows felt sore from his weight, and he began to wonder where the bus was that was going to take him away to loneliness. He went down to the terrace, carrying his suitcase, and stood in the archway. There was no sound of a coming bus—no sound at all, in fact, except a splashing and a flapping and a murmuring to the left and right of him. A forward step or two showed him that there were two long washing troughs, one on each side of the archway, each trough shaded by a stone gallery and further enclosed in a sort of trellis of leaning kneading women.

Mr. Robinson noticed uneasily that he could not see one woman's face; all were so deeply bent and absorbed. After a moment, however, a woman's voice from the row behind him asked him if he was waiting for the bus. He turned to reply, hoping to break the spell by finding an ingenuous rustic face lifted to look at him. But all the faces were bent once more, and it was another woman behind him again who told him that the bus had left ten minutes before. Once more the speaker bent over her work before Mr. Robinson had time to turn and see her face. "What a curious protracted accident," he thought, and had time to curse his strange isolation before he realized the irritation of being unable to leave St. Pierre for another half dozen hours. He flung his suitcase into the hall of the inn and walked off up a path that led through the vineyards. As if the whole affair had been prearranged, all the dogs on the terrace rose up and followed him, yawning and stretching surreptitiously, like workers reluctantly leaving their homes at the sound of a factory whistle.

Mr. Robinson, true to his habit, concentrated his attention on—or rather diffused it to embrace—the colors about him. The leaves of the vines especially held his eye; they wore the same frosty bloom that grapes themselves often wear—a sky-blue dew on the green leaf. Two magpies, with a bottle-green sheen on their wings, gave their police-rattle cry as he came near and then flew off, flaunting their long tails clumsily. A hundred feet higher, where the ground became too steep even for vines, Mr. Robinson found a grove of gnarled old olive trees, edging a thick wood of Spanish chestnuts. Here he sat down and looked between the tree-trunks and over the distorted shadows at the uneven yellow land and the thin blade of mat-blue sea stabbing the farthest hills. The dogs stood round him, expecting him to rise in a minute and lead them on again. Seeing that he still sat where he was, they wagged their tails tolerantly but invitingly. Finally they resigned themselves to the inevitable and began philosophically walking about the grove, sniffing gently at various points in search of a makeshift stationary amusement.

Mr. Robinson watched them with a growing sense of comfort. "Here," he thought, "are the good undeliberate beasts again; I knew they would

save me. They don't shut themselves away from life in their little indi-
vidualities, or account uniquely for their lusts on the silly ground of
personality. Their bodies aren't prisons—they're just dormitories. . . ."
He delighted in watching the dogs busily engrossed in being alive without
self-consciousness. After all, he thought, he did not really depend on
men. (For he had been doubting his prized detachment most painfully.)

One of the dogs discovered a mouse-hole and, after thrusting his nose
violently into it to verify the immediacy of the smell, began digging, but
not very cleverly because he was too large a dog for such petty sports.
The other dogs hurried to the spot and, having verified the smell for
themselves, stood restively round the first discoverer, wearing the irritable
look we all wear when watching some one else bungle over something we
feel (erroneously) that we could do very much better ourselves. Finally
they pushed the original dog aside and began trying to dig, all in the
same spot, but, finding this impossible, they tapped different veins of the
same lode-smell. Soon a space of some ten feet square was filled with a
perfect tornado of flying dust, clods, grass, and piston-like forepaws. Hind
legs remained rooted while forelegs did all the work, but whenever the
accumulation of earth to the rear of each dog became inconveniently
deep, hindlegs, with a few impatient strong strokes, would dash the heap
away to some distance—even as far as Mr. Robinson's boots. Quite suddenly all the dogs, with one impulse, admitted themselves beaten; they
concluded without rancor that the area was unmistakably mouseless. They
signified their contempt for the place in the usual canine manner, and
walked away, sniffing, panting, sniffing again for some new excitement.

Mr. Robinson, who had been, for the duration of the affair, a dog in
spirit, expecting at every second that a horrified mouse would emerge
from this cyclone of attack, imitated his leaders and quieted down with
an insouciance equal to theirs. But he had escaped from the menace of
humanity; he was eased—he was sleepy. . . .

He slept for a great many hours, and when he awoke the sunlight was
slanting down at the same angle as the hill, throwing immense shadows
across the vineyards. The dogs had gone home. And there, on a space of
flattened earth between two spreading tree-roots, was a mouse and its
family. Mr. Robinson, all mouse now, with no memory of his canine past,
lay quite still on his side. The mother mouse moved in spasms, stopping
to quiver her nose over invisible interests in the dust. Her brood were like
little curled feathers, specks of down blown about by a fitful wind. There
seemed to be only one license to move shared by this whole mouse family;
when mother stopped, one infant mouse would puff forward, and as soon
as its impulse expired, another thistledown brother would glide erratically
an inch or two. In this leisurely way the family moved across the space
of earth and into the grass, appearing again and again between the green
blades. Mr. Robinson lay still, sycophantically reverent.

Between two blades of grass the senior mouse came out onto a little plateau, about eighteen inches away from Mr. Robinson's unwinking eye. At that range Mr. Robinson could see its face as clearly as one sees the face of a wife over a breakfast table. It was a dignified but greedy face; its eyes, in so far as they had any expression at all, expressed a cold heart; its attraction lay in its texture, a delicious velvet—and that the mouse would never allow a human finger, however friendly, to enjoy. It would have guarded its person as a classical virgin guarded her honor. As soon as Mr. Robinson saw the mouse's remote expression he felt as a lost sailor on a sinking ship might feel, who throws his last rope—and no saving hands grasp it.

He heard the sound of human footsteps behind him. There was a tiny explosion of flight beside him—and the mouse family was not there. Through the little grove marched a line of men in single file, going home from their work in the vineyards over the hill. Mr. Robinson sat up and noticed, with a cold heart, that all the men wore the rush hats of the country pulled down against the low last light of the sun, and that not one face was visible.

Mr. Robinson sat for some time with his face in his hands. He felt his eyes with his finger, and the shape of his nose and cheekbone; he bit his finger with his strong teeth. Here was a face—the only human face in the world. Suddenly craving for the sight of that friend behind the mirror, he got up and walked back to the Trois Moineaux. He found himself very hungry, having starved all day; but his isolation gave him a so much deeper sense of lack than did his empty stomach that, although dinner was in progress among the bands of light and shade on the terrace, his first act was to run to his room and stand before the mirror. There was a mistiness in the mirror. He rubbed it with his hand. The mistiness persisted—a compact haze of blankness that exactly covered the reflection of his face. He moved to a different angle—he moved the mirror—he saw clearly the reflection of the room, of his tweed-clad figure, of his tie, of his suitcase in the middle of the floor; but his face remained erased, like an unsatisfactory charcoal sketch. Filled with an extraordinary fear, he stood facing the mirror for some minutes, feeling with tremulous fingers for his eyes, his lips, his forehead. There seemed to him to be the same sensation of haze in his sense of touch as in his eyesight—a nervelessness —a feeling of nauseating contact with a dead thing. It was like touching with an unsuspecting hand one's own limb numbed by cold or by an accident of position.

Mr. Robinson walked downstairs, dazed, and out onto the terrace. As before, the shadowed tables looking out over the edge of the terrace were already surrounded by laughing, chattering parties. Mr. Robinson took his seat, as before, under the olive tree. "Bring me a bottle of . . . Sauterne," he said to the waiter (for he remembered that his late unmarried sister used to sustain upon this wine a reputation for wit in the boarding house in which she had lived). "And, waiter, isn't there a table free looking out at the view? I can't see anything here." It was not the view he craved, of course, but only a point of vantage from which to see the faces of his mysterious noisy neighbors. His need for seeing faces was more immediate than ever, now that his one friend had failed him.

"There will be tables free there in a moment," said the waiter. "They are all going to dance soon. They're only waiting for the moon." And the waiter nodded his shadowed face towards a distant hill, behind which—looking at this moment like a great far red fire—the moon was coming up. "Look, the moon, the moon, the moon, look . . ." every one on the terrace was saying. And a few moments later, the moon—now completely round but cut in half by a neat bar of cloud, took flight lightly from the top of the hill.

There was a scraping of chairs, the scraping of a gramophone, and half a dozen couples of young men and women began dancing between the tall Italian urns and the olive trees on the terrace. Mr. Robinson poured himself out a large tumbler of Sauterne. "Waiter, I don't want a table at the edge now—I want one near the dancers—I want to see their faces."

"There are no tables free in the center of the terrace now. Several are vacant at the edge."

"I can see a table there, near the dancers, with only two chairs occupied. Surely I could sit with them."

"That table is taken by a large party, but most of them are dancing. They will come back there in a moment."

Mr. Robinson, disregarding the waiter and clutching his tumbler in one hand and his bottle in the other, strode to the table he had chosen. "I'm *too* lonely—I must sit here."

"So lonely, poo-oo-oor man," said the woman at the table, a stout middle-aged woman with high shoulders and a high bosom clad in saxe-blue sequins. She turned her face towards him in the pink light of the moon. Mr. Robinson, though desperate, was not surprised. Her face was the same blank—the same terrible disc of nothingness that he had seen in his mirror. Mr. Robinson looked at her companion in dreadful certainty. A twin blank faced him.

"Sh-lonely, eh?" came a thick young voice out of nothingness. "Well, m'lad, you'll be damn sight lonelier yet in minute 'f y' come buttin' in on—"

"Ow, Ronnie," expostulated his frightful friend—but at that moment the gramophone fell silent and the dancers came back to their table. Mr. Robinson scanned the spaces that should have been their faces one by one; they were like discs of dazzle seen after unwisely meeting the eye of the sun.

"'This old feller sayzzz—lonely—pinched your chair, Belle—"

"Never mind, duckie," said Belle—and threw herself across Mr. Robinson's knee. "Plenty of room for little me."

The white emptiness of her face that was no face blocked out Mr. Robinson's view of the world.

"Oh, my God!" she cried, jumping up sudddenly. "I know why he's lonely—why—the man's not alive. Look at his face!"

"I am—I am—I am—" shouted Mr. Robinson in terror. "I'll show you I am . . ." He lurched after her and dragged her among the dancers as the music began again. He shut his eyes. He could hear her wild animal shrieks of laughter and feel her thin struggling body under his hands.

Mr. Robinson sat, quite still but racked by confusion, excitement, and disgust, beside the road on the wall of a vineyard, watching the last star slip down into the haze that enhaloed the hills. The moon had gone long ago. All Mr. Robinson's heart was set on catching the bus this morning; to him the dawn that was even now imperceptibly replacing the starlight was only a herald of the bus and of escape. He had no thoughts and no plans beyond catching the bus. He knew that he was cold, but flight would warm him; that he was hungry and thirsty, but flight would nourish him; that he was exhausted and broken-hearted, but flight would ease and comfort him.

A white glow crowned a hill, behind which the sky had long been pearly, and in a minute an unbearably bright ray shot from the hill into Mr. Robinson's eyes. The dazzling domed brow of the sun rose between a tree and a crag, and a lily-white light rushed into the valley.

The bus, crackling and crunching, waddled round the bend. Mr. Robinson hailed it with a distraught cry and gesture.

"*Enfin . . . très peu de places, m'sieu—n'y a qu'un tout p'tit coin par ici . . .*"

Mr. Robinson had no need now to look at the face of the driver, or at the rows of senseless sunlit ghosts that filled the bus. He knew his curse by now. He climbed into the narrow place indicated beside the driver. The bus lurched on down the narrow winding road that overhung the steep vineyards of the valley. Far below—so far below that one could not see the movement of the water—a yellow stream enmeshed its rocks in a net of plaited strands.

Mr. Robinson sat beside the driver, not looking at that phantom faceless face—so insulting to the comfortable sun—but looking only at the road that was leading him to escape. How far to flee he did not know, but all the hope there was, he felt, lay beyond the farthest turn of the road. After one spellbound look at the sun-blinded face of St. Pierre, clinging to its hivelike hill, he looked forward only, at the winding perilous road.

And his acute eyes saw, in the middle of the way, half a dozen specks of live fur, blowing about a shallow rut. . . . The bus's heavy approach had already caused a certain panic in the mouse family. One atom blew one way, one another; there was a sort of little muddled maze of running mice in the road.

Mr. Robinson's heart seemed to burst. Before he was aware, he had sprung to his feet and seized the wheel of the bus from the driver. He had about twenty seconds in which to watch the mice scuttling into the grass—to watch the low loose wall of the outer edge of the road crumble beneath the plunging weight of the bus. He saw, leaning crazily towards him, the face—the *face*—rolling eyes, tight grinning lips—of the driver, looking down at death. There, far down, was the yellow net of the river, spread to catch them all.

COMMENT AND QUESTION

1. Is Mr. Robinson, who hated "this strangling *me*," self-engrossed?

2. Two key questions are: Why does Mr. Robinson see no faces? Why does he finally see the driver's face?

3. Two lines of interest develop simultaneously in this story and produce a single revelation. One is the failure to see faces, the other, Mr. Robinson's interest in animals.

   a. Begin with the proprietor who stands with his back against the light and trace all the people who are faceless, ending with the episode of the mirror on p. 24.

   b. Begin with the dog who lays his head on Mr. Robinson's knee and notice all the animals through the mouse on p. 23. Why do animals console Mr. Robinson? Does he see their faces?

4. Why does Mr. Robinson feel like a lost sailor on a sinking ship when he observes the mouse on p. 24? Why does this incident occur almost simultaneously with the incident of the mirror on p. 24?

5. How does the woman at the dance merely confirm what the reader already knows?

6. The final incident contains all the threads of the story, faceless people, animals, Mr. Robinson's acute sight, a bus.

Why does Mr. Robinson try to rescue the mouse? What reward does he receive? What price does he pay?

THE HAPPY AUTUMN FIELDS

BY ELIZABETH BOWEN

ELIZABETH BOWEN (1899–   ) was born in
Ireland and lives in Bowen's Court, County
Cork, Ireland. Her book of short stories, *Ivy
Gripped the Steps* (1946), reflects the emo-
tional tension of life in England during the
second World War. Other collections of her
short stories include *Joining Charles* (1929),
Look at All Those Roses (1941), and *The
Cat Jumps* (1949). She has written a number
of novels: *The Death of the Heart* (1939),
The Heat of the Day (1949), *The Hotel* and
To the North (1950), *Friends and Relations*
(1951), *The House in Paris* and *The Last
September* (1952), and *A World of Love*
(1955).

T HE family walking party, though it comprised so many, did not deploy
or straggle over the stubble but kept in a procession of threes and twos.
Papa, who carried his Alpine stick, led, flanked by Constance and little
Arthur. Robert and Cousin Theodore, locked in studious talk, had Emily
attached but not quite abreast. Next came Digby and Lucius, taking, to
left and right, imaginary aim at rooks. Henrietta and Sarah brought up
the rear.

It was Sarah who saw the others ahead on the blond stubble, who
knew them, knew what they were to each other, knew their names and
knew her own. It was she who felt the stubble under her feet, and who
heard it give beneath the tread of the others a continuous different more
distant soft stiff scrunch. The field and all these outlying fields in view
knew as Sarah knew that they were Papa's. The harvest had been good
and was now in: he was satisfied—for this afternoon he had made the

THE HAPPY AUTUMN FIELDS   Reprinted from *Ivy Gripped the Steps* by Elizabeth
Bowen, by permission of Alfred A. Knopf, Inc. and Messrs. Jonathan Cape Ltd.
Copyright 1941, 1946 by Elizabeth Bowen.

instinctive choice of his most womanly daughter, most nearly infant son. Arthur, whose hand Papa was holding, took an anxious hop, a skip and a jump to every stride of the great man's. As for Constance—Sarah could often see the flash of her hat-feather as she turned her head, the curve of her close bodice as she turned her torso. Constance gave Papa her attention but not her thoughts, for she had already been sought in marriage.

The landowners' daughters, from Constance down, walked with their beetle-green, mole or maroon skirts gathered up and carried clear of the ground, but for Henrietta, who was still ankle-free. They walked inside a continuous stuffy sound, but left silence behind them. Behind them, rooks that had risen and circled, sun striking blue from their blue-black wings, planed one by one to the earth and settled to peck again. Papa and the boys were dark-clad as the rooks but with no sheen, but for their white collars.

It was Sarah who located the thoughts of Constance, knew what a twisting prisoner was Arthur's hand, felt to the depths of Emily's pique at Cousin Theodore's inattention, rejoiced with Digby and Lucius at the imaginary fall of so many rooks. She felt back, however, as from a rocky range, from the converse of Robert and Cousin Theodore. Most she knew that she swam with love at the nearness of Henrietta's young and alert face and eyes which shone with the sky and queried the afternoon.

She recognized the colour of valediction, tasted sweet sadness, while from the cottage inside the screen of trees wood-smoke rose melting pungent and blue. This was the eve of the brothers' return to school. It was like a Sunday; Papa had kept the late afternoon free; all (all but one) encircling Robert, Digby and Lucius, they walked the estate the brothers would not see again for so long. Robert, it could be felt, was not unwilling to return to his books; next year he would go to college like Theodore; besides, to all this they saw he was not the heir. But in Digby and Lucius aiming and popping hid a bodily grief, the repugnance of victims, though these two were further from being heirs than Robert.

Sarah said to Henrietta: "To think they will not be here to-morrow!"

"*Is* that what you are thinking about?" Henrietta asked, with her subtle taste for the truth.

"More, I was thinking that you and I will be back again by one another at table. . . ."

"You know we are always sad when the boys are going, but we are never sad when the boys have gone." The sweet reciprocal guilty smile that started on Henrietta's lips finished on those of Sarah. "Also," the young sister said, "we know this is only something happening again. It happened last year, and it will happen next. But oh how should I feel, and how should you feel, if it were something that had not happened before?"

"For instance, when Constance goes to be married?"

"Oh, I don't mean *Constance!*" said Henrietta.

"So long," said Sarah, considering, "as, whatever it is, it happens to both of us?" She must never have to wake in the early morning except to the birdlike stirrings of Henrietta, or have her cheek brushed in the dark by the frill of another pillow in whose hollow did not repose Henrietta's cheek. Rather than they should cease to lie in the same bed she prayed they might lie in the same grave. "You and I will stay as we are," she said, "then nothing can touch one without touching the other."

"So you say; so I hear you say!" exclaimed Henrietta, who then, lips apart, sent Sarah her most tormenting look. "But I cannot forget that you chose to be born without me; that you would not wait—" But here she broke off, laughed outright and said: "Oh, *see!*"

Ahead of them there had been a dislocation. Emily took advantage of having gained the ridge to kneel down to tie her bootlace so abruptly that Digby all but fell over her, with an exclamation. Cousin Theodore had been civil enough to pause beside Emily, but Robert, lost to all but what he was saying, strode on, head down, only just not colliding into Papa and Constance, who had turned to look back. Papa, astounded, let go of Arthur's hand, whereupon Arthur fell flat on the stubble.

"Dear me," said the affronted Constance to Robert.

Papa said: "What is the matter there? May I ask, Robert, where you are going, sir? Digby, remember that is your sister Emily."

"Cousin Emily is in trouble," said Cousin Theodore.

Poor Emily, telescoped in her skirts and by now scarlet under her hat-brim, said in a muffled voice: "It is just my bootlace, Papa."

"Your bootlace, Emily?"

"I was just tying it."

"Then you had better tie it.— Am I to think," said Papa, looking round them all, "that you must all go down like a pack of ninepins because Emily has occasion to stoop?"

At this Henrietta uttered a little whoop, flung her arms round Sarah, buried her face in her sister and fairly suffered with laughter. She could contain this no longer; she shook all over. Papa, who found Henrietta so hopelessly out of order that he took no notice of her except at table, took no notice, simply giving the signal for the others to collect themselves and move on. Cousin Theodore, helping Emily to her feet, could be seen to see how her heightened colour became her, but she dispensed with his hand chillily, looked elsewhere, touched the brooch at her throat and said: "Thank you, I have not sustained an accident." Digby apologized to Emily, Robert to Papa and Constance. Constance righted Arthur, flicking his breeches over with her handkerchief. All fell into their different steps and resumed their way.

Sarah, with no idea how to console laughter, coaxed, "Come, come,

come," into Henrietta's ear. Between the girls and the others the distance widened; it began to seem that they would be left alone.

"And why not?" said Henrietta, lifting her head in answer to Sarah's thought.

They looked around them with the same eyes. The shorn uplands seemed to float on the distance, which extended dazzling to tiny blue glassy hills. There was no end to the afternoon, whose light went on ripening now they had scythed the corn. Light filled the silence which, now Papa and the others were out of hearing, was complete. Only screens of trees intersected and knolls made islands in the vast fields. The mansion and the home farm had sunk for ever below them in the expanse of woods, so that hardly a ripple showed where the girls dwelled.

The shadow of the same rook circling passed over Sarah then over Henrietta, who in their turn cast one shadow across the stubble. "But, Henrietta, we cannot stay here for ever."

Henrietta immediately turned her eyes to the only lonely plume of smoke, from the cottage. "Then let us go and visit the poor old man. He is dying and the others are happy. One day we shall pass and see no more smoke; then soon his roof will fall in, and we shall always be sorry we did not go to-day."

"But he no longer remembers us any longer."

"All the same, he will feel us there in the door."

"But can we forget this is Robert's and Digby's and Lucius's good-bye walk? It would be heartless of both of us to neglect them."

"Then how heartless Fitzgeorge is!" smiled Henrietta.

"Fitzgeorge is himself, the eldest and in the Army. Fitzgeorge I'm afraid is not an excuse for us."

A resigned sigh, or perhaps the pretence of one, heaved up Henrietta's still narrow bosom. To delay matters for just a moment more she shaded her eyes with one hand, to search the distance like a sailor looking for a sail. She gazed with hope and zeal in every direction but that in which she and Sarah were bound to go. Then— "Oh, but Sarah, here *they* are, coming—they are!" she cried. She brought out her handkerchief and began to fly it, drawing it to and fro through the windless air.

In the glass of the distance, two horsemen came into view, cantering on a grass track between the fields. When the track dropped into a hollow they dropped with it, but by now the drumming of hoofs was heard. The reverberation filled the land, the silence and Sarah's being; not watching for the riders to reappear she instead fixed her eyes on her sister's handkerchief which, let hang limp while its owner intently waited, showed a bitten corner as well as a damson stain. Again it became a flag, in furious motion.— "Wave too, Sarah, wave too! Make your bracelet flash!"

"They must have seen us if they will ever see us," said Sarah, standing still as a stone.

Henrietta's waving at once ceased. Facing her sister she crunched up her handkerchief, as though to stop it acting a lie. "I can see you are shy," she said in a dead voice. "So shy you won't even wave to *Fitzgeorge?*"

Her way of not speaking the *other* name had a hundred meanings; she drove them all in by the way she did not look at Sarah's face. The impulsive breath she had caught stole silently out again, while her eyes—till now at their brightest, their most speaking—dulled with uncomprehending solitary alarm. The ordeal of awaiting Eugene's approach thus became for Sarah, from moment to moment, torture.

Fitzgeorge, Papa's heir, and his friend Eugene, the young neighbouring squire, struck off the track and rode up at a trot with their hats doffed. Sun striking low turned Fitzgeorge's flesh to coral and made Eugene blink his dark eyes. The young men reined in; the girls looked up the horses. "And my father, Constance, the others?" Fitzgeorge demanded, as though the stubble had swallowed them.

"Ahead, on the way to the quarry, the other side of the hill."

"We heard you were all walking together," Fitzgeorge said, seeming dissatisfied.

"We are following."

"What, alone?" said Eugene, speaking for the first time.

"Forlorn!" glittered Henrietta, raising two mocking hands.

Fitzgeorge considered, said "Good" severely, and signified to Eugene that they would ride on. But too late: Eugene had dismounted. Fitzgeorge saw, shrugged and flicked his horse to a trot; but Eugene led his slowly between the sisters. Or rather, Sarah walked on his left hand, the horse on his right and Henrietta the other side of the horse. Henrietta, acting like somebody quite alone, looked up at the sky, idly holding one of the empty stirrups. Sarah, however, looked at the ground, with Eugene inclined as though to speak but not speaking. Enfolded, dizzied, blinded as though inside a wave, she could feel his features carved in brightness above her. Alongside the slender stepping of his horse, Eugene matched his naturally long free step to hers. His elbow was through the reins; with his fingers he brushed back the lock that his bending to her had sent falling over his forehead. She recorded the sublime act and knew what smile shaped his lips. So each without looking trembled before an image, while slow colour burned up the curves of her cheeks. The consummation would be when their eyes met.

At the other side of the horse, Henrietta began to sing. At once her pain, like a scientific ray, passed through the horse and Eugene to penetrate Sarah's heart.

We surmount the skyline: the family come into our view, we into theirs. They are halted, waiting, on the decline to the quarry. The handsome statufied group in strong yellow sunshine, aligned by Papa and crowned by Fitzgeorge, turn their judging eyes on the laggards, waiting to close their ranks round Henrietta and Sarah and Eugene. One more moment and it will be too late; no further communication will be possible. Stop oh stop Henrietta's heartbreaking singing! Embrace her close again! Speak the only possible word! Say—oh, say what? Oh, the word is lost!

"*Henrietta . . .*"

A shock of striking pain in the knuckles of the outflung hand—Sarah's? The eyes, opening, saw that the hand had struck, not been struck: there was a corner of a table. Dust, whitish and gritty, lay on the top of the table and on the telephone. Dull but piercing white light filled the room and what was left of the ceiling; her first thought was that it must have snowed. If so, it was winter now.

Through the calico stretched and tacked over the window came the sound of a piano: someone was playing Tchaikovsky badly in a room without windows or doors. From somewhere else in the hollowness came a cascade of hammering. Close up, a voice: "Oh, *awake,* Mary?" It came from the other side of the open door, which jutted out between herself and the speaker—he on the threshold, she lying on the uncovered mattress of a bed. The speaker added: "I had been going away."

Summoning words from somewhere she said: "Why? I didn't know you were here."

"Evidently—Say, who is 'Henrietta'?"

Despairing tears filled her eyes. She drew back her hurt hand, began to suck at the knuckle and whimpered, "I've hurt myself."

A man she knew to be "Travis," but failed to focus, came round the door saying: Really I don't wonder." Sitting down on the edge of the mattress he drew her hand away from her lips and held it: the act, in itself gentle, was accompanied by an almost hostile stare of concern. "Do listen, Mary," he said. "While you've slept I've been all over the house again, and I'm less than ever satisfied that it's safe. In your normal senses you'd never attempt to stay here. There've been alerts, and more than alerts, all day; one more bang anywhere near, which may happen at any moment, could bring the rest of this down. You keep telling me that you have things to see to—but do you know what chaos the rooms are in? Till they've gone ahead with more clearing, where can you hope to start? And if there *were* anything you could do, you couldn't do it. Your own nerves know that, if you don't: it was almost frightening, when I looked in just now, to see the way you were sleeping—you've shut up shop."

She lay staring over his shoulder at the calico window. He went on: "You don't like it here. Your self doesn't like it. Your will keeps driving your self, but it can't be driven the whole way—it makes its own get-out: sleep. Well, I want you to sleep as much as you (really) do. But *not* here. So I've taken a room for you in a hotel; I'm going now for a taxi, you can practically make the move without waking up."

"No, I can't get into a taxi without waking."

"Do you realize you're the last soul left in the terrace?"

"Then who is that playing the piano?"

"Oh, one of the furniture-movers in Number Six. I didn't count the jaquerie; of course *they're* in possession—unsupervised, teeming, having a high old time. While I looked in on you in here ten minutes ago they were smashing out that conservatory at the other end. Glass being done in in cold blood—it was brutalizing. You never batted an eyelid; in fact, I thought you smiled." He listened. "Yes, the piano—they are highbrow all right. You know there's a workman downstairs lying on your blue sofa looking for pictures in one of your French books?"

"No," she said, "I've no idea who is there."

"Obviously. With the lock blown off your front door anyone who likes can get in and out."

"Including you."

"Yes. I've had a word with a chap about getting that lock back before to-night. As for you, you don't know what is happening."

"I did," she said, locking her fingers before her eyes.

The unreality of this room and of Travis's presence preyed on her as figments of dreams that one knows to be dreams can do. This environment's being in semi-ruin struck her less than its being some sort of device or trap; and she rejoiced, if anything, in its decrepitude. As for Travis, he had his own part in the conspiracy to keep her from the beloved two. She felt he began to feel he was now unmeaning. She was struggling not to contemn him, scorn him for his ignorance of Henrietta, Eugene, her loss. His possessive angry fondness was part, of course, of the story of him and Mary, which like a book once read she remembered clearly but with indifference. Frantic at being delayed here, while the moment awaited her in the cornfield, she all but afforded a smile at the grotesquerie of being saddled with Mary's body and lover. Rearing up her head from the bare pillow, she looked, as far as the crossed feet, along the form inside which she found herself trapped: the irrelevant body of Mary, weighted down to the bed, wore a short black modern dress, flaked with plaster. The toes of the black suède shoes by their sickly whiteness showed Mary must have climbed over fallen ceilings; dirt engraved the fate-lines in Mary's palms.

This inspired her to say: "But I've made a start; I've been pulling out things of value or things I want."

For answer Travis turned to look down, expressively, at some object out of her sight, on the floor close by the bed. "*I* see," he said, "a musty old leather box gaping open with God knows what—junk, illegible letters, diaries, yellow photographs, chiefly plaster and dust. Of all things, Mary! —after a missing will?"

"Everything one unburies seems the same age."

"Then what are these, where do they come from—family stuff?"

"No idea," she yawned into Mary's hand. "They may not even be mine.

Having a house like this that had empty rooms must have made me store more than I knew, for years. I came on these, so I wondered. Look if you like."

He bent and began to go through the box—it seemed to her, not unsuspiciously. While he blew grit off packets and fumbled with tapes she lay staring at the exposed laths of the ceiling, calculating. She then said: "Sorry if I've been cranky, about the hotel and all. Go away just for two hours, then come back with a taxi, and I'll go quiet. Will that do?"

"Fine—except why not now?"

"Travis . . ."

"Sorry. It shall be as you say . . . You've got some good morbid stuff in this box, Mary—so far as I can see at a glance. The photographs seem more your sort of thing. Comic but lyrical. All of one set of people—a beard, a gun and a pot hat, a schoolboy with a moustache, a phaeton drawn up in front of mansion, a group on steps, a *carte de visite* of two young ladies hand-in-hand in front of a painted field—"

"*Give that to me!*"

She instinctively tried, and failed, to unbutton the bosom of Mary's dress: it offered no hospitality to the photograph. So she could only fling herself over on the mattress, away from Travis, covering the two faces with her body. Racked by that oblique look of Henrietta's she recorded, too, a sort of personal shock at having seen Sarah for the first time.

Travis's hand came over her, and she shuddered. Wounded, he said: "Mary . . ."

"Can't you leave *me* alone?"

She did not move or look till he had gone out saying: "Then, in two hours." She did not therefore see him pick up the dangerous box, which he took away under his arm, out of her reach.

They were back. Now the sun was setting behind the trees, but its rays passed dazzling between the branches into the beautiful warm red room. The tips of the ferns in the jardiniere curled gold, and Sarah, standing by the jardiniere, pinched at a leaf of scented geranium. The carpet had a great centre wreath of pomegranates, on which no tables or chairs stood, and its whole circle was between herself and the others.

No fire was lit yet, but where they were grouped was a hearth. Henrietta sat on a low stool, resting her elbow above her head on the arm of Mamma's chair, looking away intently as though into a fire, idle. Mamma embroidered, her needle slowed down by her thoughts; the length of tatting with roses she had already done overflowed stiffly over her supple skirts. Stretched on the rug at Mamma's feet, Arthur looked through an album of Swiss views, not liking them but vowed to be very quiet. Sarah, from where she stood, saw fuming cateracts and null eternal snows as poor Arthur kept turning over the pages, which had tissue paper between.

Against the white marble mantlepiece stood Eugene. The dark red shadows gathering in the drawing-room as the trees drowned more and more of the sun would reach him last, perhaps never: it seemed to Sarah that a lamp was lighted behind his face. He was the only gentleman with the ladies: Fitzgeorge had gone to the stables, Papa to give an order; Cousin Theodore was consulting a dictionary; in the gunroom Robert, Lucius and Digby went through the sad rites, putting away their guns. All this was known to go on but none of it could be heard.

This particular hour of subtle light—not to be fixed by the clock, for it was early in winter and late in summer and in spring and autumn now, about Arthur's bedtime—had always, for Sarah, been Henrietta's. To be with her indoors or out, upstairs or down, was to share the same crepitation. Her spirit ran on past yours with a laughing shiver into an element of its own. Leaves and branches and mirrors in empty rooms became animate. The sisters rustled and scampered and concealed themselves where nobody else was in play that was full of fear, fear that was full of play. Till, by dint of making each other's hearts beat violently, Henrietta so wholly and Sarah so nearly lost all human reason that Mama had been known look at them searchingly as she sat instated for evening among the calm amber lamps.

But now Henrietta had locked the hour inside her breast. By spending it seated beside mamma, in young imitation of Constance the Society daughter, she disclaimed for ever anything else. It had always been she who with one fierce act destroyed any toy that might be outgrown. She sat with straight back, poising her cheek remotely against her finger. Only by never looking at Sarah did she admit their eternal loss.

Eugene, not long returned from a foreign tour, spoke of travel, addressing himself to Mamma, who thought but did not speak of her wedding journey. But every now and then she had to ask Henrietta to pass the scissors or tray of carded wools, and Eugene seized every such moment to look at Sarah. Into eyes always brilliant with melancholy he dared begin to allow no other expression. But this in itself declared the conspiracy of still undeclared love. For her part she looked at him as though he, transfigured by the strange light, were indeed a picture, a picture who could not see her. The wallpaper now flamed scarlet behind his shoulder. Mamma, Henrietta, even unknowing Arthur were in no hurry to raise their heads.

Henrietta said: "If I were a man I should take my bride to Italy."

"There are mules in Switzerland," said Arthur.

"Sarah," said Mamma, who turned in her chair mildly, "where are you, my love; do you never mean to sit down?"

"To Naples," said Henrietta.

"Are you not thinking of Venice?" said Eugene.

"No," returned Henrietta, "why should I be? I should like to climb the volcano. But then I am not a man, and am still less likely ever to be a bride."

"Arthur . . ." Mamma said.

"Mamma?"

"Look at the clock."

Arthur sighed politely, got up and replaced the album on the circular table, balanced upon the rest. He offered his hand to Eugene, his cheek to Henrietta and to Mamma; then he started towards Sarah, who came to meet him. "Tell me, Arthur," she said, embracing him, "what did you do to-day?"

Arthur only stared with his button blue eyes. "You were there too; we went for a walk in the cornfield, with Fitzgeorge on his horse, and I fell down." He pulled out of her arms and said: "I must go back to my beetle." He had difficulty, as always, in turning the handle of the mahogany door. Mamma waited till he had left the room, then said: "Arthur is quite a man now; he no longer comes running to me when he has hurt himself. Why, I did not even know he had fallen down. Before we know, he will be going away to school too." She sighed and lifted her eyes to Eugene. "To-morrow is to be a sad day."

Eugene with a gesture signified his own sorrow. The sentiments of Mamma could have been uttered only here in the drawing-room, which for all its size and formality was lyrical and almost exotic. There was a look like velvet in darker parts of the air; sombre window draperies let out gushes of lace; the music on the pianoforte bore tender titles, and the harp though unplayed gleamed in a corner, beyond sofas, whatnots, arm-chairs, occasional tables that all stood on tottering little feet. At any moment a tinkle might have been struck from the lustres' drops of the brighter day, a vibration from the musical instruments, or a quiver from the fringes and ferns. But the towering vases upon the consoles, the albums piled on the tables, the shells and figurines on the flights of brackets, all had, like the alabaster Leaning Tower of Pisa, an equilibrium of their own. Nothing would fall or change. And everything in the drawing-room was muted, weighted, pivoted by Mamma. When she added: "We shall not feel quite the same," it was to be understood that she would not have spoken thus from her place at the opposite end of Papa's table.

"Sarah," said Henrietta curiously, "what made you ask Arthur what he had been doing? Surely you have not forgotten to-day?"

The sisters were seldom known to address or question one another in public; it was taken that they knew each other's minds. Mamma, though untroubled, looked from one to the other. Henrietta continued: "No day, least of all to-day, is like any other— Surely that must be true?" she said to Eugene. "You will never forget my waving my handkerchief?"

Before Eugene had composed an answer, she turned to Sarah: "Or *you*, them riding across the fields?"

Eugene also slowly turned his eyes on Sarah, as though awaiting with something like dread her answer to the question he had not asked. She drew a light little gold chair into the middle of the wreath of the carpet, where no one ever sat, and sat down. She said: "But since then I think I have been asleep."

"Charles the First walked and talked half an hour after his head was cut off," said Henrietta mockingly. Sarah in anguish pressed the palms of her hands together upon a shred of geranium leaf.

"How else," she said, "could I have had such a bad dream?"

"That must be the explanation!" said Henrietta.

"A trifle fanciful," said Mamma.

However rash it might be to speak at all, Sarah wished she knew how to speak more clearly. The obscurity and loneliness of her trouble was not to be borne. How could she put into words the feeling of dislocation, the formless dread that had been with her since she found herself in the drawing-room? The source of both had been what she must call her dream. How could she tell the others with what vehemence she tried to attach her being to each second, not because each was singular in itself, each a drop condensed from the mist of love in the room, but because she apprehended that the seconds were numbered? Her hope was that the others at least half knew. Were Henrietta and Eugene able to understand how completely, how nearly for ever, she had been swept from them, would they not without fail each grasp one of her hands?— She went so far as to throw her hands out, as though alarmed by a wasp. The shred of geranium fell to the carpet.

Mamma, tracing this behaviour of Sarah's to only one cause, could not but think reproachfully of Eugene. Delightful as his conversation had been, he would have done better had he paid this call with the object of interviewing Papa. Turning to Henrietta she asked her to ring for the lamps, as the sun had set.

Eugene, no longer where he had stood, was able to make no gesture towards the bell-rope. His dark head was under the tide of dusk; for, down on one knee on the edge of the wreath, he was feeling over the carpet for what had fallen from Sarah's hand. In the inevitable silence rooks on the return from the fields could be heard streaming over the house; their sound filled the sky and even the room, and it appeared so useless to ring the bell that Henrietta stayed quivering by Mama's chair. Eugene rose, brought out his fine white handkerchief and, while they watched, enfolded carefully in it what he had just found, then returned the handkerchief to his breast pocket. This was done so deep in the reverie that accompanies any final act that Mamma instinctively murmured to Henrietta: "But you will be my child when Arthur has gone."

The door opened for Constance to appear on the threshold. Behind her queenly figure globes approached, swimming in their own light: these

were the lamps for which Henrietta had not rung, but these first were
put on the hall tables. "Why, Mamma," exclaimed Constance, "I cannot
see who is with you!"

"Eugene is with us," said Henrietta, "but on the point of asking if he
may send for his horse."

"Indeed?" said Constance to Eugene. "Fitzgeorge has been asking for
you, but I cannot tell where he is now."

The figures of Emily, Lucius and Cousin Theodore crisscrossed the
lamplight there in the hall, to mass behind Constance's in the drawing-
room door. Emily, over her sister's shoulder, said: "Mama, Lucius wishes
to ask you whether for once he may take his guitar to school."—"One
objection, however," said Cousin Theodore, "is that Lucius's trunk is
already locked and strapped." "Since Robert is taking his box of inks,"
said Lucius, "I do not see why I should not take my guitar."— "But
Robert," said Constance, "will soon be going to college."

Lucius squeezed past the others into the drawing-room in order to look
anxiously at Mamma, who said: "You have thought of this late; we must
go and see." The others parted to let Mamma, followed by Lucius, out.
Then Constance, Emily and Cousin Theodore deployed and sat down in
different parts of the drawing-room, to await the lamps.

"I am glad the rooks have done passing over," said Emily, "they make
me nervous."—"Why," yawned Constance haughtily, "what do you think
could happen?" Robert and Digby silently came in.

Eugene said to Sarah: "I shall be back to-morrow."

"But, oh—" she began. She turned to cry: "Henrietta!"

"Why, what is the matter?" said Henrietta, unseen at the back of the
gold chair. "What could be sooner than to-morrow?"

"But something terrible may be going to happen."

"There cannot fail to be to-morrow," said Eugene gravely.

"*I* will see that there is to-morrow," said Henrietta.

"You will never let me out of your sight?"

Eugene, addressing himself to Henrietta, said: "Yes, promise her what
she asks."

Henrietta cried: "She *is* never out of my sight. Who are you to ask
me that, you Eugene? Whatever tries to come between me and Sarah
becomes nothing. Yes, come to-morrow, come sooner, come—when you
like, but no one will ever be quite alone with Sarah. You do not even
know what you are trying to do. It is *you* who are making something terrible happen.— Sarah, tell him that that is true! Sarah—"

The others, in the dark on the chairs and sofas, could be felt to turn
their judging eyes upon Sarah, who, as once before, could not speak—

—The house rocked; simultaneously the calico window split and more
ceiling fell, though not on the bed. The enormous dull sound of the

explosion died, leaving a minor trickle of dissolution still to be heard in parts of the house. Until the choking stinging plaster dust had had time to settle, she lay with lips pressed close, nostrils not breathing and eyes shut. Remembering the box, Mary wondered if it had been again buried. No, she found, looking over the edge of the bed: that had been unable to happen because the box was missing. Travis, who must have taken it, would when he came back no doubt explain why. She looked at her watch, which had stopped, which was not surprising; she did not remember winding it for the last two days, but then she could not remember much. Through the torn window appeared the timelessness of an impermeably clouded late summer afternoon.

There being nothing left, she wished he would come to take her to the hotel. The one way back to the fields was barred by Mary's surviving the fall of ceiling. Sarah was right in doubting that there would be tomorrow: Eugene, Henrietta were lost in time to the woman weeping there on the bed, no longer reckoning who she was.

At last she heard the taxi, then Travis hurrying up the littered stairs. "Mary, you're all right, Mary—*another?*" Such a helpless white face came round the door that she could only hold out her arms and say: "Yes, but where have *you* been?"

"You said two hours. But I wish—"

"I have missed you."

"Have you? Do you know you are crying?"

"Yes. How are we to live without natures? We only know inconvenience now, not sorrow. Everything pulverizes so easily because it is rot-dry; one can only wonder that it makes so much noise. The source, the sap must have dried up, or the pulse must have stopped, before you and I were conceived. So much flowed through people; so little flows through us. All we can do is imitate love or sorrow.— Why did you take away my box?"

He only said: "It is in my office."

She continued: "What has happened is cruel: I am left with a fragment torn out of a day, a day I don't even know where or when; and now how am I to help laying that like a pattern against the poor stuff of everything else?— Alternatively, I am a person drained by a dream. I cannot forget the climate of those hours. Or life at that pitch, eventful— not happy, no, but strung like a harp. I have had a sister called Henrietta."

"And I have been looking inside your box. What else can you expect?— I have had to write off this day, from the work point of view, thanks to you. So could I sit and do nothing for the last two hours? I just glanced through this and that—still, I know the family."

"You said it was morbid stuff."

"Did I? I still say it gives off something."

She said: "And then there was Eugene."

"Probably. I don't think I came on much of his except some notes he must have made for Fitzgeorge from some book on scientific farming. Well, there it is: I have sorted everything out and put it back again, all but a lock of hair that tumbled out of a letter I could not trace. So I've got the hair in my pocket."

"What colour is it?"

"Ash-brown. Of course, it is a bit—desiccated. Do you want it?"

"No," she said with a shudder. "Really, Travis, what revenges you take!"

"I didn't look at it that way," he said puzzled.

"Is the taxi waiting?" Mary got off the bed and, picking her way across the room, began to look about for things she ought to take with her, now and then stopping to brush her dress. She took the mirror out of her bag to see how dirty her face was. "Travis—" she said suddenly.

"Mary?"

"Only, I—"

"That's all right. Don't let us imitate anything just at present."

In the taxi, looking out of the window, she said: "I suppose, then, that I am descended from Sarah?"

"No," he said, "that would be impossible. There must be some reason why you should have those papers, but that is not the one. From all negative evidence Sarah, like Henrietta, remained unmarried. I found no mention of either, after a certain date, in the letters of Constance, Robert or Emily, which makes it seem likely both died young. Fitzgeorge refers, in a letter to Robert written in his old age, to some friend of their youth who was thrown from his horse and killed, riding back after a visit to their home. The young man, whose name doesn't appear, was alone; and the evening, which was in autumn, was fine though late. Fitzgeorge wonders, and says he will always wonder, what made the horse shy in those empty fields."

COMMENT AND QUESTION

1. *Chronology.* Half of this story takes place in World War Two, during the day and night bombing of London. The other half takes place about 1850.

2. *The impression of Victorian life.* In this story the reader will find a contrast drawn between the calm, well-ordered, traditional life of Victorian England and the chaos of life in World War Two. The author makes a significant point about Victorian life. She shows that under the Victorian surface, under the equanimity and propriety, lay repressed tension and passion. The solidity of Victorian life is best seen in the description of the drawing room in the third section. But what is hap-

pening beneath the surface? Awakened love and the violence of death are in the room.

3. *Sarah and Henrietta.* At least three times we are given clues which indicate that Henrietta is irrepressible, unstable, and ungovernable, all of which help to explain her final act. Clearly Henrietta waved her handkerchief once more as Eugene rode home across the darkening autumn fields. Do you know what a sister fixation is? The final paragraph of this story is frightening in its Freudian implications.

4. *Symbols.*

a. In the scene in the drawing room when Constance brings the lamps, she exclaims to her mother, "I cannot see who is with you." The principals, of course, are there: Eugene, Sarah, and Henrietta. Henrietta's answer contains the symbolic implications. Love and death are in the room. Henrietta's statement, "Eugene is with us," carries the promise of love. The second half of Henrietta's statement carries the threat of death.

b. Notice that the drawing room carpet has a center wreath of pomegranates. Pomegranates are forever associated with the mythological tale of Ceres and her daughter, Proserpine. Seized by Pluto and carried off to the underworld, Proseprine refused to eat until she could be restored to light. But one day she ate six seeds of a pomegranate. As a result, when she was finally restored to the light of day, it was for six months only. The other six months she was forced to spend underground.

Sarah, too, is torn by divided emotions. When she is asked the veiled question, "Do you love Eugene?", she places her chair in the middle of the wreath of pomegranates in the carpet and answers evasively.

c. Notice how the bomb that awakens Mary comes at the climax of the Victorian story.

5. *The purpose of the author.* The experience of Mary in "The Happy Autumn Fields," is a kind of resistance against a wartime life which had robbed her of personal identity and personal emotion. A serious student will want to read Miss Bowen's preface to her collection of stories, *Ivy Gripped the Steps,* from which "The Happy Autumn Fields," is taken. The stories in this collection reveal in their consecutive arrangement "a rising tide of hallucination." In her preface Miss Bowen tells how and why she came to write this particular story.

THEY WEREN'T GOING TO DIE

BY KAY BOYLE

KAY BOYLE (1903–   ) was born in St. Paul, Minnesota, but during most of her adult life she has lived in Europe. She has published several volumes of short stories, a number of novels, and a collection of poems. She has won the O. Henry Memorial Award twice, in 1935 with "White Horses of Vienna," and in 1941 with "Defeat." In the ten years between 1940 and 1950 she was represented four times in the *O. Henry Memorial Award Prize Stories* collection. These four stories, "Monsieur Panalitus," "Their Name Is Macaroni," "The Canals of Mars," and "Summer Evening," reflect both the upheaval and the aftermath of the second World War.

THEY were most of them rather tall men, tall, lanky black men with their heads carried high and with dignity on their smooth straight necks. If you walked behind a group of them wandering idly and with almost girl-like flippancy of gesture down the road, you could hear their shy, giddy laughter and speech, and you saw at once that the uniform they wore had nothing to do with their bones or their gait. The tunics and trousers and boots had all been made for somebody else, for some other race of men who knew when they came to a town what they wanted: *bistrot*, or a *tabac*, or paper and ink to write to somebody at home. They were never made for the softly hee-heeing, melodiously murmuring Senegalese, who went plucking the heads off daisies and nudging each other like schoolgirls as they ambled through the springtime evening toward the river and fields, out of the direction of and the setting for war. Their necks

---

rose rounded and smooth from the khaki cloth, with a little spring in the
arch of them just before the hair began growing high on their pates, and
from the back like this you could see the ears lying close to the small,
elegantly fashioned skulls.

There was a general term for them, for the Senegalese: one that covered
the whole foolish, aimless-seeming catastrophe of them, the long, loose-
hanging hands and the narrow hips and the quickly lipped and unlipped
smiles. In cinema theaters they were recognized as this, where they might
be seen in the actualities of the week marching half indolently in military
formation across the screen toward what nobody had taken the trouble to
show them a picture of or told them how loud the noise was going to be.
And Frenchmen, marking with colored pins on the wall map the drastic
sweeping line of the German descent through France, would put their
fingers down south of Lyon and speak the name for them again and again.
They would say: "Here's where we're pushing the *chair de canon* up,"
and if the black men had heard it they would not have known what it
meant or, anyway, that it was meant for them. But they wouldn't have
heard it because they would have been wandering off toward the river,
the incongruous army boots heavy and dusty on their feet, and daisies or
the flowers of other weeds broken off and brushing switchlike in their
hands. They knew they were going to kill people, maybe a lot of people,
smiling big softlipped smiles and looking sideways in the evening at each
other, but they hadn't come all the way out here just to die. They hadn't
walked down the hills of home, descending the paths with their hands
in their fathers' or their uncles' or their male cousins' or their older
brothers' hands toward the colonial towns and military service, for absolutely nothing. They had taken a long time learning which was the right
and which was the left, and how to count up to forty-six or -seven, and
what the foreign orders meant. In a little while they knew they were going
to start singing again, and do the belly dance to the tom-toms that summer, but one thing they weren't going to do: they certainly weren't going
to die.

Twenty or more of them had been billeted in the Count's stable on his
property south of the city, and the first evening the Count left them alone.
But in the morning he put on his gray tweed jacket and smoothed his
oiled, thinning hair back in his hands and stepped down the driveway to
look them over in the sun: a big, well-manicured gentleman of fifty maybe,
with heavy shoulders and a sveltely corseted *tour de taille,* and his pince-
nez hanging on a ribbon. He had been an Anglophile so long that it
showed by this time in the way his eyelids fell halfway over his sight and
hung there, and the way his chin returned to his throat and vanished
whenever he opened his mouth to speak. He stood in the stable door with
the light behind him, the height and the weight exaggerated so, and the
baby lieutenant whose family kept a good hotel on the water front at

Cannes stood before him in the darkness of the stable, not quite certain how to address him or exactly what to say. But the Count said at once:

"I gathered there was someone too young for it in command," and he snapped the pince-nez on the high hard arch of the nose his ancestors had handed down from one generation to the next. There it hung between the hard, well-shaven jowls, as outmoded as the battle-ax tacked up among the relics of another time and the armorial bearings in the dining hall. "There's one of them got into the house," the Count said. "I saw the back of him making down the corridor as I came out," and the little lieutenant straightened up like a flash and settled his leather belt in a military way.

"I'll have it taken care of at once, Monsieur," he said, but the Count wasn't finished with him yet. He took off his pince-nez and with the rim of one glass he tapped the lieutenant sharply on the khaki breast where the decorations hadn't yet been pinned.

"I don't know what the army's composed of this time or what kind of war you're running, young man," he said, and the lieutenant's color ran up under his delicate skin to his black silk brows, and he bit his lip. "As far as I can see there's no discipline, no order, not an ounce of stamina in the superiors." He drew up his heavy, stooping shoulders in the London-cut tweed and sucked his waist in, as if for military bearing, and looked down on the young officer with his bleak, withering eye.

"I feel certain it won't happen again, Monsieur," the little officer said, but for all of that it happened three times again that day.

It seemed there was nothing to be done with the tall, black, grinning fool who went sidling out of the loft no matter whom the lieutenant set to guard him, and went ambling back through the château's ancient, imported trees and in through the window or the door and down the ground-floor corridor to the place he liked so well. There they found him the first time when they searched the house, and there he was the second, and the third, not even taking the trouble to lock the door as other people did when they entered this particular place. He was sitting on the window sill above the porcelain receptacle, his puttees unwound and his breeches drawn up high, and his bare black feet hung down in the water that was there for another use entirely. The servants said they could hear him laughing out loud all the way in the kitchen whenever he pulled the chain and the water flushed up across his shins. Even the third time the lieutenant opened the door, the black man was sitting there, smiling right across his face, and reaching up to pull the chain again.

"What in the name of God do you think you're in France for?" the Count exploded before the lieutenant could clear his own throat of the youthful hesitation in it and snap the orders out.

"Kill Boche," said the Senegalese, with his feet dabbling in the water still. "Come kill Boche," he said, and he was reaching up to pull the porcelain handle when the lieutenant took him by the neck of his tunic and jerked him off the sill.

The weather held six weeks for war that time as it never did for pleasure, and the Count told the lieutenant that afternoon to get the blacks busy on the soil. His gardeners had been mobilized and he had been making out with a boy as best as he could, but now he had had quite enough of this military horseplay. The potato plants were waiting for the earth to be hoed up compactly around them, so a half dozen of the Senegalese were set to that, stripped to the waist and bent like oarsmen under the sun. Others were put to work the length of the strawberry beds, weeding and raking out between the clumps of low glossy leaves and the just-shedding strawberry flowers beneath the southern wall. The pear trees had been trained to spread out like vines across the hot stones of the wall, and on the other side the main road from Lyon led on around the curve and dropped down the hill to the village. Whenever the Senegalese turned their heads that way they could see over the top of the wall, through the pear leaves, whatever happened to be passing by.

They could see the trees and the fields and the waters of the river moving off beyond, and they leaned on the rake handles and the spade handles, talking among themselves. They would strike at the ground a little, and then the Senegalese melody rose sweetly on their tongues and they would pause again, giggling like women at each other. It was not from indolence that they ceased to turn the earth or pluck the weeds out of the Count's rich soil, nor out of what might have been native languor that they leaned on their implements and looked off through the leaves. They might have been merely waiting there, waiting for the name and the look of the thing that was to come, and work was not in them, for this was not the promise that had been made. The Count came out after tea and he saw them leaning in these long, loose attitudes of ease, their big hands hanging from their idle wrists, or clasped at rest on the rake handles and the spade handles and the hoes. There they had paused, like children halted on the edge of Christmas Eve, the blood humming with it, the babble of credulity tittering from lip to ear to eye.

"What are you canaille waiting for?" the little lieutenant called out as he hurried across the drive. He was beginning to play his part quite well, although in a panicky, puerile way. The Senegalese shifted the instruments in their hands, and moved their feet, and looked out toward the river. "What are you waiting for to get on with the job?" he shouted out, and one of the black men lifted his hand like a black lily drooping from the wrist and moved it toward the sky.

"Kill Boche," he said. "Waiting for the sun to go."

The Count seemed to have set the worldly manner aside for the moment, and he opened his arms in his gray tweed jacket and looked around in mock bewilderment.

"But where is the Boche? There's no Boche here as far as I can see," he said. It was he, by his own cunning, who was to establish himself the unmistakable master of the situation as he was the master of the château and the lawn. "Everything's very peaceful and quiet here," he went on saying, and as he spoke to the blacks he put an innocent look on his long, outmoded face. He was going to get the better of them in their own way now, steal their blue-black thunder from them by his utter guilelessness and charm. "No Boche, no kill," he said, and his chin collapsed into his neck as he smiled around the vegetable garden at them. "Work," he said, and he made the gestures of spading, hoeing, raking before them on the air.

"Boche tomorrow, maybe Boche tonight," said the black man, and he lifted his hand again and moved it in casual indication from place to place. "Kill Boche there—there—there—there," he said, letting it fall from the wrist once toward the trees and once toward the wall and twice beyond it, and the Senegalese music of talk rose on their tongues again, then waned and died.

It was just before six that evening that the first motorcycle was heard coming down the road. The three Senegalese near the pear trees straightened up from the strawberry beds and their vision came level with the top of the wall and sought beyond it. They saw first the trees on the other side and then the surface of the road and at last the color of the solitary rider's jacket as he came leaning to the handle bars. They spoke the word or gave the sign in silence, and then their feet raced naked and wild back across the garden and the drive to where the guns were stacked in the stable yard, their legs reaching, their mouths splitting wide. They went so fast they were back in time for the second one: he dropped from his machine just where the brass studs began marking the curve of the turn and the motorcycle ran of itself a little way down the hill before it hit the tree. The third had a sidecar with a machine gunner riding in it, but neither the driver on the leather saddle nor the gunner behind his curved glass shield had time to see the khaki drape of the turbans or the guns along the wall. It did not make the turn this time but ran with the two dead men on its seats into the ditch and sputtered out there, and the others coming along behind were thirty seconds too late to see. There they came hastening down the road from Lyon, sidecar after sidecar of them driving fast, and as they came the black men picked them off over the garden wall and jumped up and down on the strawberry plants on their naked feet in glee.

The seventh or eighth was a single rider again, and this time the warning was there, splattered out on the road before him. He lifted his head to the pear leaves on top of the wall and braked so that the tires cried aloud, and swung the machine on its haunches, rearing and pawing the air. When he poured into speed and streamed back up the road, crouched flat to the bars, the black men's hearts stood still in pain. They waited there for a moment, and then they looked at each other and they could no longer find the sounds of laughter or speech. It might have been just after six on Christmas Day, and the stockings emptied, the presents all opened, the candles on the tree put out. They hadn't quite got over it when the nimble little tank came down the road, its eyes, like those of a snail, fingering them out, nor when the second tank came down behind it and the piece of the garden wall suddenly blew in.

The look of disappointment was on their faces still when the Count came out to have a look at them lying there. The machine gunners who had finished them off were removing their smoked goggles just inside the gate, and the German officer was chatting amiably with the Count as he walked with him out through the rose garden which shielded the vegetable beds from the drive. There were the black men, foolish-looking and rather giddy even in death, lying among the strawberry flowers and the potato plants.

"The staff will be along almost at once," the German officer was saying in a rather heavy but easy French. "I'd like to get this cleaned up without delay. It's a charming place, really charming. Regrettable that it was necessary to touch the wall."

The Count put his pince-nez on with a hand that did not tremble, and as the thought struck him with singular force, *Gentlemen, actually well-bred men this time,* he said aloud:

"The bodies removed?" and he felt himself sickening and turned the other way.

"Buried," said the German officer pleasantly. He had a kid glove, as scrupulously clean as if just lifted from the haberdasher's counter, on the hand with which he touched the Count's tweed. "I'm sorry to give you all this trouble," he said. "The staff will require most of the bedrooms for the moment at least." Then he turned toward the black men again and gave his orders. "Right where they are," he said shortly. "Snipers' burial." "Right there—there, you mean?" said the Count. He was thinking confusedly of the potato plants and the strawberry flowers, but he could not bring himself to turn and look at them again.

COMMENT AND QUESTION

1. The title of this story is made to apply obviously to the Senegalese. But it applies with most force to some other people in the story. Who are they?

2. When Hitler invaded France in 1940, France had a supposedly impregnable Maginot line and a fine army. But she collapsed swiftly. This story holds a clue to the shattering fall of France in the second World War.

3. Between 1870 and 1940, Germany invaded France three times. What details in the story reflect this history?

4. This story was published first in *The New Yorker* and reflects the understatement so characteristic of the style of the magazine. But unlike many *New Yorker* stories, "They Weren't Going to Die" develops emotion, here a warm sympathy for the Senegalese. Miss Boyle arouses also a feeling of injustice and pain because of the dishonor done to the Senegalese. In all fairness, were the Senegalese really snipers?

5. "What in the name of God do you think you're in France for?" Like the title, this question of the Count's is ironical and holds the theme of the story.

6. At the end of the story the Count is confused. What conflicting ideas and emotions seem to be possessing him?

7. Notice the recurring metaphor concerning Christmas. How does this metaphor help to explain the actions of the Senegalese?

THE HANDS OF
MR. OTTERMOLE

BY THOMAS BURKE

THOMAS BURKE (1887–1945) was born in London. He established his reputation with his stories about the East End of London. His collections of short stories include *Limehouse Nights* (1919), *More Limehouse Nights* (1921), and *A Tea-Shop in Limehouse* (1931).

MURDER (said old Quong)—oblige me by passing my pipe—murder is one of the simplest things in the world to do. Killing a man is a much simpler matter than killing a duck. Not always so safe, perhaps, but simpler. But to certain gifted people it is both simple and entirely safe. Many minds of finer complexion than my own have discoloured themselves in seeking to name the identity of the author of those wholesale murders which took place last year. Who that man or woman really was, I know no more than you do, but I have a theory of the person it could have been; and if you are not pressed for time I will elaborate that theory into a little tale.

As I had the rest of that evening and the whole of the next day for dalliance in my ivory tower, I desired that he would tell me the story; and, having reckoned up his cash register and closed the ivory gate, he told me —between then and the dawn—his story of the Mallon End murders. Paraphrased and condensed, it came out something like this.

At six o'clock of a January evening Mr. Whybrow was walking home through the cobweb alleys of London's East End. He had left the golden clamour of the great High Street to which the tram had brought him from the river and his daily work, and was now in the chess-board of byways that is called Mallon End. None of the rush and gleam of the High Street trickled into these byways. A few paces south—a flood-tide of life, foaming and beating. Here—only slow shuffling figures and muffled pulses. He was in the sink of London, the last refuge of European vagrants.

As though in tune with the street's spirit, he too walked slowly, with head down. It seemed that he was pondering some pressing trouble, but he was not. He had no trouble. He was walking slowly because he had been on his feet all day, and he was bent in abstraction because he was wondering whether the Missis would have herrings for his tea, or haddock; and he was trying to decide which would be the more tasty on a night like this. A wretched night it was, of damp and mist, and the mist wandered into his throat and his eyes, and the damp had settled on pavement and roadway, and where the sparse lamp-light fell it sent up a greasy sparkle that chilled one to look at. By contrast it made his speculations more agreeable, and made him ready for that tea—whether herring or haddock. His eye turned from the glum bricks that made his horizon, and went forward half a mile. He saw a gas-lit kitchen, a flamy fire and a spread tea-table. There was toast in the hearth and a singing kettle on the side and a piquant effusion of herrings, or maybe of haddock, or perhaps sausages. The vision gave his aching feet a throb of energy. He shook imperceptible damp from his shoulders, and hastened towards its reality.

But Mr. Whybrow wasn't going to get any tea that evening—or any other evening. Mr. Whybrow was going to die. Somewhere within a hundred yards of him another man was walking: a man much like Mr. Whybrow and much like any other man, but without the only quality that enables mankind to live peaceably together and not as madmen in a jungle. A man with a dead heart eating into itself and bringing forth the foul organisms that arise from death and corruption. And that thing in man's shape, or a whim or a settled idea—one cannot know—had said within himself that Mr. Whybrow should never taste another herring. Not that Mr. Whybrow had injured him. Not that he had any dislike of Mr. Whybrow. Indeed, he knew nothing of him save as a familiar figure about the streets. But, moved by a force that had taken possession of his empty cells, he had picked on Mr. Whybrow with that blind choice that makes us pick one restaurant table that has nothing to mark it from four or five other tables, or one apple from a dish of half-a-dozen equal apples; or that drives Nature to send a cyclone upon one corner of this planet, and destroy five hundred lives in that corner, and leave another five hundred in the same corner unharmed. So this man had picked on Mr. Whybrow, as he might have picked on you or me, had we been within his daily observation; and even now he was creeping through the blue-toned streets, nursing his large white hands, moving ever closer to Mr. Whybrow's tea-table, so closer to Mr. Whybrow himself.

He wasn't, this man, a bad man. Indeed, he had many of the social and amiable qualities, and passed as a respectable man, as most successful criminals do. But the thought had come into his mouldering mind that he would like to murder somebody, and, as he held no fear of God or man, he was going to do it, and would then go home to *his* tea. I don't say that flippantly, but as a statement of fact. Strange as it may seem to the humane, murderers must and do sit down to meals after a murder. There is no reason why they shouldn't, and many reasons why they should. For one thing, they need to keep their physical and mental vitality at full beat for the business of covering their crime. For another, the strain of their effort makes them hungry, and satisfaction at the accomplishment of a desired thing brings a feeling of relaxation towards human pleasures. It is accepted among non-murderers that the murderer is always overcome by fear for his safety and horror at his act; but this type is rare. His own safety is, of course, his immediate concern, but vanity is a marked quality of most murderers, and that, together with the thrill of conquest, makes him confident that he can secure it, and when he has restored his strength with food he goes about securing it as a young hostess goes about the arranging of her first big dinner—a little anxious, but no more. Criminologists and detectives tell us that *every* murderer, however intelligent or cunning, always makes one slip in his tactics—one little slip that brings the affair home to him. But that is only half-true. It is true only of the murderers who are caught. Scores of murderers are not caught: therefore scores of murderers do not make any mistake at all. This man didn't.

As for horror or remorse, prison chaplains, doctors and lawyers have told us that of murderers they have interviewed under condemnation and the shadow of death, only one here and there has expressed any contrition for his act, or shown any sign of mental misery. Most of them display only exasperation at having been caught when so many have gone undiscovered, or indignation at being condemned for a perfectly reasonable act. However normal and humane they may have been before the murder, they are utterly without conscience after it. For what is conscience? Simply a polite nickname for superstition, which is a polite nickname for fear. Those who associate remorse with murder are, no doubt, basing their ideas on the world-legend of the remorse of Cain, or are projecting their own frail minds into the mind of the murderer, and getting false reactions. Peaceable folk cannot hope to make contact with this mind, for they are not merely different in mental type from the murderer: they are different in their personal chemistry and construction. Some men can and do kill, not one man, but two or three, and go calmly about their daily affairs. Other men could not, under the most agonising provocation, bring themselves even to wound. It is men of this sort who imagine the murderer in torments of remorse and fear of the law, whereas he is actually sitting down to his tea.

The man with the large white hands was as ready for his tea as Mr. Whybrow was, but he had something to do before he went to it. When he had done that something, and made no mistake about it, he would be even more ready for it, and would go to it as comfortably as he went to it the day before, when his hands were stainless.

Walk on, then, Mr. Whybrow, walk on; and as you walk, look your last upon the familiar features of your nightly journey. Follow your jack-o'-lantern tea-table. Look well upon its warmth and colour and kindness; feed your eyes with it, and tease your nose with its gentle domestic odours; for you will never sit down to it. Within ten minutes' pacing of you a pursuing phantom has spoken in his heart, and you are doomed. There you go —you and phantom—two nebulous dabs of mortality, moving through green air along pavements of powder-blue, the one to kill, the other to be killed. Walk on. Don't annoy your burning feet by hurrying, for the more slowly you walk, the longer you will breathe the green air of this January dusk, and see the dreamy lamplight and the little shops, and hear the agreeable commerce of the London crowd and the haunting pathos of the street-organ. These things are dear to you, Mr. Whybrow. You don't know it now, but in fifteen minutes you will have two seconds in which to realise how inexpressibly dear they are.

Walk on, then, across this crazy chess-board. You are in Lagos Street now, among the tents of the wanderers of Eastern Europe. A minute or so, and you are in Loyal Lane, among the lodging-houses that shelter the useless and the beaten of London's camp-followers. The lane holds the smell of them, and its soft darkness seems heavy with the wail of the futile. But you are not sensitive to impalpable things, and you plod through it, unseeing, as you do every evening, and come to Blean Street, and plod through that. From basement to sky rise the tenements of an alien colony. Their windows slot the ebony of their walls with lemon. Behind those windows strange life is moving, dressed with forms that are not of London or of England, yet, in essence, the same agreeable life that you have been living, and to-night will live no more. From high above you comes a voice crooning *The Song of Katta*. Through a window you see a family keeping a religious rite. Through another you see a woman pouring out tea for her husband. You see a man mending a pair of boots; a mother bathing her baby. You have seen all these things before, and never noticed them. You do not notice them now, but if you knew that you were never going to see them again, you would notice them. You never *will* see them again, not because your life has run its natural course, but because a man whom you have often passed in the street has at his own solitary pleasure decided to usurp the awful authority of nature, and destroy you. So perhaps it's as well that you don't notice them, for your part in them is ended. No more for you these pretty moments of our earthly travail: only one moment of terror, and then a plunging darkness.

Closer to you this shadow of massacre moves, and now he is twenty yards behind you. You can hear his footfall, but you do not turn your head. You are familiar with footfalls. You are in London, in the easy security of your daily territory, and footfalls behind you, your instinct tells you, are no more than a message of human company.

But can't you hear something in those footfalls—something that goes with a widdershins beat? Something that says: *Look out, look out. Beware, beware.* Can't you hear the very syllables of *murd-er-er, murd-er-er?* No; there is nothing in footfalls. They are neutral. The foot of villainy falls with the same quiet note as the foot of honesty. But those footfalls, Mr. Whybrow, are bearing on to you a pair of hands, and there *is* something in hands. Behind you that pair of hands is even now stretching its muscles in preparation for your end. Every minute of your days you have been seeing human hands. Have you ever realised the sheer horror of hands—those appendages that are a symbol for our moments of trust and affection and salutation? Have you thought of the sickening potentialities that lie within the scope of that five-tentacled member? No, you never have; for all the human hands that you have seen have been stretched to you in kindness or fellowship. Yet, though the eyes can hate, and the lips can sting, it is only that dangling member that can gather the accumulated essence of evil, and electrify it into currents of destruction. Satan may enter into man by many doors, but in the hands alone can he find the servants of his will.

Another minute, Mr. Whybrow, and you will know all about the horror of human hands.

You are nearly home now. You have turned into your street—Caspar Street—and you are in the centre of the chess-board. You can see the front window of your little four-roomed house. The street is dark, and its three lamps give only a smut of light that is more confusing than darkness. It is dark—empty, too. Nobody about; no lights in the front parlours of the houses, for the families are at tea in their kitchens; and only a random glow in a few upper rooms occupied by lodgers. Nobody about but you and your following companion, and you don't notice him. You see him so often that he is never seen. Even if you turned your head and saw him, you would only say "Good-evening" to him, and walk on. A suggestion that he was a possible murderer would not even make you laugh. It would be too silly.

And now you are at your gate. And now you have found your door-key. And now you are in, and hanging up your hat and coat. The Missis has just called a greeting from the kitchen, whose smell is an echo of that greeting (herrings!) and you have answered it, when the door shakes under a sharp knock.

Go away, Mr. Whybrow. Go away from that door. Don't touch it. Get right away from it. Get out of the house. Run with the Missis to the back garden, and over the fence. Or call the neighbours. But don't touch that door. Don't, Mr. Whybrow, don't open . . .

Mr. Whybrow opened the door.

That was the beginning of what became known as London's Strangling Horrors. Horrors they were called because they were something more than murders: they were motiveless, and there was an air of black magic about them. Each murder was committed at a time when the street where the bodies were found was empty of any perceptible or possible murderer. There would be an empty alley. There would be a policeman at its end. He would turn his back on the empty alley for less than a minute. Then he would look round and run into the night with news of another strangling. And in any direction he looked nobody to be seen and no report to be had of anybody being seen. Or he would be on duty in a long quiet street, and suddenly be called to a house of dead people whom a few seconds earlier he had seen alive. And, again, whichever way he looked nobody to be seen; and although police whistles put an immediate cordon around the area, and searched all houses, no possible murderer to be found.

The first news of the murder of Mr. and Mrs. Whybrow was brought by the station sergeant. He had been walking through Caspar Street on his way to the station for duty, when he noticed the open door of No. 98. Glancing in, he saw by the gaslight of the passage a motionless body on the floor. After a second look he blew his whistle, and when the constables answered him he took one to join him in a search of the house, and sent others to watch all neighbouring streets, and make inquiries at adjoining houses. But neither in the house nor in the streets was anything found to indicate the murderer. Neighbours on either side, and opposite, were questioned, but they had seen nobody about, and had heard nothing. One had heard Mr. Whybrow come home—the scrape of his latch-key in the door was so regular an evening sound, he said, that you could set your watch by it for half-past six—but he had heard nothing more than the sound of the opening door until the sergeant's whistle. Nobody had been seen to enter the house or leave it, by front or back, and the necks of the dead people carried no fingerprints or other traces. A nephew was called in to go over the house, but he could find nothing missing; and anyway his uncle possessed nothing worth stealing. The little money in the house was untouched, and there were no signs of any disturbance of the property, or even of struggle. No signs of anything but brutal and wanton murder.

Mr. Whybrow was known to neighbours and work-mates as a quiet, likeable, home-loving man; such a man as could not have any enemies. But, then, murdered men seldom have. A relentless enemy who hates a man to the point of wanting to hurt him seldom wants to murder him, since to do that puts him beyond suffering. So the police were left with an impossible situation: no clue to the murderer and no motive for the murders; only the fact that they had been done.

The first news of the affair sent a tremor through London generally, and an electric thrill through all Mallon End. Here was a murder of two inoffensive people, not for gain and not for revenge; and the murderer, to whom, apparently, killing was a casual impulse, was at large. He had left no traces, and, provided he had no companions, there seemed no reason why he should not remain at large. Any clear-headed man who stands alone, and has no fear of God or man, can, if he chooses, hold a city, even a nation, in subjection; but your everyday criminal is seldom clear-headed, and dislikes being lonely. He needs, if not the support of confederates, at least somebody to talk to; his vanity needs the satisfaction of perceiving at first hand the effect of his work. For this he will frequent bars and coffee-shops and other public places. Then, sooner or later, in a glow of comradeship, he will utter the one word too much; and the nark, who is everywhere, has an easy job.

But though the doss-houses and saloons and other places were "combed" and set with watches, and it was made known by whispers that good money and protection were assured to those with information, nothing attaching to the Whybrow case could be found. The murderer clearly had no friends and kept no company. Known men of this type were called up and questioned, but each was able to give a good account of himself; and in a few days the police were at a dead end. Against the constant public gibe that the thing had been done almost under their noses, they became restive, and for four days each man of the force was working his daily beat under a strain. On the fifth day they became still more restive.

It was the season of annual teas and entertainments for the children of the Sunday Schools, and on an evening of fog, when London was a world of groping phantoms, a small girl, in the bravery of best Sunday frock and shoes, shining face and new-washed hair, set out from Logan Passage for St. Michael's Parish Hall. She never got there. She was not actually dead until half-past six, but she was as good as dead from the moment she left her mother's door. Somebody like a man, pacing the street from which the Passage led, saw her come out; and from that moment she was dead. Through the fog somebody's large white hands reached after her, and in fifteen minutes they were about her.

At half-past six a whistle screamed trouble, and those answering it found the body of little Nellie Brinoff in a warehouse entry in Minnow Street. The sergeant was first among them, and he posted his men to useful points, ordering them here and there in the tart tones of repressed rage, and berating the officer whose beat the street was. "I saw you, Magson, at the end of the lane. What were you up to there? You were there ten minutes before you turned." Magson began an explanation about keeping an eye on a suspicious-looking character at that end, but the sergeant cut him short: "Suspicious character be damned. You don't want to look for suspicious characters. You want to look for *murderers*. Messing about . . . and then this happens right where you ought to be. Now think what they'll say."

With the speed of ill news came the crowd, pale and perturbed; and on the story that the unknown monster had appeared again, and this time to a child, their faces streaked the fog with spots of hate and horror. But then came the ambulance and more police, and swiftly they broke up the crowd; and as it broke the sergeant's thought was thickened into words, and from all sides came low murmurs of "Right under their noses." Later inquiries showed that four people of the district, above suspicion, had passed that entry at intervals of seconds before the murder, and seen nothing and heard nothing. None of them had passed the child alive or seen her dead. None of them had seen anybody in the street except themselves. Again the police were left with no motive and with no clue.

And now the district, as you will remember, was given over, not to panic, for the London public never yields to that, but to apprehension and dismay. If these things were happening in their familiar streets, then anything might happen. Wherever people met—in the streets, the markets and the shops—they debated the one topic. Women took to bolting their windows and doors at the first fall of dusk. They kept their children closely under their eye. They did their shopping before dark, and watched anxiously, while pretending they weren't watching, for the return of their husbands from work. Under the Cockney's semi-humorous resignation to disaster, they hid an hourly foreboding. By the whim of one man with a pair of hands the structure and tenour of their daily life were shaken, as they always can be shaken by any man contemptuous of humanity and fearless of its laws. They began to realise that the pillars that supported the peaceable society in which they lived were mere straws that anybody could snap; that laws were powerful only so long as they were obeyed; that the police were potent only so long as they were feared. By the power of his hands this one man had made a whole community do something new: he had made it think, and left it gasping at the obvious.

And then, while it was yet gasping under his first two strokes, he made his third. Conscious of the horror that his hands had created, and hungry as an actor who has once tasted the thrill of the multitude, he made fresh advertisement of his presence; and on Wednesday morning, three days after the murder of the child, the papers carried to the breakfast-tables of England the story of a still more shocking outrage.

At 9:32 on Tuesday night a constable was on duty in Jarnigan Road, and at that time spoke to a fellow-officer named Petersen at the top of Clemming Street. He had seen this officer walk down that street. He could swear that the street was empty at that time, except for a lame boot-black whom he knew by sight, and who passed him and entered a tenement on the side opposite that on which his fellow-officer was walking. He had the habit, as all constables had just then, of looking constantly behind him and around him, whichever way he was walking, and he was certain that the street was empty. He passed his sergeant at 9:33, saluted him, and answered his inquiry for anything seen. He reported that he had seen nothing, and passed on. His beat ended at a short distance from Clemming Street, and, having paced it, he turned and came again at 9:34 to the top of the street. He had scarcely reached it before he heard the hoarse voice of the sergeant: "Gregory! You there? Quick. Here's another. My God, it's Petersen! Garotted. Quick, call 'em up!"

That was the third of the Strangling Horrors, of which there were to be a fourth and a fifth; and the five horrors were to pass into the unknown and unknowable. That is, unknown as far as authority and the public were concerned. The identity of the murderer *was* known, but to two men only. One was the murderer himself; the other was a young journalist.

This young man, who was covering the affairs for his paper, the *Daily Torch*, was no smarter than the other zealous newspaper men who were hanging about these byways in the hope of a sudden story. But he was patient, and he hung a little closer to the case than the other fellows, and by continually staring at it he at last raised the figure of the murderer like a genie from the stones on which he had stood to do his murders.

After the first few days the men had given up any attempt at exclusive stories, for there was none to be had. They met regularly at the police-station, and what little information there was they shared. The officials were agreeable to them, but no more. The sergeant discussed with them the details of each murder; suggested possible explanations of the man's methods; recalled from the past those cases that had some similarity; and on the matter of motive reminded them of the motiveless Neil Cream and the wanton John Williams, and hinted that work was being done which would soon bring the business to an end; but about that work he would not say a word. The Inspector, too, was gracefully garrulous on the thesis of Murder, but whenever one of the party edged the talk towards what was being done in this immediate matter, he glided past it. Whatever the officials knew, they were not giving it to newspaper men. The business had fallen heavily upon them, and only by a capture made by their own efforts could they rehabilitate themselves in official and public esteem. Scotland Yard, of course, was at work, and had all the station's material; but the station's hope was that they themselves would have the honour of settling the affair; and however useful the co-operation of the Press might be in other cases, they did not want to risk a defeat by a premature dis-closure of their theories and plans.

So the sergeant talked at large, and propounded one interesting theory after another, all of which the newspaper men had thought of themselves.

The young man soon gave up these morning lectures on the Philosophy of Crime, and took to wandering about the streets and making bright stories out of the effect of the murders on the normal life of the people. A melancholy job made more melancholy by the district. The littered roadways, the crestfallen houses, the bleared windows—all held the acid misery that evokes no sympathy: the misery of the frustrated poet. The misery was the creation of the aliens, who were living in this makeshift fashion because they had no settled homes, and would neither take the trouble to make a home where they *could* settle, nor get on with their wandering.

There was little to be picked up. All he saw and heard were indignant faces, and wild conjectures of the murderer's identity and of the secret of his trick of appearing and disappearing unseen. Since a policeman himself had fallen a victim, denunciations of the force had ceased, and the unknown was now invested with a cloak of legend. Men eyed other men, as though thinking: It might be *him*. It might be *him*. They were no longer looking for a man who had the air of a Madame Tussaud murderer; they were looking for a man, or perhaps some harridan woman, who had done these particular murders. Their thoughts ran mainly on the foreign set. Such ruffianism could scarcely belong to England, nor could the bewildering cleverness of the thing. So they turned to Roumanian gipsies and Turkish carpet-sellers. There, clearly, would be found the "warm" spot. These Eastern fellows—they knew all sorts of tricks, and they had no real religion—nothing to hold them within bounds. Sailors returning from those parts had told tales of conjurors who made themselves invisible; and there were tales of Egyptian and Arab potions that were used for abysmally queer purposes. Perhaps it *was* possible to them; you never knew. They were so slick and cunning, and they had such gliding movements; no Englishman could melt away as they could. Almost certainly the murderer would be found to be one of that sort—with some dark trick of his own—and just because they were sure that he *was* a magician, they felt that it was useless to look for him. He was a power, able to hold them in subjection and to hold himself untouchable. Superstition, which so easily cracks the frail shell of reason, had got into them. He could do anything he chose: he would never be discovered. These two points they settled, and they went about the streets in a mood of resentful fatalism.

They talked of their ideas to the journalist in half-tones, looking right and left, as though HE might overhear them and visit them. And though all the district was thinking of him and ready to pounce upon him, yet, so strongly had he worked upon them, that if any man in the street—say, a small man of commonplace features and form—had cried "*I* am the Monster!" would their stifled fury have broken into flood and have borne him down and engulfed him? Or would they not suddenly have seen something unearthly in that everyday face and figure, something unearthly in his everyday boots, something unearthly about his hat, something that marked him as one whom none of their weapons could alarm or pierce? And would they not momentarily have fallen back from this devil, as the devil fell back from the Cross made by the sword of Faust, and so have given him time to escape? I do not know; but so fixed was their belief in his invincibility that it is at least likely that they would have made this hesitation, had such an occasion arisen. But it never did. To-day this commonplace fellow, his murder lust glutted, is still seen and observed among them as he was seen and observed all the time; but because nobody then dreamt, or now dreams, that he was what he was, they observed him then, and observe him now, as people observe a lamp-post.

Almost was their belief in his invincibility justified; for, five days after the murder of the policeman Petersen, when the experience and inspiration of the whole detective force of London were turned towards his identification and capture, he made his fourth and fifth strokes.

At nine o'clock that evening, the young newspaper man, who hung about every night until his paper was away, was strolling along Richards Lane. Richards Lane is a narrow street, partly a stall-market, and partly residential. The young man was in the residential section, which carries on one side small working-class cottages, and on the other the wall of a railway goods-yard. The great wall hung a blanket of shadow over the lane, and the shadow and the cadaverous outline of the now deserted market stalls gave it the appearance of a living lane that had been turned to frost in the moment between breath and death. The very lamps, that elsewhere were nimbuses of gold, had here the rigidity of gems. The journalist, feeling this message of frozen eternity, was telling himself that he was tired of the whole thing, when in one stroke the frost was broken. In the moment between one pace and another silence and darkness were racked by a high scream and through the scream a voice: "Help! help! *He's here!*"

Before he could think what movement to make, the lane came to life. As though its invisible populace had been waiting on that cry, the door of every cottage was flung open, and from them and from the alleys poured shadowy figures bent in question-mark form. For a second or so they stood as rigid as the lamps; then a police whistle gave them direction, and the flock of shadows sloped up the street. The journalist followed them, and others followed him. From the main street and from surrounding streets they came, some risen from unfinished suppers, some disturbed in their ease of slippers and shirt-sleeves, some stumbling on infirm limbs, and some upright, and armed with pokers or the tools of their trade. Here and there above the wavering cloud of heads moved the bold helmets of policemen. In one dim mass they surged upon a cottage whose doorway was marked by the sergeant and two constables; and voices of those behind urged them on with "Get in! Find him! Run round the back! Over the wall!" and those in front cried: "Keep back! Keep back!"

And now the fury of a mob held in thrall by unknown peril broke loose. He was here—on the spot. Surely this time he *could not* escape. All minds were bent upon the cottage; all energies thrust towards its doors and windows and roof; all thought was turned upon one unknown man and his extermination. So that no one man saw any other man. No man saw the narrow, packed lane and the mass of struggling shadows, and all forgot to look among themselves for the monster who never lingered upon his victims. All forgot, indeed, that they, by their mass crusade of vengeance, were affording him the perfect hiding-place. They saw only the house, and they heard only the rending of woodwork and the smash of glass at back and front, and the police giving orders or crying with the chase; and they pressed on.

But they found no murderer. All they found was news of murder and a glimpse of the ambulance, and for their fury there was no other object than the police themselves, who fought against this hampering of their work.

The journalist managed to struggle through to the cottage door, and to get the story from the constable stationed there. The cottage was the home of a pensioned sailor and his wife and daughter. They had been at supper, and at first it appeared that some noxious gas had smitten all three in mid-action. The daughter lay dead on the hearth-rug, with a piece of bread-and-butter in her hand. The father had fallen sideways from his chair, leaving on his plate a filled spoon of rice-pudding. The mother lay half under the table, her lap filled with the pieces of a broken cup and splashes of cocoa. But in three seconds the idea of gas was dismissed. One glance at their necks showed that this was the Strangler again; and the police stood and looked at the room and momentarily shared the fatalism of the public. They were helpless.

This was his fourth visit, making seven murders in all. He was to do, as you know, one more—and to do it that night; and then he was to pass into history as the unknown London horror, and return to the decent life that he had always led, remembering little of what he had done, and worried not at all by the memory. Why did he stop? Impossible to say. Why did he begin? Impossible again. It just happened like that; and if he thinks at all of those days and nights, I surmise that he thinks of them as we think of foolish or dirty little sins that we committed in childhood. We say that they were not really sins, because we were not then consciously ourselves: we had not come to realisation; and we look back at that foolish little creature that we once were, and forgive him because he didn't know. So, I think, with this man.

There are plenty like him. Eugene Aram, after the murder of Daniel Clarke, lived a quiet, contented life for fourteen years, unhaunted by his crime and unshaken in his self-esteem. Dr. Crippen murdered his wife, and then lived pleasantly with his mistress in the house under whose floor he had buried the wife. Constance Kent, found Not Guilty of the murder of her young brother, led a peaceful life for five years before she confessed. George Joseph Smith and William Palmer lived amiably among their fellows untroubled by fear or by remorse for their poisonings and drownings. Charles Peace, at the time he made his one unfortunate essay, had settled down into a respectable citizen with an interest in antiques. It happened that, after a lapse of time, these men were discovered, but more murderers than we guess are living decent lives to-day, and will die in decency, undiscovered and unsuspected. As this man will.

But he had a narrow escape, and it was perhaps this narrow escape that brought him to a stop. The escape was due to an error of judgment on the part of the journalist.

As soon as he had the full story of the affair, which took some time, he spent fifteen minutes on the telephone, sending the story through, and at the end of the fifteen minutes, when the stimulus of the business had left him, he felt physically tired and mentally dishevelled. He was not yet free to go home; the paper would not go away for another hour; so he turned into a bar for a drink and some sandwiches.

It was then, when he had dismissed the whole business from his mind, and was looking about the bar and admiring the landlord's taste in watch-chains and his air of domination, and was thinking that the landlord of a well-conducted tavern had a more comfortable life than a newspaper man, that his mind received from nowhere a spark of light. He was not thinking about the Strangling Horrors; his mind was on his sandwich. As a public-house sandwich, it was a curiosity. The bread had been thinly cut, it was buttered, and the ham was not two months stale; it was ham as it should be. His mind turned to the inventor of this refreshment, the Earl of Sandwich, and then to George the Fourth, and then to the Georges, and to the legend of that George who was worried to know how the apple got into the apple-dumpling. He wondered whether George would have been equally puzzled to know how the ham got into the ham sandwich, and how long it would have been before it occurred to him that the ham could not have got there unless somebody had put it there. He got up to order another sandwich, and in that moment a little active corner of his mind settled the affair. If there was ham in his sandwich, somebody must have put it there. If seven people had been murdered, somebody must have been there to murder them. There was no aeroplane or automobile that would go into a man's pocket; therefore that somebody must have escaped either by running away or standing still; and again therefore—

He was visualising the front-page story that his paper would carry if his theory were correct, and if—a matter of conjecture—his editor had the necessary nerve to make a bold stroke, when a cry of "Time, gentlemen, please! All out!" reminded him of the hour. He got up and went out into a world of mist, broken by the ragged discs of roadside puddles and the streaming lightning of motor-buses. He was certain that he had *the* story, but, even if it were proved, he was doubtful whether the policy of his paper would permit him to print it. It had one great fault. It was truth, but it was impossible truth. It rocked the foundations of everything that newspaper readers believed and that newspaper editors helped them to believe. They might believe that Turkish carpet-sellers had the gift of making themselves invisible. They would not believe this.

As it happened, they were not asked to, for the story was never written. As his paper had by now gone away, and as he was nourished by his refreshment and stimulated by his theory, he thought he might put in an extra half-hour by testing that theory. So he began to look about for the man he had in mind—a man with white hair, and large white hands; otherwise an everyday figure whom nobody would look twice at. He wanted to spring his idea on this man without warning, and he was going to place himself within reach of a man armoured in legends of dreadfulness and grue. This might appear to be an act of supreme courage—that one man, with no hope of immediate outside support, should place himself at the mercy of one who was holding a whole parish in terror. But it wasn't. He didn't think about the risk. He didn't think about his duty to his employers or loyalty to his paper. He was moved simply by an instinct to follow a story to its end.

He walked slowly from the tavern and crossed into Fingal Street, making for Deever Market, where he had hope of finding his man. But his journey was shortened. At the corner of Lotus Street he saw him—or a man who looked like him. This street was poorly lit, and he could see little of the man: but he *could* see white hands. For some twenty paces he stalked him; then drew level with him; and at a point where the arch of a railway crossed the street, he saw that this was his man. He approached him with the current conversational phrase of the district: "Well, seen anything of the murderer?" The man stopped to look sharply at him; then, satisfied that the journalist was not the murderer, said:

"Eh? No, nor's anybody else, curse it. Doubt if they ever will."

"I don't know. I've been thinking about them, and I've got an idea."

"So?"

"Yes. Came to me all of a sudden. Quarter of an hour ago. And I'd felt that we'd all been blind. It's been staring us in the face."

The man turned again to look at him, and the look and the movement held suspicion of this man who seemed to know so much. "Oh? Has it? Well, if you're so sure, why not give us the benefit of it?"

"I'm going to." They walked level, and were nearly at the end of the little street where it meets Deever Market, when the journalist turned casually to the man. He put a finger on his arm. "Yes, it seems to me quite simple now. But there's still one point I don't understand. One little thing I'd like to clear up. I mean the motive. Now, as man to man, tell me, Sergeant Ottermole, just *why* did you kill all those inoffensive people?"

The sergeant stopped, and the journalist stopped. There was just enough light from the sky, which held the reflected light of the continent of London, to give his a sight of the sergeant's face, and the sergeant's face was turned to him with a wide smile of such urbanity and charm that the journalist's eyes were frozen as they met it. The smile stayed for some seconds. Then said the sergeant: "Well, to tell you the truth, Mister Newspaper Man, I don't know. I really don't know. In fact, I've been worried about it myself. But I've got an idea—just like you. Everybody knows that we can't control the workings of our minds. Don't they? Ideas come into our minds without asking. But everybody's supposed to be able to control his body. Why? Eh? We get our minds from lord-knows-where—from people who were dead hundreds of years before we were born. Mayn't we get our bodies in the same way? Our faces—our legs—our heads —they aren't completely ours. We don't make 'em. They come to us. And couldn't ideas come into our bodies like ideas come into our minds? Eh? Can't ideas live in nerve and muscle as well as in brain? Couldn't it be that parts of our bodies aren't really us, and couldn't ideas come into those parts all of a sudden, like ideas come into—into"—he shot his arms out, showing the great white-gloved hands and hairy wrists; shot them out so swiftly to the journalist's throat that his eyes never saw them—"into *my* hands!"

COMMENT AND QUESTION

Some of the details in this story seem to reflect the exploits of Jack the Ripper, who once terrorized the East End of London. Further comment cannot be made on this detective story without giving the plot away.

PAUL'S CASE

BY WILLA CATHER

WILLA CATHER (1876–1947) was born in Virginia but moved to Nebraska when still a child. Two of her best novels, *O Pioneers!* (1913) and *My Ántonia* (1918), are excellent studies of the Middle West. In 1923 she won the Pulitzer Prize with *One of Ours*, a novel of the first World War. *Death Comes for the Archbishop* (1927), a sympathetic portrayal of Catholic missionaries in New Mexico; *A Lost Lady* (1923), a pioneer novel of the Middle West; and *Shadows on the Rock* (1931), a picture of life in early Quebec—these three novels reveal Miss Cather as a versatile artist. Her books of short stories include *The Troll Garden* (1905), *Youth and the Bright Medusa* (1920), *Obscure Destinies* (1932), and *The Old Beauty and Others* (1948).

IT WAS Paul's afternoon to appear before the faculty of the Pittsburgh High School to account for his various misdemeanours. He had been suspended a week ago, and his father had called at the Principal's office and confessed his perplexity about his son. Paul entered the faculty room suave and smiling. His clothes were a trifle outgrown, and the tan velvet on the collar of his open overcoat was frayed and worn; but for all that there was something of the dandy about him, and he wore an opal pin in his neatly knotted black four-in-hand, and a red carnation in his buttonhole. This latter adornment the faculty somehow felt was not properly significant of the contrite spirit befitting a boy under the ban of suspension.

Paul was tall for his age and very thin, with high, cramped shoulders

PAUL'S CASE Reprinted from *Youth and the Bright Medusa* by Willa Cather, by permission of Alfred A. Knopf, Inc. Copyright 1905, 1932 by Willa Cather.

and a narrow chest. His eyes were remarkable for a certain hysterical brilliancy, and he continually used them in a conscious, theatrical sort of way, peculiarly offensive in a boy. The pupils were abnormally large, as though he were addicted to belladonna, but there was a glassy glitter about them which that drug does not produce.

When questioned by the Principal as to why he was there, Paul stated, politely enough, that he wanted to come back to school. This was a lie, but Paul was quite accustomed to lying; found it, indeed, indispensable for overcoming friction. His teachers were asked to state their respective charges against him, which they did with such a rancour and aggrievedness as evinced that this was not a usual case. Disorder and impertinence were among the offences named, yet each of his instructors felt that it was scarcely possible to put into words the real cause of the trouble, which lay in a sort of hysterically defiant manner of the boy's; in the contempt which they all knew he felt for them, and which he seemingly made not the least effort to conceal. Once, when he had been making a synopsis of a paragraph at the blackboard, his English teacher had stepped to his side and attempted to guide his hand. Paul had started back with a shudder and thrust his hands violently behind him. The astonished woman could scarcely have been more hurt and embarrassed had he struck at her. The insult was so involuntary and definitely personal as to be unforgettable. In one way and another, he had made all his teachers, men and women alike, conscious of the same feeling of physical aversion. In one class he habitually sat with his hand shading his eyes; in another he always looked out of the window during the recitation; in another he made a running commentary on the lecture, with humorous intent.

His teachers felt this afternoon that his whole attitude was symbolized by his shrug and his flippantly red carnation flower, and they fell upon him without mercy, his English teacher leading the pack. He stood through it smiling, his pale lips parted over his white teeth. (His lips were continually twitching, and he had a habit of raising his eyebrows that was contemptuous and irritating to the last degree.) Older boys than Paul had broken down and shed tears under that ordeal, but his set smile did not once desert him, and his only sign of discomfort was the nervous trembling of the fingers that toyed with the buttons of his overcoat, and an occasional jerking of the other hand which held his hat. Paul was always smiling, always glancing about him, seeming to feel that people might be watching him and trying to detect something. This conscious expression, since it was as far as possible from boyish mirthfulness, was usually attributed to insolence or "smartness."

As the inquisition proceeded, one of his instructors repeated an impertinent remark of the boy's, and the Principal asked him whether he thought that a courteous speech to make to a woman. Paul shrugged his shoulders slightly and his eyebrows twitched.

"I don't know," he replied. "I didn't mean to be polite or impolite, either. I guess it's a sort of way I have, of saying things regardless."

The Principal asked him whether he didn't think that a way it would be well to get rid of. Paul grinned and said he guessed so. When he was told that he could go, he bowed gracefully and went out. His bow was like a repetition of the scandalous red carnation.

His teachers were in despair, and his drawing master voiced the feeling of them all when he declared there was something about the boy which none of them understood. He added: "I don't really believe that smile of his comes altogether from insolence; there's something sort of haunted about it. The boy is not strong, for one thing. There is something wrong about the fellow."

The drawing master had come to realize that, in looking at Paul, one saw only his white teeth and the forced animation of his eyes. One warm afternoon the boy had gone to sleep at his drawing-board, and his master had noted with amazement what a white, blue-veined face it was; drawn and wrinkled like an old man's about the eyes, the lips twitching even in his sleep.

His teachers left the building dissatisfied and unhappy; humiliated to have felt so vindictive toward a mere boy, to have uttered this feeling in cutting terms, and to have set each other on, as it were, in the gruesome game of intemperate reproach. One of them remembered having seen a miserable street cat set at bay by a ring of tormentors.

As for Paul, he ran down the hill whistling the Soldiers' Chorus from *Faust*, looking wildly behind him now and then to see whether some of his teachers were not there to witness his light-heartedness. As it was now late in the afternoon and Paul was on duty that evening as usher at Carnegie Hall, he decided that he would not go home to supper.

When he reached the concert hall the doors were not yet open. It was chilly outside, and he decided to go up into the picture gallery—always deserted at this hour—where there were some of Raffelli's gay studies of Paris streets and an airy blue Venetian scene or two that always exhilarated him. He was delighted to find no one in the gallery but the old guard, who sat in the corner, a newspaper on his knee, a black patch over one eye and the other closed. Paul possessed himself of the place and walked confidently up and down, whistling under his breath. After a while he sat down before a blue Rico and lost himself. When he bethought him to look at his watch, it was after seven o'clock, and he rose with a start and ran downstairs, making a face at Augustus Cæsar, peering out from the cast-room, and an evil gesture at the Venus of Milo as he passed her on the stairway.

When Paul reached the ushers' dressing-room half-a-dozen boys were there already, and he began excitedly to tumble into his uniform. It was one of the few that at all approached fitting, and Paul thought it very becoming—though he knew the tight, straight coat accentuated his narrow chest, about which he was exceedingly sensitive. He was always excited while he dressed, twanging all over to the tuning of the strings and the preliminary flourishes of the horns in the music-room; but tonight he seemed quite beside himself, and he teased and plagued the boys until, telling him that he was crazy, they put him down on the floor and sat on him.

Somewhat calmed by his suppression, Paul dashed out to the front of the house to seat the early comers. He was a model usher. Gracious and smiling he ran up and down the aisles. Nothing was too much trouble for him; he carried messages and brought programs as though it were his greatest pleasure in life, and all the people in his section thought him a charming boy, feeling that he remembered and admired them. As the house filled, he grew more and more vivacious and animated, and the colour came to his cheeks and lips. It was very much as though this were a great reception and Paul were the host. Just as the musicians came out to take their places, his English teacher arrived with checks for the seats which a prominent manufacturer had taken for the season. She betrayed some embarrassment when she handed Paul the tickets, and a *hauteur* which subsequently made her feel very foolish. Paul was startled for a moment, and had the feeling of wanting to put her out; what business had she here among all these fine people and gay colours? He looked her over and decided that she was not appropriately dressed and must be a fool to sit downstairs in such togs. The tickets had probably been sent her out of kindness, he reflected, as he put down a seat for her, and she had about as much right to sit there as he had.

When the symphony began Paul sank into one of the rear seats with a long sigh of relief, and lost himself as he had done before the Rico. It was not that symphonies, as such, meant anything in particular to Paul, but the first sigh of the instruments seemed to free some hilarious spirit within him; something that struggled there like the Genius in the bottle found by the Arab fisherman. He felt a sudden zest of life; the lights danced before his eyes and the concert hall blazed into unimaginable splendour. When the soprano soloist came on, Paul forgot even the nastiness of his teacher's being there, and gave himself up to the peculiar intoxication such personages always had for him. The soloist chanced to be a German woman, by no means in her first youth, and the mother of many children; but she wore a satin gown and a tiara, and she had that indefinable air of achievement, that world-shine upon her, which always blinded Paul to any possible defects.

After a concert was over, Paul was often irritable and wretched until he got to sleep,—and tonight he was even more than usually restless. He had the feeling of not being able to let down; of its being impossible to give up this delicious excitement which was the only thing that could be called living at all. During the last number he withdrew and, after hastily changing his clothes in the dressing-room, slipped out to the side door where the singer's carriage stood. Here he began pacing rapidly up and down the walk, waiting to see her come out.

Over yonder the Schenley, in its vacant stretch, loomed big and square through the fine rain, the windows of its twelve stories glowing like those of a lighted card-board house under a Christmas tree. All the actors and singers of any importance stayed there when they were in the city, and a number of the big manufacturers of the place lived there in the winter. Paul had often hung about the hotel, watching the people go in and out, longing to enter and leave school-masters and dull care behind him for ever.

At last the singer came out, accompanied by the conductor, who helped her into her carriage and closed the door with a cordial *auf wiedersehen*, —which set Paul to wondering whether she were not an old sweetheart of his. Paul followed the carriage over to the hotel, walking so rapidly as not to be far from the entrance when the singer alighted and disappeared behind the swinging glass doors which were opened by a negro in a tall hat and a long coat. In the moment that the door was ajar, it seemed to Paul that he, too, entered. He seemed to feel himself go after her up the steps, into the warm, lighted building, into an exotic, a tropical world of shiny, glistening surfaces and basking ease. He reflected upon the mysterious dishes that were brought into the dining-room, the green bottles in buckets of ice, as he had seen them in the supper party pictures of the Sunday supplement. A quick gust of wind brought the rain down with sudden vehemence, and Paul was startled to find that he was still outside in the slush of the gravel driveway; that his boots were letting in the water and his scanty overcoat was clinging wet about him; that the lights in front of the concert hall were out, and that the rain was driving in sheets between him and the orange glow of the windows above him. There it was, what he wanted—tangibly before him, like the fairy world of a Christmas pantomime; as the rain beat in his face, Paul wondered whether he were destined always to shiver in the black night outside, looking up at it.

He turned and walked reluctantly toward the car tracks. The end had to come sometime; his father in his nightclothes at the top of the stairs, explanations that did not explain, hastily improvised fictions that were forever tripping him up, his upstairs room and its horrible yellow wall-paper, the creaking bureau with the greasy plush collar-box, and over his painted wooden bed the pictures of George Washington and John Calvin, and the framed motto, "Feed my Lambs," which had been worked in red worsted by his mother, whom Paul could not remember.

Half an hour later, Paul alighted from the Negley Avenue car and went slowly down one of the side streets off the main thoroughfare. It was a highly respectable street, where all the houses were exactly alike, and where business men of moderate means begot and reared large families of children, all of whom went to Sabbath-school and learned the shorter catechism, and were interested in arithmetic; all of whom were as exactly alike as their homes, and of a piece with the monotony in which they lived. Paul never went up Cordelia Street without a shudder of loathing. His home was next the house of the Cumberland minister. He approached it tonight with the nerveless sense of defeat, the hopeless feeling of sinking back forever into ugliness and commonness that he had always had when he came home. The moment he turned into Cordelia Street he felt the waters close above his head. After each of these orgies of living, he experienced all the physical depression which follows a debauch; the loathing of respectable beds, of common food, of a house permeated by kitchen odours; a shuddering repulsion for the flavourless, colourless mass of every-day existence; a morbid desire for cool things and soft lights and fresh flowers.

The nearer he approached the house, the more absolutely unequal Paul felt to the sight of it all; his ugly sleeping chamber; the cold bath-room with the grimy zinc tub, the cracked mirror, the dripping spiggots; his father, at the top of the stairs, his hairy legs sticking out from his night-shirt, his feet thrust into carpet slippers. He was so much later than usual that there would certainly be inquiries and reproaches. Paul stopped short before the door. He felt that he could not be accosted by his father to-night; that he could not toss again on that miserable bed. He would not go in. He would tell his father that he had no car fare, and it was raining so hard he had gone home with one of the boys and stayed all night.

Meanwhile, he was wet and cold. He went around to the back of the house and tried one of the basement windows, found it open, raised it cautiously, and scrambled down the cellar wall to the floor. There he stood, holding his breath, terrified by the noise he had made; but the floor above him was silent, and there was no creak on the stairs. He found a soap-box, and carried it over to the soft ring of light that streamed from the furnace door, and sat down. He was horribly afraid of rats, so he did not try to sleep, but sat looking distrustfully at the dark, still terrified lest he might have awakened his father. In such reactions, after one of the experiences which made days and nights out of the dreary blanks of the calendar, when his senses were deadened, Paul's head was always singularly clear. Suppose his father had heard him getting in at the window and had come down and shot him for a burglar? Then, again, suppose his father had come down, pistol in hand, and he had cried out in time to save himself, and his father had been horrified to think how nearly he had killed him? Then, again, suppose a day should come when his father would remember that night, and wish there had been no warning cry to stay his hand? With this last supposition Paul entertained himself until daybreak.

The following Sunday was fine; the sodden November chill was broken by the last flash of autumnal summer. In the morning Paul had to go to church and Sabbath-school, as always. On seasonable Sunday afternoons the burghers of Cordelia Street usually sat out on their front "stoops," and talked to their neighbours on the next stoop, or called to those across the street in neighbourly fashion. The men sat placidly on gay cushions placed upon the steps that led down to the sidewalk, while the women, in their Sunday "waists," sat in rockers on the cramped porches, pretending to be greatly at their ease. The children played in the streets; there were so many of them that the place resembled the recreation grounds of a kindergarten. The men on the steps—all in their shirt sleeves, their vests unbuttoned—sat with their legs well apart, their stomachs comfortably protruding, and talked of the prices of things, or told anecdotes of the sagacity of their various chiefs and overlords. They occasionally looked over the multitude of squabbling children, listened affectionately to their high-pitched, nasal voices, smiling to see their own proclivities reproduced in their offspring, and interspersed their legends of the iron kings with remarks about their sons' progress at school, their grades in arithmetic, and the amounts they had saved in their toy banks.

On this last Sunday of November, Paul sat all the afternoon on the lowest step of his "stoop," staring into the street, while his sisters, in their rockers, were talking to the minister's daughters next door about how many shirt-waists they had made in the last week, and how many waffles some one had eaten at the last church supper. When the weather was warm, and his father was in a particularly jovial frame of mind, the girls made lemonade, which was always brought out in a red-glass pitcher, ornamented with forget-me-nots in blue enamel. This the girls thought very fine, and the neighbours joked about the suspicious colour of the pitcher.

Today Paul's father, on the top step, was talking to a young man who shifted a restless baby from knee to knee. He happened to be the young man who was daily held up to Paul as a model, and after whom it was his father's dearest hope that he would pattern. This young man was of a ruddy complexion, with a compressed, red mouth, and faded, near-sighted eyes, over which he wore thick spectacles, with gold bows that curved about his ears. He was clerk to one of the magnates of a great steel corporation, and was looked upon in Cordelia Street as a young man with a future. There was a story that, some five years ago—he was now barely twenty-six—he had been a trifle "dissipated," but in order to curb his appetites and save the loss of time and strength that a sowing of wild oats might have entailed, he had taken his chief's advice, oft reiterated to his employés, and at twenty-one had married the first woman whom he

could persuade to share his fortunes. She happened to be an angular
school-mistress, much older than he, who also wore thick glasses, and who
had now borne him four children, all near-sighted, like herself.

The young man was relating how his chief, now cruising in the Mediterranean, kept in touch with all the details of the business, arranging his
office hours on his yacht just as though he were at home, and "knocking
off work enough to keep two stenographers busy." His father told, in turn,
the plan his corporation was considering, of putting in an electric railway
plant at Cairo. Paul snapped his teeth; he had an awful apprehension
that they might spoil it all before he got there. Yet he rather liked to hear
these legends of the iron kings, that were told and retold on Sundays and
holidays; these stories of palaces in Venice, yachts on the Mediterranean,
and high play at Monte Carlo appealed to his fancy, and he was interested in the triumphs of cash boys who had become famous, though he
had no mind for the cash-boy stage.

After supper was over, and he had helped to dry the dishes, Paul
nervously asked his father whether he could go to George's to get some
help in his geometry, and still more nervously asked for car-fare. This
latter request he had to repeat, as his father, on principle, did not like
to hear requests for money, whether much or little. He asked Paul whether
he could not go to some boy who lived nearer, and told him that he ought
not to leave his school work until Sunday; but he gave him the dime. He
was not a poor man, but he had a worthy ambition to come up in the
world. His only reason for allowing Paul to usher was that he thought a
boy ought to be earning a little.

Paul bounded upstairs, scrubbed the greasy odour of the dish-water
from his hands with the ill-smelling soap he hated, and then shook over
his fingers a few drops of violet water from the bottle he kept hidden in
his drawer. He left the house with his geometry conspicuously under his
arm, and the moment he got out of Cordelia Street and boarded a downtown car, he shook off the lethargy of two deadening days, and began
to live again.

The leading juvenile of the permanent stock company which played
at one of the downtown theatres was an acquaintance of Paul's, and the
boy had been invited to drop in at the Sunday-night rehearsals whenever
he could. For more than a year Paul had spent every available moment
loitering about Charley Edwards's dressing-room. He had won a place
among Edwards's following not only because the young actor, who could
not afford to employ a dresser, often found him useful, but because he
recognized in Paul something akin to what churchmen term "vocation."

It was at the theatre and at Carnegie Hall that Paul really lived; the
rest was but a sleep and a forgetting. This was Paul's fairy tale, and it had
for him all the allurement of a secret love. The moment he inhaled the
gassy, painty, dusty odour behind the scenes, he breathed like a prisoner

set free, and felt within him the possibility of doing or saying splendid, brilliant things. The moment the cracked orchestra beat out the overture from *Martha*, or jerked at the serenade from *Rigoletto*, all stupid and ugly things slid from him, and his senses were deliciously, yet delicately fired.

Perhaps it was because, in Paul's world, the natural nearly always wore the guise of ugliness, that a certain element of artificiality seemed to him necessary in beauty. Perhaps it was because his experience of life elsewhere was so full of Sabbath-school picnics, petty economies, wholesome advice as to how to succeed in life, and the unescapable odours of cooking, that he found this existence so alluring, these smartly-clad men and women so attractive, that he was so moved by these starry apple orchards that bloomed perennially under the lime-light.

It would be difficult to put it strongly enough how convincingly the stage entrance of that theatre was for Paul the actual portal of Romance. Certainly none of the company ever suspected it, least of all Charley Edwards. It was very like the old stories that used to float about London of fabulously rich Jews, who had subterranean halls, with palms, and fountains, and soft lamps and richly apparelled women who never saw the disenchanting light of London day. So, in the midst of that smoke-palled city, enamoured of figures and grimy toil, Paul had his secret temple, his wishing-carpet, this bit of blue-and-white Mediterranean shore bathed in perpetual sunshine.

Several of Paul's teachers had a theory that his imagination had been perverted by garish fiction; but the truth was, he scarcely ever read at all. The books at home were not such as would either tempt or corrupt a youthful mind, and as for reading the novels that some of his friends urged upon him—well, he got what he wanted much more quickly from music; any sort of music, from an orchestra to a barrel organ. He needed only the spark, the indescribable thrill that made his imagination master of his senses, and he could make plots and pictures enough of his own. It was equally true that he was not stagestruck—not, at any rate, in the usual acceptation of that expression. He had no desire to become an actor, any more than he had to become a musician. He felt no necessity to do any of these things; what he wanted was to see, to be in the atmosphere, float on the wave of it, to be carried out, blue league after blue league, away from everything.

After a night behind the scenes, Paul found the schoolroom more than ever repulsive; the bare floors and naked walls; the prosy men who never wore frock coats, or violets in their buttonholes; the women with their dull gowns, shrill voices, and pitiful seriousness about prepositions that govern the dative. He could not bear to have the other pupils think, for a moment, that he took these people seriously; he must convey to them that he considered it all trivial, and was there only by way of a joke, anyway. He had autograph pictures of all the members of the stock company which he showed his classmates, telling them the most incredible stories of his familiarity with these people, of his acquaintance with the soloists who came to Carnegie Hall, his suppers with them and the flowers he sent them. When these stories lost their effect, and his audience grew listless, he would bid all the boys good-bye, announcing that he was going to travel for awhile; going to Naples, to California, to Egypt. Then, next Monday, he would slip back, conscious and nervously smiling; his sister was ill, and he would have to defer his voyage until spring.

Matters went steadily worse with Paul at school. In the itch to let his instructors know how heartily he despised them, and how thoroughly he was appreciated elsewhere, he mentioned once or twice that he had no time to fool with theorems; adding—with a twitch of the eyebrows and a touch of that nervous bravado which so perplexed them—that he was helping the people down at the stock company; they were old friends of his.

The upshot of the matter was, that the Principal went to Paul's father, and Paul was taken out of school and put to work. The manager at Carnegie Hall was told to get another usher in his stead; the doorkeeper at the theatre was warned not to admit him to the house; and Charley Edwards remorsefully promised the boy's father not to see him again.

The members of the stock company were vastly amused when some of Paul's stories reached them—especially the women. They were hardworking women, most of them supporting indolent husbands or brothers, and they laughed rather bitterly at having stirred the boy to such fervid and florid inventions. They agreed with the faculty and with his father, that Paul's was a bad case.

The east-bound train was ploughing through a January snow-storm; the dull dawn was beginning to show grey when the engine whistled a mile out of Newark. Paul started up from the seat where he had lain curled in uneasy slumber, rubbed the breath-misted window glass with his hand, and peered out. The snow was whirling in curling eddies above the white bottom lands, and the drifts lay already deep in the fields and along the fences, while here and there the long dead grass and dried weed stalks protruded black above it. Lights shone from the scattered houses, and a gang of labourers who stood beside the track waved their lanterns.

Paul had slept very little, and he felt grimy and uncomfortable. He had made the all-night journey in a day coach because he was afraid if he took a Pullman he might be seen by some Pittsburgh business man who had noticed him in Denny & Carson's office. When the whistle woke him, he clutched quickly at his breast pocket, glancing about him with an uncertain smile. But the little, clay-bespattered Italians were still sleeping, the slatternly women across the aisle were in open-mouthed oblivion, and even the crumby, crying babies were for the nonce stilled. Paul settled back to struggle with his impatience as best he could.

When he arrived at the Jersey City station, he hurried through his breakfast, manifestly ill at ease and keeping a sharp eye about him. After he reached the Twenty-third Street station, he consulted a cabman, and had himself driven to a men's furnishing establishment which was just opening for the day. He spent upward of two hours there, buying with endless reconsidering and great care. His new street suit he put on in the fitting-room; the frock coat and dress clothes he had bundled into the cab with his new shirts. Then he drove to a hatter's and a shoe house. His next errand was at Tiffany's, where he selected silver mounted brushes and a scarf-pin. He would not wait to have his silver marked, he said. Lastly, he stopped at a trunk shop on Broadway, and had his purchases packed into various travelling bags.

It was a little after one o'clock when he drove up to the Waldorf, and, after settling with the cabman, went into the office. He registered from Washington; said his mother and father had been abroad, and that he had come down to await the arrival of their steamer. He told his story plausibly and had no trouble, since he offered to pay for them in advance, in engaging his rooms; a sleeping-room, sitting-room and bath.

Not once, but a hundred times Paul had planned this entry into New York. He had gone over every detail of it with Charley Edwards, and in his scrap book at home there were pages of description about New York hotels, cut from the Sunday papers.

When he was shown to his sitting-room on the eighth floor, he saw at a glance that everything was as it should be; there was but one detail in his mental picture that the place did not realize, so he rang for the bell boy and sent him down for flowers. He moved about nervously until the boy returned, putting away his new linen and fingering it delightedly as he did so. When the flowers came, he put them hastily into water, and then tumbled into a hot bath. Presently he came out of his white bath-room, resplendent in his new silk underwear, and playing with the tassels of his red robe. The snow was whirling so fiercely outside his windows that he could scarcely see across the street; but within, the air was deliciously soft and fragrant. He put the violets and jonquils on the tabouret beside the couch, and threw himself down with a long sigh, covering himself with a Roman blanket. He was thoroughly tired; he had been in such haste, he had stood up to such a strain, covered so much ground in the last twenty-four hours, that he wanted to think how it had all come about. Lulled by the sound of the wind, the warm air, and the cool fragrance of the flowers, he sank into deep, drowsy retrospection.

It had been wonderfully simple; when they had shut him out of the theatre and concert hall, when they had taken away his bone, the whole thing was virtually determined. The rest was a mere matter of opportunity. The only thing that at all surprised him was his own courage—for he realized well enough that he had always been tormented by fear, a sort of apprehensive dread that, of late years, as the meshes of the lies he had told closed about him, had been pulling the muscles of his body tighter and tighter. Until now, he could not remember a time when he had not been dreading something. Even when he was a little boy, it was always there—behind him, or before, or on either side. There had always been the shadowed corner, the dark place into which he dared not look, but from which something seemed always to be watching him—and Paul had done things that were not pretty to watch, he knew.

But now he had a curious sense of relief, as though he had at last thrown down the gauntlet to the thing in the corner.

Yet it was but a day since he had been sulking in the traces; but yesterday afternoon that he had been sent to the bank with Denny & Carson's deposit, as usual—but this time he was instructed to leave the book to be balanced. There was above two thousand dollars in checks, and nearly a thousand in the bank notes which he had taken from the book and quietly transferred to his pocket. At the bank he had made out a new deposit slip. His nerves had been steady enough to permit of his returning to the office, where he had finished his work and asked for a full day's holiday tomorrow, Saturday, giving a perfectly reasonable pretext. The bank book, he knew, would not be returned before Monday or Tuesday, and his father would be out of town for the next week. From the time he slipped the bank notes into his pocket until he boarded the night train for New York, he had not known a moment's hesitation.

How astonishingly easy it had all been; here he was, the thing done; and this time there would be no awakening, no figure at the top of the stairs. He watched the snow flakes whirling by his window until he fell asleep.

When he awoke, it was four o'clock in the afternoon. He bounded up with a start; one of his precious days gone already! He spent nearly an hour in dressing, watching every stage of his toilet carefully in the mirror. Everything was quite perfect; he was exactly the kind of boy he had always wanted to be.

When he went downstairs, Paul took a carriage and drove up Fifth avenue toward the Park. The snow had somewhat abated; carriages and tradesmen's wagons were hurrying soundlessly to and fro in the winter twilight; boys in woollen mufflers were shovelling off the doorsteps; the avenue stages made fine spots of colour against the white street. Here and there on the corners whole flower gardens blooming behind glass windows, against which the snow flakes stuck and melted; violets, roses, carnations, lilies of the valley—somehow vastly more lovely and alluring that they blossomed thus unnaturally in the snow. The Park itself was a wonderful stage winter-piece.

When he returned, the pause of the twilight had ceased, and the tune of the streets had changed. The snow was falling faster, lights streamed from the hotels that reared their many stories fearlessly up into the storm, defying the raging Atlantic winds. A long, black stream of carriages poured down the avenue, intersected here and there by other streams, tending horizontally. There were a score of cabs about the entrance of his hotel, and his driver had to wait. Boys in livery were running in and out of the awning stretched across the sidewalk, up and down the red velvet carpet laid from the door to the street. Above, about, within it all, was the rumble and roar, the hurry and toss of thousands of human beings as hot for pleasure as himself, and on every side of him towered the glaring affirmation of the omnipotence of wealth.

The boy set his teeth and drew his shoulders together in a spasm of realization; the plot of all dramas, the text of all romances, the nerve-stuff of all sensations was whirling about him like the snow flakes. He burnt like a faggot in a tempest.

When Paul came down to dinner, the music of the orchestra floated up the elevator shaft to greet him. As he stepped into the thronged corridor, he sank back into one of the chairs against the wall to get his breath. The lights, the chatter, the perfumes, the bewildering medley of colour— he had, for a moment, the feeling of not being able to stand it. But only for a moment; these were his own people, he told himself. He went slowly about the corridors, through the writing-rooms, smoking-rooms, reception-rooms, as though he were exploring the chambers of an enchanted palace, built and peopled for him alone.

When he reached the dining-room he sat down at a table near a window. The flowers, the white linen, the many-coloured wine glasses, the gay toilettes of the women, the low popping of corks, the undulating repetitions of the *Blue Danube* from the orchestra, all flooded Paul's dream with bewildering radiance. When the roseate tinge of his champagne was added—that cold, precious, bubbling stuff that creamed and foamed in his glass—Paul wondered that there were honest men in the world at all. This was what all the world was fighting for, he reflected; this was what all the struggle was about. He doubted the reality of his past. Had he ever known a place called Cordelia Street, a place where fagged looking business men boarded the early car? Mere rivets in a machine they seemed to Paul,— sickening men, with combings of children's hair always hanging to their coats, and the smell of cooking in their clothes. Cordelia Street—Ah, that belonged to another time and country! Had he not always been thus, had he not sat here night after night, from as far back as he could remember, looking pensively over just such shimmering textures, and slowly twirling the stem of a glass like this one between his thumb and middle finger? He rather thought he had.

He was not in the least abashed or lonely. He had no especial desire to meet or to know any of these people; all he demanded was the right to look on and conjecture, to watch the pageant. The mere stage properties were all he contended for. Nor was he lonely later in the evening, in his loge at the Opera. He was entirely rid of his nervous misgivings, of his forced aggressiveness, of the imperative desire to show himself different from his surroundings. He felt now that his surroundings explained him. Nobody questioned the purple; he had only to wear it passively. He had only to glance down at his dress coat to reassure himself that here it would be impossible for anyone to humiliate him.

He found it hard to leave his beautiful sitting-room to go to bed that night, and sat long watching the raging storm from his turret window. When he went to sleep, it was with the lights turned on in his bedroom; partly because of his old timidity, and partly so that, if he should wake in the night, there would be no wretched moment of doubt, no horrible suspicion of yellow wall-paper, or of Washington and Calvin above his bed.

On Sunday morning the city was practically snowbound. Paul breakfasted late, and in the afternoon he fell in with a wild San Francisco boy, a freshman at Yale, who said he had run down for a "little flyer" over Sunday. The young man offered to show Paul the night side of the town, and the two boys went off together after dinner, not returning to the hotel until seven o'clock the next morning. They had started out in the confiding warmth of a champagne friendship, but their parting in the elevator was singularly cool. The freshman pulled himself together to make his train, and Paul went to bed. He awoke at two o'clock in the afternoon, very thirsty and dizzy, and rang for ice-water, coffee, and the Pittsburgh papers.

On the part of the hotel management, Paul excited no suspicion. There was this to be said for him, that he wore his spoils with dignity and in no way made himself conspicuous. His chief greediness lay in his ears and eyes, and his excesses were not offensive ones. His dearest pleasures were the grey winter twilights in his sitting-room; his quiet enjoyment of his flowers, his clothes, his wide divan, his cigarette and his sense of power. He could not remember a time when he had felt so at peace with himself. The mere release from the necessity of petty lying, lying every day and every day, restored his self-respect. He had never lied for pleasure, even at school; but to make himself noticed and admired, to assert his difference from other Cordelia Street boys; and he felt a good deal more manly, more honest, even, now that he had no need for boastful pretensions, now that he could, as his actor friends used to say, "dress the part." It was characteristic that remorse did not occur to him. His golden days went by without a shadow, and he made each as perfect as he could.

On the eighth day after his arrival in New York, he found the whole affair exploited in the Pittsburgh papers, exploited with a wealth of detail which indicated that local news of a sensational nature was at a low ebb. The firm of Denny & Carson announced that the boy's father had refunded the full amount of his theft, and that they had no intention of prosecuting. The Cumberland minister had been interviewed, and expressed his hope of yet reclaiming the motherless lad, and Paul's Sabbath-school teacher declared that she would spare no effort to that end. The rumour had reached Pittsburgh that the boy had been seen in a New York hotel, and his father had gone East to find him and bring him home.

Paul had just come in to dress for dinner; he sank into a chair, weak in the knees, and clasped his head in his hands. It was to be worse than jail, even; the tepid waters of Cordelia Street were to close over him finally and forever. The grey monotony stretched before him in hopeless, unrelieved years; Sabbath-school, Young People's Meeting, the yellow-papered room, the damp dish-towels; it all rushed back upon him with sickening vividness. He had the old feeling that the orchestra had suddenly stopped, the sinking sensation that the play was over. The sweat broke out on his face, and he sprang to his feet, looking about him with his white, conscious smile, and winked at himself in the mirror. With something of the childish belief in miracles with which he had so often gone to class, all his lessons unlearned, Paul dressed and dashed whistling down the corridor to the elevator.

He had no sooner entered the dining-room and caught the measure of the music, than his remembrance was lightened by his old elastic power of claiming the moment, mounting with it, and finding it all sufficient. The glare and glitter about him, the mere scenic accessories had again, and for the last time, their old potency. He would show himself that he was game, he would finish the thing splendidly. He doubted, more than ever, the existence of Cordelia Street, and for the first time he drank his wine recklessly. Was he not, after all, one of these fortunate beings? Was he not still himself, and in his own place? He drummed a nervous accompaniment to the music and looked about him, telling himself over and over that it had paid.

He reflected drowsily, to the swell of the violin and the chill sweetness of his wine, that he might have done it more wisely. He might have caught an outbound steamer and been well out of their clutches before now. But the other side of the world had seemed too far away and too uncertain then; he could not have waited for it; his need had been too sharp. If he had to choose over again, he would do the same thing to-morrow. He looked affectionately about the dining-room, now gilded with a soft mist. Ah, it had paid indeed!

Paul was awakened next morning by a painful throbbing in his head and feet. He had thrown himself across the bed without undressing, and had slept with his shoes on. His limbs and hands were lead heavy, and his tongue and throat were parched. There came upon him one of those fateful attacks of clear-headedness that never occurred except when he was physically exhausted and his nerves hung loose. He lay still and closed his eyes and let the tide of realities wash over him.

His father was in New York; "stopping at some joint or other," he told himself. The memory of successive summers on the front stoop fell upon him like a weight of black water. He had not a hundred dollars left; and he knew now, more than ever, that money was everything, the wall that stood between all he loathed and all he wanted. The thing was winding itself up; he had thought of that on his first glorious day in New York, and had even provided a way to snap the thread. It lay on his dressing-table now; he had got it out last night when he came blindly up from dinner,— but the shiny metal hurt his eyes, and he disliked the look of it, anyway.

He rose and moved about with a painful effort, succumbing now and again to attacks of nausea. It was the old depression exaggerated; all the world had become Cordelia Street. Yet somehow he was not afraid of anything, was absolutely calm; perhaps because he had looked into the dark corner at last, and knew. It was bad enough, what he saw there; but somehow not so bad as his long fear of it had been. He saw everything clearly now. He had a feeling that he had made the best of it, that he had lived the sort of life he was meant to live, and for half an hour he sat staring at the revolver. But he told himself that was not the way, so he went downstairs and took a cab to the ferry.

When Paul arrived at Newark, he got off the train and took another cab, directing the driver to follow the Pennsylvania tracks out of the town. The snow lay heavy on the roadways and had drifted deep in the open fields. Only here and there the dead grass or dried weed stalks projected, singularly black, above it. Once well into the country, Paul dismissed the carriage and walked, floundering along the tracks, his mind a medley of irrelevant things. He seemed to hold in his brain an actual picture of everything he had seen that morning. He remembered every feature of both his drivers, the toothless old woman from whom he had bought the red flowers in his coat, the agent from whom he had got his ticket, and all of his fellow-passengers on the ferry. His mind, unable to cope with vital matters near at hand, worked feverishly and deftly at sorting and grouping these images. They made for him a part of the ugliness of the world, of the ache in his head, and the bitter burning on his tongue. He stooped and put a handful of snow into his mouth as he walked, but that, too, seemed hot. When he reached a little hillside, where the tracks ran through a cut some twenty feet below him, he stopped and sat down.

The carnations in his coat were drooping with the cold, he noticed; all their red glory over. It occurred to him that all the flowers he had seen in the show windows that first night must have gone the same way, long before this. It was only one splendid breath they had, in spite of their brave mockery at the winter outside the glass. It was a losing game in the end, it seemed, this revolt against the homilies by which the world is run. Paul took one of the blossoms carefully from his coat and scooped a little hole in the snow, where he covered it up. Then he dozed a while, from his weak condition, seeming insensible to the cold.

The sound of an approaching train woke him, and he started to his feet, remembering only his resolution, and afraid lest he should be too late. He stood watching the approaching locomotive, his teeth chattering, his lips drawn away from them in a frightened smile; once or twice he glanced nervously sidewise, as though he were being watched. When the right moment came, he jumped. As he fell, the folly of his haste occurred to him with merciless clearness, the vastness of what he had left undone. There flashed through his brain, clearer than ever before, the blue of Adriatic water, the yellow of Algerian sands.

He felt something strike his chest,—his body was being thrown swiftly through the air, on and on, immeasurably far and fast, while his limbs gently relaxed. Then, because the picture making mechanism was crushed, the disturbing visions flashed into black, and Paul dropped back into the immense design of things.

COMMENT AND QUESTION

1. *The theme.* The theme of "Paul's Case" is a familiar one in the writing of Willa Cather. It is the conflict between the demands of art and the demands of a civilization hostile or alien to art. It is the conflict between the artist, who lives through his senses, and the drab citizen, who respects dullness and mediocrity. In such a conflict the great artist often survives because of his genius. "Paul's Case" is made human because Paul is not a great artist. He does not have even fifth-rate artistic ability. He seems to have no creative powers. He is simply a sensitive, romantic adolescent who wants to enjoy beauty.

2. *Paul's quest.* The major question in this story is: Could Paul have reconciled his desires with what his environment offered him? It is clear that he tried to adjust. In the first half of the story we see Paul seeking fulfillment. Where does he turn to satisfy his senses? Where is he happy? In the second half of the story Paul seeks fulfillment again. What drives him into this second attempt? At the end of the story, the problem still remains. Was Paul's problem insoluble? Could someone have helped Paul? If so, who?

3. *Paul's likes.* The reader who understands Paul, Paul's problem, and Paul's solution to his problem knows that he could have helped Paul. The reader of this story can play the rôle of a psychiatrist. He can begin his study of Paul's case by recalling a sound psychological observation: "Tell me what you like and I'll tell you what you are." Let the reader determine what Paul likes and he will know what Paul is.

It is not enough to say that Paul likes beauty. The specific quality of

Paul's "likes" holds the clue to Paul's mistakes, to his inability to adjust. For example, Paul likes flowers—not just flowers—but violets and roses behind the plate glass windows of a florist's shop in a snowstorm. He likes music—not just music—but a singer in a satin gown and tiara, emanating success. He likes stories of a king of finance on his yacht in the Mediterranean, but is not interested in the cash-boy stage of the rise to power. The list of what Paul likes must be both extensive and definite if the reader is to understand Paul. (What Paul dislikes is important, also. For example, Paul did not live in a slum. What, then, did he dislike in his home?)

4. *Paul's mistake.* The next step is the most difficult. What Paul likes must be translated into general terms. Thus the violets and roses in midwinter are *costly;* the singer is *successful* and *theatrical;* a king of finance is *romantic.* A list of five or six terms describing the inner quality of Paul's desires brings the reader face to face with the problem of Paul's maladjustment. Several passages are particularly significant at this point. Notice the following:

a. "Perhaps it was because, in Paul's world, the natural nearly always wore the guise of ugliness, that a certain amount of artificiality seemed to him necessary in beauty."

b. "He seemed to feel himself go after her up the steps, into the warm, lighted building, into an exotic, a tropical world of shiny, glistening surfaces and basking ease. He reflected upon the mysterious dishes that were brought into the dining-room, the green bottles in buckets of ice. . . ."

c. ". . . and on every side of him towered the glaring affirmation of the omnipotence of wealth."

5. *A solution for Paul.* What, then, was Paul's mistake in his search for beauty? To appreciate life through his senses was with him a psychological necessity and a truly legitimate necessity. But he could have found beauty, even in Pittsburgh. How? Could Paul have created beauty? What kind of work would have made him happy?

6. *Paul's character.* Not only Paul's problem but also Paul's character and personality play a part in Paul's final decision. Paul was adolescent. He had the nervous susceptibility, the sentimentality, the active imagination, the preoccupation with the ego, of the adolescent. Study the passage where the drawing master observes Paul asleep. Study the scene in the cellar.

What characteristics of Paul do the following passages illustrate?

a. "He had never lied for pleasure, even at school; but to make himself noticed and admired. . . ."

b. "He needed only the spark [music], the indescribable thrill that made his imagination master of his senses. . . ."

c. "The boy set his teeth and drew his shoulders together in a spasm of realization; the plot of all dramas, the text of all romance, the nerve-stuff of all sensations was whirling about him like the snow flakes. He burnt like a faggot in a tempest."

7. *The carnation.* The episode of the carnation at the end of the story is symbolic. It embodies Paul's life and Paul's problem. It explains why Paul will not go home to Cordelia Street. What is the relation between this episode and Paul's final act? One sentence from this passage is especially significant: "It was a losing game in the end, it seemed, this revolt against the homilies by which the world is run." This sentence, in fact, states the theme of the story.

8. *The structure.* For a story which has interested countless readers, the action is curiously static. The action does not really begin until the reader is three-fifths of the way through the story. Although the first four episodes are represented as a continuous plot, they are merely four habitual actions of Paul's. The author presents in these episodes a case history. We see Paul alternating between what he likes and dislikes, between school and a concert, home and the theater. The story begins when Paul is forced to choose between the alternatives, and he runs away to New York.

THE NEW VILLA

BY ANTON CHEKHOV

ANTON CHEKHOV (1860–1904) was born in
Tagarog, South Russia. He came of a family
of liberated serfs, was educated in his own
town and at the University of Moscow, where
he received a degree in medicine in 1884.
He practiced little. Instead, between 1889 and
1900 he established his reputation in Russia
as a master of the short story. After 1916,
when he began to be translated into English,
his reputation spread. A great many of his
stories are now available in English. He was
associated with the Moscow Art Theater, and
his major plays are *The Sea Gull, Three
Sisters, The Cherry Orchard,* and *Uncle
Vanya.*

Two miles from the village of Obrutchanovo a huge bridge was being
built. From the village, which stood up high on the steep river-bank, its
trellis-like skeleton could be seen, and in foggy weather and on still winter
days, when its delicate iron girders and all the scaffolding around was
covered with hoar frost, it presented a picturesque and even fantastic
spectacle. Kutcherov, the engineer who was building the bridge, a stout,
broad-shouldered, bearded man in a soft crumpled cap drove through the
village in his racing droshky or his open carriage. Now and then on
holidays navvies working on the bridge would come to the village; they
begged for alms, laughed at the women, and sometimes carried off something. But that was rare; as a rule the days passed quietly and peacefully
as though no bridge-building were going on, and only in the evening,

THE NEW VILLA   By Anton Chekhov from *The Witch and Other Stories.* Reprinted by permission of the Macmillan Co. and Chatto & Windus Ltd.

when camp fires gleamed near the bridge, the wind faintly wafted the songs of the navvies. And by day there was sometimes the mournful clang of metal, don-don-don.

It happened that the engineer's wife came to see him. She was pleased with the river-banks and the gorgeous view over the green valley with trees, churches, flocks, and she began begging her husband to buy a small piece of ground and to build them a cottage on it. Her husband agreed. They bought sixty acres of land, and on the high bank in a field, where in earlier days the cows of Obrutchanovo used to wander, they built a pretty house of two storeys with a terrace and a verandah, with a tower and a flagstaff on which a flag fluttered on Sundays—they built it in about three months, and then all the winter they were planting big trees, and when spring came and everything began to be green there were already avenues to the new house, a gardener and two labourers in white aprons were digging near it, there was a little fountain, and a globe of looking-glass flashed so brilliantly that it was painful to look at. The house had already been named the New Villa.

On a bright, warm morning at the end of May two horses were brought to Obrutchanovo to the village blacksmith, Rodion Petrov. They came from the New Villa. The horses were sleek, graceful beasts, as white as snow, and strikingly alike.

"Perfect swans!" said Rodion, gazing at them with reverent admiration.

His wife Stepanida, his children and grandchildren came out into the street to look at them. By degrees a crowd collected. The Lytchkovs, father and son, both men with swollen faces and entirely beardless, came up bareheaded. Kozov, a tall, thin old man with a long, narrow beard, came up leaning on a stick with a crook handle: he kept winking with his crafty eyes and smiling ironically as though he knew something.

"It's only that they are white; what is there in them?" he said. "Put mine on oats, and they will be just as sleek. They ought to be in a plough and with a whip, too. . . ."

The coachman simply looked at him with disdain, but did not utter a word. And afterwards, while they were blowing up the fire at the forge, the coachman talked while he smoked cigarettes. The peasants learned from him various details: his employers were wealthy people; his mistress, Elena Ivanovna, had till her marriage lived in Moscow in a poor way as a governess; she was kind-hearted, compassionate, and fond of helping the poor. On the new estate, he told them, they were not going to plough or to sow, but simply to live for their pleasure, live only to breathe the fresh air. When he had finished and led the horses back a crowd of boys followed him, the dogs barked, and Kozov, looking after him, winked sarcastically.

"Landowners, too-oo!" he said. "They have built a house and set up horses, but I bet they are nobodies—landowners, too-oo."

Kozov for some reason took a dislike from the first to the new house, to the white horses, and to the handsome, well-fed coachman. Kozov was a solitary man, a widower; he had a dreary life (he was prevented from working by a disease which he sometimes called a rupture and sometimes worms); he was maintained by his son, who worked at a confectioner's in Harkov and sent him money; and from early morning till evening he sauntered at leisure about the river or about the village; if he saw, for instance, a peasant carting a log, or fishing, he would say: "That log's dry wood—it is rotten," or, "They won't bite in weather like this." In times of drought he would declare that there would not be a drop of rain till the frost came; and when the rains came he would say that everything would rot in the fields, that everything was ruined. And as he said these things he would wink as though he knew something.

At the New Villa they burned Bengal lights and sent up fireworks in the evenings, and a sailing-boat with red lanterns floated by Obrutchanovo. One morning the engineer's wife, Elena Ivanovna, and her little daughter drove to the village in a carriage with yellow wheels and a pair of dark bay ponies; both mother and daughter were wearing broadbrimmed straw hats, bent down over their ears.

This was exactly at the time when they were carting manure, and the blacksmith Rodion, a tall, gaunt old man, bareheaded and barefooted, was standing near his dirty and repulsive-looking cart and, flustered, looked at the ponies, and it was evident by his face that he had never seen such little horses before.

"The Kutcherov lady has come!" was whispered around. "Look, the Kutcherov lady has come!"

Elena Ivanovna looked at the huts as though she were selecting one, and then stopped at the very poorest, at the windows of which there were so many children's heads—flaxen, red, and dark. Stepanida, Rodion's wife, a stout woman, came running out of the hut; her kerchief slipped off her grey head; she looked at the carriage facing the sun, and her face smiled and wrinkled up as though she were blind.

"This is for your children," said Elena Ivanovna, and she gave her three roubles.

Stepanida suddenly burst into tears and bowed down to the ground. Rodion, too, flopped to the ground, displaying his brownish bald head, and as he did so he almost caught his wife in the ribs with the fork. Elena Ivanovna was overcome with confusion and drove back.

II

The Lytchkovs, father and son, caught in their meadows two cart-horses, a pony, and a broad-faced Aalhaus bull-calf, and with the help of readheaded Volodka, son of the blacksmith Rodion, drove them to the

village. They called the village elder, collected witnesses, and went to
look at the damage.

"All right, let 'em!" said Kozov, winking, "le-et 'em! Let them get out
of it if they can, the engineers! Do you think there is no such thing as law?
All right! Send for the police inspector, draw up a statement! . . ."

"Draw up a statement," repeated Volodka.

"I don't want to let this pass!" shouted the younger Lytchkov. He
shouted louder and louder, and his beardless face seemed to be more and
more swollen. "They've set up a nice fashion! Leave them free, and they
will ruin all the meadows! You've no sort of right to ill-treat people! We
are not serfs now!"

"We are not serfs now!" repeated Volodka.

"We got on all right without a bridge," said the elder Lytchkov
gloomily; "we did not ask for it. What do we want a bridge for? We
don't want it!"

"Brothers, good Christians, we cannot leave it like this!"

"All right, let 'em!" said Kozov, winking. "Let them get out of it if
they can! Landowners, indeed!"

They went back to the village, and as they walked the younger Lytchkov
beat himself on the breast with his fist and shouted all the way, and
Volodka shouted, too, repeating his words. And meanwhile quite a crowd
had gathered in the village round the thoroughbred bull-calf and the
horses. The bull-calf was embarrassed and looked up from under his
brows, but suddenly lowered his muzzle to the ground and took to his
heels, kicking up his hind legs; Kozov was frightened and waved his stick
at him, and they all burst out laughing. Then they locked up the beasts
and waited.

In the evening the engineer sent five roubles for the damage, and the
two horses, the pony and the bull-calf, without being fed or given water,
returned home, their heads hanging with a guilty air as though they were
convicted criminals.

On getting the five roubles the Lytchkovs, father and son, the village
elder and Volodka, punted over the river in a boat and went to a hamlet
on the other side where there was a tavern, and there had a long carousal.
Their singing and the shouting of the younger Lytchkov could be heard
from the village. Their women were uneasy and did not sleep all night.
Rodion did not sleep either.

"It's a bad business," he said, sighing and turning from side to side.
"The gentleman will be angry, and then there will be trouble. . . . They
have insulted the gentleman. . . . Oh, they've insulted him. It's a bad
business. . . ."

It happened that the peasants, Rodion amongst them, went into their
forest to divide the clearings for mowing, and as they were returning home

they were met by the engineer. He was wearing a red cotton shirt and high boots; a setter dog with its long tongue hanging out, followed behind him.

"Good-day, brothers," he said.

The peasants stopped and took off their hats.

"I have long wanted to have a talk with you, friends," he went on. "This is what it is. Ever since the early spring your cattle have been in my copse and garden every day. Everything is trampled down; the pigs have rooted up the meadow, are ruining everything in the kitchen garden, and all the undergrowth in the copse is destroyed. There is no getting on with your herdsmen; one asks them civilly, and they are rude. Damage is done on my estate every day and I do nothing—I don't fine you or make a complaint; meanwhile you impounded my horses and my bull-calf and exacted five roubles. Was that right? Is that neighbourly?" he went on, and his face was so soft and persuasive, and his expression was not forbidding. "Is that the way decent people behave? A week ago one of your people cut down two oak saplings in my copse. You have dug up the road to Eresnevo, and now I have to go two miles round. Why do you injure me at every step? What harm have I done you? For God's sake, tell me! My wife and I do our utmost to live with you in peace and harmony; we help the peasants as we can. My wife is a kind, warm-hearted woman; she never refuses you help. That is her dream—to be of use to you and your children. You reward us with evil for our good. You are unjust, my friends. Think of that. I ask you earnestly to think it over. We treat you humanely; repay us in the same coin."

He turned and went away. The peasants stood a little longer, put on their caps and walked away. Rodion, who always understood everything that was said to him in some peculiar way of his own, heaved a sigh and said:

"We must pay. 'Repay in coin, my friends' . . . he said."

They walked to the village in silence. On reaching home Rodion said his prayer, took off his boots, and sat down on the bench beside his wife. Stepanida and he always sat side by side when they were at home, and always walked side by side in the street; they ate and they drank and they slept always together, and the older they grew the more they loved one another. It was hot and crowded in their hut, and there were children everywhere—on the floors, in the windows, on the stove. . . . In spite of her advanced years Stepanida was still bearing children, and now, looking at the crowd of children, it was hard to distinguish which were Rodion's and which were Volodka's. Volodka's wife, Lukerya, a plain young woman with prominent eyes and a nose like the beak of a bird, was kneading dough in a tub; Volodka was sitting on the stove with his legs hanging.

"On the road near Nikita's buckwheat . . . the engineer with his dog . . ." Rodion began, after a rest, scratching his ribs and his elbow.

" 'You must pay,' says he . . . 'coin,' says he. . . . Coin or no coin, we shall have to collect ten kopecks from every hut. We've offended the gentleman very much. I am sorry for him. . . .'"

"We've lived without a bridge," said Volodka, not looking at anyone, "and we don't want one."

"What next; the bridge is a government business."

"We don't want it."

"Your opinion is not asked. What is it to you?"

" 'Your opinion is not asked,' " Volodka mimicked him. "We don't want to drive anywhere; what do we want with a bridge? If we have to, we can cross by the boat."

Someone from the yard outside knocked at the window so violently that it seemed to shake the whole hut.

"Is Volodka at home?" he heard the voice of the younger Lytchkov. "Volodka, come out, come along."

Volodka jumped down off the stove and began looking for his cap.

"Don't go, Volodka," said Rodion diffidently. "Don't go with them, son. You are foolish, like a little child; they will teach you no good; don't go!"

"Don't go, son," said Stepanida, and she blinked as thought about to shed tears. "I bet they are calling you to the tavern."

" 'To the tavern,' " Volodka mimicked.

"You'll come back drunk again, you currish Herod," said Lukerya, looking at him angrily. "Go along, go along, and may you burn up with vodka, you tailless Satan!"

"You hold your tongue," shouted Volodka.

"They've married me to a fool, they've ruined me, a luckless orphan, you red-headed drunkard . . ." wailed Lukerya, wiping her face with a hand covered with dough. "I wish I had never set eyes on you."

Volodka gave her a blow on the ear and went off.

III

Elena Ivanovna and her little daughter visited the village on foot. They were out for a walk. It was a Sunday, and the peasant women and girls were walking up and down the street in their brightly-coloured dresses. Rodion and Stepanida, sitting side by side at their door, bowed and smiled to Elena Ivanovna and her little daughter as to acquaintances. From the windows more than a dozen children stared at them; their faces expressed amazement and curiosity, and they could be heard whispering:

"The Kutcherov lady had come! The Kutcherov lady!"

"Good-morning," said Elena Ivanovna, and she stopped; she paused, and then asked: "Well, how are you getting on?"

"We get along all right, thank God," answered Rodion, speaking rapidly. "To be sure we get along."

"The life we lead!" smiled Stepanida. "You can see our poverty your-self, dear lady! The family is fourteen souls in all, and only two bread-winners. We are supposed to be blacksmiths, but when they bring us a horse to shoe we have no coal, nothing to buy it with. We are worried to death, lady," she went on, and laughed. "Oh, oh, we are worried to death."

Elena Ivanovna sat down at the entrance and, putting her arm round her little girl, pondered something, and judging from the little girl's expression, melancholy thoughts were straying through her mind, too; as she brooded she played with the sumptuous lace on the parasol she had taken out of her mother's hands.

"Poverty," said Rodion, "a great deal of anxiety—you see no end to it. Here, God sends no rain . . . our life is not easy, there is no deny-ing it."

"You have a hard time in this life," said Elena Ivanovna, "but in the other world you will be happy."

Rodion did not understand her, and simply coughed into his clenched hand by way of reply. Stepanida said:

"Dear lady, the rich men will be all right in the next world, too. The rich put up candles, pay for services; the rich give to beggars, but what can the poor man do? He has no time to make the sign of the cross. He is the beggar of beggars himself; how can he think of his soul? And many sins come from poverty; from trouble we snarl at one another like dogs, we haven't a good word to say to one another, and all sorts of things happen, dear lady—God forbid! It seems we have no luck in this world nor the next. All the luck has fallen to the rich."

She spoke gaily; she was evidently used to talking of her hard life. And Rodion smiled, too; he was pleased that his old woman was so clever, so ready of speech.

"It is only on the surface that the rich seem to be happy," said Elena Ivanovna. "Every man has his sorrow. Here my husband and I do not live poorly, we have means, but are we happy? I am young, but I have had four children; my children are always being ill. I am ill, too, and con-stantly being doctored."

"And what is your illness?" asked Rodion.

"A woman's complaint. I get no sleep; a continual headache gives me no peace. Here I am sitting and talking, but my head is bad, I am weak all over, and I should prefer the hardest labour to such a condition. My soul, too, is troubled; I am in continual fear for my children, my husband. Every family has its own trouble of some sort; we have ours. I am not of noble birth. My grandfather was a simple peasant, my father was a trades-man in Moscow; he was a plain, uneducated man, too, while my husband's parents were wealthy and distinguished. They did not want him to marry me, but he disobeyed them, quarrelled with them, and they have not forgiven us to this day. That worries my husband; it troubles him and keeps him in constant agitation; he loves his mother, loves her dearly. So I am uneasy, too, my soul is in pain."

Peasants, men and women, were by now standing round Rodion's hut and listening. Kozov came up, too, and stood twitching his long, narrow beard. The Lytchkovs, father and son, drew near.

"And say what you like, one cannot be happy and satisfied if one does not feel in one's proper place." Elena Ivanovna went on. "Each of you has his strip of land, each of you works and knows what he is working for; my husband builds bridges—in short, everyone has his place, while I, I simply walk about. I have not my bit to work. I don't work, and feel as though I were an outsider. I am saying all this that you may not judge from outward appearances; if a man is expensively dressed and has means it does not prove that he is satisfied with his life."

She got up to go away and took her daughter by the hand.

"I like your place here very much," she said, and smiled, and from that faint, diffident smile one could tell how unwell she really was, how young and how pretty; she had a pale, thinnish face with dark eyebrows and fair hair. And the little girl was just such another as her mother: thin, fair, and slender. There was a fragrance of scent about them.

"I like the river and the forest and the village," Elena Ivanovna went on; "I could live here all my life, and I feel as though here I should get strong and find my place. I want to help you—I want to dreadfully—to be of use, to be a real friend to you. I know your need, and what I don't know I feel, my heart guesses. I am sick, feeble, and for me perhaps it is not possible to change my life as I would. But I have children. I will try to bring them up that they may be of use to you, may love you. I shall impress upon them continually that their life does not belong to them, but to you. Only I beg you earnestly, I beseech you, trust us, live in friendship with us. My husband is a kind, good man. Don't worry him, don't irritate him. He is sensitive to every trifle, and yesterday, for instance, your cattle were in our vegetable garden, and one of your people broke down the fence to the bee-hives, and such an attitude to us drives my husband to despair. I beg you," she went on in an imploring voice, and she clasped her hands on her bosom—"I beg you to treat us as good neighbours; let us live in peace! There is a saying, you know, that even a bad peace is better than a good quarrel, and, 'Don't buy property, but buy neighbours.' I repeat my husband is a kind man and good; if all goes well we promise to do everything in our power for you; we will mend the roads, we will build a school for your children. I promise you."

"Of course we thank you humbly, lady," said Lytchkov the father, looking at the ground; "you are educated people; it is for you to know best. Only, you see, Voronov, a rich peasant at Eresnevo, promised to build a school; he, too, said, 'I will do this for you,' 'I will do that for you,' and he only put up the framework and refused to go on. And then they made the peasants put the roof on and finish it; it cost them a thousand roubles. Voronov did not care; he only stroked his beard, but the peasants felt it a bit hard."

"That was a crow, but now there's a rook, too," said Kozov, and he winked.

There was the sound of laughter.

"We don't want a school," said Volodka sullenly. "Our children go to Petrovskoe, and they can go on going there; we don't want it."

Elena Ivanovna seemed suddenly intimidated; her face looked paler and thinner, she shrank into herself as though she had been touched with something coarse, and walked away without uttering another word. And she walked more and more quickly, without looking round.

"Lady," said Rodion, walking after her, "lady, wait a bit; hear what I would say to you."

He followed her without his cap, and spoke softly as though begging.

"Lady, wait and hear what I will say to you."

They had walked out of the village, and Elena Ivanovna stopped beside a cart in the shade of an old mountain ash.

"Don't be offended, lady," said Rodion. "What does it mean? Have patience. Have patience for a couple of years. You will live here, you will have patience, and it will all come round. Our folks are good and peaceable; there's no harm in them; it's God's truth I'm telling you. Don't mind Kozov and the Lytchkovs, and don't mind Volodka. He's a fool; he listens to the first that speaks. The others are quiet folks; they are silent. Some would be glad, you know, to say a word from the heart and to stand up for themselves, but cannot. They have a heart and a conscience, but no tongue. Don't be offended . . . have patience. . . . What does it matter?"

Elena Ivanovna looked at the broad, tranquil river, pondering, and tears flowed down her cheeks. And Rodion was troubled by those tears; he almost cried himself.

"Never mind . . ." he muttered. "Have patience for a couple of years. You can have the school, you can have the roads, only not all at once. If you went, let us say, to sow corn on that mound you would first have to weed it out, to pick out all the stones, and then to plough, and work and work . . . and with the people, you see, it is the same . . . you must work and work until you overcome them."

The crowd had moved away from Rodion's hut, and was coming along the street towards the mountain ash. They began singing songs and playing the concertina, and they kept coming closer and closer. . . .

"Mamma, let us go away from here," said the little girl, huddling up to her mother, pale and shaking all over; "let us go away, mamma!"

"Where?"

"To Moscow. . . . Let us go, mamma."

The child began crying.

Rodion was utterly overcome; his face broke into profuse perspiration; he took out of his pocket a little crooked cucumber, like a half-moon, covered with crumbs of rye bread, and began thrusting it into the little girl's hands.

"Come, come," he muttered, scowling severely; "take the little cucumber, eat it up. . . . You mustn't cry. Mamma will whip you. . . . She'll tell your father of you when you get home. Come, come. . . ."

They walked on, and he still followed behind them, wanting to say something friendly and persuasive to them. And seeing that they were both absorbed in their own thoughts and their own griefs, and not noticing him, he stopped and, shading his eyes from the sun, looked after them for a long time till they disappeared into their copse.

IV

The engineer seemed to grow irritable and petty, and in every trivial incident saw an act of robbery or outrage. His gate was kept bolted even by day, and at night two watchmen walked up and down the garden beating a board; and they gave up employing anyone from Obrutchanovo as a labourer. As ill-luck would have it someone (either a peasant or one of the workmen) took the new wheels off the cart and replaced them by old ones, then soon afterwards two bridles and a pair of pincers were carried off, and murmurs arose even in the village. People began to say that a search should be made at the Lytchkovs' and at Volodka's, and then the bridles and the pincers were found under the hedge in the engineer's garden; someone had thrown them down there.

It happened that the peasants were coming in a crowd out of the forest, and again they met the engineer on the road. He stopped, and without wishing them good-day he began, looking angrily first at one, then at another:

"I have begged you not to gather mushrooms in the park and near the yard, but to leave them for my wife and children, but your girls come before daybreak and there is not a mushroom left. . . . Whether one asks you or not it makes no difference. Entreaties, and friendliness, and persuasion I see are all useless."

He fixed his indignant eyes on Rodion and went on:

"My wife and I behaved to you as human beings, as to our equals, and you? But what's the use of talking! It will end by our looking down upon you. There is nothing left!"

And making an effort to restrain his anger, not to say too much, he turned and went on.

On getting home Rodion said his prayer, took off his boots, and sat down beside his wife.

"Yes . . ." he began with a sigh. "We were walking along just now, and Mr. Kutcherov met us. . . . Yes. . . . He saw the girls at daybreak. . . . 'Why don't they bring mushrooms,' he said . . . 'to my wife and children?' he said. . . . And then he looked at me and he said: 'I and my wife will look after you,' he said. I wanted to fall down at his feet, but I hadn't the courage. . . . God give him health. . . . God bless him! . . ."

Stephania crossed herself and sighed.

"They are kind, simple-hearted people," Rodion went on. " 'We shall look after you.' . . . He promised me that before everyone. In our old age . . . it wouldn't be a bad thing. . . . I should always pray for them. . . . Holy Mother, bless them. . . ."

The Feast of the Exaltation of the Cross, the fourteenth of September, was the festival of the village church. The Lytchkovs, father and son, went across the river early in the morning and returned to dinner drunk; they spent a long time going about the village, alternately singing and swearing; then they had a fight and went to the New Villa to complain. First Lytchkov the father went into the yard with a long ashen stick in his hands. He stopped irresolutely and took off his hat. Just at that moment the engineer and his family were sitting on the verandah, drinking tea.

"What do you want?" shouted the engineer.

"Your honour . . ." Lytchkov began, and burst into tears. "Show the Divine mercy, protect me . . . my son makes my life a misery . . . your honour. . . ."

Lytchkov the son walked up, too; he, too, was bareheaded and had a stick in his hand; he stopped and fixed his drunken senseless eyes on the verandah.

"It is not my business to settle your affairs," said the engineer. "Go to the rural captain or the police officer."

"I have been everywhere. . . . I have lodged a petition . . ." said Lytchkov the father, and he sobbed. "Where can I go now? He can kill me now, it seems. He can do anything. Is that the way to treat a father? A father?"

He raised his stick and hit his son on the head; the son raised his stick and struck his father just on his bald patch such a blow that the stick bounced back. The father did not even flinch, but hit his son again and again on the head. And so they stood and kept hitting one another on the head, and it looked not so much like a fight as some sort of a game. And peasants, men and women, stood in a crowd at the gate and looked into the garden, and the faces of all were grave. They were the peasants who had come to greet them for the holiday, but seeing the Lytchkovs, they were ashamed and did not go in.

The next morning Elena Ivanovna went with the children to Moscow. And there was a rumour that the engineer was selling his house. . . .

V

The peasants had long ago grown used to the sight of the bridge, and it was difficult to imagine the river at that place without a bridge. The heap of rubble left from the building of it had long been overgrown with grass, the navvies were forgotten, and instead of the strains of the "Dubinushka" that they used to sing, the peasants heard almost every hour the sounds of a passing train.

The New Villa has long ago been sold; now it belongs to a government clerk who comes here from the town for the holidays with his family, drinks tea on the terrace, and then goes back to the town again. He wears a cockade on his cap; he talks and clears his throat as though he were a very important official, though he is only of the rank of a collegiate secretary, and when the peasants bow he makes no response.

In Obrutchanovo everyone has grown older; Kozov is dead. In Rodion's hut there are even more children. Volodka has grown a long red beard. They are still as poor as ever.

In the early spring the Obrutchanovo peasants were sawing wood near the station. And after work they were going home; they walked without haste one after the other. Broad saws curved over their shoulders; the sun was reflected in them. The nightingales were singing in the bushes on the bank, larks were trilling in the heavens. It was quiet at the New Villa; there was not a soul there, and only golden pigeons—golden because the sunlight was streaming upon them—were flying over the house. All of them—Rodion, the two Lytchkovs, and Volodka—thought of the white horses, the little ponies, the fireworks, the boat with the lanterns; they remembered how the engineer's wife, so beautiful and so grandly dressed, had come into the village and talked to them in such a friendly way. And it seemed as though all that had never been; it was like a dream or a fairy-tale.

They trudged along, tired out, and mused as they went. . . . In their village, they mused, the people were good, quiet, sensible, fearing God, and Elena Ivanovna, too, was quiet, kind, and gentle; it made one sad to look at her, but why had they not got on together? Why had they parted like enemies? How was it that some mist had shrouded from their eyes what mattered most, and had let them see nothing but damage done by cattle, bridles, pincers, and all those trivial things which now, as they remembered them, seemed so nonsensical? How was it that with the new owner they lived in peace, and yet had been on bad terms with the engineer?

And not knowing what answer to make to these questions they were all silent except Volodka, who muttered something.

"What is it?" Rodion asked.

"We lived without a bridge . . ." said Volodka gloomily. "We lived without a bridge, and did not ask for one . . . and we don't want it. . . ."

No one answered him and they walked on in silence with drooping heads.

COMMENT AND QUESTION

1. The events in "The New Villa" occur about 1900 in the Russia of the Czars.

2. In many of his stories and plays Chekhov unmasks the idle and the ineffectual, the liar and the troublemaker, the self-deceived and the sentimental well-wisher. How many of these types appear in "The New Villa"?

3. Rodion is an important character. How does he differ from the other characters? Does he have great intelligence? What childlike errors does he make about the incident of the mushrooms and also about the engineer's phrase, "repay us in the same coin"?

4. Study Rodion's comments on work near the end of section III. Through Rodion Chekhov expresses one of the most important ideas not only of this story but also of his writing as a whole—the gospel of work. Chekhov felt that serious, earnest work would root out the laziness, the indifference, the boredom of the Russian society of his time and would engender a social revolution. In "The New Villa" Chekhov includes both gentry and peasants in his criticism.

5. In section III, study the conversation on poverty between Stepanida and Elena. Where is the irony? Is Elena self-deceived? Does she take a neurotic pleasure in her suffering? Is her charity self-conscious? Does she speak of work? Notice the parasol.

6. What is the ironical connection between the conversation on poverty and an early comment by the coachman: "On the new estate, he told them, they were not going to plough or sow, but simply to live for their pleasure, live only to breathe the fresh air"?

7. The bridge is clearly a symbol. Its purpose in the story is emphasized by the repeated comment: "We don't want a bridge."

8. Are the conflicts between the engineer and the peasants trivial? Why does the engineer become so angry about the mushrooms when he had been so tractable about the peasants' cutting down trees and digging up the road?

9. In section IV, what serious weakness does the engineer show in the incident where the Lytchkov son beats his father? As a peasant, Lytchkov was appealing to the engineer to assume what great responsibility?

10. The tone in this story is often comic. See the description of the impounded animals, the statements of Rodion, the picture of Lytchkov beating his father. What does this tone contribute?

The melancholy tone, set early by "the mournful clang of metal, don-don-don," is equally characteristic of Chekhov.

11. Chekhov often communicates through moods. What is the mood of the first paragraph? What is the mood of the last incident in section V? Are the questions the men ask themselves in this last incident answered by Volodka's last statement?

HOOK

BY WALTER VAN TILBURG CLARK

WALTER VAN TILBURG CLARK (1909–   )
was born in Maine but has spent most of his
life in Nevada. Much of his writing reflects
the history and culture of the West. He has
published a collection of short stories, *The
Watchful Gods* (1950). He has also published three novels, *The Ox-Bow Incident*
(1940), *The City of Trembling Leaves*
(1945), and *The Track of the Cat* (1949).

Hook, the hawks' child, was hatched in a dry spring among the oaks
beside the seasonal river, and was struck from the nest early. In the
drouth his single-willed parents had to extend their hunting ground by
more than twice, for the ground creatures upon which they fed died and
dried by the hundreds. The range became too great for them to wish to
return and feed Hook, and when they had lost interest in each other they
drove Hook down into the sand and brush and went back to solitary
courses over the bleaching hills.

Unable to fly yet, Hook crept over the ground, challenging all large
movements with recoiled head, erected, rudimentary wings, and the
small rasp of his clattering beak. It was during this time of abysmal
ignorance and continual fear that his eyes took on the first quality of a
hawk, that of being wide, alert and challenging. He dwelt, because of
his helplessness, among the rattling brush which grew between the oaks
and the river. Even in his thickets and near the water, the white sun was
the dominant presence. Except in the dawn, when the land wind stirred,
or in the late afternoon, when the sea wind became strong enough to

HOOK   From *The Watchful Gods and Other Stories* by Walter Van Tilburg
Clark. Reprinted by permission of Random House, Inc. Copyright, 1940, by
Walter Van Tilburg Clark.

penetrate the half-mile inland to this turn in the river, the sun was the major force, and everything was dry and motionless under it. The brush, small plants and trees alike husbanded the little moisture at their hearts; the moving creatures waited for dark, when sometimes the sea fog came over and made a fine, soundless rain which relieved them.

The two spacious sounds of his life environed Hook at this time. One was the great rustle of the slopes of yellowed wild wheat, with over it the chattering rustle of the leaves of the California oaks, already as harsh and individually tremulous as in autumn. The other was the distant whisper of the foaming edge of the Pacific, punctuated by the hollow shoring of the waves. But these Hook did not yet hear, for he was attuned by fear and hunger to the small, spasmodic rustlings of live things. Dry, shrunken, and nearly starved, and with his plumage delayed, he snatched at beetles, dragging in the sand to catch them. When swifter and stronger birds and animals did not reach them first, which was seldom, he ate the small, silver fish left in the mud by the failing river. He watched, with nearly chattering beak, the quick, thin lizards pause, very alert, and raise and lower themselves, but could not catch them because he had to raise his wings to move rapidly, which startled them.

Only one sight and sound not of his world of microscopic necessity was forced upon Hook. That was the flight of the big gulls from the beaches, which sometimes, in quealing play, came spinning back over the foothills and the river bed. For some inherited reason, the big, ship-bodied birds did not frighten Hook, but angered him. Small and chewed-looking, with his wide, already yellowing eyes glaring up at them, he would stand in an open place on the sand in the sun and spread his shaping wings and clatter his bill like shaken dice. Hook was furious about the swift, easy passage of gulls.

His first opportunity to leave off living like a ground owl came acci-dentally. He was standing in the late afternoon in the red light under the thicket, his eyes half-filmed with drowse and the stupefaction of starvation, when suddenly something beside him moved, and he struck, and killed a field mouse driven out of the wheat by thirst. It was a poor mouse, shriveled and lice ridden, but in striking, Hook had tasted blood, which raised nest memories and restored his nature. With started neck plumage and shining eyes, he tore and fed. When the mouse was de-voured, Hook had entered hoarse adolescence. He began to seek with a conscious appetite, and to move more readily out of shelter. Impelled by the blood appetite, so glorious after his long preservation upon the flaky and bitter stuff of bugs, he ventured even into the wheat in the open sun beyond the oaks, and discovered the small trails and holes among the roots. With his belly often partially filled with flesh, he grew rapidly in strength and will. His eyes were taking on their final change, their yellow growing deeper and more opaque, their stare more constant, their challenge less desperate. Once during this transformation, he surprised a ground squirrel, and although he was ripped and wing-bitten and could not hold his prey, he was not dismayed by the conflict, but exalted. Even while the wing was still drooping and the pinions not grown back, he was excited by other ground squirrels and pursued them futilely, and was angered by their dusty escapes. He realized that his world was a great arena for killing, and felt the magnificence of it.

The two major events of Hook's young life occurred in the same day. A little after dawn he made the customary essay and succeeded in flight. A little before sunset, he made his first sustained flight of over two hundred yards, and at its termination struck and slew a great buck squirrel whose thrashing and terrified gnawing and squealing gave him a wild delight. When he had gorged on the strong meat, Hook stood upright, and in his eyes was the stare of the hawk, never flagging in intensity but never swelling beyond containment. After that the stare had only to grow more deeply challenging and more sternly controlled as his range and deadliness increased. There was no change in kind. Hook had mastered the first of the three hungers which are fused into the single, flaming will of a hawk, and he had experienced the second.

The third and consummating hunger did not awaken in Hook until the following spring, when the exultation of space had grown slow and steady in him, so that he swept freely with the wind over the miles of coastal foothills, circling, and ever in sight of the sea, and used without struggle the warm currents lifting from the slopes, and no longer desired to scream at the range of his vision, but intently sailed above his shadow swiftly climbing to meet him on the hillsides, sinking away and rippling across the brush-grown canyons.

That spring the rains were long, and Hook sat for hours, hunched and angry under their pelting, glaring into the fogs of the river valley, and killed only small, drenched things flooded up from their tunnels. But when the rains had dissipated, and there were sun and sea wind again, the game ran plentiful, the hills were thick and shining green, and the new river flooded about the boulders where battered turtles climbed up to shrink and sleep. Hook then was scorched by the third hunger. Ranging farther, often forgetting to kill and eat, he sailed for days with growing rage, and woke at night clattering on his dead tree limb, and struck and struck and struck at the porous wood of the trunk, tearing it away. After days, in the draft of a coastal canyon miles below his own hills, he came upon the acrid taint he did not know but had expected, and sailing down it, felt his neck plumes rise and his wings quiver so that he swerved unsteadily. He saw the unmated female perched upon the tall and jagged stump of a tree that had been shorn by storm, and he stooped, as if upon game. But she was older than he, and wary of the gripe of his importunity, and banked off screaming, and he screamed also at the intolerable delay.

At the head of the canyon, the screaming pursuit was crossed by another male with a great wing-spread, and the light golden in the fringe of his plumage. But his more skillful opening played him false against the ferocity of the twice-balked Hook. His rising maneuver for position was cut short by Hook's wild, upward swoop, and at the blow he raked desperately and tumbled off to the side. Dropping, Hook struck him again, struggled to clutch, but only raked and could not hold, and, diving, struck once more in passage, and then beat up, yelling triumph, and saw the crippled antagonist side-slip away, half-tumble once, as the ripped wing failed to balance, then steady and glide obliquely into the cover of brush on the canyon side. Beating hard and stationary in the wind above the bush that covered his competitor, Hook waited an instant, but when the bush was still, screamed again, and let himself go off with the current, reseeking, infuriated by the burn of his own wounds, the thin choke-thread of the acrid taint.

On a hilltop projection of stone two miles inland, he struck her down, gripping her rustling body with his talons, beating her wings down with his wings, belting her head when she whimpered or thrashed, and at last clutching her neck with his hook and, when her coy struggles had given way to stillness, succeeded.

In the early summer, Hook drove the three young ones from their nest, and went back to lone circling above his own range. He was complete.

II

Throughout that summer and the cool, growthless weather of the winter, when the gales blew in the river canyon and the ocean piled upon the shore, Hook was master of the sky and the hills of his range. His flight became a lovely and certain thing, so that he played with the treacherous currents of the air with a delicate ease surpassing that of the gulls. He could sail for hours, searching the blanched grasses below him with telescopic eyes, gaining height against the wind, descending in mile-long, gently declining swoops when he curved and rode back, and never beating either wing. At the swift passage of his shadow within their vision, gophers, ground squirrels and rabbits froze, or plunged gibbering into their tunnels beneath matted turf. Now, when he struck, he killed easily in one hard-knuckled blow. Occasionally, in sport, he soared up over the river and drove the heavy and weaponless gulls downstream again, until they would no longer venture inland.

There was nothing which Hook feared now, and his spirit was wholly belligerent, swift and sharp, like his gaze. Only the mixed smells and incomprehensible activities of the people at the Japanese farmer's home, inland of the coastwise highway and south of the bridge across Hook's river, troubled him. The smells were strong, unsatisfactory and never clear, and the people, though they behaved foolishly, constantly running in and out of their built-up holes, were large, and appeared capable, with fearless eyes looking up at him, so that he instinctively swerved aside from them. He cruised over their yard, their gardens, and their bean fields, but he would not alight close to their buildings.

But this one area of doubt did not interfere with his life. He ignored it, save to look upon it curiously as he crossed, his afternoon shadow sliding in an instant over the chicken-and-crate-cluttered yard, up the side of the unpainted barn, and then out again smoothly, just faintly, liquidly rippling over the furrows and then over the stubble of the grazing slopes. When the season was dry, and the dead earth blew on the fields, he extended his range to satisfy his great hunger, and again narrowed it when the fields were once more alive with the minute movements he could not only see but anticipate.

Four times that year he was challenged by other hawks blowing up from behind the coastal hills to scud down his slopes, but two of these he slew in mid-air, and saw hurtle down to thump on the ground and lie still while he circled, and a third, whose wing he tore, he followed closely to earth and beat to death in the grass, making the crimson jet out from its breast and neck into the pale wheat. The fourth was a strong flier and experienced fighter, and theirs was a long, running battle, with brief, rising flurries of striking and screaming, from which down and plumage soared off.

Here, for the first time, Hook felt doubts, and at moments wanted to drop away from the scoring, burning talons and the twisted hammer strokes of the strong beak, drop away shrieking, and take cover and be still. In the end, when Hook, having outmaneuvered his enemy and come above him, wholly in control, and going with the wind, tilted and plunged for the death rap, the other, in desperation, threw over on his back and struck up. Talons locked, beaks raking, they dived earthward. The earth grew and spread under them amazingly, and they were not fifty feet above it when Hook, feeling himself turning toward the underside, tore free and beat up again on heavy, wrenched wings. The other, stroking swiftly, and so close to down that he lost wing plumes to a bush, righted himself and planed up, but flew on lumberingly between the hills and did not return. Hook screamed the triumph, and made a brief pretense of pursuit, but was glad to return, slow and victorious, to his dead tree.

In all these encounters Hook was injured, but experienced only the fighter's pride and exultation from the sting of wounds received in successful combat. And in each of them he learned new skill. Each time the wounds healed quickly, and left him a more dangerous bird.

In the next spring, when the rains and the night chants of the little frogs were past, the third hunger returned upon Hook with a new violence. In his quest, he came into the taint of a young hen. Others too were drawn by the unnerving perfume, but only one of them, the same with which Hook had fought his great battle, was a worthy competitor. This hunter drove off two, while two others, game but neophytes, were glad enough that Hook's impatience would not permit him to follow and kill. Then the battle between the two champions fled inland, and was a tactical marvel, but Hook lodged the neck-breaking blow, and struck again as they dropped past the treetops. The blood had already begun to pool on the gray, fallen foliage as Hook flapped up between branches, too spent to cry his victory. Yet his hunger would not let him rest until, late in the second day, he drove the female to ground, among the laurels of a strange river canyon.

When the two fledglings of this second brood had been driven from the nest, and Hook had returned to his own range, he was not only complete, but supreme. He slept without concealment on his bare limb, and did not open his eyes when, in the night, the heavy-billed cranes coughed in the shadows below him.

III

The turning point of Hook's career came that autumn, when the brush in the canyons rustled dryly and the hills, mowed close by the cattle, smoked under the wind as if burning. One midafternoon, when the black clouds were torn on the rim of the sea and the surf flowered white and high on the rocks, raining in over the low cliffs, Hook rode the wind diagonally across the river mouth. His great eyes, focused for small things stirring in the dust and leaves, overlooked so large and slow a movement as that of the Japanese farmer rising from the brush and lifting the two black eyes of his shotgun. Too late Hook saw and, startled, swerved, but wrongly. The surf muffled the reports, and nearly without sound, Hook felt the minute whips of the first shot, and the astounding, breath-breaking blow of the second.

Beating his good wing, tasting the blood that quickly swelled into his beak, he tumbled off with the wind and struck into the thickets on the far side of the river mouth. The branches tore him. Wild with rage, he thrust up and clattered his beak, challenging, but when he had fallen over twice, he knew that the trailing wing would not carry, and then heard the boots of the hunter among the stones in the river bed and, seeing him loom at the edge of the bushes, crept back among the thickest brush and was still. When he saw the boots stand before him, he reared back, lifting his good wing and cocking his head for the serpent-like blow, his beak open but soundless, his great eyes hard and very shining. The boots passed on. The Japanese farmer, who believed that he had lost chickens, and who had cunningly observed Hook's flight for many afternoons, until he could plot it, did not greatly want a dead hawk.

When Hook could hear nothing but the surf and the wind in the thicket,

he let the sickness and shock overcome him. The fine film of the inner lid
dropped over his big eyes. His heart beat frantically, so that it made the
plumage of his shot-aching breast throb. His own blood throttled his
breathing. But these things were nothing compared to the lightning of
pain in his left shoulder, where the shot had bunched, shattering the airy
bones so the pinions trailed on the ground and could not be lifted. Yet,
when a sparrow lit in the bush over him, Hook's eyes flew open again,
hard and challenging, his good wing was lifted and his beak strained open.
The startled sparrow darted piping out over the river.

Throughout that night, while the long clouds blew across the stars and
the wind shook the bushes about him, and throughout the next day, while
the clouds still blew and massed until there was no gleam of sunlight on
the sand bar, Hook remained stationary, enduring his sickness. In the
second evening, the rains began. First there was a long, running patter of
drops upon the beach and over the dry trees and bushes. At dusk there
came a heavier squall, which did not die entirely, but slacked off to a
continual, spaced splashing of big drops, and then returned with the front
of the storm. In long, misty curtains, gust by gust, the rain swept over the
sea, beating down its heaving, and coursed up the beach. The little jets of
dust ceased to rise about the drops in the fields, and the mud began to
gleam. Among the boulders of the river bed, darkling pools grew slowly.

Still Hook stood behind his tree from the wind, only gentle drops reaching him, falling from the upper branches and then again from the brush.
His eyes remained closed, and he could still taste his own blood in his
mouth, though it had ceased to come up freshly. Out beyond him, he
heard the storm changing. As rain conquered the sea, the heave of the
surf became a hushed sound, often lost in the crying of the wind. Then
gradually, as the night turned toward morning, the wind also was broken
by the rain. The crying became fainter, the rain settled toward steadiness,
and the creep of the waves could be heard again, quiet and regular upon
the beach.

At dawn there was no wind and no sun, but everywhere the roaring
of the vertical, relentless rain. Hook then crept among the rapid drippings
of the bushes, dragging his torn sail, seeking better shelter. He stopped
often and stood with the shutters of film drawn over his eyes. At mid-
morning he found a little cave under a ledge at the base of the sea cliff.
Here, lost without branches and leaves about him, he settled to await
improvement.

When, at midday of the third day, the rain stopped altogether, and the
sky opened before a small, fresh wind, letting light through to glitter
upon a tremulous sea, Hook was so weak that his good wing trailed also
to prop him upright, and his open eyes were lusterless. But his wounds
were hardened, and he felt the return of hunger. Beyond his shelter, he
heard the gulls flying in great numbers and crying their joy at the cleared

air. He could even hear, from the fringe of the river, the ecstatic and unstinted bubblings and chirpings of the small birds. The grassland, he felt, would be full of the stirring anew of the close-bound life, the un-drowned insects clicking as they dried out, the snakes slithering down, heads half erect, into the grasses where the mice, gophers and ground squirrels ran and stopped and chewed and licked themselves smoother and drier.

With the aid of this hunger, and on the crutches of his wings, Hook came down to stand in the sun beside his cave, whence he could watch the beach. Before him, in ellipses on tilting planes, the gulls flew. The surf was rearing again, and beginning to shelve and hiss on the sand. Through the white foam-writing it left, the long-billed pipers twinkled in bevies, escaping each wave, then racing down after it to plunge their fine drills into the minute double holes where the sand crabs bubbled. In the third row of breakers two seals lifted sleek, streaming heads and barked, and over them, trailing his spider legs, a great crane flew south. Among the stones at the foot of the cliff, small red and green crabs made a little, continuous rattling and knocking. The cliff swallows glittered and twanged on aerial forays.

The afternoon began auspiciously for Hook also. One of the two gulls which came squabbling above him dropped a freshly caught fish to the sand. Quickly Hook was upon it. Gripping it, he raised his good wing and cocked his head with open beak at the many gulls which had circled and come down at once toward the fall of the fish. The gulls sheered off, cursing raucously. Left alone on the sand, Hook devoured the fish and, after resting in the sun, withdrew again to his shelter.

IV

In the succeeding days, between rains, he foraged on the beach. He learned to kill and crack the small green crabs. Along the edge of the river mouth, he found the drowned bodies of mice and squirrels and even sparrows. Twice he managed to drive feeding gulls from their catch, charging upon them with buffeting wing and clattering beak. He grew stronger slowly, but the shot sail continued to drag. Often, at the choking thought of soaring and striking and the good, hot-blood kill, he strove to take off, but only the one wing came up, winnowing with a hiss, and drove him over onto his side in the sand. After these futile trials, he would rage and clatter. But gradually he learned to believe that he could not fly, that his life must now be that of the discharged nestling again. Denied the joy of space, without which the joy of loneliness was lost, the joy of battle and killing, the blood lust, became his whole concentration. It was his hope, as he charged feeding gulls, that they would turn and offer battle, but they never did. The sandpipers, at his approach, fled peeping, or, like a quiver of arrows shot together, streamed out over the surf in a long curve. Once, pent beyond bearing, he disgraced himself by shrieking challenge at the business-like heron which flew south every evening at the same time. The heron did not even turn his head, but flapped and glided on.

Hook's shame and anger became such that he stood awake at night. Hunger kept him awake also, for these little leavings of the gulls could not sustain his great body in its renewed violence. He became aware that the gulls slept at night in flocks on the sand, each with one leg tucked under him. He discovered also that the curlews and the pipers, often mingling, likewise slept, on the higher remnant of the bar. A sensation of evil delight filled him in the consideration of protracted striking among them.

There was only half of a sick moon in a sky of running but far-separated clouds on the night when he managed to stalk into the center of the sleeping gulls. This was light enough, but so great was his vengeful pleasure that there broke from him a shrill scream of challenge as he first struck. Without the power of flight behind it, the blow was not murderous, and this newly discovered impotence made Hook crazy, so that he screamed again and again as he struck and tore at the felled gull. He slew the one, but was twice knocked over by its heavy flounderings, and all the others rose above him, weaving and screaming, protesting in the thin moonlight. Wakened by their clamor, the wading birds also took wing, startled and plaintive. When the beach was quiet again, the flocks had settled elsewhere, beyond his pitiful range, and he was left alone beside the single kill. It was a disappointing victory. He fed with lowering spirit.

Thereafter, he stalked silently. At sunset he would watch where the gulls settled along the miles of beach, and after dark he would come like a sharp shadow among them, and drive with his hook on all sides of him, till the beatings of a poorly struck victim sent the flock up. Then he would turn vindictively upon the fallen and finish them. In his best night, he killed five from one flock. But he ate only a little from one, for the vigor resulting from occasional repletion strengthened only his ire, which became so great at such a time that food revolted him. It was not the joyous, swift, controlled hunting anger of a sane hawk, but something quite different, which made him dizzy if it continued too long, and left him unsatisfied with any kill.

Then one day, when he had very nearly struck a gull while driving it from a gasping yellowfin, the gull's wing rapped against him as it broke for its running start, and, the trailing wing failing to support him, he was knocked over. He flurried awkwardly in the sand to regain his feet, but his mastery of the beach was ended. Seeing him, in clear sunlight, struggling after the chance blow, the gulls returned about him in a flashing cloud, circling and pecking on the wing. Hook's plumage showed quick little jets of irregularity here and there. He reared back, clattering and erecting the good wing, spreading the great, rusty tail for balance. His eyes shone with a little of the old pleasure. But it died, for he could reach none of them. He was forced to turn and dance awkwardly on the sand, trying to clash bills with each tormentor. They banked up quealing and returned, weaving about him in concentric and overlapping circles. His scream was lost in their clamor, and he appeared merely to be hopping clumsily with his mouth open. Again he fell sideways. Before he could right himself, he was bowled over, and a second time, and lay on his side, twisting his neck to reach them and clappering in blind fury, and was struck three times by three successive gulls, shrieking their flock triumph.

Finally he managed to roll to his breast, and to crouch with his good wing spread wide and the other stretched nearly as far, so that he extended like a gigantic moth, only his snake head, with its now silent scimitar, erect. One great eye blazed under its level brow, but where the other had been was a shallow hole from which thin blood trickled to his russet gap.

In this crouch, by short stages, stopping repeatedly to turn and drive the gulls up, Hook dragged into the river canyon and under the stiff cover of the bitter-leafed laurel. There the gulls left him, soaring up with great clatter of their valor. Till nearly sunset Hook, broken spirited and enduring his hardening eye socket, heard them celebrating over the waves.

When his will was somewhat replenished, and his empty eye socket had stopped the twitching and vague aching which had forced him often to roll ignominiously to rub it in the dust, Hook ventured from the protective lacings of his thicket. He knew fear again, and the challenge of his remaining eye was once more strident, as in adolescence. He dared not return to the beaches, and with a new, weak hunger, the home hunger, enticing him, made his way by short hunting journeys back to the wild wheat slopes and the crisp oaks. There was in Hook an unwonted sensation now, that of the ever-neighboring possibility of death. This sensation was beginning, after his period as a mad bird on the beach, to solidify him into his last stage of life. When, during his slow homeward passage, the gulls wafted inland over him, watching the earth with curious, miserish eyes, he did not cower, but neither did he challenge, either by opened beak or by raised shoulder. He merely watched carefully, learning his first lessons in observing the world with one eye.

At first the familiar surroundings of the bend in the river and the tree with the dead limb to which he could not ascend, aggravated his humiliation, but in time, forced to live cunningly and half-starved, he lost much of his savage pride. At the first flight of a strange hawk over his realm, he was wild at his helplessness, and kept twisting his head like an owl, or spinning in the grass like a small and feathered dervish, to keep the hateful beauty of the wind-rider in sight. But in the succeeding weeks, as one after another coasted his beat, his resentment declined, and when one of the raiders, a haughty yearling, sighted his up-staring eye, and plunged and struck him dreadfully, and failed to kill him only because he dragged under a thicket in time, the second of his great hungers was gone. He had no longer the true lust to kill, no joy of battle, but only the poor desire to fill his belly.

Then truly he lived in the wheat and the brush like a ground owl, ridden with ground lice, dusty or muddy, ever half-starved, forced to sit for hours by small holes for petty and unsatisfying kills. Only once during the final months before his end did he make a kill where the breath of danger recalled his valor, and then the danger was such as a hawk with wings and eyes would scorn. Waiting beside a gopher hole, surrounded by the high, yellow grass, he saw the head emerge, and struck, and was amazed that there writhed in his clutch the neck and dusty coffin-skull of a rattlesnake. Holding his grip, Hook saw the great, thick body slither up after, the tip an erect, strident blur, and writhe on the dirt of the gopher's mound. The weight of the snake pushed Hook about, and once threw him down, and the rising and falling whine of the rattles made the moment terrible, but the vaulted mouth, gaping from the closeness of Hook's gripe, so that the pale, envenomed sabers stood out free, could not reach him. When Hook replaced the grip of his beak with the grip of his talons, and was free to strike again and again at the base of the head, the struggle was over. Hook tore and fed on the fine, watery flesh, and left the tattered armor and the long, jointed bone for the marching ants.

When the heavy rains returned, he ate well during the period of the first escapes from flooded burrows, and then well enough, in a vulture's way, on the drowned creatures. But as the rains lingered, and the burrows hung full of water, and there were no insects in the grass and no small birds sleeping in the thickets, he was constantly hungry, and finally unbearably hungry. His sodden and ground-broken plumage stood out raggedly about him, so that he looked fat, even bloated, but underneath it his skin clung to his bones. Save for his great talons and clappers, and the rain in his down, he would have been like a handful of air. He often stood for a long time under some bush or ledge, heedless of the drip, his one eye filmed over, his mind neither asleep or awake, but between. The gurgle and swirl of the brimming river, and the sound of chunks of the bank cut away to splash and dissolve in the already muddy flood, became familiar to him, and yet a torment, as if that great, ceaselessly working power of water ridiculed his frailty, within which only the faintest spark of valor still glimmered. The last two nights before the rain ended, he huddled under the floor of the bridge on the coastal highway, and heard the palpitant thunder of motors swell and roar over him. The trucks shook the bridge so that Hook, even in his famished lassitude, would sometimes open his one great eye wide and startled.

V

After the rains, when things became full again, bursting with growth and sound, the trees swelling, the thickets full of song and chatter, the fields, turning green in the sun, alive with rustling passages, and the moonlit nights strained with the song of the peepers all up and down the river and in the pools in the fields, Hook had to bear the return of the one hunger left him. At times this made him so wild that he forgot himself and screamed challenge from the open ground. The fretfulness of it spoiled his hunting, which was now entirely a matter of patience. Once he was in despair, and lashed himself through the grass and thickets, trying to rise when that virgin scent drifted for a few moments above the current of his own river. Then, breathless, his beak agape, he saw the strong suitor ride swiftly down on the wind over him, and heard afar the screaming fuss of the harsh wooing in the alders. For that moment even the battle heart beat in him again. The rim of his good eye was scarlet, and a little bead of new blood stood in the socket of the other. With beak and talon, he ripped at a fallen log, and made loam and leaves fly from about it.

But the season of love passed over to the nesting season, and Hook's love hunger, unused, shriveled in him with the others, and there remained in him only one stern quality befitting a hawk, and that the negative one, the remnant, the will to endure. He resumed his patient, plotted hunting, now along a field of the Japanese farmer, but ever within reach of the river thickets.

Growing tough and dry again as the summer advanced, inured to the family of the farmer, whom he saw daily, stooping and scraping with sticks in the ugly, open rows of their fields, where no lovely grass rustled and no life stirred save the shameless gulls, which walked at the heels of the workers, gobbling the worms and grubs as they turned up, Hook became nearly content with his shard of life. The only longing or resentment to pierce him was that which he suffered occasionally when forced to hide at the edge of the mile-long bean field from the wafted cruising and the restive, down-bent gaze of one of his own kind. For the rest, he was without flame, a snappish, dust-colored creature, fading into the grasses he trailed through, and suited to his petty ways.

At the end of that summer, for the second time in his four years, Hook underwent a drouth. The equinoctial period passed without a rain. The laurel and the rabbit-brush dropped dry leaves. The foliage of the oaks shriveled and curled. Even the night fogs in the river canyon failed. The farmer's red cattle on the hillside lowed constantly, and could not feed on the dusty stubble. Grass fires broke out along the highway, and ate fast in the wind, filling the hollows with the smell of smoke, and died in the dirt of the shorn hills. The river made no sound. Scum grew on its vestigial pools, and turtles died and stank among the rocks. The dust rode before the wind, and ascended and flowered to nothing between the hills, and every sunset was red with the dust in the air. The people in the farmer's house quarreled, and even struck one another. Birds were silent, and only the hawks flew much. The animals lay breathing hard for very long spells, and ran and crept jerkily. Their flanks were fallen in, and their eyes were red.

At first Hook gorged at the fringe of the grass fires on the multitudes of tiny things that came running and squeaking. But thereafter there were the blackened strips on the hills, and little more in the thin, crackling grass. He found mice and rats, gophers and ground-squirrels, and even rabbits, dead in the stubble and under the thickets, but so dry and flesh-less that only a faint smell rose from them, even on the sunny days. He starved on them. By early December he had wearily stalked the length of the eastern foothills, hunting at night to escape the voracity of his own kind, resting often upon his wings. The queer trail of his short steps and great horned toes zigzagged in the dust and was erased by the wind at dawn. He was nearly dead, and could make no sound through the horn funnels of his clappers.

Then one night the dry wind brought him, with the familiar, lifeless dust, another familiar scent, troublesome, mingled and unclear. In his vision-dominated brain he remembered the swift circle of his flight a year past, crossing in one segment, his shadow beneath him, a yard cluttered with crates and chickens, a gray barn and then again the plowed land and the stubble. Traveling faster than he had for days, impatient of his shrunken sweep, Hook came down to the farm. In the dark wisps of cloud blown among the stars over him, but no moon, he stood outside the wire of the chicken run. The scent of fat and blooded birds reached him from the shelter, and also within the enclosure was water. At the breath of the water, Hook's gorge contracted, and his tongue quivered and clove in its groove of horn. But there was the wire. He stalked its perimeter and found no opening. He beat it with his good wing, and felt it cut but not give. He wrenched at it with his beak in many places, but could not tear it. Finally, in a fury which drove the thin blood through him, he leaped repeatedly against it, beating and clawing. He was thrown back from the last leap as from the first, but in it he had risen so high as to clutch with his beak at the top wire. While he lay on his breast on the ground, the significance of this came upon him.

Again he leapt, clawed up the wire, and, as he would have fallen, made even the dead wing bear a little. He grasped the top and tumbled within. There again he rested flat, searching the dark with quick-turning head. There was no sound or motion but the throb of his own body. First he drank at the chill metal trough hung for the chickens. The water was cold, and loosened his tongue and his tight throat, but it also made him drunk and dizzy, so that he had to rest again, his claws spread wide to brace him. Then he walked stiffly, to stalk down the scent. He trailed it up the runway. Then there was the stuffy, body-warm air, acrid with droppings, full of soft rustlings as his talons clicked on the board floor. The thick, white shapes showed faintly in the darkness. Hook struck quickly, driving a hen to the floor with one blow, its neck broken and stretched out stringily. He leaped the still pulsing body, and tore it. The rich, streaming blood was overpowering to his dried senses, his starved, leathery body. After a few swallows, the flesh choked him. In his rage, he struck down another hen. The urge to kill took him again, as in those nights on the beach. He could let nothing go. Balked of feeding, he was compelled to slaughter. Clattering, he struck again and again. The henhouse was suddenly filled with the squawking and helpless rushing and buffeting of the terrified, brainless fowls.

Hook reveled in mastery. Here was game big enough to offer weight against a strike, and yet unable to soar away from his blows. Turning in the midst of the turmoil, cannily, his fury caught at the perfect pitch, he struck unceasingly. When the hens finally discovered the outlet, and streamed into the yard, to run around the fence, beating and squawking, Hook followed them, scraping down the incline, clumsy and joyous. In the yard, the cock, a bird as large as he, and much heavier, found him out and gave valiant battle. In the dark, and both earthbound, there was little skill, but blow upon blow, and only chance parry. The still squawking hens pressed into one corner of the yard. While the duel went on, a dog, excited by the sustained scuffling, began to bark. He continued to bark, running back and forth along the fence on one side. A light flashed on in an uncurtained window of the farmhouse, and streamed whitely over the crates littering the ground.

Enthralled by his old battle joy, Hook knew only the burly cock before him. Now, in the farthest reach of the window light, they could see each other dimly. The Japanese farmer, with his gun and lantern, was already at the gate when the finish came. The great cock leapt to jab with his spurs and, toppling forward with extended neck as he fell, was struck and extinguished. Blood had loosened Hook's throat. Shrilly he cried his triumph. It was a thin and exhausted cry, but within him as good as when he shrilled in mid-air over the plummeting descent of a fine foe in his best spring.

The light from the lantern partially blinded Hook. He first turned and ran directly from it, into the corner where the hens were huddled. They fled apart before his charge. He essayed the fence, and on the second try, in his desperation, was out. But in the open dust, the dog was on him, circling, dashing in, snapping. The farmer, who at first had not fired because of the chickens, now did not fire because of the dog, and, when he saw that the hawk was unable to fly, relinquished the sport to the dog, holding the lantern up in order to see better. The light showed his own flat, broad, dark face as sunken also, the cheekbones very prominent, and showed the torn-off sleeves of his shirt and the holes in the knees of his overalls. His wife, in a stained wrapper, and barefooted, heavy black hair hanging around a young, passionless face, joined him hesitantly, but watched, fascinated and a little horrified. His son joined them too, encouraging the dog, but quickly grew silent. Courageous and cruel death, however it may afterward sicken the one who has watched it, is impossible to look away from.

In the circle of the light, Hook turned to keep the dog in front of him. His one eye gleamed with malevolence. The dog was an Airedale, and large. Each time he pounced, Hook stood ground, raising his good wing, the pinions newly torn by the fence, opening his beak soundlessly, and, at the closest approach, hissed furiously, and at once struck. Hit and ripped twice by the whetted horn, the dog recoiled more quickly from several subsequent jumps and, infuriated by his own cowardice, began to bark wildly. Hook maneuvered to watch him, keeping his head turned to avoid losing the foe on the blind side. When the dog paused, safely away, Hook watched him quietly, wing partially lowered, beak closed, but at the first move again lifted the wing and gaped. The dog whined, and the man spoke to him encouragingly. The awful sound of his voice made Hook for an instant twist his head to stare up at the immense figures behind the light. The dog again sallied, barking, and Hook's head spun back. His wing was bitten this time, and with a furious side-blow, he caught the dog's nose. The dog dropped him with a yelp, and then, smarting, came on more warily, as Hook propped himself up from the ground again between his wings. Hook's artificial strength was waning, but his heart still stood to the battle, sustained by a fear of such dimension as he had never known before, but only anticipated when the arrogant young hawk had driven him to cover. The dog, unable to find any point at which the merciless, unwinking eye was not watching him, the parted beak waiting, paused and whimpered again.

"Oh, kill the poor thing," the woman begged.

The man, though, encouraged the dog again, saying, "Sick him; sick him."

The dog rushed bodily. Unable to avoid him, Hook was bowled down, snapping and raking. He left long slashes, as from the blade of a knife, on the dog's flank, but before he could right himself and assume guard again, was caught by the good wing and dragged, clattering, and seeking to make a good stroke from his back. The man followed them to keep the light on them, and the boy went with him, wetting his lips with his tongue and keeping his fists closed tightly. The woman remained behind, but could not help watching the diminished conclusion.

In the little, palely shining arena, the dog repeated his successful maneuver three times, growling but not barking, and when Hook thrashed up from the third blow, both wings were trailing, and dark, shining streams crept on his black-fretted breast from the shoulders. The great eye flashed more furiously than it ever had in victorious battle, and the beak still gaped, but there was no more clatter. He faltered when turning to keep front; the broken wings played him false even as props. He could not rise to use his talons.

The man had tired of holding the lantern up, and put it down to rub his arm. In the low, horizontal light, the dog charged again, this time throwing the weight of his forepaws against Hook's shoulder, so that Hook was crushed as he struck. With his talons up, Hook raked at the dog's belly, but the dog conceived the finish, and furiously worried the feathered bulk. Hook's neck went limp, and between his gaping clappers came only a faint chittering, as from some small kill of his own in the grasses.

In this last conflict, however, there had been some minutes of the supreme fire of the hawk whose three hungers are perfectly fused in the one will; enough to burn off a year of shame.

Between the great sails the light body lay caved and perfectly still. The dog, smarting from his cuts, came to the master and was praised. The woman, joining them slowly, looked at the great wingspread, her husband raising the lantern that she might see it better.

"Oh, the brave bird," she said.

COMMENT AND QUESTION

1. The conflict here is the most universal of all conflicts. It is summed up in the third paragraph from the end: "In this last conflict, however, there had been some minutes of the supreme fire of the hawk whose three hungers are perfectly fused in the one will. . . ." What are the three hungers? What is the one will?

2. Explain the deep satisfaction produced in the reader by the last battle of Hook. Does this last battle arouse any other feelings in the reader?

3. What forces must Hook contend with? At what point is his supremacy complete?

4. What are Hook's fears?

5. What terms besides "barbaric" may be used to describe Hook?

6. This story tries to present life through sense impressions. The recording of sight and sound is especially keen. The student should note the most vivid passages.

7. Do we experience the life of Hook only through sense impressions? Are we given other insights? Is Hook given any "human" reactions? Does the story make ethical and moral judgments?

8. Show how the first three paragraphs establish most of the important motifs in the story, the drouth, the gulls, etc.

9. Notice that "Hook" is divided into five parts. If you will write a title for each part, you will see quite clearly the structural logic of the story.

THE SECRET SHARER

BY JOSEPH CONRAD

JOSEPH CONRAD (1857–1924), a Pole by birth, is one of the greatest of English novelists, and probably the greatest writer of sea stories in the English language. He was born Jósef Téodor Konrad Korzeniowski near Kiev, the Ukraine (Russian Poland). He went to sea as a young man in 1873 and followed the sea for twenty years. His voyages to Australia, South Africa, South America, and the Orient are reflected in his writing. When he was thirty-eight he published his first novel, *Almayer's Folly*. His better known novels are *Lord Jim* (1900), *Nostromo* (1904), and *Victory* (1915). His better known short stories and *novelle* are "The Lagoon," "Youth," "The Heart of Darkness," "The Secret Sharer," and "The Nigger of the Narcissus."

O N MY right hand there were lines of fishing-stakes resembling a mysterious system of half-submerged bamboo fences, incomprehensible in its division of the domain of tropical fishes, and crazy of aspect as if abandoned forever by some nomad tribe of fishermen now gone to the other end of the ocean; for there was no sign of human habitation as far as the eye could reach. To the left a group of barren islets, suggesting ruins of stone walls, towers, and blockhouses, had its foundations set in a blue sea that itself looked solid, so still and stable did it lie below my feet; even the track of light from the westering sun shone smoothly, without that animated glitter which tells of an imperceptible ripple. And when I turned my head to take a parting glance at the tug which had just left us anchored outside the bar, I saw the straight line of the flat shore joined to the stable sea, edge to edge, with a perfect and unmarked closeness, in one leveled floor half brown, half blue under the enormous dome of the sky. Corresponding in their insignificance to the islets of the sea, two small clumps of trees, one on each side of the only fault in the impeccable joint, marked the mouth of the river Meinam we had just left on the first preparatory stage of our homeward journey; and, far back on the inland level, a larger and loftier mass, the grove surrounding the great Paknam pagoda, was the only thing on which the eye could rest from the vain task of exploring the monotonous sweep of the horizon. Here and there gleams as of a few scattered pieces of silver marked the windings of the great river; and on the nearest of them, just within the bar, the tug steaming right into the land became lost to my sight, hull and funnel and masts, as though the impassive earth had swallowed her up without an effort, without a tremor. My eye followed the light cloud of her smoke, now here, now there, above the plain, according to the devious curves of the stream, but always fainter and farther away, till I lost it at last behind the miter-shaped hill of the great pagoda. And then I was left alone with my ship, anchored at the head of the Gulf of Siam.

She floated at the starting-point of a long journey, very still in an immense stillness, the shadows of her spars flung far to the eastward by the setting sun. At that moment I was alone on her decks. There was not a sound in her—and around us nothing moved, nothing lived, not a canoe on the water, not a bird in the air, not a cloud in the sky. In this breathless pause at the threshold of a long passage we seemed to be measuring our fitness for a long and arduous enterprise, the appointed task of both our existences to be carried out, far from all human eyes, with only sky and sea for spectators and for judges.

There must have been some glare in the air to interfere with one's sight, because it was only just before the sun left us that my roaming eyes made out beyond the highest ridge of the principal islet of the group something which did away with the solemnity of perfect solitude. The tide of darkness flowed on swiftly; and with tropical suddenness a swarm of stars came out above the shadowy earth, while I lingered yet, my hand resting lightly on my ship's rail as if on the shoulder of a trusted friend. But, with all that multitude of celestial bodies staring down at one, the comfort of quiet communion with her was gone for good. And there were also disturbing sounds by this time—voices, footsteps forward; the steward flitted along the main deck, a busily ministering spirit; a hand-bell tinkled urgently under the poop-deck. . . .

I found my two officers waiting for me near the supper table, in the lighted cuddy. We sat down at once, and as I helped the chief mate, I said:

"Are you aware that there is a ship anchored inside the islands? I saw her mastheads above the ridge as the sun went down."

He raised sharply his simple face, overcharged by a terrible growth of whisker, and emitted his usual ejaculations: "Bless my soul, sir! You don't say so!"

My second mate was a round-cheeked, silent young man, grave beyond his years, I thought; but as our eyes happened to meet I detected a slight quiver on his lips. I looked down at once. It was not my part to encourage sneering on board my ship. It must be said, too, that I knew very little of my officers. In consequence of certain events of no particular significance, except to myself, I had been appointed to the command only a fortnight before. Neither did I know much of the hands forward. All these people had been together for eighteen months or so, and my position was that of the only stranger on board. I mention this because it has some bearing on what is to follow. But what I felt most was my being a stranger to the ship; and if all the truth must be told, I was somewhat of a stranger to myself. The youngest man on board (barring the second mate), and untried as yet by a position of the fullest responsibilty, I was willing to take the adequacy of the others for granted. They had simply to be equal to their tasks; but I wondered how far I should turn out faithful to that ideal conception of one's own personality every man sets up for himself secretly.

Meantime the chief mate, with an almost visible effect of collaboration on the part of his round eyes and frightful whiskers, was trying to evolve a theory of the anchored ship. His dominant trait was to take all things into earnest consideration. He was of a painstaking turn of mind. As he used to say, he "liked to account to himself" for practically everything that came in his way, down to a miserable scorpion he had found in his cabin a week before. The why and the wherefore of that scorpion—how it got on board and came to select his room rather than the pantry (which was a dark place and more what a scorpion would be partial to), and how on earth it managed to drown itself in the inkwell of his writing-desk—had exercised him infinitely. The ship within the islands was much more easily accounted for; and just as we were about to rise from table he made his pronouncement. She was, he doubted not, a ship from home lately arrived. Probably she drew too much water to cross the bar except at the top of spring tides. Therefore she went into that natural harbor to wait for a few days in preference to remaining in an open roadstead.

"That's so," confirmed the second mate, suddenly, in his slightly hoarse voice. "She draws over twenty feet. She's the Liverpool ship *Sephora* with a cargo of coal. Hundred and twenty-three days from Cardiff."

We looked at him in surprise.

"The tugboat skipper told me when he came on board for your letters, sir," explained the young man. "He expects to take her up the river the day after tomorrow."

After thus overwhelming us with the extent of his information he slipped out of the cabin. The mate observed regretfully that he "could not account for that young fellow's whims." What prevented him telling us all about it at once, he wanted to know.

I detained him as he was making a move. For the last two days the crew had had plenty of hard work, and the night before they had very little sleep. I felt painfully that I—a stranger—was doing something unusual when I directed him to let all hands turn in without setting an anchor-watch. I proposed to keep on deck myself till one o'clock or thereabouts. I would get the second mate to relieve me at that hour.

"He will turn out the cook and the steward at four," I concluded, "and then give you a call. Of course at the slightest sign of any sort of wind we'll have the hands up and make a start at once."

He concealed his astonishment. "Very well, sir." Outside the cuddy he put his head in the second mate's door to inform him of my unheard-of caprice to take a five hours' anchor-watch on myself. I heard the other raise his voice incredulously—"What? The Captain himself?" Then a few more murmurs, a door closed, then another. A few moments later I went on deck.

My strangeness, which had made me sleepless, had prompted that unconventional arrangement, as if I had expected in those solitary hours of the night to get on terms with the ship of which I knew nothing, manned by men of whom I knew very little more. Fast alongside a wharf, littered like any ship in port with a tangle of unrelated things, invaded by unrelated shore people, I had hardly seen her yet properly. Now, as she lay cleared for sea, the stretch of her main-deck seemed to me very fine under the stars. Very fine, very roomy for her size, and very inviting. I descended the poop and paced the waist, my mind picturing to myself the coming passage through the Malay Archipelago, down the Indian Ocean, and up the Atlantic. All its phases were familiar enough to me, every characteristic, all the alternatives which were likely to face me on the high seas— everything! . . . except the novel responsibility of command. But I took heart from the reasonable thought that the ship was like other ships, the men like other men, and that the sea was not likely to keep any special surprises expressly for my discomfiture.

Arrived at that comforting conclusion, I bethought myself of a cigar and went below to get it. All was still down there. Everybody at the after end of the ship was sleeping profoundly. I came out again on the quarter-deck, agreeably at ease in my sleeping-suit on that warm breathless night, barefooted, a glowing cigar in my teeth, and, going forward, I was met by the profound silence of the fore end of the ship. Only as I passed the door of the forecastle I heard a deep, quiet, trustful sigh of some sleeper inside. And suddenly I rejoiced in the great security of the sea as compared with the unrest of the land, in my choice of that untempted life presenting no disquieting problems, invested with an elementary moral beauty by the absolute straightforwardness of its appeal and by the singleness of its purpose.

The riding-light in the fore-rigging burned with a clear, untroubled, as if symbolic, flame, confident and bright in the mysterious shades of the night. Passing on my way aft along the other side of the ship, I observed that the rope side-ladder, put over, no doubt, for the master of the tug when he came to fetch away our letters, had not been hauled in as it should have been. I became annoyed at this, for exactitude in small matters is the very soul of discipline. Then I reflected that I had myself peremptorily dismissed my officers from duty, and by my own act had prevented the anchor-watch being formally set and things properly attended to. I asked myself whether it was wise ever to interfere with the established routine of duties even from the kindest of motives. My action might have made me appear eccentric. Goodness only knew how that absurdly whiskered mate would "account" for my conduct, and what the whole ship thought of that informality of their new captain. I was vexed with myself.

Not from compunction certainly, but, as it were mechanically, I proceeded to get the ladder in myself. Now a side-ladder of that sort is a light affair and comes in easily, yet my vigorous tug, which should have brought it flying on board, merely recoiled upon my body in a totally unexpected jerk. What the devil! . . . I was so astounded by the immovableness of that ladder that I remained stock-still, trying to account for it to myself like that imbecile mate of mine. In the end, of course, I put my head over the rail.

The side of the ship made an opaque belt of shadow on the darkling glassy shimmer of the sea. But I saw at once something elongated and pale floating very close to the ladder. Before I could form a guess a faint flash of phosphorescent light, which seemed to issue suddenly from the naked body of a man, flickered in the sleeping water with the elusive, silent play of summer lightning in a night sky. With a gasp I saw revealed to my stare a pair of feet, the long legs, a broad livid back immersed right up to the neck in a greenish cadaverous glow. One hand, awash, clutched the bottom rung of the ladder. He was complete but for the head. A headless corpse! The cigar dropped out of my gaping mouth with a tiny plop and a short hiss quite audible in the absolute stillness of all things under heaven. At that I suppose he raised up his face, a dimly pale oval in the shadow of the ship's side. But even then I could only barely make out down there the shape of his black-haired head. However, it was enough for the horrid, frost-bound sensation which had gripped me about the chest to pass off. The moment of vain exclamations was past, too. I only climbed on the spare spar and leaned over the rail as far as I could, to bring my eyes nearer to that mystery floating alongside.

As he hung by the ladder, like a resting swimmer, the sea-lightning played about his limbs at every stir; and he appeared in it ghastly, silvery, fish-like. He remained as mute as a fish, too. He made no motion to get out of the water, either. It was inconceivable that he should not attempt to come on board, and strangely troubling to suspect that perhaps he did not want to. And my first words were prompted by just that troubled incertitude.

"What's the matter?" I asked in my ordinary tone, speaking down to the face upturned exactly under mine.

"Cramp," it answered, no louder. Then slightly anxious, "I say, no need to call anyone."

"I was not going to," I said.

"Are you alone on deck?"

"Yes."

I had somehow the impression that he was on the point of letting go the ladder to swim away beyond my ken—mysterious as he came. But, for the moment, this being appearing as if he had risen from the bottom of the sea (it was certainly the nearest land to the ship) wanted only to know the time. I told him. And he, down there, tentatively:

"I suppose your captain's turned in?"

"I am sure he isn't," I said.

He seemed to struggle with himself, for I heard something like the low, bitter murmur of doubt. "What's the good?" His next words came out with a hesitating effort.

"Look here, my man. Could you call him out quietly?"

I thought the time had come to declare myself.

"I am the captain."

I heard a "By Jove!" whispered at the level of the water. The phosphorescence flashed in the swirl of the water all about his limbs, his other hand seized the ladder.

"My name's Leggatt."

The voice was calm and resolute. A good voice. The self-possession of that man had somehow induced a corresponding state in myself. It was very quietly that I remarked:

"You must be a good swimmer."

"Yes. I've been in the water practically since nine o'clock. The question for me now is whether I am to let go this ladder and go on swimming till I sink from exhaustion, or—to come on board here."

I felt this was no mere formula of desperate speech, but a real alternative in the view of a strong soul. I should have gathered from this that he was young; indeed, it is only the young who are ever confronted by such clear issues. But at the time it was pure intuition on my part. A mysterious communication was established already between us two—in the face of that silent, darkened tropical sea. I was young, too; young enough to make no comment. The man in the water began suddenly to climb up the ladder, and I hastened away from the rail to fetch some clothes.

Before entering the cabin I stood still, listening in the lobby at the foot of the stairs. A faint snore came through the closed door of the chief mate's room. The second mate's door was on the hook, but the darkness in there was absolutely soundless. He, too, was young and could sleep like a stone. Remained the steward, but he was not likely to wake up before he was called. I got a sleeping-suit out of my room and, coming back on deck, saw the naked man from the sea sitting on the mainhatch, glimmering white in the darkness, his elbows on his knees and his head in his hands. In a moment he had concealed his damp body in a sleeping-suit of the same gray-stripe pattern as the one I was wearing and followed me like my double on the poop. Together we moved right aft, barefooted, silent.

"What is it?" I asked in a deadened voice, taking the lighted lamp out of the binnacle, and raising it to his face.

"An ugly business."

He had rather regular features: a good mouth; light eyes under somewhat heavy, dark eyebrows; a smooth, square forehead; no growth on his cheeks; a small, brown mustache, and a well-shaped, round chin. His expression was concentrated, meditative, under the inspecting light of the lamp I held up to his face; such as a man thinking hard in solitude might wear. My sleeping-suit was just right for his size. A well-knit young fellow of twenty-five at most. He caught his lower lip with the edge of white, even teeth.

"Yes," I said, replacing the lamp in the binnacle. The warm, heavy tropical night closed upon his head again.

"There's a ship over there," he murmured.

"Yes, I know. The *Sephora*. Did you know of us?"

"Hadn't the slightest idea. I am the mate of her—" He paused and corrected himself. "I should say I *was*."

"Aha! Something wrong?"

"Yes. Very wrong indeed. I've killed a man."

"What do you mean? Just now?"

"No, on the passage. Weeks ago. Thirty-nine south. When I say a man—"

"Fit of temper," I suggested, confidently.

The shadowy, dark head, like mine, seemed to nod imperceptibly

above the ghostly gray of my sleeping-suit. It was, in the night, as though
I had been faced by my own reflection in the depths of a somber and
immense mirror.

"A pretty thing to have to own up to for a Conway boy," murmured
my double, distinctly.

"You're a Conway boy?"

"I am," he said, as if startled. Then, slowly . . . "Perhaps you too—"

It was so; but being a couple of years older I had left before he joined.
After a quick interchange of dates a silence fell; and I thought suddenly
of my absurd mate with his terrific whiskers and the "Bless my soul—you
don't say so" type of intellect. My double gave me an inkling of his
thoughts by saying: "My father's a parson in Norfolk. Do you see me
before a judge and jury on that charge? For myself I can't see the necessity. There are fellows that an angel from heaven— And I am not that.
He was one of those creatures that are just simmering all the time with
a silly sort of wickedness. Miserable devils that have no business to live at
all. He wouldn't do his duty and wouldn't let anybody else do theirs. But
what's the good of talking! You know well enough the sort of ill-condi-
tioned snarling cur—"

He appealed to me as if our experiences had been as identical as our
clothes. And I knew well enough the pestiferous danger of such a character where there are no means of legal repression. And I knew well
enough also that my double there was no homicidal ruffian. I did not
think of asking him for details, and he told me the story roughly in
brusque, disconnected sentences. I needed no more. I saw it all going on
as though I were myself inside that other sleeping-suit.

"It happened while we were setting a reefed foresail, at dusk. Reefed
foresail! You understand the sort of weather. The only sail we had left
to keep the ship running; so you may guess what it had been like for days.
Anxious sort of job, that. He gave me some of his cursed insolence at the
sheet. I tell you I was overdone with this terrific weather that seemed to
have no end to it. Terrific, I tell you—and a deep ship. I believe the fellow
himself was half crazed with funk. It was no time for gentlemanly reproof,
so I turned round and felled him like an ox. He up and at me. We closed
just as an awful sea made for the ship. All hands saw it coming and took
to the rigging, but I had him by the throat, and went on shaking him like
a rat, the men above us yelling, 'Look out! look out!' Then a crash as if
the sky had fallen on my head. They say that for over ten minutes hardly
anything was to be seen of the ship—just the three masts and a bit of the
forecastle head and of the poop all awash driving along in a smother of
foam. It was a miracle that they found us, jammed together behind the
forebits. It's clear that I meant business, because I was holding him by
the throat still when they picked us up. He was black in the face. It was
too much for them. It seems they rushed us aft together, gripped as we

were, screaming 'Murder!' like a lot of lunatics, and broke into the cuddy. And the ship running for her life, touch and go all the time, any minute her last in a sea fit to turn your hair gray only a-looking at it. I understand that the skipper, too, started raving like the rest of them. The man had been deprived of sleep for more than a week, and to have this sprung on him at the height of a furious gale nearly drove him out of his mind. I wonder they didn't fling me overboard after getting the carcass of their precious ship-mate out of my fingers. They had rather a job to separate us, I've been told. A sufficiently fierce story to make an old judge and a respectable jury sit up a bit. The first thing I heard when I came to myself was the maddening howling of that endless gale, and on that the voice of the old man. He was hanging on to my bunk, staring into my face out of his sou'wester.

" 'Mr. Leggatt, you have killed a man. You can act no longer as chief mate of this ship.' "

His care to subdue his voice made it sound monotonous. He rested a hand on the end of the skylight to steady himself with, and all that time did not stir a limb, so far as I could see. "Nice little tale for a quiet tea-party," he concluded in the same tone.

One of my hands, too, rested on the end of the skylight; neither did I stir a limb, so far as I knew. We stood less than a foot from each other. It occurred to me that if old "Bless my soul—you don't say so" were to put his head up the companion and catch sight of us, he would think he was seeing double, or imagine himself come upon a scene of weird witchcraft; the strange captain having a quiet confabulation by the wheel with his own gray ghost. I became very much concerned to prevent anything of the sort. I heard the other's soothing undertone.

"My father's a parson in Norfolk," it said. Evidently he had forgotten he had told me this important fact before. Truly a nice little tale.

"You had better slip down into my stateroom now," I said, moving off stealthily. My double followed my movements; our bare feet made no sound; I let him in, closed the door with care, and, after giving a call to the second mate, returned on deck for my relief.

"Not much sign of any wind yet," I remarked when he approached.

"No, sir. Not much," he assented, sleepily, in his hoarse voice, with just enough deference, no more, and barely suppressing a yawn.

"Well, that's all you have to look out for. You have got your orders."

"Yes, sir."

I paced a turn or two on the poop and saw him take up his position face forward with his elbow in the ratlines of the mizzen-rigging before I went below. The mate's faint snoring was still going on peacefully. The cuddy lamp was burning over the table on which stood a vase with flowers, a polite attention from the ship's provision merchant—the last flowers we should see for the next three months at the very least. Two bunches of bananas hung from the beam symmetrically, one on each side of the rudder-casing. Everything was as before in the ship—except that two of her captain's sleeping-suits were simultaneously in use, one motionless in the cuddy, the other keeping very still in the captain's stateroom.

It must be explained here that my cabin had the form of the capital letter L, the door being within the angle and opening into the short part of the letter. A couch was to the left, the bed-place to the right; my writing-desk and the chronometers' table faced the door. But anyone opening it, unless he stepped right inside, had no view of what I call the long (or vertical) part of the letter. It contained some lockers surmounted by a bookcase; and a few clothes, a thick jacket or two, caps, oilskin coat, and such like, hung on hooks. There was at the bottom of that part a door opening into my bath-room, which could be entered also directly from the saloon. But that way was never used.

The mysterious arrival had discovered the advantage of this particular shape. Entering my room, lighted strongly by a gift bulkhead lamp swung on gimbals above my writing-desk, I did not see him anywhere till he stepped out quietly from behind the coats hung in the recessed part.

"I heard somebody moving about, and went in there at once," he whispered.

I, too, spoke under my breath.

"Nobody is likely to come in here without knocking and getting permission."

He nodded. His face was thin and the sunburn faded, as though he had been ill. And no wonder. He had been, I heard presently, kept under arrest in his cabin for nearly seven weeks. But there was nothing sickly in his eyes or in his expression. He was not a bit like me, really; yet, as we stood leaning over my bed-place, whispering side by side, with our dark heads together and our backs to the door, anybody bold enough to open it stealthily would have been treated to the uncanny sight of a double captain busy talking in whispers with his other self.

"But all this doesn't tell me how you came to hang on to our side-ladder," I inquired, in the hardly audible murmurs we used, after he had told me something more of the proceedings on board the *Sephora* once the bad weather was over.

"When we sighted Java Head I had had time to think all those matters out several times over. I had six weeks of doing nothing else, and with only an hour or so every evening for a tramp on the quarter-deck."

He whispered, his arms folded on the side of my bed-place, staring through the open port. And I could imagine perfectly the manner of this thinking out—a stubborn if not a steadfast operation; something of which I should have been perfectly incapable.

"I reckoned it would be dark before we closed with the land," he continued, so low that I had to strain my hearing, near as we were to each other, shoulder touching shoulder almost. "So I asked to speak to the old man. He always seemed very sick when he came to see me—as if he could not look me in the face. You know, that foresail saved the ship. She was too deep to have run long under bare poles. And it was I that managed to set it for him. Anyway, he came. When I had him in my cabin—he stood by the door looking at me as if I had the halter round my neck already—I asked him right away to leave my cabin door unlocked at night while the ship was going through Sunda Straits. There would be the Java coast within two or three miles, off Angier Point. I wanted nothing more. I've had a prize for swimming my second year in the Conway."

"I can believe it," I breathed out.

"God only knows why they locked me in every night. To see some of their faces you'd have thought they were afraid I'd go about at night strangling people. Am I a murdering brute? Do I look it? By Jove! if I had been he wouldn't have trusted himself like that into my room. You'll say I might have chucked him aside and and bolted out, there and then— it was dark already. Well, no. And for the same reason I wouldn't think of trying to smash the door. There would have been a rush to stop me at the noise, and I did not mean to get into a confounded scrimmage. Somebody else might have got killed—for I would not have broken out only to get chucked back, and I did not want any more of that work. He refused, looking more sick than ever. He was afraid of the men, and also of that old second mate of his who had been sailing with him for years—a gray-headed old humbug; and his steward, too, had been with him devil knows how long—seventeen years or more—a dogmatic sort of loafer who hated me like poison, just because I was the chief mate. No chief mate ever made more than one voyage in the *Sephora*, you know. Those two old chaps ran the ship. Devil only knows what the skipper wasn't afraid of (all his nerve went to pieces altogether in that hellish spell of bad weather we had)— of what the law would do to him—of his wife, perhaps. Oh, yes! she's on board. Though I don't think she would have meddled. She would have been only too glad to have me out of the ship in any way. The 'brand of Cain' business, don't you see. That's all right. I was ready enough to go off wandering on the face of the earth—and that was price enough to pay for an Abel of that sort. Anyhow, he wouldn't listen to me. 'This thing must take its course. I represent the law here.' He was shaking like a leaf. 'So you won't?' 'No!' 'Then I hope you will be able to sleep on that,' I said, and turned my back on him. 'I wonder that *you* can,' cries he, and locks the door.

"Well, after that, I couldn't. Not very well. That was three weeks ago. We have had a slow passage through the Java Sea; drifted about Carimata for ten days. When we anchored here they thought, I suppose, it was all right. The nearest land (and that's five miles) is the ship's destination; the consul would soon set about catching me; and there would have been no object in bolting to these islets there. I don't suppose there's a drop of water on them. I don't know how it was, but tonight that steward, after bringing me my supper, went out to let me eat it, and left the door unlocked. And I ate it—all there was, too. After I had finished I strolled out on the quarter-deck. I don't know that I meant to do anything. A breath of fresh air was all I wanted, I believe. Then a sudden temptation came over me. I kicked off my slippers and was in the water before I had made up my mind fairly. Somebody heard the splash and they raised an awful hullabaloo. 'He's gone! Lower the boats! He's committed suicide! No, he's swimming.' Certainly I was swimming. It's not so easy for a swimmer like me to commit suicide by drowning. I landed on the nearest islet before the boat left the ship's side. I heard them pulling about in the dark, hailing, and so on, but after a bit they gave up. Everything quieted down and the anchorage became as still as death. I sat down on a stone and began to think. I felt certain they would start searching for me at daylight. There was no place to hide on those stony things—and if there had been, what would have been the good? But now I was clear of that ship, I was not going back. So after a while I took off all my clothes, tied them up in a bundle with a stone inside, and dropped them in the deep water on the outer side of that islet. That was suicide enough for me. Let them think what they liked, but I didn't mean to drown myself. I meant to swim till I sank—but that's not the same thing. I struck out for another of these little islands, and it was from that one that I first saw your riding-light. Something to swim for. I went on easily, and on the way I came upon a flat rock a foot or two above water. In the daytime, I dare say, you might make it out with a glass from your poop. I scrambled up on it and rested myself for a bit. Then I made another start. That last spell must have been over a mile."

His whisper was getting fainter and fainter, and all the time he stared straight out through the port-hole, in which there was not even a star to be seen. I had not interrupted him. There was something that made comment impossible in his narrative, or perhaps in himself; a sort of feeling, a quality, which I can't find a name for. And when he ceased, all I found was a futile whisper: "So you swam for our light?"

"Yes—straight for it. It was something to swim for. I couldn't see any stars low down because the coast was in the way, and I couldn't see the land, either. The water was like glass. One might have been swimming in a confounded thousand-feet deep cistern with no place for scrambling out anywhere; but what I didn't like was the notion of swimming round and round like a crazed bullock before I gave out; and as I didn't mean to go back . . . No. Do you see me being hauled back, stark naked, off one of these little islands by the scruff of the neck and fighting like a wild beast? Somebody would have got killed for certain, and I did not want any of that. So I went on. Then your ladder—"

"Why didn't you hail the ship?" I asked, a little louder.

He touched my shoulder lightly. Lazy footsteps came right over our heads and stopped. The second mate had crossed from the other side of the poop and might have been hanging over the rail, for all we knew.

"He couldn't hear us talking—could he?" My double breathed into my very ear, anxiously.

His anxiety was an answer, a sufficient answer, to the question I had put to him. An answer containing all the difficulty of that situation. I closed the port-hole quietly, to make sure. A louder word might have been overheard.

"Who's that?" he whispered then.

"My second mate. But I don't know much more of the fellow than you do."

And I told him a little about myself. I had been appointed to take charge while I least expected anything of the sort, not quite a fortnight ago. I didn't know either the ship or the people. Hadn't had the time in port to look about me or size anybody up. And as to the crew, all they knew was that I was appointed to take the ship home. For the rest, I was almost as much of a stranger on board as himself, I said. And at the moment I felt it most acutely. I felt that it would take very little to make me a suspect person in the eyes of the ship's company.

He had turned about meantime; and we, the two strangers in the ship, faced each other in identical attitudes.

"Your ladder—" he murmured, after a silence. "Who'd have thought of finding a ladder hanging over at night in a ship anchored out here! I felt just then a very unpleasant faintness. After the life I've been leading for nine weeks, anybody would have got out of condition. I wasn't capable of swimming round as far as your rudder-chains. And, lo and behold! there was a ladder to get hold of. After I gripped it I said to myself, 'What's the good?' When I saw a man's head looking over I thought I would swim away presently and leave him shouting—in whatever language it was. I didn't mind being looked at. I—I liked it. And then you speaking to me so quietly—as if you had expected me—made me hold on a little longer. It had been a confounded lonely time—I don't mean while swimming. I was glad to talk a little to somebody that didn't belong to the *Sephora*. As to asking for the captain, that was a mere impulse. It could have been no use, with all the ship knowing about me and the other people pretty certain to be round here in the morning. I don't know— I wanted to be seen, to talk with somebody, before I went on. I don't know what I would have said. . . . 'Fine night, isn't it?' or something of the sort."

"Do you think they will be round here presently?" I asked with some incredulity.

"Quite likely," he said, faintly.

He looked extremely haggard all of a sudden. His head rolled on his shoulders.

"H'm. We shall see then. Meantime get into that bed," I whispered. "Want help? There."

It was a rather high bed-place with a set of drawers underneath. This amazing swimmer really needed the lift I gave him by seizing his leg. He tumbled in, rolled over on his back, and flung one arm across his eyes. And then, with his face nearly hidden, he must have looked exactly as I used to look in that bed. I gazed upon my other self for a while before drawing across carefully the two green serge curtains which ran on a brass rod. I thought for a moment of pinning them together for greater safety, but I sat down on the couch, and once there I felt unwilling to rise and hunt for a pin. I would do it in a moment. I was extremely tired, in a peculiarly intimate way, by the strain of stealthiness, by the effort of whispering and the general secrecy of this excitement. It was three o'clock by now and I had been on my feet since nine, but I was not sleepy; I could not have gone to sleep. I sat there, fagged out, looking at the curtains, trying to clear my mind of the confused sensation of being in two places at once, and greatly bothered by an exasperating knocking in my head. It was a relief to discover suddenly that it was not in my head at all, but on the outside of the door. Before I could collect myself the words "Come in" were out of my mouth, and the steward entered with a tray, bringing in my morning coffee. I had slept, after all, and I was so frightened that I shouted, "This way! I am here, steward," as though he had been miles away. He put down the tray on the table next the couch and only then said, very quietly, "I can see you are here, sir." I felt him give me a keen look, but I dared not meet his eyes just then. He must have wondered why I had drawn the curtains of my bed before going to sleep on the couch. He went out, hooking the door open as usual.

I heard the crew washing decks above me. I knew I would have been told at once if there had been any wind. Calm, I thought, and I was doubly vexed. Indeed, I felt dual more than ever. The steward reappeared suddenly in the doorway. I jumped up from the couch so quickly that he gave a start.

"What do you want here?"

"Close your port, sir—they are washing decks."

"It is closed," I said, reddening.

"Very well, sir." But he did not move from the doorway and returned my stare in an extraordinary, equivocal manner for a time. Then his eyes wavered, all his expression changed, and in a voice unusually gentle, almost coaxingly:

"May I come in to take the empty cup away, sir?"

"Of course!" I turned my back on him while he popped in and out. Then I unhooked and closed the door and even pushed the bolt. This sort of thing could not go on very long. The cabin was as hot as an oven, too. I took a peep at my double, and discovered that he had not moved, his arm was still over his eyes; but his chest heaved; his hair was wet; his chin glistened with perspiration. I reached over him and opened the port.

"I must show myself on deck," I reflected.

Of course, theoretically, I could do what I liked, with no one to say nay to me within the whole circle of the horizon; but to lock my cabin door and take the key away I did not dare. Directly I put my head out of the companion I saw the group of my two officers, the second mate bare-footed, the chief mate in long india-rubber boots, near the break of the poop, and the steward half-way down the poop-ladder talking to them eagerly. He happened to catch sight of me and dived, the second ran down on the main-deck shouting some order or other, and the chief mate came to meet me, touching his cap.

There was a sort of curiosity in his eye that I did not like. I don't know whether the steward had told them that I was "queer" only, or down-right drunk, but I know the man meant to have a good look at me. I watched him coming with a smile which, as he got into point-blank range, took effect and froze his very whiskers. I did not give him time to open his lips.

"Square the yards by lifts and braces before the hands go to breakfast."

It was the first particular order I had given on board that ship; and I stayed on deck to see it executed, too. I had felt the need of asserting myself without loss of time. That sneering young cub got taken down a peg or two on that occasion, and I also seized the opportunity of having a good look at the face of every foremast man as they filed past me to go to the after braces. At breakfast time, eating nothing myself, I presided with such frigid dignity that the two mates were only too glad to escape from the cabin as soon as decency permitted; and all the time the dual working of my mind distracted me almost to the point of insanity. I was constantly watching myself, my secret self, as dependent on my actions as my own personality, sleeping in that bed, behind that door which faced me as I sat at the head of the table. It was very much like being mad, only it was worse because one was aware of it.

I had to shake him for a solid minute, but when at last he opened his eyes it was in the full possession of his senses, with an inquiring look.

"All's well so far," I whispered. "Now you must vanish into the bath-room."

He did so, as noiseless as a ghost, and then I rang for the steward, and facing him boldly, directed him to tidy up my stateroom while I was having my bath—"and be quick about it." As my tone admitted of no excuses, he said, "Yes, sir," and ran off to fetch his dust-pan and brushes. I took a bath and did most of my dressing, splashing, and whistling softly for the steward's edification, while the secret sharer of my life stood drawn

up bolt upright in that little space, his face looking very sunken in daylight, his eyelids lowered under the stern, dark line of his eyebrows drawn
together by a slight frown.

When I left him there to go back to my room the steward was finishing
dusting. I sent for the mate and engaged him in some insignificant conversation. It was, as it were, trifling with the terrific character of his
whiskers; but my object was to give him an opportunity for a good look at
my cabin. And then I could at last shut, with a clear conscience, the door
of my stateroom and get my double back into the recessed part. There was
nothing else for it. He had to sit still on a small folding stool, half
smothered by the heavy coats hanging there. We listened to the steward
going into the bath-room out of the saloon, filling the water-bottles there,
scrubbing the bath, setting things to rights, whisk, bang, clatter—out
again into the saloon—turn the key—click. Such was my scheme for keeping my second self invisible. Nothing better could be contrived under the
circumstances. And there we sat; I at my writing-desk ready to appear
busy with some papers, he behind me out of sight of the door. It would
not have been prudent to talk in daytime; and I could not have stood the
excitement of that queer sense of whispering to myself. Now and then,
glancing over my shoulder, I saw him far back there, sitting rigidly on
the low stool, his bare feet close together, his arms folded, his head hanging on his breast—and perfectly still. Anybody would have taken him
for me.

I was fascinated by it myself. Every moment I had to glance over my
shoulder. I was looking at him when a voice outside the door said:

"Beg pardon, sir."

"Well!" . . . I kept my eyes on him, and so when the voice outside
the door announced, "There's a ship's boat coming our way, sir," I saw
him give a start—the first movement he had made for hours. But he did
not raise his bowed head.

"All right. Get the ladder over."

I hesitated. Should I whisper something to him? But what? His immobility seemed to have been never disturbed. What could I tell him he
did not know already? . . . Finally I went on deck.

II

The skipper of the *Sephora* had a thin red whisker all round his face,
and the sort of complexion that goes with hair of that color; also the particular, rather smeary shade of blue in the eyes. He was not exactly a
showy figure; his shoulders were high, his stature but middling—one leg
slightly more bandy than the other. He shook hands, looking vaguely
around. A spiritless tenacity was his main characteristic, I judged. I behaved with a politeness which seemed to disconcert him. Perhaps he was
shy. He mumbled to me as if he were ashamed of what he was saying;

gave his name (it was something like Archbold—but at this distance of years I hardly am sure), his ship's name, and a few other particulars of that sort, in the manner of a criminal making a reluctant and doleful confession. He had had terrible weather on the passage out—terrible—terrible —wife aboard, too.

By this time we were seated in the cabin and the steward brought in a tray with a bottle and glasses. "Thanks! No." Never took liquor. Would have some water, though. He drank two tumblerfuls. Terrible thirsty work. Ever since daylight had been exploring the islands round his ship.

"What was that for—fun?" I asked, with an appearance of polite interest.

"No!" He sighed. "Painful duty."

As he persisted in his mumbling and I wanted my double to hear every word, I hit upon the notion of informing him that I regretted to say I was hard of hearing.

"Such a young man, too!" he nodded, keeping his smeary blue, unintelligent eyes fastened upon me. "What was the cause of it—some disease?" he inquired, without the least sympathy and as if he thought that, if so, I'd got no more than I deserved.

"Yes; disease," I admitted in a cheerful tone which seemed to shock him. But my point was gained, because he had to raise his voice to give me his tale. It is not worth while to record that version. It was just over two months since all this had happened, and he had thought so much about it that he seemed completely muddled as to its bearings, but still immensely impressed.

"What would you think of such a thing happening on board your own ship? I've had the *Sephora* for these fifteen years. I am a well-known shipmaster."

He was densely distressed—and perhaps I should have sympathized with him if I had been able to detach my mental vision from the unsuspected sharer of my cabin as though he were my second self. There he was on the other side of the bulkhead, four or five feet from us, no more, as we sat in the saloon. I looked politely at Captain Archbold (if that was his name), but it was the other I saw, in a gray sleeping-suit, seated on a low stool, his bare feet close together, his arms folded, and every word said between us falling into the ears of his dark head bowed on his chest.

"I have been at sea now, man and boy, for seven-and-thirty years, and I've never heard of such a thing happening in an English ship. And that it should be my ship. Wife on board, too."

I was hardly listening to him.

"Don't you think," I said, "that the heavy sea which, you told me, came aboard just then might have killed the man? I have seen the sheer weight of a sea kill a man very neatly, by simply breaking his neck."

"Good God!" he uttered, impressively, fixing his smeary blue eyes on

me. "The sea! No man killed by the sea ever looked like that." He seemed
positively scandalized at my suggestion. And as I gazed at him, certainly
not prepared for anything original on his part, he advanced his head close
to mine and thrust his tongue out at me so suddenly that I couldn't help
starting back.

After scoring over my calmness in this graphic way he nodded wisely.
If I had seen the sight, he assured me, I would never forget it as long as
I lived. The weather was too bad to give the corpse a proper sea burial.
So next day at dawn they took it up on the poop, covering its face with a
bit of bunting; he read a short prayer, and then, just as it was, in its
oilskins and long boots, they launched it amongst those mountainous seas
that seemed ready every moment to swallow up the ship herself and the
terrified lives on board of her.

"That reefed foresail saved you," I threw in.

"Under God—it did," he exclaimed fervently. "It was by a special
mercy, I firmly believe, that it stood some of those hurricane squalls."

"It was the setting of that sail which—" I began.

"God's own hand in it," he interrupted me. "Nothing less could have
done it. I don't mind telling you that I hardly dared give the order. It
seemed impossible that we could touch anything without losing it, and
then our last hope would have been gone."

The terror of that gale was on him yet. I let him go on for a bit, then
said, casually—as if returning to a minor subject:

"You were very anxious to give up your mate to the shore people, I
believe?"

He was. To the law. His obscure tenacity on that point had in it something incomprehensible and a little awful; something, as it were, mystical,
quite apart from his anxiety that he should not be suspected of "coun-
tenancing any doings of that sort." Seven-and-thirty virtuous years at sea,
of which over twenty of immaculate command, and the last fifteen in the
Sephora, seemed to have laid him under some pitiless obligation.

"And you know," he went on, groping shamefacedly amongst his feelings, "I did not engage that young fellow. His people had some interest
with my owners. I was in a way forced to take him on. He looked very
smart, very gentlemanly, and all that. But do you know—I never liked him,
somehow. I am a plain man. You see, he wasn't exactly the sort for the
chief mate of a ship like the *Sephora*."

I had become so connected in thoughts and impressions with the secret
sharer of my cabin that I felt as if I, personally, were being given to understand that I, too, was not the sort that would have done for the chief
mate of a ship like the *Sephora*. I had no doubt of it in my mind.

"Not at all the style of man. You understand," he insisted, superfluously,
looking hard at me.

I smiled urbanely. He seemed at a loss for a while.

"I suppose I must report a suicide."

"Beg pardon?"

"Sui-cide! That's what I'll have to write to my owners directly I get in."

"Unless you manage to recover him before tomorrow," I assented, dispassionately. . . . "I mean, alive."

He mumbled something which I really did not catch, and I turned my ear to him in a puzzled manner. He fairly bawled:

"The land—I say, the mainland is at least seven miles off my anchorage."

"About that."

My lack of excitement, of curiosity, of surprise, of any sort of pronounced interest, began to arouse his distrust. But except for the felicitous pretense of deafness I had not tried to pretend anything. I had felt utterly incapable of playing the part of ignorance properly, and therefore was afraid to try. It is also certain that he had brought some ready-made suspicions with him, and that he viewed my politeness as a strange and unnatural phenomenon. And yet how else could I have received him? Not heartily! That was impossible for psychological reasons, which I need not state here. My only object was to keep off his inquiries. Surlily? Yes, but surliness might have provoked a point-blank question. From its novelty to him and from its nature, punctilious courtesy was the manner best calculated to restrain the man. But there was the danger of his breaking through my defense bluntly. I could not, I think, have met him by a direct lie, also for psychological (not moral) reasons. If he had only known how afraid I was of his putting my feeling of identity with the other to the test! But, strangely enough—(I thought of it only afterwards)—I believe that he was not a little disconcerted by the reverse side of that weird situation, by something in me that reminded him of the man he was seeking—suggested a mysterious similitude to the young fellow he had distrusted and disliked from the first.

However that might have been, the silence was not very prolonged. He took another oblique step.

"I reckon I had no more than a two-mile pull to your ship. Not a bit more."

"And quite enough, too, in this awful heat," I said.

Another pause full of mistrust followed. Necessity, they say, is mother of invention, but fear, too, is not barren of ingenious suggestions. And I was afraid he would ask me point-blank for news of my other self.

"Nice little saloon, isn't it?" I remarked, as if noticing for the first time the way his eyes roamed from one closed door to the other. "And very well fitted out, too. Here, for instance," I continued, reaching over the back of my seat negligently and flinging the door open, "is my bath-room."

He made an eager movement, but hardly gave it a glance. I got up, shut the door of the bath-room, and invited him to have a look round, as if I were very proud of my accommodation. He had to rise and be shown round, but he went through the business without any raptures whatever.

"And now we'll have a look at my stateroom," I declared, in a voice as loud as I dared to make it, crossing the cabin to the starboard side with purposely heavy steps.

He followed me in and gazed around. My intelligent double had vanished. I played my part.

"Very convenient—isn't it?"

"Very nice. Very comf . . ." He didn't finish and went out brusquely as if to escape from some unrighteous wiles of mine. But it was not to be. I had been too frightened not to feel vengeful; I felt I had him on the run, and I meant to keep him on the run. My polite insistence must have had something menacing in it, because he gave in suddenly. And I did not let him off a single item; mate's room, pantry, storerooms, the very sail-locker which was also under the poop—he had to look into them all. When at last I showed him out on the quarter-deck he drew a long, spiritless sigh, and mumbled dismally that he must really be going back to his ship now. I desired my mate, who had joined us, to see to the captain's boat.

The man of whiskers gave a blast on the whistle which he used to wear hanging round his neck, and yelled, "Sephora's away!" My double down there in my cabin must have heard, and certainly could not feel more relieved than I. Four fellows came running out from somewhere forward and went over the side, while my own men, appearing on deck too, lined the rail. I escorted my visitor to the gangway ceremoniously, and nearly overdid it. He was a tenacious beast. On the very ladder he lingered, and in that unique, guiltily conscientious manner of sticking to the point:

"I say . . . you . . . you don't think that—"

I covered his voice loudly:

"Certainly not. . . . I am delighted. Good-by."

I had an idea of what he meant to say, and just saved myself by the privilege of defective hearing. He was too shaken generally to insist, but my mate, close witness of that parting, looked mystified and his face took on a thoughtful cast. As I did not want to appear as if I wished to avoid all communication with my officers, he had the opportunity to address me.

"Seems a very nice man. His boat's crew told our chaps a very extraordinary story, if what I am told by the steward is true. I suppose you had it from the captain, sir?"

"Yes. I had a story from the captain."

"A very horrible affair—isn't it, sir?"

"It is."

"Beats all these tales we hear about murders in Yankee ships."

"I don't think it beats them. I don't think it resembles them in the least."

"Bless my soul—you don't say so! But of course I've no acquaintance whatever with American ships, not I, so I couldn't go against your knowledge. It's horrible enough for me. . . . But the queerest part is that those fellows seemed to have some idea the man was hidden aboard here. They had really. Did you ever hear of such a thing?"

"Preposterous—isn't it?"

We were walking to and fro athwart the quarter-deck. No one of the crew forward could be seen (the day was Sunday), and the mate pursued:

"There was some little dispute about it. Our chaps took offense. 'As if we would harbor a thing like that,' they said. 'Wouldn't you like to look for him in our coal-hole?' Quite a tiff. But they made it up in the end. I suppose he did drown himself. Don't you, sir?"

"I don't suppose anything."

"You have no doubt in the matter, sir?"

"None whatever."

I left him suddenly. I felt I was producing a bad impression, but with my double down there it was most trying to be on deck. And it was almost as trying to be below. Altogether a nerve-trying situation. But on the whole I felt less torn in two when I was with him. There was no one in the whole ship whom I dared take into my confidence. Since the hands had got to know his story, it would have been impossible to pass him off for anyone else, and an accidental discovery was to be dreaded now more than ever. . . .

The steward being engaged in laying the table for dinner, we could talk only with our eyes when I first went down. Later in the afternoon we had a cautious try at whispering. The Sunday quietness of the ship was against us; the stillness of air and water around her was against us; the elements, the men were against us—everything was against us in our secret partnership; time itself—for this could not go on forever. The very trust in Providence was, I suppose, denied to his guilt. Shall I confess that this thought cast me down very much? And as to the chapter of accidents which counts for so much in the book of success, I could only hope that it was closed. For what favorable accident could be expected?

"Did you hear everything?" were my first words as soon as we took up our position side by side, leaning over my bed-place.

He had. And the proof of it was his earnest whisper, "The man told you he hardly dared to give the order."

I understood the reference to be to that saving foresail.

"Yes. He was afraid of it being lost in the setting."

"I assure you he never gave the order. He may think he did, but he never gave it. He stood there with me on the break of the poop after the maintopsail blew away, and whimpered about our last hope—positively whimpered about it and nothing else—and the night coming on! To hear one's skipper go on like that in such weather was enough to drive any fellow out of his mind. It worked me up into a sort of desperation. I just took it into my own hands and went away from him, boiling, and— But what's the use telling you? *You* know! . . . Do you think that if I had not been pretty fierce with them I should have got the men to do anything? Not it! The bo's'n perhaps? Perhaps! It wasn't a heavy sea—it was a sea gone mad! I suppose the end of the world will be something like that; and a man may have the heart to see it coming once and be done with it—but to have to face it day after day— I don't blame anybody. I was precious little better than the rest. Only—I was an officer of that old coal-wagon, anyhow—"

"I quite understand," I conveyed that sincere assurance into his ear. He was out of breath with whispering; I could hear him pant slightly. It was all very simple. The same strung-up force which had given twenty-four men a chance, at least, for their lives, had, in a sort of recoil, crushed an unworthy mutinous existence.

But I had no leisure to weigh the merits of the matter—footsteps in the saloon, a heavy knock. "There's enough wind to get under way with, sir." Here was the call of a new claim upon my thoughts and even upon my feelings.

"Turn the hands up," I cried through the door. "I'll be on deck directly."

I was going out to make the acquaintance of my ship. Before I left the cabin our eyes met—the eyes of the only two strangers on board. I pointed to the recessed part where the little campstool awaited him and laid my finger on my lips. He made a gesture—somewhat vague—a little mysterious, accompanied by a faint smile, as if of regret.

This is not the place to enlarge upon the sensations of a man who feels for the first time a ship move under his feet to his own independent word. In my case they were not unalloyed. I was not wholly alone with my command; for there was that stranger in my cabin. Or rather, I was not completely and wholly with her. Part of me was absent. That mental feeling of being in two places at once affected me physically as if the mood of secrecy had penetrated my very soul. Before an hour had elapsed since the ship had begun to move, having occasion to ask the mate (he stood by my side) to take a compass bearing of the Pagoda, I caught myself reaching up to his ear in whispers. I say I caught myself, but enough had escaped to startle the man. I can't describe it otherwise than by saying that he shied. A grave, preoccupied manner, as though he were in possession of some perplexing intelligence, did not leave him henceforth. A little later I moved away from the rail to look at the compass with such a stealthy gait that the helmsman noticed it—and I could not help noticing the unusual roundness of his eyes. These are trifling instances, though it's to no commander's advantage to be suspected of ludicrous eccentricities. But I was also more seriously affected. There are to a seaman certain words, gestures, that should in given conditions come as naturally, as instinctively as the winking of a menaced eye. A certain order should spring on to his lips without thinking; a certain sign should get itself made, so to speak, without reflection. But all unconscious alertness had abandoned me. I had to make an effort of will to recall myself back (from the cabin) to the conditions of the moment. I felt that I was appearing an irresolute commander to those people who were watching me more or less critically.

And, besides, there were the scares. On the second day out, for instance, coming off the deck in the afternoon (I had straw slippers on my bare feet) I stopped at the open pantry door and spoke to the steward. He was doing something there with his back to me. At the sound of my voice he nearly jumped out of his skin, as the saying is, and incidentally broke a cup.

"What on earth's the matter with you?" I asked, astonished.

He was extremely confused. "Beg your pardon, sir. I made sure you were in your cabin."

"You see I wasn't."

"No, sir. I could have sworn I had heard you moving in there not a moment ago. It's most extraordinary . . . very sorry, sir."

I passed on with an inward shudder. I was so identified with my secret double that I did not even mention the fact in those scanty, fearful whispers we exchanged. I suppose he had made some slight noise of some kind or other. It would have been miraculous if he hadn't at one time or another. And yet, haggard as he appeared, he looked always perfectly self-controlled, more than calm—almost invulnerable. On my suggestion he remained almost entirely in the bath-room, which, upon the whole, was the safest place. There could be really no shadow of an excuse for anyone ever wanting to go in there, once the steward had done with it. It was a very tiny place. Sometimes he reclined on the floor, his legs bent, his head sustained on one elbow. At others I would find him on the camp-stool, sitting in his gray sleeping-suit and with his cropped dark hair like a patient, unmoved convict. At night I would smuggle him into my bed-place, and we would whisper together, with the regular footfalls of the officer of the watch passing and repassing over our heads. It was an infinitely miserable time. It was lucky that some tins of fine preserves were stowed in a locker in my stateroom; hard bread I could always get hold of; and so he lived on stewed chicken, paté de foie gras, asparagus, cooked oysters, sardines—on all sorts of abominable sham delicacies out of tins. My early morning coffee he always drank; and it was all I dared do for him in that respect.

Every day there was the horrible maneuvering to go through so that my room and then the bath-room should be done in the usual way. I came to hate the sight of the steward, to abhor the voice of that harmless man. I felt that it was he who would bring on the disaster of discovery. It hung like a sword over our heads.

The fourth day out, I think (we were then working down the east side of the Gulf of Siam, tack for tack, in light winds and smooth water)—the fourth day, I say, of this miserable juggling with the unavoidable, as we sat at our evening meal, that man, whose slightest movement I dreaded, after putting down the dishes ran up on deck busily. This could not be dangerous. Presently he came down again; and then it appeared that he had remembered a coat of mine which I had thrown over a rail to dry after having been wetted in a shower which had passed over the ship in the afternoon. Sitting stolidly at the head of the table I became terrified at the sight of the garment on his arm. Of course he made for my door. There was no time to lose.

"Steward," I thundered. My nerves were so shaken that I could not govern my voice and conceal my agitation. This was the sort of thing that made my terrifically whiskered mate tap his forehead with his fore-finger. I had detected him using that gesture while talking on deck with a confidential air to the carpenter. It was too far to hear a word, but I had no doubt that this pantomime could only refer to the strange new captain.

"Yes, sir," the pale-faced steward turned resignedly to me. It was this maddening course of being shouted at, checked without rhyme or reason, arbitrarily chased out of my cabin, suddenly called into it, sent flying out of his pantry on incomprehensible errands, that accounted for the growing wretchedness of his expression.

"Where are you going with that coat?"

"To your room, sir."

"Is there another shower coming?"

"I'm sure I don't know, sir. Shall I go up again and see, sir?"

"No! never mind."

My object was attained, as of course my other self in there would have heard everything that passed. During this interlude my two officers never raised their eyes off their respective plates; but the lip of that confounded cub, the second mate, quivered visibly.

I expected the steward to hook my coat on and come out at once. He was very slow about it; but I dominated my nervousness sufficiently not to shout after him. Suddenly I became aware (it could be heard plainly enough) that the fellow for some reason or other was opening the door of the bath-room. It was the end. The place was literally not big enough to swing a cat in. My voice died in my throat and I went stony all over. I expected to hear a yell of surprise and terror, and made a movement, but had not the strength to get on my legs. Everything remained still. Had my second self taken the poor wretch by the throat? I don't know what I could have done next moment if I had not seen the steward come out of my room, close the door, and then stand quietly by the sideboard.

"Saved," I thought. "But, no! Lost! Gone! He was gone!"

I laid my knife and fork down and leaned back in my chair. My head swam. After a while, when sufficiently recovered to speak in a steady voice, I instructed my mate to put the ship round at eight o'clock himself.

"I won't come on deck," I went on. "I think I'll turn in, and unless the wind shifts I don't want to be disturbed before midnight. I feel a bit seedy."

"You did look middling bad a little while ago," the chief mate remarked without showing any great concern.

They both went out, and I stared at the steward clearing the table. There was nothing to be read on that wretched man's face. But why did he avoid my eyes I asked myself. Then I thought I should like to hear the sound of his voice.

"Steward!"

"Sir!" Startled as usual.

"Where did you hang up that coat?"

"In the bath-room, sir." The usual anxious tone. "It's not quite dry yet, sir."

For some time longer I sat in the cuddy. Had my double vanished as he had come? But of his coming there was an explanation, whereas his disappearance would be inexplicable. . . . I went slowly into my dark room, shut the door, lighted the lamp, and for a time dared not turn round. When at last I did I saw him standing bolt-upright in the narrow recessed part. It would not be true to say I had a shock, but an irresistible doubt of his bodily existence flitted through my mind. Can it be, I asked myself, that he is not visible to other eyes than mine? It was like being haunted. Motionless, with a grave face, he raised his hands slightly at me in a gesture which meant clearly, "Heavens! what a narrow escape!" Narrow indeed. I think I had come creeping quietly as near insanity as any man who has not actually gone over the border. That gesture restrained me, so to speak.

The mate with the terrific whiskers was now putting the ship on the other tack. In the moment of profound silence which follows upon the hands going to their stations I heard on the poop his raised voice: "Hard alee!" and the distant shout of the order repeated on the maindeck. The sails, in that light breeze, made but a faint fluttering noise. It ceased. The ship was coming round slowly; I held my breath in the renewed stillness of expectation; one wouldn't have thought that there was a single living soul on her decks. A sudden brisk shout, "Mainsail haul!" broke the spell, and in the noisy cries and rush overhead of the men running away with the main-brace we two, down in my cabin, came together in our usual position by the bed-place.

He did not wait for my question. "I heard him fumbling here and just managed to squat myself down in the bath," he whispered to me. "The fellow only opened the door and put his arm in to hang the coat up. All the same—"

"I never thought of that," I whispered back, even more appalled than before at the closeness of the shave, and marveling at that something unyielding in his character which was carrying him through so finely. There was no agitation in his whisper. Whoever was being driven distracted, it was not he. He was sane. And the proof of his sanity was continued when he took up the whispering again.

"It would never do for me to come to life again."

It was something that a ghost might have said. But what he was alluding to was his old captain's reluctant admission of the theory of suicide. It would obviously serve his turn—if I had understood at all the view which seemed to govern the unalterable purpose of his action.

"You must maroon me as soon as ever you can get amongst these islands off the Cambodge shore," he went on.

"Maroon you! We are not living in a boy's adventure tale," I protested. His scornful whispering took me up.

"We aren't indeed! There's nothing of a boy's tale in this. But there's nothing else for it. I want no more. You don't suppose I am afraid of what can be done to me? Prison or gallows or whatever they may please. But you don't see me coming back to explain such things to an old fellow in a wig and twelve respectable tradesmen, do you? What can they know whether I am guilty or not—or of *what* I am guilty, either? That's my affair. What does the Bible say? 'Driven off the face of the earth.' Very well. I am off the face of the earth now. As I came at night so I shall go."

"Impossible!" I murmured. "You can't."

"Can't? . . . Not naked like a soul on the Day of Judgment. I shall freeze on to this sleeping-suit. The Last Day is not yet—and . . . you have understood thoroughly. Didn't you?"

I felt suddenly ashamed of myself. I may say truly that I understood—and my hesitation in letting that man swim away from my ship's side had been a mere sham sentiment, a sort of cowardice.

"It can't be done now till next night," I breathed out. "The ship is on the off-shore tack and the wind may fail us."

"As long as I know that you understand," he whispered. "But of course you do. It's a great satisfaction to have got somebody to understand. You seem to have been there on purpose." And in the same whisper, as if we two whenever we talked had to say things to each other which were not fit for the world to hear, he added, "It's very wonderful."

We remained side by side talking in our secret way—but sometimes silent or just exchanging a whispered word or two at long intervals. And as usual he stared through the port. A breath of wind came now and again into our faces. The ship might have been moored in dock, so gently and on an even keel she slipped through the water, that did not murmur even at our passage, shadowy and silent like a phantom sea.

At midnight I went on deck, and to my mate's great surprise put the ship round on the other tack. His terrible whiskers flitted round me in silent criticism. I certainly should not have done it if it had been only a question of getting out of that sleepy gulf as quickly as possible. I believe he told the second mate, who relieved him, that it was a great want of judgment. The other only yawned. That intolerable cub shuffled about so sleepily and lolled against the rails in such a slack, improper fashion that I came down on him sharply.

"Aren't you properly awake yet?"

"Yes, sir! I am awake."

"Well, then, be good enough to hold yourself as if you were. And keep a look-out. If there's any current we'll be closing with some islands before daylight."

The east side of the gulf is fringed with islands, some solitary, others in groups. On the blue background of the high coast they seem to float on silvery patches of calm water, arid and gray, or dark green and rounded like clumps of evergreen bushes, with the larger ones, a mile or two long, showing the outlines of ridges, ribs of gray rock under the dank mantle of matted leafage. Unknown to trade, to travel, almost to geography, the manner of life they harbor is an unsolved secret. There must be villages—settlements of fishermen at least—on the largest of them, and some communication with the world is probably kept up by native craft. But all that forenoon, as we headed for them, fanned along by the faintest of breezes, I saw no sign of man or canoe in the field of the telescope I kept on pointing at the scattered group.

At noon I gave no orders for a change of course, and the mate's whiskers became much concerned and seemed to be offering themselves unduly to my notice. At last I said:

"I am going to stand right in. Quite in—as far as I can take her."

The stare of extreme surprise imparted an air of ferocity also to his eyes, and he looked truly terrific for a moment.

"We're not doing well in the middle of the gulf," I continued, casually. "I am going to look for the land breezes tonight."

"Bless my soul! Do you mean, sir, in the dark amongst the lot of all them islands and reefs and shoals?"

"Well—if there are any regular land breezes at all on this coast one must get close inshore to find them, mustn't one?"

"Bless my soul!" he exclaimed again under his breath. All that afternoon he wore a dreamy, contemplative appearance which in him was a mark of perplexity. After dinner I went into my stateroom as if I meant to take some rest. There we two bent our dark heads over a half-unrolled chart lying on my bed.

"There," I said. "It's got to be Koh-ring. I've been looking at it ever since sunrise. It has got two hills and a low point. It must be inhabited. And on the coast opposite there is what looks like the mouth of a biggish river—with some town, no doubt, not far up. It's the best chance for you that I can see."

"Anything. Koh-ring let it be."

He looked thoughtfully at the chart as if surveying chances and distances from a lofty height—and following with his eyes his own figure wandering on the blank land of Cochin-China, and then passing off that piece of paper clean out of sight into uncharted regions. And it was as if the ship had two captains to plan her course for her. I had been so worried and restless running up and down that I had not had the patience to dress that day. I had remained in my sleeping-suit, with straw slippers and a soft floppy hat. The closeness of the heat in the gulf had been most oppressive, and the crew were used to see me wandering in that airy attire.

"She will clear the south point as she heads now," I whispered into his ear. "Goodness only knows when, though, but certainly after dark. I'll edge her in to half a mile, as far as I may be able to judge in the dark—"

"Be careful," he murmured, warningly—and I realized suddenly that all my future, the only future for which I was fit, would perhaps go irretrievably to pieces in any mishap to my first command.

I could not stop a moment longer in the room. I motioned him to get out of sight and made my way on the poop. That unplayful cub had the watch. I walked up and down for a while thinking things out, then beckoned him over.

"Send a couple of hands to open the two quarter-deck ports," I said, mildly.

He actually had the impudence, or else so forgot himself in his wonder at such an incomprehensible order, as to repeat:

"Open the quarter-deck ports! What for, sir?"

"The only reason you need concern yourself about is because I tell you to do so. Have them opened wide and fastened properly."

He reddened and went off, but I believe made some jeering remark to the carpenter as to the sensible practice of ventilating a ship's quarter-deck. I know he popped into the mate's cabin to impart the fact to him because the whiskers came on deck, as it were by chance, and stole glances at me from below—for signs of lunacy or drunkenness, I suppose.

A little before supper, feeling more restless than ever, I rejoined, for a moment, my second self. And to find him sitting so quietly was surprising, like something against nature, inhuman.

I developed my plan in a hurried whisper.

"I shall stand in as close as I dare and then put her round. I will presently find means to smuggle you out of here into the sail-locker, which communicates with the lobby. But there is an opening, a sort of square for hauling the sails out, which gives straight on the quarter-deck and which is never closed in fine weather, so as to give air to the sails. When the ship's way is deadened in stays and all the hands are aft at the main-braces you will have a clear road to slip out and get overboard through the open quarter-deck port. I've had them both fastened up. Use a rope's end to lower yourself into the water so as to avoid a splash—you know. It could be heard and cause some beastly complication."

He kept silent for a while, then whispered, "I understand."

"I won't be there to see you go," I began with an effort. "The rest . . . I only hope I have understood, too."

"You have. From first to last"—and for the first time there seemed to be a faltering, something strained in his whisper. He caught hold of my arm, but the ringing of the supper bell made me start. He didn't, though; he only released his grip.

After supper I didn't come below again till well past eight o'clock. The faint, steady breeze was loaded with dew; and the wet, darkened sails held all there was of propelling power in it. The night, clear and starry, sparkled darkly, and the opaque, lightless patches shifting slowly against the low stars were the drifting islets. On the port bow there was a big one more distant and shadowily imposing by the great space of sky it eclipsed.

On opening the door I had a back view of my very own self looking at a chart. He had come out of the recess and was standing near the table.

"Quite dark enough," I whispered.

He stepped back and leaned against my bed with a level, quiet glance. I sat on the couch. We had nothing to say to each other. Over our heads the officer of the watch moved here and there. Then I heard him move quickly. I knew what that meant. He was making for the companion; and presently his voice was outside my door.

"We are drawing in pretty fast, sir. Land looks rather close."

"Very well," I answered. "I am coming on deck directly."

I waited till he was gone out of the cuddy, then rose. My double moved too. The time had come to exchange our last whispers, for neither of us was ever to hear each other's natural voice.

"Look here!" I opened a drawer and took out three sovereigns. "Take this anyhow. I've got six and I'd give you the lot, only I must keep a little money to buy some fruit and vegetables for the crew from native boats as we go through Sunda Straits."

He shook his head.

"Take it," I urged him, whispering desperately. "No one can tell what—"

He smiled and slapped meaningly the only pocket of the sleeping-jacket. It was not safe, certainly. But I produced a large old silk handkerchief of mine, and tying the three pieces of gold in a corner, pressed it on him. He was touched, I suppose, because he took it at last and tied it quickly round his waist under the jacket, on his bare skin.

Our eyes met; several seconds elapsed, till, our glances still mingled, I extended my hand and turned the lamp out. Then I passed through the cuddy, leaving the door of my room wide open. . . . "Steward!"

He was still lingering in the pantry in the greatness of his zeal, giving a rub-up to a plated cruet stand the last thing before going to bed. Being careful not to wake up the mate, whose room was opposite, I spoke in an undertone.

He looked round anxiously. "Sir!"

"Can you get me a little hot water from the galley?"

"I am afraid, sir, the galley fire's been out for some time now."

"Go and see."

He flew up the stairs.

"Now," I whispered, loudly, into the saloon—too loudly, perhaps, but I was afraid I couldn't make a sound. He was by my side in an instant—the double captain slipped past the stairs—through a tiny dark passage . . . a sliding door. We were in the sail-locker, scrambling on our knees over the sails. A sudden thought struck me. I saw myself wandering barefooted, bareheaded, the sun beating on my dark poll. I snatched off my floppy hat and tried hurriedly in the dark to ram it on my other self. He dodged and fended off silently. I wonder what he thought had come to me before he understood and suddenly desisted. Our hands met gropingly, lingered united in a steady, motionless clasp for a second. . . . No word was breathed by either of us when they separated.

I was standing quietly by the pantry door when the steward returned.

"Sorry, sir. Kettle barely warm. Shall I light the spirit-lamp?"

"Never mind."

I came out on deck slowly. It was now a matter of conscience to shave the land as close as possible—for now he must go overboard whenever the ship was put in stays. Must! There could be no going back for him. After a moment I walked over to leeward and my heart flew into my mouth at the nearness of the land on the bow. Under any other circumstances I would not have held on a minute longer. The second mate had followed me anxiously.

I looked on till I felt I could command my voice.

"She will weather," I said then in a quiet tone.

"Are you going to try that, sir?" he stammered out incredulously.

I took no notice of him and raised my tone just enough to be heard by the helmsman.

"Keep her good full."

"Good full, sir."

The wind fanned my cheek, the sails slept, the world was silent. The strain of watching the dark loom of the land grow bigger and denser was too much for me. I had shut my eyes—because the ship must go closer. She must! The stillness was intolerable. Were we standing still?

When I opened my eyes the second view started my heart with a thump. The black southern hill of Koh-ring seemed to hang right over the ship like a towering fragment of the everlasting night. On that enormous mass of blackness there was not a gleam to be seen, not a sound to be heard. It was gliding irresistibly towards us and yet seemed already within reach of the hand. I saw the vague figures of the watch grouped in the waist, gazing in awed silence.

"Are you going on, sir?" inquired an unsteady voice at my elbow.

I ignored it. I had to go on.

"Keep her full. Don't check her way. That won't do now," I said, warningly.

"I can't see the sails very well," the helmsman answered me, in strange, quavering tones.

Was she close enough? Already she was, I won't say in the shadow of the land, but in the very blackness of it, already swallowed up as it were, gone too close to be recalled, gone from me altogether.

"Give the mate a call," I said to the young man who stood at my elbow as still as death. "And turn all hands up."

My tone had a borrowed loudness reverberated from the height of the land. Several voices cried out together: "We are all on deck, sir."

Then stillness again, with the great shadow gliding closer, towering higher, without a light, without a sound. Such a hush had fallen on the ship that she might have been a bark of the dead floating in slowly under the very gate of Erebus.

"My God! Where are we?"

It was the mate moaning at my elbow. He was thunderstruck, and as it were deprived of the moral support of his whiskers. He clapped his hands and absolutely cried out, "Lost!"

"Be quiet," I said, sternly.

He lowered his tone, but I saw the shadowy gesture of his despair. "What are we doing here?"

"Looking for the land wind."

He made as if to tear his hair, and addressed me recklessly.

"She will never get out. You have done it, sir. I knew it'd end in something like this. She will never weather, and you are too close now to stay. She'll drift ashore before she's round. O my God!"

I caught his arm as he was raising it to batter his poor devoted head, and shook it violently.

"She's ashore already," he wailed, trying to tear himself away.

"Is she? . . . Keep good full there!"

"Good full, sir," cried the helmsman in a frightened, thin, child-like voice.

I hadn't let go the mate's arm and went on shaking it. "Ready about, do you hear? You go forward"—shake—"and stop there"—shake—"and hold your noise"—shake—"and see these head-sheets properly overhauled"—shake, shake—shake.

And all the time I dared not look towards the land lest my heart should fail me. I released my grip at last and he ran forward as if fleeing for dear life.

I wondered what my double there in the sail-locker thought of this commotion. He was able to hear everything—and perhaps he was able to understand why, on my conscience, it had to be thus close—no less. My first order "Hard alee!" re-echoed ominously under the towering shadow of Koh-ring as if I had shouted in a mountain gorge. And then I watched the land intently. In that smooth water and light wind it was impossible to feel the ship coming-to. No! I could not feel her. And my second self was making now ready to slip out and lower himself overboard. Perhaps he was gone already . . . ?

The great black mass brooding over our very mastheads began to pivot away from the ship's side silently. And now I forgot the secret stranger ready to depart, and remembered only that I was a total stranger to the ship. I did not know her. Would she do it? How was she to be handled?

I swung the mainyard and waited helplessly. She was perhaps stopped, and her very fate hung in the balance, with the black mass of Koh-ring like the gate of the everlasting night towering over her taffrail. What would she do now? Had she way on her yet? I stepped to the side swiftly, and on the shadowy water I could see nothing except a faint phosphorescent flash revealing the glassy smoothness of the sleeping surface. It was impossible to tell—and I had not learned yet the feel of my ship. Was she moving? What I needed was something easily seen, a piece of paper, which I could throw overboard and watch. I had nothing on me. To run down for it I didn't dare. There was no time. All at once my strained, yearning stare distinguished a white object floating within a yard of the ship's side. White on the black water. A phosphorescent flash passed under it. What was that thing? . . . I recognized my own floppy hat. It must have fallen off his head . . . and he didn't bother. Now I had what I wanted—the saving mark for my eyes. But I hardly thought of my other self, now gone from the ship, to be hidden forever from all friendly faces, to be a fugitive and a vagabond on the earth, with no brand of the curse on his sane forehead to stay a slaying hand . . . too proud to explain.

And I watched the hat—the expression of my sudden pity for his mere flesh. It had been meant to save his homeless head from the dangers of the sun. And now—behold—it was saving the ship, by serving me for a mark to help out the ignorance of my strangeness. Ha! It was drifting forward, warning me just in time that the ship had gathered sternway.

"Shift the helm," I said in a low voice to the seaman standing still like a statue.

The man's eyes glistened wildly in the binnacle light as he jumped round to the other side and spun round the wheel.

I walked to the break of the poop. On the overshadowed deck all hands stood by the forebraces waiting for my order. The stars ahead seemed to be gliding from right to left. And all was so still in the world that I heard the quiet remark, "She's round," passed in a tone of intense relief between two seamen.

"Let go and haul."

The foreyards ran round with a great noise, amidst cheery cries. And now the frightful whiskers made themselves heard giving various orders. Already the ship was drawing ahead. And I was alone with her. Nothing! no one in the world should stand now between us, throwing a shadow on the way of silent knowledge and mute affection, the perfect communion of a seaman with his first command.

Walking to the taffrail, I was in time to make out, on the very edge of a darkness thrown by a towering black mass like the very gateway of Erebus—yes, I was in time to catch an evanescent glimpse of my white hat left behind to mark the spot where the secret sharer of my cabin and of my thoughts, as though he were my second self, had lowered himself into the water to take his punishment: a free man, a proud swimmer striking out for a new destiny.

COMMENT AND QUESTION

1. *The intention of Conrad.* The world of Conrad is both dark and bright, dark in its picture of evil, bright in its picture of the worth of a human being. To Conrad, as to Hardy, evil is a powerful constituent of the framework of the universe. And Conrad, like Hardy, is a master at describing evil, evil with the odds in its favor, evil ranging the world freely, with humanity as its natural prey.

Against this black background, Conrad's ideal characters glow very bright. Although they have human frailty, they are moved by an obscure sense of their moral destiny. Beset by the hostile forces of evil, they nevertheless achieve self-fulfillment and preserve their moral integrity. In their greatest moments they rise to defend their ideals against the dark power which seeks to conquer them. If they lose their lives, they still win, because they have been true to their own conscience.

"The Secret Sharer" dramatizes some of these ideas. It is not a somber story, except for one brief moment, when, at the close, the mass of Koh-ring seems instinct with evil. Rather, it is a hopeful story and reveals Conrad's conception of the moral worth and dignity of a human being.

The reader will find on p. 117 a sentence which states the theme of the story quite explicitly. In the second paragraph, also, Conrad describes his purpose in specific symbols.

2. *The sense of isolation.* Study the first two paragraphs for setting and mood. Consider, also, that on the ship the captain is utterly alone. Alone, except for what? Study the last two paragraphs. Is the captain still alone?

What part does the idea of solitude or isolation play in Conrad's conception of a human being? What part does it play in Conrad's idea that a man can betray only his own conscience?

3. *The symbolic level.* A story with symbolic intentions must be studied first for plot and for character motivation. The details of the plot and of character motivation are then translated into the symbolic meaning. In "The Secret Sharer" the symbolic meanings are rooted in the actions and motives of a captain who is taking command of his ship. The captain's first watch, the discussion with Captain Archbold about the reefed foresail, the maneuvering to catch a breeze—all these incidents on the plot level have a parallel significance on the symbolic level.

The following is a brief exercise in translating the details of the plot level into the symbolic level. Notice, here, that just as in "The Bench of Desolation," the initial impulse toward self-fulfillment must spring from the hero or protagonist, himself. The first halting efforts of the captain are seen in the episode on pages 119–120.

a. *Plot level:* The captain's first act on his ship is to stand a five hours' anchor watch. What effect does this sudden and unusual order have upon the position of the rope side-ladder? What part does the rope side-ladder play in the appearance of Leggatt?

Symbolic level: Almost indirectly, the captain's first assertion of his command brings to light his secret self. What does this incident mean in the progress of the story as a whole?

b. *Plot level:* The captain is afraid that Leggatt won't come on board, is even more afraid that Leggatt doesn't want to come on board. In his uncertainty the capatin delays telling who he is. Then the captain firmly declares his identity. What happens?

Symbolic level: Positive self-assertion results in an active response of the secret self. What does the captain's uncertainty mean? What does the sudden swirl of phosphorescence mean?

4. *The captain and Leggatt.*

a. What physical qualities or accidents of background make the captain and Leggatt sharers of the same identity? But how do they differ in their personalities? Notice Leggatt's words, the expression on his face, his attitude toward the crew when he is a ship's officer, his conduct in a crisis on the *Sephora*, his attitude toward his own destiny. Compare Leggatt with the captain.

b. What symbolic quality is embodied in Leggatt's ability as a swimmer? While telling of his escape, Leggatt says: "I meant to swim till I sank—but that's not the same thing [as suicide]." This moral ideal—this perseverance in a struggle against odds—is typical of Conrad and keynotes the character of Leggatt.

c. Both Leggatt and the captain are "suspect." What actions of the captain arouse the apprehension of his crew? Could both the sentence stating the theme and the second paragraph of the story refer to Leggatt as well as to the captain?

d. Study the episode of Leggatt on board the *Sephora*. Who gave the order for setting the reefed foresail? Who should have given the order?

e. How does his conversation with Leggatt during the first night in the cabin affect the captain? What action does the captain perform the next morning?

5. *The captain of the Sephora.* Captain Archbold is part of the symbolism of this story. Study the description of him at the beginning of section II. Notice the tone he uses when he identifies himself.

What are Captain Archbold's relations with his officers and crew?

Remember that Captain Archbold has come looking for the secret self in order to shackle him. Is Captain Archbold then a threat, a warning, or an object lesson? Or all three? Explain the reflection of the protagonist on p. 133: "If he had only known how afraid I was of his putting my feeling of identity with the other to the test!"

6. *The test.*

a. *The odds.* The odds are heavy against the successful outcome of the test. This position is typical of Conrad. His human beings are the more remarkable because they valiantly face great odds. A paragraph on p. 135 lists some of the odds. During the test both Leggatt and the captain are dressed in sleeping-suits. Some critics have said that the sleeping-suit is a symbol of the unconscious. Could not the detail of the sleeping-suit also mean that both men are defenseless?

b. *The darkness.* The test occurs in darkness. Darkness has long been a symbol of what? The darkness is made blacker by the mass of Koh-ring. Explain the symbolic intention of: "Such a hush had fallen on the ship that she might have been a bark of the dead floating in slowly under the very gates of Erebus." What part does Koh-ring play on the plot level? On the symbolic level?

c. *The light in the darkness.* What does the captain see in the darkness? Why is this object important?

7. *Additional meanings.* In *The Art of Modern Fiction* Mr. Ray B. West, Jr., and Mr. Robert Wooster Stallman present a detailed analysis of "The Secret Sharer." They find three allegories in the story, a moral, a psychological, and an aesthetic. The present discussion has considered only the moral allegory.

The student might explore the possibilities of a psychological and an aesthetic allegory. For the psychological allegory, consider that Leggatt comes up out of darkness, naked. He goes back down into darkness, dressed like the captain. Leggatt and the captain never hear each other's natural voice. And the phosphorescence in black waters always reveals the presence of the secret self.

THE BLUE HOTEL

BY STEPHEN CRANE

STEPHEN CRANE (1871–1900) was born in
New Jersey. He served as a correspondent in
the Greco-Turkish War and in Cuba in the
Spanish-American War. He was only twenty-
nine when he died in England, but in his
short lifetime he wrote brilliantly and published a number of novels and many short
stories. His first novel, *Maggie* (1896), was
privately printed because no publisher would
print it. His next novel, *The Red Badge of
Courage* (1895), written before he had seen
a battlefield, made him famous. This novel
and two short stories, "The Open Boat" and
"The Blue Hotel" have become American
classics.

T HE PALACE HOTEL at Fort Romper was painted a light blue, a shade
that is on the legs of a kind of heron, causing the bird to declare its position against any background. The Palace Hotel, then, was always screaming and howling in a way that made the dazzling winter landscape of
Nebraska seem only a gray swampish hush. It stood alone on the prairie,
and when the snow was falling the town two hundred yards away was
not visible. But when the traveler alighted at the railway station he was
obliged to pass the Palace Hotel before he could come upon the company
of low clapboard houses which composed Fort Romper, and it was not
to be thought that any traveler could pass the Palace Hotel without looking at it. Pat Scully, the proprietor, had proved himself a master of
strategy when he chose his paints. It is true that on clear days, when

the great transcontinental expresses, long lines of swaying Pullmans, swept through Fort Romper, passengers were overcome at the sight, and the cult that knows the brown-reds and the subdivisions of the dark greens of the East expressed shame, pity, horror, in a laugh. But to the citizens of this prairie town and to the people who would naturally stop there, Pat Scully had performed a feat. With this opulence and splendor, these creeds, classes, egotisms, that streamed through Romper on the rails day after day, they had no color in common.

As if the displayed delights of such a blue hotel were not sufficiently enticing, it was Scully's habit to go every morning and evening to meet the leisurely trains that stopped at Romper and work his seductions upon any man that he might see wavering, gripsack in hand.

One morning, when a snow-crusted engine dragged its long string of freight cars and its one passenger coach to the station, Scully performed the marvel of catching three men. One was a shaky and quick-eyed Swede, with a great shining cheap valise; one was a tall bronzed cowboy, who was on his way to a ranch near the Dakota line; one was a little silent man from the East, who didn't look it, and didn't announce it. Scully practically made them prisoners. He was so nimble and merry and kindly that each probably felt it would be the height of brutality to try to escape. They trudged off over the creaking board sidewalks in the wake of the eager little Irishman. He wore a heavy fur cap squeezed tightly down on his head. It caused his two red ears to stick out stiffly, as if they were made of tin.

At last, Scully, elaborately, with boisterous hospitality, conducted them through the portals of the blue hotel. The room which they entered was small. It seemed to be merely a proper temple for an enormous stove, which, in the center, was humming with godlike violence. At various points on its surface the iron had become luminous and glowed yellow from the heat. Beside the stove Scully's son Johnnie was playing High-Five with an old farmer who had whiskers both gray and sandy. They were quarreling. Frequently the old farmer turned his face toward a box of sawdust—colored brown from tobacco juice—that was behind the stove, and spat with an air of great impatience and irritation. With a loud flourish of words Scully destroyed the game of cards, and bustled his son upstairs with part of the baggage of the new guests. He himself conducted them to three basins of the coldest water in the world. The cowboy and the Easterner burnished themselves fiery red with this water, until it seemed to be some kind of metal-polish. The Swede, however, merely dipped his fingers gingerly and with trepidation. It was notable that throughout this series of small ceremonies the three travelers were made to feel that Scully was very benevolent. He was conferring great favors upon them. He handed the towel from one to another with an air of philanthropic impulse.

Afterward they went to the first room, and, sitting about the stove, listened to Scully's officious clamor at his daughters, who were preparing the midday meal. They reflected in the silence of experienced men who tread carefully amid new people. Nevertheless, the old farmer, stationary, invincible in his chair near the warmest part of the stove, turned his face from the sawdust-box frequently and addressed a glowing commonplace to the strangers. Usually he was answered in short but adequate sentences by either the cowboy or the Easterner. The Swede said nothing. He seemed to be occupied in making furtive estimates of each man in the room. One might have thought that he had the sense of silly suspicion which comes to guilt. He resembled a badly frightened man.

Later, at dinner, he spoke a little, addressing his conversation entirely to Scully. He volunteered that he had come from New York, where for ten years he had worked as a tailor. These facts seemed to strike Scully as fascinating, and afterward he volunteered that he had lived at Romper for fourteen years. The Swede asked about the crops and the price of labor. He seemed barely to listen to Scully's extended replies. His eyes continued to rove from man to man.

Finally, with a laugh and a wink, he said that some of these Western communities were very dangerous; and after his statement he straightened his legs under the table, tilted his head, and laughed again, loudly. It was plain that the demonstration had no meaning to the others. They looked at him wondering and in silence.

II

As the men trooped heavily back into the front room, the two little windows presented views of a turmoiling sea of snow. The huge arms of the wind were making attempts—mighty, circular, futile—to embrace the flakes as they sped. A gate-post like a still man with a blanched face stood aghast amid this profligate fury. In a hearty voice Scully announced the presence of a blizzard. The guests of the blue hotel, lighting their pipes, assented with grunts of lazy masculine contentment. No island of the sea could be exempt in the degree of this little room with its humming stove. Johnnie, son of Scully, in a tone which defined his opinion of his ability as a card-player, challenged the old farmer of both gray and sandy whiskers to a game of High-Five. The farmer agreed with a contemptuous and bitter scoff. They sat close to the stove, and squared their knees under a wide board. The cowboy and the Easterner watched the game with interest. The Swede remained near the window, aloof, but with a countenance that showed signs of an inexplicable excitement.

The play of Johnnie and the gray-beard was suddenly ended by another quarrel. The old man arose while casting a look of heated scorn at his adversary. He slowly buttoned his coat, and then stalked with fabulous dignity from the room. In the discreet silence of all other men the Swede laughed. His laughter rang somehow childish. Men by this time had begun to look at him askance, as if they wished to inquire what ailed him.

A new game was formed jocosely. The cowboy volunteered to become the partner of Johnnie, and they all then turned to ask the Swede to throw in his lot with the little Easterner. He asked some questions about the game, and, learning that it wore many names, and that he had played it when it was under an alias, he accepted the invitation. He strode toward the men nervously, as if he expected to be assaulted. Finally, seated, he gazed from face to face and laughed shrilly. This laugh was so strange that the Easterner looked up quickly, the cowboy sat intent and with his mouth open, and Johnnie paused, holding the cards with still fingers.

Afterward there was a short silence. Then Johnnie said, "Well, let's get at it. Come on now!" They pulled their chairs forward until their knees were bunched under the board. They began to play, and their interest in the game caused the others to forget the manner of the Swede.

The cowboy was a board-whacker. Each time that he held superior cards he whanged them, one by one, with exceeding force, down upon the improvised table, and took the tricks with a glowing air of prowess and pride that sent thrills of indignation into the hearts of his opponents. A game with a board-whacker in it is sure to become intense. The countenances of the Easterner and the Swede were miserable whenever the cowboy thundered down his aces and kings, while Johnnie, his eyes gleaming with joy, chuckled and chuckled.

Because of the absorbing play none considered the strange ways of the Swede. They paid strict heed to the game. Finally, during a lull caused by a new deal, the Swede suddenly addressed Johnnie: "I suppose there have been a good many men killed in this room." The jaws of the others dropped and they looked at him.

"What in hell are you talking about?" said Johnnie.

The Swede laughed again his blatant laugh, full of a kind of false courage and defiance. "Oh, you know what I mean all right," he answered.

"I'm a liar if I do!" Johnnie protested. The card was halted, and the men stared at the Swede. Johnnie evidently felt that as the son of the proprietor, he should make a direct inquiry. "Now, what might you be drivin' at, mister?" he asked. The Swede winked at him. It was a wink full of cunning. His fingers shook on the edge of the board. "Oh, maybe you think I have been to nowheres. Maybe you think I'm a tenderfoot?"

"I don't know nothin' about you," answered Johnnie, "and I don't give a damn where you've been. All I got to say is that I don't know what you're driving at. There hain't never been nobody killed in this room."

The cowboy, who had been steadily gazing at the Swede, then spoke: "What's wrong with you, mister?"

Apparently it seemed to the Swede that he was formidably menaced. He shivered and turned white near the corners of his mouth. He sent an appealing glance in the direction of the little Easterner. During these moments he did not forget to wear his air of advanced pot-valor. "They say they don't know what I mean," he remarked mockingly to the Easterner.

The latter answered after prolonged and cautious reflection. "I don't understand you," he said, impassively.

The Swede made a movement then which announced that he thought he had encountered treachery from the only quarter where he had expected sympathy, if not help. "Oh, I see you are all against me, I see—"

The cowboy was in a state of deep stupefaction. "Say," he cried, as he tumbled the deck violently down upon the board, "say, what are you gittin' at, hey?"

The Swede sprang up with the celerity of a man escaping from a snake on the floor. "I don't want to fight!" he shouted. "I don't want to fight!"

The cowboy stretched his long legs indolently and deliberately. His hands were in his pockets. He spat into the sawdust-box. "Well, who the hell thought you did?" he inquired.

The Swede backed rapidly toward a corner of the room. His hands were out protectingly in front of his chest, but he was making an obvious struggle to control his fright. "Gentlemen," he quavered, "I suppose I am going to be killed before I can leave this house! I suppose I am going to be killed before I can leave this house!" In his eyes was the dying-swan look. Through the windows could be seen the snow turning blue in the shadow of dusk. The wind tore at the house, and some loose thing beat regularly against the clapboards like a spirit tapping.

A door opened, and Scully himself entered. He paused in surprise as he noted the tragic attitude of the Swede. Then he said, "What's the matter here?"

The Swede answered him swiftly and eagerly: "These men are going to kill me."

"Kill you!" ejaculated Scully. "Kill you! What are you talkin'?"

The Swede made the gesture of a martyr.

Scully wheeled sternly upon his son. "What is this, Johnnie?"

The lad had grown sullen. "Damned if I know," he answered. "I can't make no sense to it." He began to shuffle the cards, fluttering them together with an angry snap. "He says a good many men have been killed in this room, or something like that. And he says he's goin' to be killed here too. I don't know what ails him. He's crazy, I shouldn't wonder."

Scully then looked for explanation to the cowboy, but the cowboy simply shrugged his shoulders.

"Kill you?" said Scully again to the Swede. "Kill you? Man, you're off your nut."

"Oh, I know," burst out the Swede. "I know what will happen. Yes,

I'm crazy—yes. Yes, of course, I'm crazy—yes. But I know one thing—" There was a sort of sweat of misery and terror upon his face. "I know I won't get out of here alive."

The cowboy drew a deep breath, as if his mind was passing into the last stages of dissolution. "Well, I'm doggoned," he whispered to himself.

Scully wheeled suddenly and faced his son. "You've been troublin' this man!"

Johnnie's voice was loud with its burden of grievance. "Why, good Gawd, I ain't done nothin' to 'im."

The Swede broke in. "Gentlemen, do not disturb yourselves. I will leave this house. I will go away, because"—he accused them dramatically with his glance—"because I do not want to be killed."

Scully was furious with his son. "Will you tell me what is the matter, you young divil? What's the matter, anyhow? Speak out!"

"Blame it!" cried Johnnie in despair, "don't I tell you I don't know? He —he says we want to kill him, and that's all I know. I can't tell what ails him."

The Swede continued to repeat: "Never mind, Mr. Scully; never mind. I will leave this house. I will go away, because I do not wish to be killed. Yes, of course, I am crazy—yes. But I know one thing! I will go away. I will leave this house. Never mind, Mr. Scully; never mind. I will go away."

"You will not go 'way," said Scully. "You will not go 'way until I hear the reason of this business. If anybody has troubled you I will take care of him. This is my house. You are under my roof, and I will not allow any peaceable man to be troubled here." He cast a terrible eye upon Johnnie, the cowboy, and the Easterner.

"Never mind, Mr. Scully; never mind. I will go away. I do not wish to be killed." The Swede moved toward the door which opened upon the stairs. It was evidently his intention to go at once for his baggage.

"No, no," shouted Scully peremptorily; but the white-faced man slid by him and disappeared. "Now," said Scully severely, "what does this mane?"

Johnnie and the cowboy cried together: "Why, we didn't do nothin' to 'im!"

Scully's eyes were cold. "No," he said, "you didn't?"

Johnnie swore a deep oath. "Why, this is the wildest loon I ever see. We didn't do nothin' at all. We were jest sittin' here playin' cards, and he—"

The father suddenly spoke to the Easterner, "Mr. Blanc," he asked, "what has these boys been doin'?"

The Easterner reflected again. "I didn't see anything wrong at all," he said at last, slowly.

Scully began to howl. "But what does it mane?" He stared ferociously at his son. "I have a mind to lather you for this, me boy."

Johnnie was frantic. "Well, what have I done?" he bawled at his father.

III

"I think you are tongue-tied," said Scully finally to his son, the cowboy, and the Easterner; and at the end of this scornful sentence he left the room.

Upstairs the Swede was swiftly fastening the straps of his great valise. Once his back happened to be half turned toward the door, and, hearing a noise there, he wheeled and sprang up, uttering a loud cry. Scully's wrinkled visage showed grimly in the light of the small lamp he carried. This yellow effulgence, streaming upward, colored only his prominent features, and left his eyes, for instance, in mysterious shadow. He resembled a murderer.

"Man! man!" he exclaimed, "have you gone daffy?"

"Oh, no! Oh, no!" rejoined the other. "There are people in this world who know pretty nearly as much as you do—understand?"

For a moment they stood gazing at each other. Upon the Swede's deathly pale cheeks were two spots brightly crimson and sharply edged, as if they had been carefully painted. Scully placed the light on the table and sat himself on the edge of the bed. He spoke ruminatively. "By cracky, I never heard of such a thing in my life. It's a complete muddle. I can't, for the soul of me, think how you ever got this idea into your head." Presently he lifted his eyes and asked: "And did you sure think they were going to kill you?"

The Swede scanned the old man as if he wished to see into his mind. "I did," he said at last. He obviously suspected that this answer might precipitate an outbreak. As he pulled on a strap his whole arm shook, the elbow wavering like a bit of paper.

Scully banged his hand impressively on the footboard of the bed. "Why, man, we're goin' to have a line of ilictric street-cars in this town next spring."

" 'A line of electric street-cars,' " repeated the Swede, stupidly.

"And," said Scully, "there's a new railroad goin' to be built down from Broken Arm to here. Not to mintion the four churches and the smashin' big brick schoolhouse. Then there's the big factory, too. Why, in two years Romper'll be a met-tro-*pol*-is."

Having finished the preparation of his baggage, the Swede straightened himself. "Mr. Scully," he said, with sudden hardihood, "how much do I owe you?"

"You don't owe me anythin'," said the old man, angrily.

"Yes, I do," retorted the Swede. He took seventy-five cents from his pocket and tendered it to Scully; but the latter snapped his fingers in disdainful refusal. However, it happened that they both stood gazing in a strange fashion at three silver pieces on the Swede's open palm.

"I'll not take your money," said Scully at last. "Not after what's been goin' on here." Then a plan seemed to strike him. "Here," he cried, picking up his lamp and moving toward the door. "Here! Come with me a minute."

"No," said the Swede, in overwhelming alarm.

"Yes," urged the old man. "Come on! I want you to come and see a picter—just across the hall—in my room."

The Swede must have concluded that his hour was come. His jaw dropped and his teeth showed like a dead man's. He ultimately followed Scully across the corridor, but he had the step of one hung in chains.

Scully flashed the light high on the wall of his own chamber. There was revealed a ridiculous photograph of a little girl. She was leaning against a balustrade of gorgeous decoration, and the formidable bang to her hair was prominent. The figure was as graceful as an upright sled-stake, and, withal, it was of the hue of lead. "There," said Scully, tenderly, "that's the picter of my little girl that died. Her name was Carrie. She had the purtiest hair you ever saw! I was that fond of her, she—"

Turning then, he saw that the Swede was not contemplating the picture at all, but, instead, was keeping keen watch on the gloom in the rear.

"Look, man!" cried Scully, heartily. "That's the picter of my little gal that died. Her name was Carrie. And then here's the picter of my oldest boy, Michael. He's a lawyer in Lincoln, an' doin' well. I gave that boy a grand eddication, and I'm glad for it now. He's a fine boy. Look at 'im now. Ain't he bold as blazes, him there in Lincoln, an honored an' respicted gintleman! An honored and respicted gintleman," concluded Scully with a flourish. And, so saying, he smote the Swede jovially on the back.

The Swede faintly smiled.

"Now," said the old man, "there's only one more thing." He dropped suddenly to the floor and thrust his head beneath the bed. The Swede could hear his muffled voice. "I'd keep it under me piller if it wasn't for that boy Johnnie. Then there's the old woman— Where is it now? I never put it twice in the same place. Ah, now come out with you!"

Presently he backed clumsily from under the bed, dragging with him an old coat rolled into a bundle. "I've fetched him," he muttered. Kneeling on the floor, he unrolled the coat and extracted from its heart a large yellow-brown whisky-bottle.

His first maneuver was to hold the bottle up to the light. Reassured, apparently, that nobody had been tampering with it, he thrust it with a generous movement toward the Swede.

The weak-kneed Swede was about to eagerly clutch this element of strength, but he suddenly jerked his hand away and cast a look of horror upon Scully.

"Drink," said the old man affectionately. He had risen to his feet, and now stood facing the Swede.

There was a silence. Then again Scully said: "Drink!"

The Swede laughed wildly. He grabbed the bottle, put it to his mouth; and as his lips curled absurdly around the opening and his throat worked, he kept his glance, burning with hatred, upon the old man's face.

IV

After the departure of Scully the three men, with the cardboard still upon their knees, preserved for a long time an astounded silence. Then Johnnie said: "That's the doddangedest Swede I ever see."

"He ain't no Swede," said the cowboy, scornfully.

"Well, what is he then?" cried Johnnie. "What is he then?"

"It's my opinion," replied the cowboy deliberately, "he's some kind of a Dutchman." It was a venerable custom of the country to entitle as Swedes all light-haired men who spoke with a heavy tongue. In consequence the idea of the cowboy was not without its daring. "Yes, sir," he repeated, "It's my opinion this feller is some kind of a Dutchman."

"Well, he says he's a Swede, anyhow," muttered Johnnie, sulkily. He turned to the Easterner: "What do you think, Mr. Blanc?"

"Oh, I don't know," replied the Easterner.

"Well, what do you think makes him act that way?" asked the cowboy.

"Why, he's frightened." The Easterner knocked his pipe against a rim of the stove. "He's clear frightened out of his boots."

"What at?" cried Johnnie and the cowboy together.

The Easterner reflected over his answer.

"What at?" cried the others again.

"Oh, I don't know, but it seems to me this man has been reading dime novels, and he thinks he's right out in the middle of it—the shootin' and stabbin' and all."

"But," said the cowboy, deeply scandalized, "this ain't Wyoming, ner none of them places. This is Nebrasker."

"Yes," added Johnnie, "an' why don't he wait till he gits *out West?*"

The traveled Easterner laughed. "It isn't different there even—not in these days. But he thinks he's right in the middle of hell."

Johnnie and the cowboy mused long.

"It's awful funny," remarked Johnnie at last.

"Yes," said the cowboy. "This is a queer game. I hope we don't git snowed in, because then we'd have to stand this here man bein' around with us all the time. That wouldn't be no good."

"I wish pop would throw him out," said Johnnie.

Presently they heard a loud stamping on the stairs, accompanied by ringing jokes in the voice of old Scully, and laughter, evidently from the Swede. The men around the stove stared vacantly at each other. "Gosh!"

said the cowboy. The door flew open, and old Scully, flushed and anec-dotal, came into the room. He was jabbering at the Swede, who followed him, laughing bravely. It was the entry of two roisterers from a banquet hall.

"Come now," said Scully sharply to the three seated men, "move up and give us a chance at the stove." The cowboy and the Easterner obedi-ently sidled their chairs to make room for the new-comers. Johnnie, how-ever, simply arranged himself in a more indolent attitude, and then remained motionless.

"Come! Git over, there," said Scully.

"Plenty of room on the other side of the stove," said Johnnie.

"Do you think we want to sit in the draught?" roared the father.

But the Swede here interposed with a grandeur of confidence. "No, no. Let the boy sit where he likes," he cried in a bullying voice to the father.

"All right! All right!" said Scully, deferentially. The cowboy and the Easterner exchanged glances of wonder.

The five chairs were formed in a cresent about one side of the stove. The Swede began to talk; he talked arrogantly, profanely, angrily. Johnnie, the cowboy, and the Easterner maintained a morose silence, while old Scully appeared to be receptive and eager, breaking in con-stantly with sympathetic ejaculations.

Finally the Swede announced that he was thirsty. He moved in his chair, and said that he would go for a drink of water.

"I'll git it for you," cried Scully at once.

"No," said the Swede, contemptuously. "I'll get it for myself." He arose and stalked with the air of an owner off into the executive parts of the hotel.

As soon as the Swede was out of hearing Scully sprang to his feet and whispered intensely to the others: "Upstairs he thought I was tryin' to poison 'im."

"Say," said Johnnie, "this makes me sick. Why don't you throw 'im out in the snow?"

"Why, he's all right now," declared Scully. "It was only that he was from the East, and he thought this was a tough place. That's all. He's all right now."

The cowboy looked with admiration upon the Easterner. "You were straight," he said. "You were on to that there Dutchman."

"Well," said Johnnie to his father, "he may be all right now, but I don't see it. Other time he was scared, but now he's too fresh."

Scully's speech was always a combination of Irish brogue and idiom, Western twang and idiom, and scraps of curiously formal diction taken from the story-books and newspapers. He now hurled a strange mass of language at the head of his son. "What do I keep? What do I keep? What do I keep?" he demanded, in a voice of thunder. He slapped his knee impressively, to indicate that he himself was going to make reply, and that all should heed. "I keep a hotel," he shouted. "A hotel, do you mind? A guest under my roof has sacred privileges. He is to be intimidated by none. Not one word shall he hear that would prijudice him in favor of goin' away. I'll not have it. There's no place in this here town where they can say they iver took in a guest of mine because he was afraid to stay here." He wheeled suddenly upon the cowboy and the Easterner. "Am I right?"

"Yes, Mr. Scully," said the cowboy, "I think you're right."

"Yes, Mr. Scully," said the Easterner, "I think you're right."

V

At six-o'clock supper, the Swede fizzed like a firewheel. He sometimes seemed on the point of bursting into riotous song, and in all his madness he was encouraged by old Scully. The Easterner was encased in reserve; the cowboy sat in wide-mouthed amazement, forgetting to eat, while Johnnie wrathily demolished great plates of food. The daughters of the house, when they were obliged to replenish the biscuits, approached as warily as Indians, and, having succeeded in their purpose, fled with ill-concealed trepidation. The Swede domineered the whole feast, and he gave it the appearance of a cruel bacchanal. He seemed to have grown suddenly taller; he gazed, brutally disdainful, into every face. His voice rang through the room. Once when he jabbed out harpoon-fashion with his fork to pinion a biscuit, the weapon nearly impaled the hand of the Easterner, which had been stretched quietly out for the same biscuit.

After supper, as the men filed toward the other room, the Swede smote Scully ruthlessly on the shoulder. "Well, old boy, that was a good, square meal." Johnnie looked hopefully at his father; he knew that shoulder was tender from an old fall; and, indeed, it appeared for a moment as if Scully was going to flame out over the matter, but in the end he smiled a sickly smile and remained silent. The others understood from his manner that he was admitting his responsibility for the Swede's new viewpoint.

Johnnie, however, addressed his parent in an aside. "Why don't you license somebody to kick you downstairs?" Scully scowled darkly by way of reply.

When they were gathered about the stove, the Swede insisted on another game of High-Five. Scully gently deprecated the plan at first, but the Swede turned a wolfish glare upon him. The old man subsided, and the Swede canvassed the others. In his tone there was always a great threat. The cowboy and the Easterner both remarked indifferently that they would play. Scully said that he would presently have to go to meet the 6:58 train, and so the Swede turned menacingly upon Johnnie. For a moment their glances crossed like blades, and then Johnnie smiled and said, "Yes, I'll play."

They formed a square, with the little board on their knees. The Easterner and the Swede were again partners. As the play went on, it was noticeable that the cowboy was not board-whacking as usual. Meanwhile, Scully, near the lamp, had put on his spectacles and, with an appearance curiously like an old priest, was reading a newspaper. In time he went out to meet the 6:58 train, and, despite his precautions, a gust of polar wind whirled into the room as he opened the door. Besides scattering the cards, it chilled the players to the marrow. The Swede cursed frightfully. When Scully returned, his entrance disturbed a cozy and friendly scene. The Swede again cursed. But presently they were once more intent, their heads bent forward and their hands moving swiftly. The Swede had adopted the fashion of board-whacking.

Scully took up his paper and for a long time remained immersed in matters which were extraordinarily remote from him. The lamp burned badly, and once he stopped to adjust the wick. The newspaper, as he turned from page to page, rustled with a slow and comfortable sound. Then suddenly he heard three terrible words: "You are cheatin'!"

Such scenes often prove that there can be little of dramatic import in environment. Any room can present a tragic front; any room can be comic. This little den was now hideous as a torture-chamber. The new faces of the men themselves had changed it upon the instant. The Swede held a huge fist in front of Johnnie's face, while the latter looked steadily over it into the blazing orbs of his accuser. The Easterner had grown pallid; the cowboy's jaw had dropped in that expression of bovine amazement which was one of his important mannerisms. After the three words, the first sound in the room was made by Scully's paper as it floated forgotten to his feet. His spectacles had also fallen from his nose, but by a clutch he had saved them in air. His hand, grasping the spectacles, now remained poised awkwardly and near his shoulder. He stared at the card-players.

Probably the silence was while a second elapsed. Then, if the floor had been suddenly twitched out from under the men they could not have moved quicker. The five had projected themselves headlong toward a common point. It happened that Johnnie, in rising to hurl himself upon the Swede, had stumbled slightly because of his curiously instinctive care for the cards and the board. The loss of the moment allowed time for the arrival of Scully, and also allowed the cowboy time to give the Swede a great push which sent him staggering back. The men found tongue together, and hoarse shouts of rage, appeal, or fear burst from every throat. The cowboy pushed and jostled feverishly at the Swede, and the Easterner and Scully clung wildly to Johnnie; but through the smoky air, above the swaying bodies of the peace-compellers, the eyes of the two warriors ever sought each other in glances of challenge that were at once hot and steely.

Of course the board had been overturned, and now the whole company of cards was scattered over the floor, where the boots of the men trampled the fat and painted kings and queens as they gazed with their silly eyes at the war that was waging above them.

Scully's voice was dominating the yells. "Stop now! Stop, I say! Stop, now—"

Johnnie, as he struggled to burst through the rank formed by Scully and the Easterner, was crying, "Well, he says I cheated! He says I cheated! I won't allow no man to say I cheated! If he says I cheated, he's a ———!"

The cowboy was telling the Swede, "Quit now! Quit, d'ye hear—"

The screams of the Swede never ceased: "He did cheat! I saw him! I saw him—"

As for the Easterner, he was importuning in a voice that was not heeded: "Wait a moment, can't you? Oh, wait a moment. What's the good of a fight over a game of cards? Wait a moment—"

In this tumult no complete sentences were clear. "Cheat"—"Quit"—"He says"—these fragments pierced the uproar and rang out sharply. It was remarkable that, whereas Scully undoubtedly made the most noise, he was the least heard of any of the riotous band.

Then suddenly there was a great cessation. It was as if each man had paused for breath; and although the room was still lighted with the anger of men, it could be seen that there was no danger of immediate conflict, and at once Johnnie, shouldering his way forward, almost succeeded in confronting the Swede. "What did you say I cheated for? What did you say I cheated for? I don't cheat, and I won't let any man say I do!"

The Swede said, "I saw you! I saw you!"

"Well," cried Johnnie, "I'll fight any man what says I cheat!"

"No, you won't," said the cowboy. "Not here."

"Ah, be still, can't you?" said Scully, coming between them.

The quiet was sufficient to allow the Easterner's voice to be heard. He was repeating, "Oh, wait a moment, can't you? What's the good of a fight over a game of cards? Wait a moment!"

Johnnie, his red face appearing above his father's shoulder, hailed the Swede again. "Did you say I cheated?"

The Swede showed his teeth. "Yes."

"Then," said Johnnie, "we must fight."

"Yes, fight," roared the Swede. He was like a demoniac. "Yes, fight! I'll show you what kind of a man I am! I'll show you who you want to fight! Maybe you think I can't fight! Maybe you think I can't! I'll show you, you skin, you card-sharp! Yes, you cheated! You cheated! You cheated!"

"Well, let's go at it, then, mister," said Johnnie, coolly.

The cowboy's brow was beaded with sweat from his efforts in intercepting all sorts of raids. He turned in despair to Scully. "What are you goin' to do now?"

A change had come over the Celtic visage of the old man. He now seemed all eagerness; his eyes glowed.

"We'll let them fight," he answered, stalwartly. "I can't put up with it any longer. I've stood this damned Swede till I'm sick. We'll let them fight."

VI

The men prepared to go out of doors. The Easterner was so nervous that he had great difficulty in getting his arms into the sleeves of his new leather coat. As the cowboy drew his fur cap down over his ears his hands trembled. In fact, Johnnie and old Scully were the only ones who displayed no agitation. These preliminaries were conducted without words.

Scully threw open the door. "Well, come on," he said. Instantly a terrific wind caused the flame of the lamp to struggle at its wick, while a puff of black smoke sprang from the chimney-top. The stove was in mid-current of the blast, and its voice swelled to equal the roar of the storm. Some of the scarred and bedabbled cards were caught up from the floor and dashed helplessly against the farther wall. The men lowered their heads and plunged into the tempest as into a sea.

No snow was falling, but great whirls and clouds of flakes, swept up from the ground by the frantic winds, were streaming southward with the speed of bullets. The covered land was blue with the sheen of an unearthly satin, and there was no other hue save where, at the low, black railway station—which seemed incredibly distant—one light gleamed like a tiny jewel. As the men floundered into a thigh-deep drift, it was known that the Swede was bawling out something. Scully went to him, put a hand on his shoulder, and projected an ear. "What's that you say?" he shouted.

"I say," bawled the Swede again, "I won't stand much show against this gang. I know you'll all pitch on me."

Scully smote him reproachfully on the arm. "Tut, man!" he yelled. The wind tore the words from Scully's lips and scattered them far alee.

"You are all a gang of—" boomed the Swede, but the storm also seized the remainder of this sentence.

Immediately turning their backs upon the wind, the men had swung around a corner to the sheltered side of the hotel. It was the function of the little house to preserve here, amid this great devastation of snow, an irregular V-shape of heavily encrusted grass, which crackled beneath the feet. One could imagine the great drifts piled against the windward side. When the party reached the comparative peace of this spot it was found that the Swede was still bellowing.

"Oh, I know what kind of a thing this is! I know you'll all pitch on me. I can't lick you all!"

Scully turned upon him panther-fashion. "You'll not have to whip all of us. You'll have to whip my son Johnnie. An' the man what troubles you durin' that time will have me to dale with."

The arrangements were swiftly made. The two men faced each other, obedient to the harsh commands of Scully, whose face, in the subtly luminous gloom, could be seen set in the austere impersonal lines that are pictured on the countenances of the Roman veterans. The Easterner's teeth were chattering, and he was hopping up and down like a mechanical toy. The cowboy stood rock-like.

The contestants had not stripped off any clothing. Each was in his ordinary attire. Their fists were up, and they eyed each other in a calm that had the elements of leonine cruelty in it.

During this pause, the Easterner's mind, like a film, took lasting impressions of three men—the iron-nerved master of the ceremony; the Swede, pale, motionless, terrible; and Johnnie, serene yet ferocious, brutish yet heroic. The entire prelude had in it a tragedy greater than the tragedy of action, and this aspect was accentuated by the long, mellow cry of the blizzard, as it sped the tumbling and wailing flakes into the black abyss of the south.

"Now!" said Scully.

The two combatants leaped forward and crashed together like bullocks. There was heard the cushioned sound of blows, and of a curse squeezing out from between the tight teeth of one.

As for the spectators, the Easterner's pent-up breath exploded from him with a pop of relief, absolute relief from the tension of the preliminaries. The cowboy bounded into the air with a yowl. Scully was immovable as from supreme amazement and fear at the fury of the fight which he himself had permitted and arranged.

For a time the encounter in the darkness was such a perplexity of flying arms that it presented no more detail than would a swiftly revolving wheel. Occasionally a face, as if illumined by a flash of light, would shine out, ghastly and marked with pink spots. A moment later, the men might have been known as shadows, if it were not for the involuntary utterance of oaths that came from them in whispers.

Suddenly a holocaust of warlike desire caught the cowboy, and he bolted forward with the speed of a broncho. "Go it, Johnnie! go it! Kill him! Kill him!"

Scully confronted him. "Kape back," he said; and by his glance the cowboy could tell that this man was Johnnie's father.

To the Easterner there was a monotony of unchangeable fighting that was an abomination. This confused mingling was eternal to his sense, which was concentrated in a longing for the end, the priceless end. Once the fighters lurched near him, and as he scrambled hastily backward he heard them breathe like men on the rack.

"Kill him, Johnnie! Kill him! Kill him! Kill him!" The cowboy's face was contorted like one of those agony masks in museums.

"Keep still," said Scully, icily.

Then there was a sudden loud grunt, incomplete, cut short, and Johnnie's body swung away from the Swede and fell with sickening heaviness to the grass. The cowboy was barely in time to prevent the mad Swede from flinging himself upon his prone adversary. "No, you don't," said the cowboy, interposing an arm. "Wait a second."

Scully was at his son's side. "Johnnie! Johnnie, me boy!" His voice had a quality of melancholy tenderness. "Johnnie! Can you go on with it?" He looked anxiously down into the bloody, pulpy face of his son.

There was a moment of silence, and then Johnnie answered in his ordinary voice, "Yes, I—it—yes."

Assisted by his father he struggled to his feet. "Wait a bit now till you git your wind," said the old man.

A few paces away the cowboy was lecturing the Swede. "No, you don't! Wait a second!"

The Easterner was plucking at Scully's sleeve. "Oh, this is enough," he pleaded. "This is enough! Let it go as it stands. This is enough!"

"Bill," said Scully, "git out of the road." The cowboy stepped aside. "Now." The combatants were actuated by a new caution as they advanced toward collision. They glared at each other, and then the Swede aimed a lightning blow that carried with it his entire weight. Johnnie was evidently half stupid from weakness, but he miraculously dodged, and his fist sent the over-balanced Swede sprawling.

The cowboy, Scully, and the Easterner burst into a cheer that was like a chorus of triumphant soldiery, but before its conclusion the Swede had scuffled agilely to his feet and come in berserk abandon at his foe. There was another perplexity of flying arms, and Johnnie's body again swung away and fell, even as a bundle might fall from a roof. The Swede instantly staggered to a little wind-waved tree and leaned upon it, breathing like an engine, while his savage and flame-lit eyes roamed from face to face as the men bent over Johnnie. There was a splendor of isolation in his situation at this time which the Easterner felt once when, lifting his eyes from the man on the ground, he beheld that mysterious and lonely figure, waiting.

"Are you any good yet, Johnnie?" asked Scully in a broken voice.

The son gasped and opened his eyes languidly. After a moment he answered, "No—I ain't—any good—any—more." Then, from shame and bodily ill, he began to weep, the tears furrowing down through the blood-stains on his face. "He was too—too—too heavy for me."

Scully straightened and addressed the waiting figure. "Stranger," he said, evenly, "it's all up with our side." Then his voice changed into that vibrant huskiness which is commonly the tone of the most simple and deadly announcements. "Johnnie is whipped."

Without replying, the victor moved off on the route to the front door of the hotel.

The cowboy was formulating new and unspellable blasphemies. The Easterner was startled to find that they were out in a wind that seemed to come direct from the shadowed arctic floes. He heard again the wail of the snow as it was flung to its grave in the south. He knew now that all this time the cold had been sinking into him deeper and deeper, and he wondered that he had not perished. He felt indifferent to the condition of the vanquished man.

"Johnnie, can you walk?" asked Scully.

"Did I hurt—hurt him any?" asked the son.

"Can you walk, boy? Can you walk?"

Johnnie's voice was suddenly strong. There was a robust impatience in it. "I asked you whether I hurt him any!"

"Yes, yes, Johnnie," answered the cowboy, consolingly; "he's hurt a good deal."

They raised him from the ground, and as soon as he was on his feet he went tottering off, rebuffing all attempts at assistance. When the party rounded the corner they were fairly blinded by the pelting of the snow. It burned their faces like fire. The cowboy carried Johnnie through the drift to the door. As they entered, some cards again rose from the floor and beat against the wall.

The Easterner rushed to the stove. He was so profoundly chilled that he almost dared to embrace the glowing iron. The Swede was not in the room. Johnnie sank into a chair and, folding his arms on his knees, buried his face in them. Scully, warming one foot and then the other at a rim of the stove, muttered to himself with Celtic mournfulness. The cowboy had removed his fur cap, and with a dazed and rueful air he was running one hand through his tousled locks. From overhead they could hear the creaking of boards, as the Swede tramped here and there in his room.

The sad quiet was broken by the sudden flinging open of a door that led toward the kitchen. It was instantly followed by an inrush of women. They precipitated themselves upon Johnnie amid a chorus of lamentation. Before they carried their prey off to the kitchen, there to be bathed and harangued with that mixture of sympathy and abuse which is a feat of their sex, the mother straightened herself and fixed old Scully with an eye of stern reproach. "Shame be upon you, Patrick Scully!" she cried. "Your own son, too. Shame be upon you!"

"There, now! Be quiet, now!" said the old man, weakly.

"Shame be upon you, Patrick Scully!" The girls, rallying to this slogan, sniffed disdainfully in the direction of those trembling accomplices, the cowboy and the Easterner. Presently they bore Johnnie away, and left the three men to dismal reflection.

VII

"I'd like to fight this here Dutchman myself," said the cowboy, breaking a long silence.

Scully wagged his head sadly. "No, that wouldn't do. It wouldn't be right. It wouldn't be right."

"Well, why wouldn't it?" argued the cowboy. "I don't see no harm in it."

"No," answered Scully, with mournful heroism. "It wouldn't be right. It was Johnnie's fight, and now we mustn't whip the man just because he whipped Johnnie."

"Yes, that's true enough," said the cowboy; "but—he better not get fresh with me, because I couldn't stand no more of it."

"You'll not say a word to him," commanded Scully, and even then they heard the tread of the Swede on the stairs. His entrance was made theatric. He swept the door back with a bang and swaggered to the middle of the room. No one looked at him. "Well," he cried, insolently, at Scully, "I s'pose you'll tell me now how much I owe you?"

The old man remained stolid. "You don't owe me nothin'."

"Huh!" said the Swede, "huh! Don't owe 'im nothin'."

The cowboy addressed the Swede. "Stranger, I don't see how you come to be so gay around here."

Old Scully was instantly alert. "Stop!" he shouted, holding his hand forth, fingers upward. "Bill, you shut up!"

The cowboy spat carelessly into the sawdust-box. "I didn't say a word, did I?" he asked.

"Mr. Scully," called the Swede, "how much do I owe you?" It was seen that he was attired for departure, and that he had his valise in his hand.

"You don't owe me nothin'," repeated Scully in the same imperturbable way.

"Huh!" said the Swede. "I guess you're right. I guess if it was any way at all, you'd owe me somethin'. That's what I guess." He turned to the cowboy. "'Kill him! Kill him! Kill him!'" he mimicked, and then guffawed victoriously. "'Kill him!'" He was convulsed with ironical humor.

But he might have been jeering the dead. The three men were immovable and silent, staring with glassy eyes at the stove.

The Swede opened the door and passed into the storm, giving one derisive glance backward at the still group.

As soon as the door was closed, Scully and the cowboy leaped to their feet and began to curse. They trampled to and fro, waving their arms and smashing into the air with their fists. "Oh, but that was a hard minute!"

wailed Scully. "That was a hard minute! Him there leerin' and scoffin'! One bang at his nose was worth forty dollars to me that minute! How did you stand it, Bill?"

"How did I stand it?" cried the cowboy in a quivering voice. "How did I stand it? Oh!"

The old man burst into sudden brogue. "I'd loike to take that Swade," he wailed, "and hould 'im down on a shtone flure and bate 'im to a jelly wid a shtick!"

The cowboy groaned in sympathy. "I'd like to git him by the neck and ha-ammer him"—he brought his hand down on a chair with a noise like a pistol-shot—"hammer that there Dutchman until he couldn't tell himself from a dead coyote!"

"I'd bate 'im until he—"

"I'd show *him* some things—"

And then together they raised a yearning, fanatic cry—"Oh-o-oh! if we only could—"

"Yes!"

"Yes!"

"And then I'd—"

"O-o-oh!"

VIII

The Swede, tightly gripping his valise, tacked across the face of the storm as if he carried sails. He was following a line of little naked, gasping trees which, he knew, must mark the way of the road. His face, fresh from the pounding of Johnnie's fists, felt more pleasure than pain in the wind and the driving snow. A number of square shapes loomed upon him finally, and he knew them as the houses of the main body of the town. He found a street and made travel along it, leaning heavily upon the wind whenever, at a corner, a terrific blast caught him.

He might have been in a deserted village. We picture the world as thick with conquering and elate humanity, but here, with the bugles of the tempest pealing, it was hard to imagine a peopled earth. One viewed the existence of man then as a marvel, and conceded a glamour of wonder to these lice which were caused to cling to a whirling, fire-smitten, ice-locked, disease-stricken, space-lost bulb. The conceit of man was explained by this storm to be the very engine of life. One was a coxcomb not to die in it. However, the Swede found a saloon.

In front of it an indomitable red light was burning, and the snowflakes were made blood-color as they flew through the circumscribed territory of the lamp's shining. The Swede pushed open the door of the saloon and entered. A sanded expanse was before him, and at the end of it four men sat about a table drinking. Down one side of the room extended a radiant bar, and its guardian was leaning upon his elbows listening to the talk of the men at the table. The Swede dropped his valise upon the floor and, smiling fraternally upon the barkeeper, said, "Gimme some whisky, will you?" The man placed a bottle, a whisky-glass, and a glass of ice-thick water upon the bar. The Swede poured himself an abnormal portion of whisky and drank it in three gulps. "Pretty bad night," remarked the bartender, indifferently. He was making the pretension of blindness which is usually a distinction of his class; but it could have been seen that he was furtively studying the half-erased blood-stains on the face of the Swede. "Bad night," he said again.

"Oh, it's good enough for me," replied the Swede, hardily, as he poured himself some more whiskey. The barkeeper took his coin and maneuvered it through its reception by the highly nickeled cash-machine. A bell rang; a card labeled "20 cts." had appeared.

"No," continued the Swede, "this isn't too bad weather. It's good enough for me."

"So?" murmured the barkeeper, languidly.

The copious drams made the Swede's eyes swim, and he breathed a trifle heavier. "Yes, I like this weather. I like it. It suits me." It was apparently his design to impart a deep significance to these words.

"So?" murmured the bartender again. He turned to gaze dreamily at the scroll-like birds and bird-like scrolls which had been drawn with soap upon the mirrors in back of the bar.

"Well, I guess I'll take another drink," said the Swede, presently. "Have something?"

"No, thanks; I'm not drinkin'," answered the bartender. Afterward he asked, "How did you hurt your face?"

The Swede immediately began to boast loudly. "Why, in a fight. I thumped the soul out of a man down here at Scully's hotel."

The interest of the four men at the table was at last aroused.

"Who was it?" said one.

"Johnnie Scully," blustered the Swede. "Son of the man what runs it. He will be pretty near dead for some weeks, I can tell you. I made a nice thing of him, I did. He couldn't get up. They carried him in the house. Have a drink?"

Instantly the men in some subtle way encased themselves in reserve. "No, thanks," said one. The group was of curious formation. Two were prominent local business men; one was the district attorney; and one was a professional gambler of the kind known as "square." But a scrutiny of the group would not have enabled an observer to pick the gambler from the men of more reputable pursuits. He was, in fact, a man so delicate in manner, when among people of fair class, and so judicious in his choice of victims, that in the strictly masculine part of the town's life he had come to be explicitly trusted and admired. People called him a thoroughbred. The fear and contempt with which his craft was regarded were undoubtedly the reason why his quiet dignity shone conspicuous above the quiet dignity of men who might be merely hatters, billiard-markers, or grocery clerks. Beyond an occasional unwary traveler who came by rail, this gambler was supposed to prey solely upon reckless and senile farmers, who, when flush with good crops, drove into town in all the pride and confidence of an absolutely invulnerable stupidity. Hearing at times in circuitous fashion of the despoilment of such a farmer, the important men of Romper invariably laughed in contempt of the victim, and if they thought of the wolf at all, it was with a kind of pride at the knowledge that he would never dare think of attacking their wisdom and courage. Besides, it was popular that this gambler had a real wife and two real children in a neat cottage in a suburb, where he led an exemplary home life; and when anyone even suggested a discrepancy in his character, the crowd immediately vociferated descriptions of this virtuous family circle. Then men who led exemplary home lives, and men who did not lead exemplary home lives, all subsided in a bunch, remarking that there was nothing more to be said.

However, when a restriction was placed upon him—as, for instance, when a strong clique of members of the new Pollywog Club refused to permit him, even as a spectator, to appear in the rooms of the organization—the candor and gentleness with which he accepted the judgment disarmed many of his foes and made his friends more desperately partisan. He invariably distinguished between himself and a respectable Romper man so quickly and frankly that his manner actually appeared to be a continual broadcast compliment.

And one must not forget to declare the fundamental fact of his entire position in Romper. It is irrefutable that in all affairs outside his business, in all matters that occur eternally and commonly between man and man, this thieving card-player was so generous, so just, so moral, that, in a contest, he could have put to flight the consciences of nine tenths of the citizens of Romper.

And so it happened that he was seated in this saloon with the two prominent local merchants and the district attorney.

The Swede continued to drink raw whisky, meanwhile babbling at the barkeeper and trying to induce him to indulge in potations. "Come on. Have a drink. Come on. What—no? Well, have a little one, then. By gawd, I've whipped a man tonight, and I want to celebrate. I whipped him good, too. Gentlemen," the Swede cried to the men at the table, "have a drink?"

"Ssh!" said the barkeeper.

The group at the table, although furtively attentive, had been pretending to be deep in talk, but now a man lifted his eyes toward the Swede and said, shortly, "Thanks. We don't want any more."

At this reply the Swede ruffled out his chest like a rooster. "Well," he exploded, "it seems I can't get anybody to drink with me in this town. Seems so, don't it? Well!"

"Ssh!" said the barkeeper.

"Say," snarled the Swede, "don't you try to shut me up. I won't have it. I'm a gentleman, and I want people to drink with me. And I want 'em to drink with me now. *Now*—do you understand?" He rapped the bar with his knuckles.

Years of experience had calloused the bartender. He merely grew sulky. "I hear you," he answered.

"Well," cried the Swede, "listen hard then. See those men over there? Well, they're going to drink with me, and don't you forget it. Now you watch."

"Hi!" yelled the barkeeper, "this won't do!"

"Why won't it?" demanded the Swede. He stalked over to the table, and by chance laid his hand upon the shoulder of the gambler. "How about this?" he asked wrathfully. "I asked you to drink with me."

The gambler simply twisted his head and spoke over his shoulder. "My friend, I don't know you."

"Oh, hell!" answered the Swede, "come and have a drink."

"Now, my boy," advised the gambler, kindly, "take your hand off my shoulder and go 'way and mind your own business." He was a little, slim man, and it seemed strange to hear him use this tone of heroic patronage to the burly Swede. The other men at the table said nothing.

"What! You won't drink with me, you little dude? I'll make you, then! I'll make you!" The Swede had grasped the gambler frenziedly at the throat, and was dragging him from his chair. The other men sprang up. The barkeeper dashed around the corner of his bar. There was a great tumult, and then was seen a long blade in the hand of the gambler. It shot forward, and a human body, this citadel of virtue, wisdom, power, was pierced as easily as if it had been a melon. The Swede fell with a cry of supreme astonishment.

The prominent merchants and the district attorney must have at once tumbled out of the place backward. The bartender found himself hanging limply to the arm of a chair and gazing into the eyes of a murderer.

"Henry," said the latter, as he wiped his knife on one of the towels that hung beneath the bar rail, "you tell 'em where to find me. I'll be home, waiting for 'em." Then he vanished. A moment afterward the barkeeper was in the street dinning through the storm for help and, moreover, companionship.

The corpse of the Swede, alone in the saloon, had its eyes fixed upon a dreadful legend that dwelt atop of the cash-machine: "This registers the amount of your purchase."

IX

Months later, the cowboy was frying pork over the stove of a little ranch near the Dakota line, when there was a quick thud of hoofs outside, and presently the Easterner entered with the letters and the papers.

"Well," said the Easterner at once, "the chap that killed the Swede has got three years. Wasn't much, was it?"

"He has? Three years?" The cowboy poised his pan of pork, while he ruminated upon the news. "Three years. That ain't much."

"No. It was a light sentence," replied the Easterner as he unbuckled his spurs. "Seems there was a good deal of sympathy for him in Romper."

"If the bartender had been any good," observed the cowboy, thoughtfully, "he would have gone in and cracked that there Dutchman on the head with a bottle in the beginnin' of it and stopped all this here murderin'."

"Yes, a thousand things might have happened," said the Easterner, tartly.

The cowboy returned his pan of pork to the fire, but his philosophy continued. "It's funny, ain't it? If he hadn't said Johnnie was cheatin' he'd be alive this minute. He was an awful fool. Game played for fun, too. Not for money. I believe he was crazy."

"I feel sorry for that gambler," said the Easterner.

"Oh, so do I," said the cowboy. "He don't deserve none of it for killin' who he did."

"The Swede might not have been killed if everything had been square."

"Might not have been killed?" exclaimed the cowboy. "Everythin' square? Why, when he said that Johnnie was cheatin' and acted like such a jackass? And then in the saloon he fairly walked up to git hurt?" With these arguments the cowboy browbeat the Easterner and reduced him to rage.

"You're a fool!" cried the Easterner, viciously. "You're a bigger jackass than the Swede by a million majority. Now let me tell you one thing. Let me tell you something. Listen! Johnnie *was* cheating!"

"'Johnnie,'" said the cowboy, blankly. There was a minute of silence, and then he said, robustly, "Why, no. The game was only for fun."

"Fun or not," said the Easterner, "Johnnie was cheating. I saw him. I know it. I saw him. And I refused to stand up and be a man. I let the Swede fight it out alone. And you—you were simply puffing around the place and wanting to fight. And then old Scully himself! We are all in it! This poor gambler isn't even a noun. He is kind of an adverb. Every sin is the result of a collaboration. We, five of us, have collaborated in the murder of this Swede. Usually there are from a dozen to forty women really involved in every murder, but in this case it seems to be only five men—you, I, Johnnie, old Scully; and that fool of an unfortunate gambler came merely as a culmination, the apex of a human movement, and gets all the punishment."

The cowboy, injured and rebellious, cried out blindly into this fog of mysterious theory: "Well, I didn't do anythin', did I?"

COMMENT AND QUESTION

1. *The power of chance.* In "The Blue Hotel," as in other stories by Crane, chance is a powerful force. It determines good and evil, rewards and punishment, life and death. But it seems to have a mysterious power. Chance circumstances in "The Blue Hotel" snowball into necessity, or fate. The Swede seems doomed from the start. In fact, the feeling of inescapable doom which hangs over the story, in spite of the play of chance events, has led critics to compare "The Blue Hotel" with Greek tragedy.

The casual events of the story seem to have a power greater than the power of acts intentionally performed by men. Like Hardy, Crane regards with sardonic amusement those actions which men call purposeful. In Hardy's *The Return of the Native*, whenever Diggory Venn tries to remedy a bad situation, he makes matters worse. With excellent motives, Venn prevents Wildeve from visiting Eustacia at night. Goaded into visiting Eustacia by day, Wildeve helps to set up the chain of events which lead to Mrs. Yeobright's death, a catastrophe unforeseen by Venn. A similar irony runs through "The Blue Hotel." The student reading "The Blue Hotel" should notice what men *do*. The motives of men have little effect on fate. Recording what men *do* is in itself a partial definition of naturalism. As a naturalistic writer, Crane has commanded attention.

2. *The background.* Some matters should be cleared up at the outset. This story is laid in a Western state, Nebraska, probably in the last decade of the nineteenth century. This fact must be understood before the reader can explain why the Swede is a frightened man at the beginning of the story. Why is the Swede afraid of card games? Why does he laugh repeatedly? Is it a laugh of nervous bravado? What frightens the Swede at the opening of section III? Why does Scully show the Swede the picture of his little girl and speak of churches and electric cars? How does the Easterner explain the Swede's actions?

3. *The five men.* Often, in this story, the reader feels that the Swede is willfully plotting his own downfall, willfully driving himself toward the end he fears the most. But the Swede is not alone. Others besides himself have helped to weave the web which entangles him. At the end of the story Crane concludes: "Every sin is the result of collaboration." The Easterner, Scully, Johnnie, the cowboy, and the gambler—these five men share the guilt of the particular sin in this story. Ironically, the gambler, who is least guilty, takes all the punishment.

The reader should trace the responsibility of these five men. By some action or by a series of actions, each one of the five confirms the fate of the Swede. Ironically, the men who think that they are helping the Swede the most are the men who are most guilty.

a. The Easterner, who is heavily responsible, is a quiet, intelligent man who is aware of the gathering forces from the beginning of the story. For example, after the first few blows he tries to stop the fight. What other actions or statements of his are conciliatory? But what is his share in the "sin"?

b. Scully also is heavily responsible from the moment the travellers leave the train. Much of the change in the Swede from the time in section II, where he cries, "I don't want to fight!" to his roar in section V, where he yells, "Yes, fight!" is due to Scully.

c. Johnnie is responsible through simple overt acts. What two acts of Johnnie influence the Swede's fate?

d. The cowboy is fairly minor. But his actions during the card games and the fight contribute also to the "sin."

e. The gambler, like Johnnie, commits an overt act but bears the least personal responsibility. The gambler "isn't even a noun," says Crane. "He is kind of an adverb." In the sentence, "A man is killed suddenly," the gambler plays the part of the "suddenly." The student should write a second sentence in which the gambler functions as a noun, and observe the difference in meaning.

4. *The Swede.* There remains the part played by the Swede himself, who walks into a saloon and straight into the conflict he had feared. The student should trace the change in the Swede from "the badly frightened man" who first enters the hotel to the man fighting in the snow. During the fight, the cowboy, Scully, and the Easterner burst into a spontaneous cheer when Johnnie sends the Swede sprawling. In the beginning of the story these men had regarded the Swede with indifference. Why do they now champion Johnnie? How far is the Swede responsible for this change?

There are four card games in the story. Study these carefully. Why was the farmer angry with Johnnie? Who are board-whackers? How far is the Swede responsible in the fourth card game?

The incident in the saloon is explained less by the character of the gambler than it is by the appearance, action, and personality of the Swede. What is the matter with the Swede's appearance? What is the bartender furtively studying? The Swede is "flown with insolence and wine," flushed with victory. How had he got into this state? Do the four men at the table realize his state? The answer to this question lies partly in the closing paragraphs of section VII. What mood had the Swede aroused in Scully and the cowboy at that point? What mood is the Swede arousing in the gambler? Is the Swede guilty of what the Greeks called *hybris*, the sin of "insolence toward the Gods"?

5. *The irony.* Some of the irony in this story has already been noted. But Crane's mocking tone hardly wavers throughout the story. The mockery is all-inclusive in the scene in the saloon, from the description of the Swede, "smiling fraternally," to the "moral" gambler and the "sulky" bartender. Even the apex of the action is treated with irony as the gambler's blade shoots forward, and the barkeeper goes "dinning through the storm for help and, moreover, companionship." The irony reaches its height at the end of section VIII, where Crane focuses our attention on the "dreadful legend" of the cash register: "This registers the amount of your purchase." Whose eyes are fixed on this sign? What is the symbolic interpretation? How does the "legend" of the cash register state the theme of the story?

The student should find other examples of irony. There is ironic humor, for example, in the repeated motif of the cards. During the fight in the hotel the cards had been scattered on the floor, "where the boots of the men trampled the fat and painted kings and queens as they gazed with their silly eyes at the war that was raging above them." The scattered cards are referred to twice more. What is Crane's purpose here?

DRY SEPTEMBER

BY WILLIAM FAULKNER

WILLIAM FAULKNER (1897–   ) has lived most of his life in Mississippi, where he was born. He served in the Canadian Air Force in the first World War. Since 1931 he has been one of the most prominent writers of fiction in America. His volumes of short stories include the following: *Idyll in the Desert* (1931), *These Thirteen* (1931), *Miss Zilphia Gant* (1932), *Doctor Martino and Other Stories* (1934), *Go Down Moses* (1942), *Knight's Gambit* (1949), and *Collected Stories of William Faulkner* (1950). He has also written a cycle of novels about a mythical locality in Mississippi. Among his best known novels are *The Sound and the Fury* (1929) and *As I Lay Dying* (1930). In 1950 he received the Nobel Prize for Literature.

THROUGH the bloody September twilight, aftermath of sixty-two rainless days, it had gone like a fire in dry grass—the rumor, the story, whatever it was. Something about Miss Minnie Cooper and a Negro. Attacked, insulted, frightened: none of them, gathered in the barber shop on that Saturday evening where the ceiling fan stirred, without freshening it, the vitiated air, sending back upon them, in recurrent surges of stale pomade and lotion, their own stale breath and odors, knew exactly what had happened.

"Except it wasn't Will Mayes," a barber said. He was a man of middle age; a thin, sand-colored man with a mild face, who was shaving a client.

DRY SEPTEMBER   From *These Thirteen* by William Faulkner. Reprinted by permission of Random House, Inc. Copyright 1931 by William Faulkner.

"I know Will Mayes. He's a good nigger. And I know Miss Minnie Cooper, too."

"What do you know about her?" a second barber said.

"Who is she?" the client said. "A young girl?"

"No," the barber said. "She's about forty, I reckon. She aint married. That's why I dont believe—"

"Believe, hell!" a hulking youth in a sweat-stained silk shirt said. "Wont you take a white woman's word before a nigger's?"

"I dont believe Will Mayes did it," the barber said. "I know Will Mayes."

"Maybe you know who did it, then. Maybe you already got him out of town, you damn niggerlover."

"I dont believe anybody did anything. I dont believe anything happened. I leave it to you fellows if them ladies that get old without getting married dont have notions that a man cant—"

"Then you are a hell of a white man," the client said. He moved under the cloth. The youth had sprung to his feet.

"You dont?" he said. "Do you accuse a white woman of lying?"

The barber held the razor poised above the half-risen client. He did not look around.

"It's this durn weather," another said. "It's enough to make a man do anything. Even to her."

Nobody laughed. The barber said in his mild, stubborn tone: "I aint accusing nobody of nothing. I just know and you fellows know how a woman that never—"

"You damn niggerlover!" the youth said.

"Shut up, Butch," another said. "We'll get the facts in plenty of time to act."

"Who is? Who's getting them?" the youth said. "Facts, hell! I—"

"You're a fine white man," the client said. "Aint you?" In his frothy beard he looked like a desert rat in the moving pictures. "You tell them, Jack," he said to the youth. "If there aint any white men in this town, you can count on me, even if I aint only a drummer and a stranger."

"That's right, boys," the barber said. "Find out the truth first. I know Will Mayes."

"Well, by God!" the youth shouted. "To think that a white man in this town—"

"Shut up, Butch," the second speaker said. "We got plenty of time."

The client sat up. He looked at the speaker. "Do you claim that anything excuses a nigger attacking a white woman? Do you mean to tell me you are a white man and you'll stand for it? You better go back North where you came from. The South dont want your kind here."

"North what?" the second said. "I was born and raised in this town."

"Well, by God!" the youth said. He looked about with a strained, baffled gaze, as if he was trying to remember what it was he wanted to say or to do. He drew his sleeve across his sweating face. "Damn if I'm going to let a white woman—"

"You tell them, Jack," the drummer said. "By God, if they—"

The screen door crashed open. A man stood in the floor, his feet apart and his heavy-set body poised easily. His white shirt was open at the throat; he wore a felt hat. His hot, bold glance swept the group. His name was McLendon. He had commanded troops at the front in France and had been decorated for valor.

"Well," he said, "are you going to sit there and let a black son rape a white woman on the streets of Jefferson?"

Butch sprang up again. The silk of his shirt clung flat to his heavy shoulders. At each armpit was a dark halfmoon. "That's what I been telling them! That's what I—"

"Did it really happen?" a third said. "This aint the first man scare she ever had, like Hawkshaw says. Wasn't there something about a man on the kitchen roof, watching her undress, about a year ago?"

"What?" the client said. "What's that?" The barber had been slowly forcing him back into the chair; he arrested himself reclining, his head lifted, the barber still pressing him down.

McLendon whirled on the third speaker. "Happen? What the hell difference does it make? Are you going to let the black sons get away with it until one really does it?"

"That's what I'm telling them!" Butch shouted. He cursed, long and steady, pointless.

"Here, here," a fourth said. "Not so loud. Dont talk so loud."

"Sure," McLendon said; "no talking necessary at all. I've done my talking. Who's with me?" He poised on the balls of his feet, roving his gaze.

The barber held the drummer's face down, the razor poised. "Find out the facts first, boys. I know Willy Mayes. It wasn't him. Let's get the sheriff and do this thing right."

McLendon whirled upon him his furious, rigid face. The barber did not look away. They looked like men of different races. The other barbers had ceased also above their prone clients. "You mean to tell me," McLendon said, "that you'd take a nigger's word before a white woman's? Why, you damn niggerloving—"

The third speaker rose and grasped McLendon's arm; he too had been a soldier. "Now, now. Let's figure this thing out. Who knows anything about what really happened?"

"Figure out hell!" McLendon jerked his arm free. "All that're with me get up from there. The ones that aint—" He roved his gaze, dragging his sleeve across his face.

Three men rose. The drummer in the chair sat up. "Here," he said, jerking at the cloth about his neck; "get this rag off me. I'm with him. I dont live here, but by God, if our mothers and wives and sisters—" He smeared the cloth over his face and flung it to the floor. McLendon stood in the floor and cursed the others. Another rose and moved toward him. The remainder sat uncomfortable, not looking at one another, then one by one they rose and joined him.

The barber picked the cloth from the floor. He began to fold it neatly. "Boys, dont do that. Will Mayes never done it. I know."

"Come on," McLendon said. He whirled. From his hip pocket protruded the butt of a heavy automatic pistol. They went out. The screen door crashed behind them reverberant in the dead air.

The barber wiped the razor carefully and swiftly, and put it away, and ran to the rear, and took his hat from the wall. "I'll be back as soon as I can," he said to the other barbers. "I cant let—" He went out, running. The two other barbers followed him to the door and caught it on the rebound, leaning out and looking up the street after him. The air was flat and dead. It had a metallic taste at the base of the tongue.

"What can he do?" the first said. The second one was saying "Jees Christ, Jees Christ" under his breath. "I'd just as lief be Will Mayes as Hawk, if he gets McLendon riled."

"Jees Christ, Jees Christ," the second whispered.

"You reckon he really done it to her?" the first said.

II

She was thirty-eight or thirty-nine. She lived in a small frame house with her invalid mother and a thin, sallow, unflagging aunt, where each morning between ten and eleven she would appear on the porch in a lace-trimmed boudoir cap, to sit swinging in the porch swing until noon. After dinner she lay down for a while, until the afternoon began to cool. Then, in one of the three or four new voile dresses which she had each summer, she would go downtown to spend the afternoon in the stores with the other ladies, where they would handle the goods and haggle over the prices in cold, immediate voices, without any intention of buying.

She was of comfortable people—not the best in Jefferson, but good people enough—and she was still on the slender side of ordinary looking, with a bright, faintly haggard manner and dress. When she was young she had had a slender, nervous body and a sort of hard vivacity which had enabled her for a time to ride upon the crest of the town's social life as exemplified by the high school party and church social period of her contemporaries while still children enough to be unclassconscious.

She was the last to realize that she was losing ground; that those among whom she had been a little brighter and louder flame than any other were beginning to learn the pleasure of snobbery—male—and retaliation—female. That was when her face began to wear that bright, haggard look. She still

carried it to parties on shadowy porticoes and summer lawns, like a mask
or a flag, with that bafflement of furious repudiation of truth in her eyes.
One evening at a party she heard a boy and two girls, all schoolmates,
talking. She never accepted another invitation.

She watched the girls with whom she had grown up as they married
and got homes and children, but no man ever called on her steadily until
the children of the other girls had been calling her "aunty" for several
years, the while their mothers told them in bright voices about how popular Aunt Minnie had been as a girl. Then the town began to see her
driving on Sunday afternoons with the cashier in the bank. He was a
widower of about forty—a high-colored man, smelling always faintly of
the barber shop or of whisky. He owned the first automobile in town, a
red runabout; Minnie had the first motoring bonnet and veil the town
ever saw. Then the town began to say: "Poor Minnie." "But she is old
enough to take care of herself," others said. That was when she began to
ask her old schoolmates that their children call her "cousin" instead of
"aunty."

It was twelve years now since she had been relegated into adultery by
public opinion, and eight years since the cashier had gone to a Memphis
bank, returning for one day each Christmas, which he spent at an annual
bachelors' party at a hunting club on the river. From behind their curtains the neighbors would see the party pass, and during the over-the-way
Christmas day visiting they would tell her about him, about how well he
looked, and how they heard that he was prospering in the city, watching
with bright, secret eyes her haggard, bright face. Usually by that hour
there would be the scent of whisky on her breath. It was supplied her by
a youth, a clerk at the soda fountain: "Sure; I buy it for the old gal. I
reckon she's entitled to a little fun."

Her mother kept to her room altogether now; the gaunt aunt ran the
house. Against that background Minnie's bright dresses, her idle and
empty days, had a quality of furious unreality. She went out in the evenings only with women now, neighbors, to the moving pictures. Each
afternoon she dressed in one of the new dresses and went downtown
alone, where her young "cousins" were already strolling in the late afternoons with their delicate, silken heads and thin, awkward arms and conscious hips, clinging to one another or shrieking and giggling with paired
boys in the soda fountain when she passed and went on along the serried
store fronts, in the doors of which the sitting and lounging men did not
even follow her with their eyes any more.

III

The barber went swiftly up the street where the sparse lights, insect-
swirled, glared in rigid and violent suspension in the lifeless air. The day
had died in a pall of dust; above the darkened square, shrouded by the

spent dust, the sky was as clear as the inside of a brass bell. Below the east was a rumor of the twice-waxed moon.

When he overtook them McLendon and three others were getting into a car parked in an alley. McLendon stooped his thick head, peering out beneath the top. "Changed your mind, did you?" he said. "Damn good thing; by God, tomorrow when this town hears about how you talked tonight—"

"Now, now," the other ex-soldier said. "Hawkshaw's all right. Come on, Hawk; jump in."

"Will Mayes never done it, boys," the barber said. "If anybody done it. Why, you all know well as I do there aint any town where they got better niggers than us. And you know how a lady will kind of think things about men when there aint any reason to, and Miss Minnie anyway—"

"Sure, sure," the soldier said. "We're just going to talk to him a little; that's all."

"Talk hell!" Butch said. "When we're through with the—"

"Shut up, for God's sake!" the soldier said. "Do you want everybody in town—"

"Tell them, by God!" McLendon said. "Tell every one of the sons that'll let a white woman—"

"Let's go; let's go: here's the other car." The second car slid squealing out of a cloud of dust at the alley mouth. McLendon started his car and took the lead. Dust lay like fog in the street. The street lights hung nimbused as in water. They drove on out of town.

A rutted lane turned at right angles. Dust hung above it too, and above all the land. The dark bulk of the ice plant, where the Negro Mayes was night watchman, rose against the sky. "Better stop here, hadn't we?" the soldier said. McLendon did not reply. He hurled the car up and slammed to a stop, the headlights glaring on the blank wall.

"Listen here, boys," the barber said; "if he's here, dont that prove he never done it? Dont it? If it was him, he would run. Dont you see he would?" The second car came up and stopped. McLendon got down; Butch sprang down beside him. "Listen, boys," the barber said.

"Cut the lights off!" McLendon said. The breathless dark rushed down. There was no sound in it save their lungs as they sought air in the parched dust in which for two months they had lived; then the diminishing crunch of McLendon's and Butch's feet, and a moment later McLendon's voice:

"Will! . . . Will!"

Below the east the wan hemorrhage of the moon increased. It heaved above the ridge, silvering the air, the dust, so that they seemed to breathe, live, in a bowl of molten lead. There was no sound of nightbird nor insect, no sound save their breathing and a faint ticking of contracting metal about the cars. Where their bodies touched one another they seemed to sweat dryly, for no more moisture came. "Christ!" a voice said; "let's get out of here."

But they didn't move until vague noises began to grow out of the darkness ahead; then they got out and waited tensely in the breathless dark. There was another sound: a blow, a hissing expulsion of breath and McLendon cursing in undertone. They stood a moment longer, then they ran forward. They ran in a stumbling clump, as though they were fleeing something. "Kill him, kill the son," a voice whispered. McLendon flung them back.

"Not here," he said. "Get him into the car." "Kill him, kill the black son!" the voice murmured. They dragged the Negro to the car. The barber had waited beside the car. He could feel himself sweating and he knew he was going to be sick at the stomach.

"What is it, captains?" the Negro said. "I aint done nothing. 'Fore God, Mr. John." Someone produced handcuffs. They worked busily about the Negro as though he were a post, quiet, intent, getting in one another's way. He submitted to the handcuffs, looking swiftly and constantly from dim face to dim face. "Who's here, captains?" he said, leaning to peer into the faces until they could feel his breath and smell his sweaty reek. He spoke a name or two. "What you all say I done, Mr. John?"

McLendon jerked the car door open. "Get in!" he said.

The Negro did not move. "What you all going to do with me, Mr. John? I aint done nothing. White folks, captains, I aint done nothing: I swear 'fore God." He called another name.

"Get in!" McLendon said. He struck the Negro. The others expelled their breath in a dry hissing and struck him with random blows and he whirled and cursed them, and swept his manacled hands across their faces and slashed the barber upon the mouth, and the barber struck him also. "Get him in there," McLendon said. They pushed at him. He ceased struggling and got in and sat quietly as the others took their places. He sat between the barber and the soldier, drawing his limbs in so as not to touch them, his eyes going swiftly and constantly from face to face. Butch clung to the running board. The car moved on. The barber nursed his mouth with his handkerchief.

"What's the matter, Hawk?" the soldier said.

"Nothing," the barber said. They regained the highroad and turned away from town. The second car dropped back out of the dust. They went on, gaining speed; the final fringe of houses dropped behind.

"Goddam, he stinks!" the soldier said.

"We'll fix that," the drummer in front beside McLendon said. On the running board Butch cursed into the hot rush of air. The barber leaned suddenly forward and touched McLendon's arm.

"Let me out, John," he said.

"Jump out, niggerlover," McLendon said without turning his head. He drove swiftly. Behind them the sourceless lights of the second car glared in the dust. Presently McLendon turned into a narrow road. It was rutted with disuse. It led back to an abandoned brick kiln—a series of reddish mounds and weed- and vine-choked vats without bottom. It had been used for pasture once, until one day the owner missed one of his mules. Although he prodded carefully in the vats with a long pole, he could not even find the bottom of them.

"John," the barber said.

"Jump out, then," McLendon said, hurling the car along the ruts. Beside the barber the Negro spoke:

"Mr. Henry."

The barber sat forward. The narrow tunnel of the road rushed up and past. Their motion was like an extinct furnace blast: cooler, but utterly dead. The car bounded from rut to rut.

"Mr. Henry," the Negro said.

The barber began to tug furiously at the door. "Look out, there!" the soldier said, but the barber had already kicked the door open and swung onto the running board. The soldier leaned across the Negro and grasped at him, but he had already jumped. The car went on without checking speed.

The impetus hurled him crashing through dust-sheathed weeds, into the ditch. Dust puffed about him, and in a thin, vicious crackling of sapless stems he lay choking and retching until the second car passed and died away. Then he rose and limped on until he reached the highroad and turned toward town, brushing at his clothes with his hands. The moon was higher, riding high and clear of the dust at last, and after a while the town began to glare beneath the dust. He went on, limping. Presently he heard cars and the glow of them grew in the dust behind him and he left the road and crouched again in the weeds until they passed. McLendon's car came last now. There were four people in it and Butch was not on the running board.

They went on; the dust swallowed them; the glare and the sound died away. The dust of them hung for a while, but soon the eternal dust absorbed it again. The barber climbed back onto the road and limped on toward town.

IV

As she dressed for supper on that Saturday evening, her own flesh felt like fever. Her hands trembled among the hooks and eyes, and her eyes had a feverish look, and her hair swirled crisp and crackling under the comb. While she was still dressing the friends called for her and sat while she donned her sheerest underthings and stockings and a new voile dress.

"Do you feel strong enough to go out?" they said, their eyes bright too, with a dark glitter. "When you have had time to get over the shock, you must tell us what happened. What he said and did; everything."

In the leafed darkness, as they walked toward the square, she began to breathe deeply, something like a swimmer preparing to dive, until she ceased trembling, the four of them walking slowly because of the terrible heat and out of solicitude for her. But as they neared the square she began to tremble again, walking with her head up, her hands clenched at her sides, their voices about her murmurous, also with that feverish, glittering quality of their eyes.

They entered the square, she in the center of the group, fragile in her fresh dress. She was trembling worse. She walked slower and slower, as children eat ice cream, her head up and her eyes bright in the haggard banner of her face, passing the hotel and the coatless drummers in chairs along the curb looking around at her: "That's the one: see? The one in pink in the middle." "Is that her? What did they do with nigger? Did they—?" "Sure. He's all right." "All right, is he?" "Sure. He went on a little trip." Then the drug store, where even the young men lounging in the doorway tipped their hats and followed with their eyes the motion of her hips and legs when she passed.

They went on, passing the lifted hats of the gentlemen, the suddenly ceased voices, deferent, protective. "Do you see?" the friends said. Their voices sounded like long, hovering sighs of hissing exultation. "There's not a Negro on the square. Not one."

They reached the picture show. It was like a miniature fairyland with its lighted lobby and colored lithographs of life caught in its terrible and beautiful mutations. Her lips began to tingle. In the dark, when the picture began, it would be all right; she could hold back the laughing so it would not waste away so fast and so soon. So she hurried on before the turning faces, the undertones of low astonishment, and they took their accustomed places where she could see the aisle against the silver glare and the young men and girls coming in two and two against it.

The lights flicked away; the screen glowed silver, and soon life began to unfold, beautiful and passionate and sad, while still the young men and girls entered, scented and sibilant in the half dark, their paired backs in silhouette delicate and sleek, their slim, quick bodies awkward, divinely young, while beyond them the silver dream accumulated, inevitably on and on. She began to laugh. In trying to suppress it, it made more noise than ever; heads began to turn. Still laughing, her friends raised her and led her out, and she stood at the curb, laughing on a high, sustained note, until the taxi came up and they helped her in.

They removed the pink voile and the sheer underthings and the stockings, and put her to bed, and cracked ice for her temples, and sent for the doctor. He was hard to locate, so they ministered to her with hushed ejaculations, renewing the ice and fanning her. While the ice was fresh and cold she stopped laughing and lay still for a time, moaning only a little. But soon the laughing welled again and her voice rose screaming.

"Shhhhhhhhhh! Shhhhhhhhhhhhhhh!" they said, freshening the ice-pack, smoothing her hair, examining it for gray; "poor girl!" Then to one another: "Do you suppose anything really happened?" their eyes darkly aglitter, secret and passionate. "Shhhhhhhhhh! Poor girl! Poor Minnie!"

V

It was midnight when McLendon drove up to his neat new house. It was trim and fresh as a birdcage and almost as small, with its clean, green-and-white paint. He locked the car and mounted the porch and entered. His wife rose from a chair beside the reading lamp. McLendon stopped in the floor and stared at her until she looked down.

"Look at that clock," he said, lifting his arm, pointing. She stood before him, her face lowered, a magazine in her hands. Her face was pale, strained, and weary-looking. "Haven't I told you about sitting up like this, waiting to see when I come in?"

"John," she said. She laid the magazine down. Poised on the balls of his feet, he glared at her with his hot eyes, his sweating face.

"Didn't I tell you?" He went toward her. She looked up then. He caught her shoulder. She stood passive, looking at him.

"Don't, John. I couldn't sleep . . . The heat; something. Please, John. You're hurting me."

"Didn't I tell you?" He released her and half struck, half flung her across the chair, and she lay there and watched him quietly as he left the room.

He went on through the house, ripping off his shirt, and on the dark, screened porch at the rear he stood and mopped his head and shoulders with the shirt and flung it away. He took the pistol from his hip and laid it on the table beside the bed, and sat on the bed and removed his shoes, and rose and slipped his trousers off. He was sweating again already, and he stooped and hunted furiously for the shirt. At last he found it and wiped his body again, and, with his body pressed against the dusty screen, he stood panting. There was no movement, no sound, not even an insect. The dark world seemed to lie stricken beneath the cold moon and the lidless stars.

COMMENT AND QUESTION

1. The title has both a literal and a symbolic meaning. Show how the title describes the two causes of the main event in the story.

2. Do the men in the barbershop seem on the defensive? If so, why should they be?

3. How does section II clinch the arguments of the barber?

4. Notice the closing passages of sections I and IV. What insight do they give into the psychology of the townspeople?

5. "Dry September" is notable for its restraint. In a story of violence, restraint will increase the tension. Study the struggle on p. 182. Study the scene in the car where Will Mayes says only, "Mr. Henry." Find other incidents where much is left unsaid.

6. Can you give a psychological explanation of the following?
    a. The barber's striking Will Mayes.
    b. Miss Minnie's hysteria.
    c. McClendon's striking his wife.

7. Where is the irony in McClendon's decoration for valor? In Miss Minnie's attending the movie with her "girl friends"?

8. Notice the opening paragraph, which both sets the tone and establishes the plot. How does this paragraph contain explicitly or implicitly the main elements of the story? What words suggest the violence to come?

Study the effect gained by the order of "attacked, insulted, frightened." Reverse the order to "frightened, insulted, attacked," and observe the difference in meaning.

THE LAST OF THE BELLES

BY F. SCOTT FITZGERALD

F. SCOTT FITZGERALD (1896–1940) was born
in Minnesota. He studied at Princeton and
served briefly in the army in the first World
War. His work reflects the climate of the jazz
age in America and of the expatriates of the
same age in Europe. He lived for a short time
in Hollywood and wrote for the motion pictures. His best novels are *The Great Gatsby*
(1925), *Tender Is the Night* (1934, revised
author's version 1951), and the unfinished *The
Last Tycoon* (1941). His short stories appear
in the following collections: *Tales of the Jazz
Age* (1922), *All the Sad Young Men* (1926),
Taps at Reveille (1935), and *The Stories of
F. Scott Fitzgerald* (1951) edited with an introduction by Malcolm Cowley.

AFTER Atlanta's elaborate and theatrical rendition of Southern charm,
we all underestimated Tarleton. It was a little hotter than anywhere we'd
been—a dozen rookies collapsed the first day in that Georgia sun—and
when you saw herds of cows drifting through the business streets, hi-yaed
by colored drovers, a trance stole down over you out of the hot light: you
wanted to move a hand or foot to be sure you were alive.

So I stayed out at camp and let Lieutenant Warren tell me about the
girls. This was fifteen years ago, and I've forgotten how I felt, except that
the days went along, one after another, better than they do now, and I
was empty-hearted, because up North she whose legend I had loved for
three years was getting married. I saw the clippings and newspaper photo-

graphs. It was "a romantic wartime wedding," all very rich and sad. I felt vividly the dark radiance of the sky under which it took place and, as a young snob, was more envious than sorry.

A day came when I went into Tarleton for a haircut and ran into a nice fellow named Bill Knowles, who was in my time at Harvard. He'd been in the National Guard division that preceded us in camp; at the last moment he had transferred to aviation and had been left behind.

"I'm glad I met you, Andy," he said with undue seriousness. "I'll hand you on all my information before I start for Texas. You see, there're really only three girls here—"

I was interested; there was something mystical about there being three girls.

"—and here's one of them now."

We were in front of a drug store and he marched me in and introduced me to a lady I promptly detested.

"The other two are Ailie Calhoun and Sally Carrol Happer."

I guessed from the way he pronounced her name that he was interested in Ailie Calhoun. It was on his mind what she would be doing while he was gone; he wanted her to have a quiet, uninteresting time.

At my age I don't even hesitate to confess that entirely unchivalrous images of Ailie Calhoun—that lovely name—rushed into my mind. At twenty-three there is no such thing as a preëmpted beauty; though, had Bill asked me, I would doubtless have sworn in all sincerity to care for her like a sister. He didn't; he was just fretting out loud at having to go. Three days later he telephoned me that he was leaving next morning and he'd take me to her house that night.

We met at the hotel and walked uptown through the flowery, hot twilight. The four white pillars of the Calhoun house faced the street, and behind them the veranda was dark as a cave with hanging, weaving, climbing vines.

When we came up the walk a girl in a white dress tumbled out of the front door, crying, "I'm so sorry I'm late!" and seeing us, added: "Why, I thought I heard you come ten minutes—"

She broke off as a chair creaked and another man, an aviator from Camp Harry Lee, emerged from the obscurity of the veranda.

"Why, Canby!" she cried. "How are you?"

He and Bill Knowles waited with the tenseness of open litigants.

"Canby, I want to whisper to you, honey," she said, after just a second. "You'll excuse us, Bill."

They went aside. Presently Lieutenant Canby, immensely displeased, said in a grim voice, "Then we'll make it Thursday, but that means sure." Scarcely nodding to us, he went down the walk, the spurs with which he presumably urged on his aeroplane gleaming in the lamplight.

"Come in—I don't just know your name——"

There she was—the Southern type in all its purity. I would have recognized Ailie Calhoun if I'd never heard Ruth Draper or read Marse Chan. She had the adroitness sugar-coated with sweet, voluble simplicity, the suggested background of devoted fathers, brothers and admirers stretching back into the South's heroic age, the unfailing coolness acquired in the endless struggle with the heat. There were notes in her voice that ordered slaves around, that withered up Yankee captains, and then soft, wheedling notes that mingled in unfamiliar loveliness with the night.

I could scarcely see her in the darkness, but when I rose to go—it was plain that I was not to linger—she stood in the orange light from the doorway. She was small and very blond; there was too much fever-colored rouge on her face, accentuated by a nose dabbed clownish white, but she shone through that like a star.

"After Bill goes I'll be sitting here all alone night after night. Maybe you'll take me to the country-club dances." The pathetic prophecy brought a laugh from Bill. "Wait a minute," Ailie murmured. "Your guns are all crooked."

She straightened my collar pin, looking up at me for a second with something more than curiosity. It was a seeking look, as if she asked, "Could it be you?" Like Lieutenant Canby, I marched off unwillingly into the suddenly insufficient night.

Two weeks later I sat with her on the same veranda, or rather she half lay in my arms and yet scarcely touched me—how she managed that I don't remember. I was trying unsuccessfully to kiss her, and had been trying for the best part of an hour. We had a sort of joke about my not being sincere. My theory was that if she'd let me kiss her I'd fall in love with her. Her argument was that I was obviously insincere.

In a lull between two of these struggles she told me about her brother who had died in his senior year at Yale. She showed me his picture—it was a handsome, earnest face with a Leyendecker forelock—and told me that when she met someone who measured up to him she'd marry. I found this family idealism discouraging; even my brash confidence couldn't compete with the dead.

The evening and other evenings passed like that, and ended with my going back to camp with the remembered smell of magnolia flowers and a mood of vague dissatisfaction. I never kissed her. We went to the vaudeville and to the country club on Saturday nights, where she seldom took ten consecutive steps with one man, and she took me to barbecues and rowdy watermelon parties, and never thought it was worth while to change what I felt for her into love. I see now that it wouldn't have been hard, but she was a wise nineteen and she must have seen that we were emotionally incompatible. So I became her confidant instead.

We talked about Bill Knowles. She was considering Bill; for, though she wouldn't admit it, a winter at school in New York and a prom at Yale had turned her eyes North. She said she didn't think she'd marry a Southern man. And by degrees I saw that she was consciously and voluntarily different from these other girls who sang nigger songs and shot craps in the country-club bar. That's why Bill and I and others were drawn to her. We recognized her.

June and July, while the rumors reached us faintly, ineffectually, of battle and terror overseas, Ailie's eyes roved here and there about the country-club floor, seeking for something among the tall young officers. She attached several, choosing them with unfailing perspicacity—save in the case of Lieutenant Canby, whom she claimed to despise, but, nevertheless, gave dates to "because he was so sincere"—and we apportioned her evenings among us all summer.

One day she broke all her dates—Bill Knowles had leave and was coming. We talked of the event with scientific impersonality—would he move her to a decision? Lieutenant Canby, on the contrary, wasn't impersonal at all; made a nuisance of himself. He told her that if she married Knowles he was going to climb up six thousand feet in his aeroplane, shut off the motor and let go. He frightened her—I had to yield him my last date before Bill came.

On Saturday night she and Bill Knowles came to the country club. They were very handsome together and once more I felt envious and sad. As they danced out on the floor the three-piece orchestra was playing *After You've Gone*, in a poignant incomplete way that I can hear yet, as if each bar were trickling off a precious minute of that time. I knew then that I had grown to love Tarleton, and I glanced about half in panic to see if some face wouldn't come in for me out of that warm, singing, outer darkness that yielded up couple after couple in organdie and olive drab. It was a time of youth and war, and there was never so much love around.

When I danced with Ailie she suddenly suggested that we go outside to a car. She wanted to know why didn't people cut in on her tonight? Did they think she was already married?

"Are you going to be?"

"I don't know, Andy. Sometimes, when he treats me as if I were sacred, it thrills me." Her voice was hushed and far away. "And then——"

She laughed. Her body, so frail and tender, was touching mine, her face was turned up to me, and there, suddenly, with Bill Knowles ten yards off, I could have kissed her at last. Our lips just touched experimentally; then an aviation officer turned a corner of the veranda near us, peered into our darkness and hesitated.

"Ailie."

"Yes."

"You heard about this afternoon?"

"What?" She leaned forward, tenseness already in her voice.

"Horace Canby crashed. He was instantly killed."

She got up slowly and stepped out of the car.

"You mean he was killed?" she said.

"Yes. They don't know what the trouble was. His motor——"

"Oh-h-h!" Her rasping whisper came through the hands suddenly covering her face. We watched her helplessly as she put her head on the side of the car, gagging dry tears. After a minute I went for Bill, who was standing in the stag line, searching anxiously about for her, and told him she wanted to go home.

I sat on the steps outside. I had disliked Canby, but his terrible, pointless death was more real to me then than the day's toll of thousands in France. In a few minutes Ailie and Bill came out. Ailie was whimpering a little, but when she saw me her eyes flexed and she came over swiftly.

"Andy"—she spoke in a quick, low voice—"of course you must never tell anybody what I told you about Canby yesterday. What he said, I mean."

"Of course not."

She looked at me a second longer as if to be quite sure. Finally she was sure. Then she sighed in such a quaint little way that I could hardly believe my ears, and her brow went up in what can only be described as mock despair.

"An-dy!"

I looked uncomfortably at the ground, aware that she was calling my attention to her involuntarily disastrous effect on men.

"Good night, Andy!" called Bill as they got into a taxi.

"Good night," I said, and almost added: "You poor fool."

II

Of course I should have made one of those fine moral decisions that people make in books, and despised her. On the contrary, I don't doubt that she could still have had me by raising her hand.

A few days later she made it all right by saying wistfully, "I know you think it was terrible of me to think of myself at a time like that, but it was such a shocking coincidence."

At twenty-three I was entirely unconvinced about anything, except that some people were strong and attractive and could do what they wanted, and others were caught and disgraced. I hoped I was of the former. I was sure Ailie was.

I had to revise other ideas about her. In the course of a long discussion with some girl about kissing—in those days people still talked about kissing more than they kissed—I mentioned the fact that Ailie had only kissed two or three men, and only when she thought she was in love. To my considerable disconcertion the girl figuratively just lay on the floor and howled.

"But it's true," I assured her, suddenly knowing it wasn't. "She told me herself."

"Ailie Calhoun! Oh, my heavens! Why, last year at the Tech spring house party——"

This was in September. We were going overseas any week now, and to bring us up to full strength a last batch of officers from the fourth training camp arrived. The fourth camp wasn't like the first three—the candidates were from the ranks; even from the drafted divisions. They had queer names without vowels in them, and save for a few young militiamen, you couldn't take it for granted that they came out of any background at all. The addition to our company was Lieutenant Earl Schoen from New Bedford, Massachusetts; as fine a physical specimen as I have ever seen. He was six-foot-three, with black hair, high color and glossy dark-brown eyes. He wasn't very smart and he was definitely illiterate, yet he was a good officer, high-tempered and commanding, and with that becoming touch of vanity that sits well on the military. I had an idea that New Bedford was a country town, and set down his bumptious qualities to that.

We were doubled up in living quarters and he came into my hut. Inside of a week there was a cabinet photograph of some Tarleton girl nailed brutally to the shack wall.

"She's no jane or anything like that. She's a society girl; goes with all the best people here."

The following Sunday afternoon I met the lady at a semi-private swimming pool in the country. When Ailie and I arrived, there was Schoen's muscular body rippling out of a bathing suit at the far end of the pool.

"Hey, lieutenant!"

When I waved back at him he grinned and winked, jerking his head toward the girl at his side. Then, digging her in the ribs, he jerked his head at me. It was a form of introduction.

"Who's that with Kitty Preston?" Ailie asked, and when I told her she said he looked like a street-car conductor, and pretended to look for her transfer.

A moment later he crawled powerfully and gracefully down the pool and pulled himself up at our side. I introduced him to Ailie.

"How do you like my girl, lieutenant?" he demanded, "I told you she was all right, didn't I?" He jerked his head toward Ailie; this time to indicate that his girl and Ailie moved in the same circles. "How about us all having dinner together down at the hotel some night?"

I left them in a moment, amused as I saw Ailie visibly making up her mind that here, anyhow, was not the ideal. But Lieutenant Earl Schoen was not to be dismissed so lightly. He ran his eyes cheerfully and inoffensively over her cute, slight figure, and decided that she would do even better than the other. Then minutes later I saw them in the water

together, Ailie swimming away with a grim little stroke she had, and
Schoen wallowing riotously around her and ahead of her, sometimes pausing and staring at her, fascinated, as a boy might look at a nautical doll.

While the afternoon passed he remained at her side. Finally Ailie came
over to me and whispered, with a laugh: "He's a following me around. He
thinks I haven't paid my carfare."

She turned quickly. Miss Kitty Preston, her face curiously flustered,
stood facing us.

"Ailie Calhoun, I didn't think it of you to go out and delib'ately try to
take a man away from another girl."—An expression of distress at the
impending scene flitted over Ailie's face—"I thought you considered yourself above anything like that."

Miss Preston's voice was low, but it held that tensity that can be felt
farther than it can be heard, and I saw Ailie's clear lovely eyes glance
about in panic. Luckily, Earl himself was ambling cheerfully and inno-
cently toward us.

"If you care for him you certainly oughtn't to belittle yourself in front
of him," said Ailie in a flash, her head high.

It was her acquaintance with the traditional way of behaving against
Kitty Preston's naïve and fierce possessiveness; or if you prefer it, Ailie's
"breeding" against the other's "commonness." She turned away.

"Wait a minute, kid!" cried Earl Schoen. "How about your address?
Maybe I'd like to give you a ring on the phone."

She looked at him in a way that should have indicated to Kitty her
entire lack of interest.

"I'm very busy at the Red Cross this month," she said, her voice as cool
as her slicked-back blond hair. "Good-by."

On the way home she laughed. Her air of having been unwittingly involved in a contemptible business vanished.

"She'll never hold that young man," she said. "He wants somebody
new."

"Apparently he wants Ailie Calhoun."

The idea amused her.

"He could give me his ticket punch to wear, like a fraternity pin. What
fun! If mother ever saw anybody like that come in the house, she'd just
lie down and die."

And to give Ailie credit, it was fully a fortnight before he did come to
her house, although he rushed her until she pretended to be annoyed at
the next country-club dance.

"He's the biggest tough, Andy," she whispered to me. "But he's so
sincere."

She used the word "tough" without the conviction it would have carried
had he been a Southern boy. She only knew it with her mind; her ear
couldn't distinguish between one Yankee voice and another. And somehow

Mrs. Calhoun didn't expire at his appearance on the threshold. The supposedly ineradicable prejudices of Ailie's parents were a convenient phenomenon that disappeared at her wish. It was her friends who were astonished. Ailie, always a little above Tarleton, whose beaus had been very carefully the "nicest" men of the camp—Ailie and Lieutenant Schoen! I grew tired of assuring people that she was merely distracting herself— and indeed every week or so there was someone new—an ensign from Pensacola, an old friend from New Orleans—but always, in between times, there was Earl Schoen.

Orders arrived for an advance party of officers and sergeants to proceed to the port of embarkation and take ship to France. My name was on the list. I had been on the range for a week and when I got back to camp, Earl Schoen buttonholed me immediately.

"We're giving a little farewell party in the mess. Just you and I and Captain Craker and three girls."

Earl and I were to call for the girls. We picked up Sally Carrol Happer and Nancy Lamar, and went on to Ailie's house; to be met at the door by the butler with the announcement that she wasn't home.

"Isn't home?" Earl repeated blankly. "Where is she?"

"Didn't leave no information about that; just said she wasn't home."

"But this is a darn funny thing!" he exclaimed. He walked around the familiar dusky veranda while the butler waited at the door. Something occurred to him. "Say," he informed me—"say, I think she's sore."

I waited. He said sternly to the butler, "You tell her I've got to speak to her a minute."

"How'm I goin' tell her that when she ain't home?"

Again Earl walked musingly around the porch. Then he nodded several times and said:

"She's sore at something that happened downtown."

In a few words he sketched out the matter to me.

"Look here; you wait in the car," I said. "Maybe I can fix this." And when he reluctantly retreated: "Oliver, you tell Miss Ailie I want to see her alone."

After some argument he bore this message and in a moment returned with a reply:

"Miss Ailie say she don't want to see that other gentleman about nothing never. She say come in if you like."

She was in the library. I had expected to see a picture of cool, outraged dignity, but her face was distraught, tumultuous, despairing. Her eyes were red-rimmed, as though she had been crying slowly and painfully, for hours.

"Oh, hello, Andy," she said brokenly. "I haven't seen you for so long. Has he gone?"

"Now, Ailie——"

"Now, Ailie!" she cried. "Now, Ailie! He spoke to me, you see. He lifted his hat. He stood there ten feet from me with that horrible—that horrible woman—holding her arm and talking to her, and then when he saw me he raised his hat. Andy, I didn't know what to do. I had to go in the drug store and ask for a glass of water, and I was so afraid he'd follow in after me that I asked Mr. Rich to let me go out the back way. I never want to see him or hear of him again."

I talked. I said what one says in such cases. I said it for half an hour. I could not move her. Several times she answered by murmuring something about his not being "sincere," and for the fourth time I wondered what the word meant to her. Certainly not constancy; it was, I half suspected, some special way she wanted to be regarded.

I got up to go. And then, unbelievably, the automobile horn sounded three times impatiently outside. It was stupefying. It said as plainly as if Earl were in the room, "All right; go to the devil then! I'm not going to wait here all night."

Ailie looked at me aghast. And suddenly a peculiar look came into her face, spread, flickered, broke into a teary, hysterical smile.

"Isn't he awful?" she cried in helpless despair. "Isn't he terrible?"

"Hurry up," I said quickly. "Get your cape. This is our last night."

And I can still feel that last night vividly, the candlelight that flickered over the rough boards of the mess shack, over the frayed paper decorations left from the supply company's party, the sad mandolin down a company street that kept picking *My Indiana Home* out of the universal nostalgia of the departing summer. The three girls lost in this mysterious men's city felt something, too—a bewitched impermanence as though they were on a magic carpet that had lighted on the Southern countryside, and any moment the wind would lift it and waft it away. We toasted ourselves and the South. Then we left our napkins and empty glasses and a little of the past on the table, and hand in hand went out into the moonlight itself. Taps had been played; there was no sound but the far-away whinny of a horse, and a loud persistent snore at which we laughed, and the leathery snap of a sentry coming to port over by the guardhouse. Craker was on duty; we others got into a waiting car, motored into Tarleton and left Craker's girl.

Then Ailie and Earl, Sally and I, two and two in the wide back seat, each couple turned from the other, absorbed and whispering, drove away into the wide, flat darkness.

We drove through pine woods heavy with lichen and Spanish moss, and between the fallow cotton fields along a road white as the rim of the world. We parked under the broken shadow of a mill where there was the sound of running water and restive squawky birds and over everything a brightness that tried to filter in anywhere—into the lost nigger cabins, the automobile, the fastnesses of the heart. The South sang to us—I wonder if they remember. I remember—the cool pale faces, the somnolent amorous eyes and the voices:

"Are you comfortable?"

"Yes; are you?"

"Are you sure you are?"

"Yes."

Suddenly we knew it was late and there was nothing more. We turned home.

Our detachment started for Camp Mills next day, but I didn't go to France after all. We passed a cold month on Long Island, marched aboard a transport with steel helmets slung at our sides and then marched off again. There wasn't any more war. I had missed the war. When I came back to Tarleton I tried to get out of the Army, but I had a regular commission and it took most of the winter. But Earl Schoen was one of the first to be demobilized. He wanted to find a good job "while the picking was good." Ailie was noncommittal, but there was an understanding between them that he'd be back.

By January the camps, which for two years had dominated the little city, were already fading. There was only the persistent incinerator smell to remind one of all that activity and bustle. What life remained centred bitterly about divisional headquarters building with the disgruntled regular officers who had also missed the war.

And now the young men of Tarleton began drifting back from the ends of the earth—some with Canadian uniforms, some with crutches or empty sleeves. A returned battalion of the National Guard paraded through the streets with open ranks for their dead, and then stepped down out of romance forever and sold you things over the counters of local stores. Only a few uniforms mingled with the dinner coats at the country-club dance.

Just before Christmas, Bill Knowles arrived unexpectedly one day and left the next—either he gave Ailie an ultimatum or she had made up her mind at last. I saw her sometimes when she wasn't busy with returned heroes from Savannah and Augusta, but I felt like an outmoded survival— and I was. She was waiting for Earl Schoen with such a vast uncertainty that she didn't like to talk about it. Three days before I got my final discharge he came.

I first happened upon them walking down Market Street together, and I don't think I've ever been so sorry for a couple in my life; though I suppose the same situation was repeating itself in every city where there had been camps. Exteriorly Earl had about everything wrong with him that could be imagined. His hat was green, with a radical feather; his suit was slashed and braided in a grotesque fashion that national advertising and the movies have put an end to. Evidently he had been to his old barber, for his hair bloused neatly on his pink, shaved neck. It wasn't as though he had been shiny and poor, but the background of mill-town dance halls and outing clubs flamed out at you—or rather flamed out at Ailie. For she had never quite imagined the reality; in these clothes even the natural grace of that magnificent body had departed. At first he boasted of his fine job; it would get them along all right until he could "see some easy money." But from the moment he came back into her world on its own terms he must have known it was hopeless. I don't know what Ailie said or how much her grief weighed against her stupefaction. She acted quickly—three days after his arrival, Earl and I went North together on the train.

"Well, that's the end of that," he said moodily. "She's a wonderful girl, but too much of a highbrow for me. I guess she's got to marry some rich guy that'll give her a great social position. I can't see that stuck-up sort of thing." And then, later: "She said to come back and see her in a year, but I'll never go back. This aristocrat stuff is all right if you got the money for it, but——"

"But it wasn't real," he meant to finish. The provincial society in which he had moved with so much satisfaction for six months already appeared to him as affected, "dudish" and artificial.

"Say, did you see what I saw getting on the train?" he asked me after a while. "Two wonderful janes, all alone. What do you say we mosey into the next car and ask them to lunch? I'll take the one in blue." Half-way down the car he turned around suddenly. "Say, Andy," he demanded, frowning; "one thing—how do you suppose she knew I used to command a street car? I never told her that."

"Search me."

III

This narrative arrives now at one of the big gaps that stared me in the face when I began. For six years, while I finished at Harvard Law and built commercial aeroplanes and backed a pavement block that went gritty under trucks, Ailie Calhoun was scarcely more than a name on a Christmas card; something that blew a little in my mind on warm nights when I remembered the magnolia flowers. Occasionally an acquaintance of Army days would ask me, "What became of that blond girl who was so popular?" but I didn't know. I ran into Nancy Lamar at the Montmartre in New York one evening and learned that Ailie had become engaged to a man in Cincinnati, had gone North to visit his family and then broken it off. She was lovely as ever and there was always a heavy beau or two. But neither Bill Knowles nor Earl Schoen had ever come back.

And somewhere about that time I heard that Bill Knowles had married a girl he met on a boat. There you are—not much of a patch to mend six years with.

Oddly enough, a girl seen at twilight in a small Indiana station started me thinking about going South. The girl, in stiff pink organdie, threw her arms about a man who got off our train and hurried him to a waiting car, and I felt a sort of pang. It seemed to me that she was bearing him off into the lost midsummer world of my early twenties, where time had stood still and charming girls, dimly seen like the past itself, still loitered along the dusky streets. I suppose that poetry is a Northern man's dream of the South. But it was months later that I sent off a wire to Ailie, and immediately followed it to Tarleton.

It was July. The Jefferson Hotel seemed strangely shabby and stuffy—a boosters' club burst into intermittent song in the dining room that my memory had long dedicated to officers and girls. I recognized the taxi driver who took me up to Ailie's house, but his "Sure, I do, lieutenant," was unconvincing. I was only one of twenty thousand.

It was a curious three days. I suppose some of Ailie's first young lustre must have gone the way of such mortal shining, but I can't bear witness to it. She was still so physically appealing that you wanted to touch the personality that trembled on her lips. No—the change was more profound than that.

At once I saw she had a different line. The modulations of pride, the vocal hints that she knew the secrets of a brighter, finer antebellum day, were gone from her voice; there was no time for them now as it rambled on in the half-laughing, half-desperate banter of the newer South. And everything was swept into this banter in order to make it go on and leave no time for thinking—the present, the future, herself, me. We went to a rowdy party at the house of some young married people, and she was the nervous, glowing centre of it. After all, she wasn't eighteen, and she was as attractive in her role of reckless clown as she had ever been in her life.

"Have you heard anything from Earl Schoen?" I asked her the second night, on our way to the country-club dance.

"No." She was serious for a moment. "I often think of him. He was the——" She hesitated.

"Go on."

"I was going to say the man I loved most, but that wouldn't be true. I never exactly loved him, or I'd have married him any old how, wouldn't I?" She looked at me questioningly. "At least I wouldn't have treated him like that."

"It was impossible."

"Of course," she agreed uncertainly. Her mood changed; she became flippant: "How the Yankees did deceive us poor little Southern girls. Ah, me!"

When we reached the country club she melted like a chameleon into the—to me—unfamiliar crowd. There was a new generation upon the floor, with less dignity than the ones I had known, but none of them were more a part of its lazy, feverish essence than Ailie. Possibly she had perceived that in her initial longing to escape from Tarleton's provincialism she had been walking alone, following a generation which was doomed to have no successors. Just where she lost the battle, waged behind the white pillars of her veranda, I don't know. But she had guessed wrong, missed out somewhere. Her wild animation, which even now called enough men around her to rival the entourage of the youngest and freshest, was an admission of defeat.

I left her house, as I had so often left it that vanished June, in a mood of vague dissatisfaction. It was hours later, tossing about my bed in the hotel, that I realized what was the matter, what had always been the matter—I was deeply and incurably in love with her. In spite of every incompatibility, she was still, she would always be to me, the most attractive girl I had ever known. I told her so next afternoon. It was one of those hot days I knew so well, and Ailie sat beside me on a couch in the darkened library.

"Oh, no, I couldn't marry you," she said, almost frightened; "I don't love you that way at all. . . . I never did. And you don't love me. I didn't mean to tell you now, but next month I'm going to marry another man. We're not even announcing it, because I've done that twice before." Suddenly it occurred to her that I might be hurt: "Andy, you just had a silly idea, didn't you? You know I couldn't ever marry a Northern man."

"Who is he?" I demanded.

"A man from Savannah."

"Are you in love with him?"

"Of course I am." We both smiled. "Of course I am! What are you trying to make me say?"

There were no doubts, as there had been with other men. She couldn't afford to let herself have doubts. I knew this because she had long ago stopped making any pretensions with me. This very naturalness, I realized, was because she didn't consider me as a suitor. Beneath her mask of an instinctive thoroughbred she had always been on to herself, and she couldn't believe that anyone not taken in to the point of uncritical worship could really love her. That was what she called being "sincere"; she felt most security with men like Canby and Earl Schoen, who were incapable of passing judgments on the ostensibly aristocratic heart.

"All right," I said, as if she had asked my permission to marry. "Now, would you do something for me?"

"Anything."

"Ride out to camp."

"But there's nothing left there, honey."

"I don't care."

We walked downtown. The taxi driver in front of the hotel repeated her objection: "Nothing there now, cap."

"Never mind. Go there anyhow."

Twenty minutes later he stopped on a wide unfamiliar plain powdered with new cotton fields and marked with isolated clumps of pine.

"Like to drive over yonder where you see the smoke?" asked the driver. "That's the new state prison."

"No. Just drive along this road. I want to find where I used to live."

An old race course, inconspicuous in the camp's day of glory, had reared its dilapidated grandstand in the desolation. I tried in vain to orient myself.

"Go along this road past that clump of trees, and then turn right—no, turn left."

He obeyed, with professional disgust.

"You won't find a single thing, darling," said Ailie. "The contractors took it all down."

We rode slowly along the margin of the fields. It might have been here—

"All right. I want to get out," I said suddenly.

I left Ailie sitting in the car, looking very beautiful with the warm breeze stirring her long, curly bob.

It might have been here. That would make the company streets down there and the mess shack, where we dined that night, just over the way.

The taxi driver regarded me indulgently while I stumbled here and there in the knee-deep underbrush, looking for my youth in a clapboard or a strip of roofing or a rusty tomato can. I tried to sight on a vaguely familiar clump of trees, but it was growing darker now and I couldn't be quite sure they were the right trees.

"They're going to fix up the old race course," Ailie called from the car. "Tarleton's getting quite doggy in its old age."

No. Upon consideration they didn't look like the right trees. All I could be sure of was this place that had once been so full of life and effort was gone, as if it had never existed, and that in another month Ailie would be gone, and the South would be empty for me forever.

COMMENT AND QUESTION

1. Ailie Calhoun is a complex character. The reader will discover this truth when he tries to reconcile some of her less attractive qualities with the fact that Andy, who is mature and perceptive, remains hopelessly in love with her throughout the story.

a. Does Ailie symbolize for Andy the lost midsummer world of his early twenties, "where time had stood still and charming girls, dimly seen like the past itself, still loitered along the dusky streets"? If so, this romantic conception must be reconciled with the following:

(1) Andy's semi-satiric portrait of Ailie in the paragraph in section I, beginning, "There she was—the Southern type in all its purity."

(2) The episode of Canby.

(3) Andy's final reflection upon Ailie in the paragraph in section III, beginning, "Beneath her mask of an instinctive thoroughbred. . . ."

b. This story was first published in 1929, when fiction writers were handling the subject of sex in what has come to be known as the "hard-boiled" manner. But "The Last of the Belles" is not a hard-boiled story; in fact, the portrait of Ailie is touched with sympathy rather than with scorn. The observations in this story, nevertheless, are acute.

What did Ailie want from love? Is a belle a coquette? What are the connotations of the two terms? What did Ailie mean by sincerity?

Is Ailie afraid of sex? If so, why is she attracted to Earl Schoen?

Consider the episode where Ailie meets Earl Schoen on the street. Ailie objects not so much to the woman with Earl as she does to an action of Earl's. What does this whole episode reveal about Ailie?

2. It has recently been recognized that a longing for wealth and social position motivated the life of Fitzgerald. But does not the author have a clear-sighted attitude toward snobbishness in this story?

In the story, "The Snows of Kilimanjaro," you will find (on p. 262) a reference to Fitzgerald in "poor Julian," and a reference to one of the stories of Fitzgerald, a story entitled "The Rich Boy." Do these references help in the interpretation of "The Last of the Belles"?

3. For a young man, Andy is unusual in his wisdom, his sensitivity, and his melancholy. He is superior to all the other characters. For example, is he not aware of his own snobbishness? Is his nostalgia ever completely explained?

4. "I suppose that poetry is a Northern man's dream of the South." This statement is a clue to the main theme of this story. This theme is seen in the title; in the phrase, "the South's heroic age"; in the significant sentence in section I, "We recognized her"; and most of all in the paragraph in section II, beginning "We drove through pine woods heavy with lichen. . . ."

Is the nostalgia in this story connected with this theme?

In one episode Earl Schoen displays a "photograph of some Tarleton girl nailed brutally to the shack wall." Does this episode merely indicate the social abyss where Earl Schoen dwells or is it related to a larger theme, the passing of "the South's heroic age"?

5. The defects in Fitzgerald's short stories are usually balanced by flashes of perception. Find the following statements and study them in their context for implications which give a depth of meaning to the story and to issues beyond the story.

a. ". . . and there was never so much love around."

b. ". . . then stepped down out of romance forever and sold you things over the counters of local stores."

c. ". . . looking for my youth in a clapboard or a strip of roofing or a rusty tomato can."

THE OTHER SIDE OF
THE HEDGE

BY EDWARD MORGAN FORSTER

EDWARD MORGAN FORSTER (1879–) has written essays, novels, and short stories. He was born in London and has lived in England most of his life, but has travelled in Italy, Greece, Egypt, and India. His best novel, *A Passage to India* (1927), is a revelation of the British and Indian character. His other novels include *Where Angels Fear to Tread* (1905), *The Longest Journey* (1907), *A Room with a View* (1908), and *Howard's End* (1910). His short stories appear in *The Collected Tales of E. M. Forster* (1947). One of his best known short stories, "The Machine Stops," was a protest against the mechanical Utopia of H. G. Wells. He has written a volume of criticism, *Aspects of the Novel* (1927).

MY PEDOMETER told me that I was twenty-five; and, though it is a shocking thing to stop walking, I was so tired that I sat down on a milestone to rest. People outstripped me, jeering as they did so, but I was too apathetic to feel resentful, and even when Miss Eliza Dimbleby, the great educationist, swept past, exhorting me to persevere, I only smiled and raised my hat.

At first I thought I was going to be like my brother, whom I had had to leave by the roadside a year or two round the corner. He had wasted his breath on singing, and his strength on helping others. But I had travelled more wisely, and now it was only the monotony of the highway that oppressed me—dust under foot and brown crackling hedges on either side, ever since I could remember.

And I had already dropped several things—indeed, the road behind was strewn with the things we all had dropped; and the white dust was settling down on them, so that already they looked no better than stones. My muscles were so weary that I could not even bear the weight of those things I still carried. I slid off the milestone into the road, and lay there prostrate, with my face to the great parched hedge, praying that I might give up.

A little puff of air revived me. It seemed to come from the hedge; and, when I opened my eyes, there was a glint of light through the tangle of boughs and dead leaves. The hedge could not be as thick as usual. In my weak, morbid state, I longed to force my way in, and see what was on the other side. No one was in sight, or I should not have dared to try. For we of the road do not admit in conversation that there is another side at all.

I yielded to the temptation, saying to myself that I would come back in a minute. The thorns scratched my face, and I had to use my arms as a shield, depending on my feet alone to push me forward. Halfway through I would have gone back, for in the passage all the things I was carrying were scraped off me, and my clothes were torn. But I was so wedged that return was impossible, and I had to wriggle blindly forward, expecting every moment that my strength would fail me, and that I should perish in the undergrowth.

Suddenly cold water closed round my head, and I seemed sinking down for ever. I had fallen out of the hedge into a deep pool. I rose to the surface at last, crying for help, and I heard someone on the opposite bank laugh and say: "Another!" And then I was twitched out and laid panting on the dry ground.

Even when the water was out of my eyes, I was still dazed, for I had never been in so large a space, nor seen such grass and sunshine. The blue sky was no longer a strip, and beneath it the earth had risen grandly into hills—clean, bare buttresses, with beech trees in their folds, and meadows and clear pools at their feet. But the hills were not high, and there was in the landscape a sense of human occupation—so that one might have called it a park or garden, if the words did not imply a certain triviality and constraint.

As soon as I got my breath, I turned to my rescuer and said:

"Where does this place lead to?"

"Nowhere, thank the Lord!" said he, and laughed. He was a man of fifty or sixty—just the kind of age we mistrust on the road—but there was no anxiety in his manner, and his voice was that of a boy of eighteen.

"But it must lead somewhere!" I cried, too much surprised at his answer to thank him for saving my life.

"He wants to know where it leads!" he shouted to some men on the hill side, and they laughed back, and waved their caps.

I noticed then that the pool into which I had fallen was really a moat which bent round to the left and to the right, and that the hedge followed it continually. The hedge was green on this side—its roots showed through the clear water, and fish swam about in them—and it was wreathed over with dog-roses and Traveller's Joy. But it was a barrier, and in a moment I lost all pleasure in the grass, the sky, the trees, the happy men and women, and realized that the place was but a prison, for all its beauty and extent.

We moved away from the boundary, and then followed a path almost parallel to it, across the meadows. I found it difficult walking, for I was always trying to out-distance my companion, and there was no advantage in doing this if the place led nowhere. I had never kept step with anyone since I left my brother.

I amused him by stopping suddenly and saying disconsolately, "This is perfectly terrible. One cannot advance: one cannot progress. Now we of the road——"

"Yes. I know."

"I was going to say, we advance continually."

"I know."

"We are always learning, expanding, developing. Why, even in my short life I have seen a great deal of advance—the Transvaal War, the Fiscal Question, Christian Science, Radium. Here for example—"

I took out my pedometer, but it still marked twenty-five, not a degree more.

"Oh, it's stopped! I meant to show you. It should have registered all the time I was walking with you. But it makes me only twenty-five."

"Many things don't work in here," he said. "One day a man brought in a Lee-Metford, and that wouldn't work."

"The laws of science are universal in their application. It must be the water in the moat that has injured the machinery. In normal conditions everything works. Science and the spirit of emulation—those are the forces that have made us what we are."

I had to break off and acknowledge the pleasant greetings of people whom we passed. Some of them were singing, some talking, some engaged in gardening, hay-making, or other rudimentary industries. They all seemed happy; and I might have been happy too, if I could have forgotten that the place led nowhere.

I was startled by a young man who came sprinting across our path, took a little fence in fine style, and went tearing over a ploughed field till he plunged into a lake, across which he began to swim. Here was true energy, and I exclaimed: "A cross-country race! Where are the others?"

"There are no others," my companion replied; and, later on, when we passed some long grass from which came the voice of a girl singing exquisitely to herself, he said again: "There are no others." I was bewildered at the waste in production, and murmured to myself, "What does it all mean?"

He said: "It means nothing but itself"—and he repeated the words slowly, as if I were a child.

"I understand," I said quietly, "but I do not agree. Every achievement is worthless unless it is a link in the chain of development. And I must not trespass on your kindness any longer. I must get back somehow to the road, and have my pedometer mended."

"First, you must see the gates," he replied, "for we have gates, though we never use them."

I yielded politely, and before long we reached the moat again, at a point where it was spanned by a bridge. Over the bridge was a big gate, as white as ivory, which was fitted into a gap in the boundary hedge. The gate opened outwards, and I exclaimed in amazement, for from it ran a road—just such a road as I had left—dusty under foot, with brown crackling hedges on either side as far as the eye could reach.

"That's my road!" I cried.

He shut the gate and said: "But not your part of the road. It is through this gate that humanity went out countless ages ago, when it was first seized with the desire to walk."

I denied this, observing that the part of the road I myself had left was not more than two miles off. But with the obstinacy of his years he repeated: "It is the same road. This is the beginning, and though it seems to run straight away from us, it doubles so often, that it is never far from our boundary and sometimes touches it." He stooped down by the moat, and traced on its moist margin an absurd figure like a maze. As we walked back through the meadows, I tried to convince him of his mistake.

"The road sometimes doubles, to be sure, but that is part of our discipline. Who can doubt that its general tendency is onward? To what goal we know not—it may be to some mountain where we shall touch the sky, it may be over precipices into the sea. But that it goes forward—who can doubt that? It is the thought of that that makes us strive to excel, each in his own way, and gives us an impetus which is lacking with you. Now that man who passed us—it's true that he ran well, and jumped well, and swam well; but we have men who can run better, and men who can jump better, and who can swim better. Specialization has produced results which would surprise you. Similarly, that girl——"

Here I interrupted myself to exclaim: "Good gracious me! I could have sworn it was Miss Eliza Dimbleby over there, with her feet in the fountain!"

He believed that it was.

"Impossible! I left her on the road, and she is due to lecture this evening at Tunbridge Wells. Why, her train leaves Cannon Street in—of course my watch has stopped like everything else. She is the last person to be here."

"People always are astonished at meeting each other. All kinds come through the hedge, and come at all times—when they are drawing ahead in the race, when they are lagging behind, when they are left for dead. I often stand near the boundary listening to the sounds of the road—you know what they are—and wonder if anyone will turn aside. It is my great happiness to help someone out of the moat, as I helped you. For our country fills up slowly, though it was meant for all mankind."

"Mankind have other aims," I said gently, for I thought him well-meaning; "and I must join them." I bade him good evening, for the sun was declining, and I wished to be on the road by nightfall. To my alarm, he caught hold of me, crying: "You are not to go yet!" I tried to shake him off, for we had no interests in common, and his civility was becoming irksome to me. But for all my struggles the tiresome old man would not let go; and, as wrestling is not my specialty, I was obliged to follow him.

It was true that I could have never found alone the place where I came in, and I hoped that, when I had seen the other sights about which he was worrying, he would take me back to it. But I was determined not to sleep in the country, for I mistrusted it, and the people too, for all their friendliness. Hungry though I was, I would not join them in their evening meals of milk and fruit, and, when they gave me flowers, I flung them away as soon as I could do so unobserved. Already they were lying down for the night like cattle—some out on the bare hillside, others in groups under the beeches. In the light of an orange sunset I hurried on with my unwelcome guide, dead tired, faint for want of food, but murmuring indomitably: "Give me life, with its struggles and victories, with its failures and hatreds, with its deep moral meaning and its unknown goal!"

At last we came to a place where the encircling moat was spanned by another bridge, and where another gate interrupted the line of the boundary hedge. It was different from the first gate; for it was half transparent like horn, and opened inwards. But through it, in the waning light, I saw again just such a road as I had left—monotonous, dusty, with brown crackling hedges on either side, as far as the eye could reach.

I was strangely disquieted at the sight, which seemed to deprive me of all self-control. A man was passing us, returning for the night to the hills, with a scythe over his shoulder and a can of some liquid in his hand. I forgot the destiny of our race. I forgot the road that lay before my eyes, and I sprang at him, wrenched the can out of his hand, and began to drink.

It was nothing stronger than beer, but in my exhausted state it overcame me in a moment. As in a dream, I saw the old man shut the gate, and heard him say: "This is where your road ends, and through this gate humanity—all that is left of it—will come in to us."

Though my senses were sinking into oblivion, they seemed to expand ere they reached it. They perceived the magic song of nightingales, and the odour of invisible hay, and stars piercing the fading sky. The man whose beer I had stolen lowered me down gently to sleep off its effects, and, as he did so, I saw that he was my brother.

COMMENT AND QUESTION

1. E. M. Forster distrusts science; its product, the machine; and the myth they have both helped to support, the idea of "progress." He exposes in his writing the mechanized and materialistic civilization which prevents man from living "by the essence that is his soul, and the essence, equally divine, that is his body." Many of his stories are fantasies, as is "The Other Side of the Hedge"; the altered perspective points up his meaning.

2. Notice the pedometer. The road is measured in years, not miles. About twenty-five centuries ago the impetus of Greek thought started the Western world in a direction it has since taken. Is there a connection?

3. Notice the two gates. Consider what they are made of, whether they open in or out and on what part of the road, and what the old man says about each gate.

In the *Odyssey* Penelope discusses a dream with the newly-arrived Odysseus, whom she has not yet recognized. Among other things, she says to him: "Stranger, in truth dreams do arise perplexed and hard to tell, dreams which come not, in man's experience, to their full issue. Two gates there are for unsubstantial dreams, one made of horn and one of ivory. The dreams that pass through the carved ivory delude and bring us tales that turn to naught; those that come through polished horn accomplish real things, whenever seen."

What, then, does Forster mean by using these two gates?

4. The meaning of the story is revealed, also, in the difference between the qualities of the road and the qualities of the life on the other side of the hedge.

5. Notice the "educationist" who exhorts on the road but later appears on the other side of the hedge. Are both of these actions in keeping with an "educationist"?

6. Does the concluding line have references beyond the obvious reference to the brother the main character had lost?

THE CAPTIVE

BY CAROLINE GORDON

CAROLINE GORDON (1895–) is a novelist, short story writer, lecturer, and teacher. She was born in Kentucky. She has published a number of novels, including *Aleck Maury, Sportsman* (1934), *The Women on the Porch* (1944), and *The Strange Children* (1951). "The Captive" is from her collection of short stories, *The Forest of the South* (1945). She is the wife of the critic Allen Tate.

W E WERE up long before day and were loading the horses at first dawn streak. Even then Tom didn't want to go.

"This ginseng don't have to get to the station," he said, "and as for the money it'll bring, we can get along without that."

"We've been without salt for three weeks now," I told him.

"There's worse things than doing without salt," Tom said.

I knew if he got to studying about it he wouldn't go and I was bound he should make the trip, Indians or no Indians. I slapped the lead horse on the rump. "Go along," I said. "I'd as soon be scalped now and have done with it as keep on thinking about it all the time."

Tom rode off without saying anything more, and I went on in the house and set about my morning work. The children were all stirring by that time. Joe felt mighty big to be the only man on the place. He was telling them what he'd do if Indians came.

"You'd better hush that up," I said. "Can't you get your mind off Indians a minute?"

All that morning, though, I was thinking about what Tom had said and wishing he hadn't had to go. It seemed like I was riding with him most of the day.

"Now he's at West Fork," I'd say to myself, and then after I'd done some more chores, "He'll be about at the crossroads now or maybe Sayler's Tavern." I knew, though, it wasn't much use to be following him that way in my mind. It'd be good dark before he could get home, and my thinking about it wouldn't hurry him.

It was around ten o'clock that I heard the first owl hooting. Over on the mountain, it seemed. Joe was in the yard feeding the chickens and he stopped stock still and threw his head back.

"You hear that, Mammy?" he asked.

I knew then that there must be something wrong with the call, or a boy like Joe wouldn't have noticed it.

I spoke up sharp, though. "I heard it," I said, "and I could hear a heap of other things if I had time to stand around with my ears open. How long you reckon it's going to take you to get those chickens fed?"

We both went on about our business without more talk, but all the time I was saying to myself that if I could get through this and see Tom Wiley riding in at the gate one more time I'd be content to bide without salt the rest of my natural life. I knew it wouldn't do to let down before the children, though, and I kept them busy doing one thing and another till dinner time. It began to rain while we were eating and it rained a long time. After it stopped raining the fog settled down, so thick you could hardly see your hand before you. And all the time the owls were calling. Calling back and forth from one mountain to another. My littlest girl, Martha, got scared, so I made all the children stay in the house and play by the fire whilst I started in on a piece of cloth I'd had in the loom a long time and never could seem to finish. I'd put a stripe through it and I was going to dye it red and make both the girls a dress out of that piece before the winter set in.

By that time the fog had risen as high as the top of the ridges and the whole house was swallowed up in it. The children kept teasing, saying it was good dark now and couldn't they have a candle.

"Yes," I said, "we're here all by ourselves and you want to go lighting candles, so they can't help finding the house."

One of the girls got to crying. "Who's coming?" she said. "Mammy, who you think's coming?"

I saw I'd got them stirred up and I'd have to settle them, for I couldn't stand to be worrying like I was and have the children crying. I gave them all a lump of sugar around and got them started on a play-party. I made out that I had the headache and if they were going to sing they'd have to sing low. It was "Hog Drovers" they were playing.

"Hog-drovers, hog-drovers, hog-drovers we air,
A-courtin' your daughter so sweet and so fair.
Kin we git lodgin' here, O here,
Kin we git lodgin' here?"

I got them started to frolicking and went back to my work. But I couldn't get my mind off something a man said to me once when we were out hunting on the Hurricane, and I made him to go right in on a bear without waiting for the other menfolks to come up.

"You're brash, Jinny," he said, "and you always been lucky, but one of these times you going to be too brash."

Sitting there listening to them owls calling, and wondering how much longer it would be before Tom got home, I got to thinking that maybe this was the time I was too brash. For I knew well there wasn't another woman in the settlements would have undertaken to stay on that place all day with nothing but a parcel of children. Still, I said to myself, it's done now and there's no undoing it. And the first thing I know, Tom will be back, and tomorrow morning it'll fair up, and I'll be thinking what a goose I was to get scared over nothing.

The children were still singing:

"Oh, this is my daughter that sets by my lap.
No pig-stealing drover kin git her from Pap.
You can't git lodgin' here, O here,
You can't git lodgin' here."

I got up and looked out of the window. It seemed to me that the fog was lifting a little. A man was coming up the path. I knew it was a white man by the walk, but I didn't know it was John Borders till he stepped up to the door.

The first thing he asked was where was Tom.

"Gone to the station with a load of ginseng," I told him. "I'm looking for him back now any minute."

He stood there looking off towards the mountain. "How long them owls been calling?" he asked.

"Off and on all evening," I said, "but owls'll hoot, dark days like this."

"Yes," he said, "and some owls'll holler like wolves and gobble like turkeys and every other kind of varmint. Jinny, you better git them children and come over to our house. Ain't no telling when Tom'll be back."

Just then an owl hooted and another one answered him from somewhere on top of the ridge. We both listened hard. It sounded like a real owl calling to his mate, but I was good and scared by that time and I thought I'd best go over to the Borderses'. It was my judgment, though, that there wasn't any hurry. Indians hardly ever come round before nightfall.

I told John that if he'd wait till I'd fastened up the stock I'd go back with him. He said that while I was doing that he'd walk out in the woods a little way. He'd been looking all day for some strayed sheep and hadn't found trace of them, but he thought they might be herded up in that gully by the spring. He went off down the path and I fastened the front door and went out the back way. I didn't fasten the back door, but I kept my eye on it all the time I was worrying with the cattle. Joe was along helping me. The cow was standing there at the pen; so I stopped and milked her while Joe went up in the triangle to look for the heifer. He found her and brought her up to the cowpen just as I finished milking. We fastened both cows up in the stable and Joe went over and saw that all the chickens were up and fastened the door on them. Then we started back to the house with the milk.

We were halfway up the path when we heard the Indians holler. We started for the house on a dead run. I could see Indians in the yard, and one Indian was coming around the house to the back door. I ran faster and slipped in the door ahead of him. Joe was right behind me. The room was so full of Indians that at first I couldn't see any of my children. The Indians was dancing around and hollering and hacking with their tomahawks. I heard one of the children screaming but I didn't know which one it was. An Indian caught me around the waist but I got away from him. I thought, I have got to do something. I fell down on my knees and crawled around between the Indians' legs, they striking at me all the time, till I found Martha, my littlest one, in the corner by the loom. She was dead and I crawled on a little way and found Sadie. She was dead, too, with her skull split open. The baby was just sitting there holding on to the bar of the loom. I caught him in my bosom and held him up to me tight; then I got to my feet. Joe was right behind me all the time and he stood up when I did. But an Indian come up and brained him with a tomahawk. I saw him go down and I knew I couldn't get any more help from him. I couldn't think of anything to do; so I worked my way over towards the door, but there was two or three Indians standing on the porch and I knew there was no use running for it. I just stood there holding the baby while the Indians pulled burning logs out of the fire onto the floor. When the blaze had sprung up they all come out onto the porch.

I made a break and got some way down the path, but an Indian run after me and caught me. He stood there, holding me tight till the other Indians come up; then he laid his hand on my head and he touched the baby too. It seemed he was claiming me for his prisoner. He had rings on his arms and ankles, and trinkets in his ears. I knew he was a chief and I thought he must be a Shawnee. I could understand some of what he said.

He was telling them they better hurry and get away before Tice Harman come home. Another Indian stepped up. I knew him—a Cherokee that come sometimes to the station. Mad Dog they called him. Tice Harman had killed his son. It come to me that they had been thinking all along that they was at Tice Harman's. I jerked my arm away from the Shawnee chief.

"You think you're burning Tice Harman's house," I said. "This ain't Tice Harman's house. It's Tom Wiley's. Tom Wiley. Tom Wiley never killed any Indians."

They looked at each other and I think they was feared. Feared because they had burned the wrong house, but feared too of Tice Harman. Mad Dog said something and laid his hand on his tomahawk, but the old chief shook his head and took hold of my arm again. He spoke, too, but so fast I couldn't tell what he was saying. The Cherokee looked mad but he turned around after a minute and called to the other Indians, and they all left the house and started off through the woods. Mad Dog went first and half a dozen young Indians after him. The old chief and I came last. He had hold of my arm and was hurrying me along, and all the time he kept talking, telling me that he had saved my life, that I was to go with him to his town to be a daughter to him to take the place of a daughter that had died.

I didn't take in much that he was saying. I kept looking back towards the burning house, thinking maybe they wasn't all dead before the Indians set fire to it. Finally I couldn't stand it no longer and I asked the old Shawnee. He pointed to one of the young Indians who was going up the ridge ahead of us. I saw something dangling from his belt and I looked away quick. I knew it was the scalps of my children.

II

We went up over the ridge and then struck north through the woods. I didn't take much notice of where we was going. I had all I could do to keep Dinny quiet—he warn't but ten months old. I let him suck all the way but it didn't do much good. We went so fast it'd jolt out of his mouth and he'd cry louder than ever. The Shawnee would grab my arm and say the other Indians would kill him sure if he kept that up. Finally I got his head down inside the waist of my dress and I held him up against me so tight he couldn't cry, and then I was scared he'd smother, but the Shawnee wouldn't let me stop to find out.

We went on, up one valley and down another, till finally we come out on level land at the foot of a mountain. The old chief made me go first, right up the mountainside. It was worse there than it was in the woods. The laurel and the ivy was so thick that sometimes he'd have to reach ahead of me and break a way through. My arms got numb and wouldn't hold the baby up. It was lucky for me I was crawling up a mountain. I would put him up ahead of me and then crawl to him, and in this way my arms would get a little ease of the burden. The old chief didn't like this, though, and every time it happened he'd slap me and tell me to go faster, go faster or they would surely kill the baby.

We got to the top of the mountain, somehow, and started down. My legs were hurting me now worse than my arms. It was going so straight down the mountainside. The back of my legs got stiff and would jerk me up every time I set my foot down, what they call stifled in a horse. I got on, somehow, though, all through that night and for most of the next day. It was near sundown when we stopped, in a rockhouse [1] at the head of a creek. The Indians must have thought they were too far for any white men to follow them. They made up a big fire and walked around it pretty careless. Two of the young Indians went off in the woods. I heard a shot and they come back dragging a little deer. They butchered it and sliced it down the middle, and slung the two haunches over the fire on forked sticks. The tenderer parts they broiled on rocks that they heated red-hot in the coals. A young buck squatted down by the fire and kept the venison turning. Soon the smell of rich meat cooking rose up in the air. The juices begun dripping down into the blaze and I thought it was a shame for all that gravy to go to waste. I asked the Shawnee to lend me a little kettle he had, and I hung it on a forked stick and caught the juices as they fell, and then poured them back over the meat. When they turned brown and rich I caught the gravy in the little kettle and sopped my fingers in it and let the baby suck them.

The old chief Crowmocker, smiled like he thought a lot of me. "White woman know," he said. "White woman teach Indian women. You make rum?"

I said I didn't know how to make rum, but there was plenty in the settlements and if he would take me back, take me just within a mile or two of the clearing, I'd undertake to furnish him and his men with all the rum they could drink.

He laughed. "White people promise," he said. "You in your cabin you forget poor Indian."

The Cherokee, Mad Dog, had been sitting there broiling the deer nose on a rock that he had got red-hot in the flames. When it was brown he brought it over and gave it to me. Then he went back and sat down, sullen like, not saying anything. The fire shone on his black eyes and on his long beak of a nose. When he moved, you could see the muscles moving, too, in his big chest and up and down his naked legs. An Indian woman would have thought him a fine-looking man, tall and well formed in every way, but it frightened me to look at him. I was glad it was the old chief and not him that had taken me prisoner. I was glad, too, that the chief was old. I'd heard tell how particular the Indians are about things like that. I thought the old chief would likely do what he said and

---

[1] A rockhouse is not a cave, but a place sheltered by an overhanging ledge of rock.

keep me for his daughter, but if it was Mad Dog he would have me for his wife.

I thought the meat never would get done, but it finally did. The Indians give me a good-size piece off the haunch and I ate it all, except a little piece I put in Dinny's mouth. He spit it out, but I kept putting it back till he got some good of it. Then I took him down to the creek and scooped up water in my hands for him. He'd been fretting because my milk was giving out, but the water and the juice from the meat quieted him a little. After we'd both had all the water we could drink I went back up the hill and sat down on a log with Dinny laying across my knees. It felt good to have his weight off my arms, but I was afraid to take my hands off him. I was feared one of them might come up and snatch him away from me any minute.

He laid there a while a-fretting and then he put his little hand up and felt my face.

"Sadie . . . ," he said. "Sadie . . ."

Sadie was the oldest girl. She played with him a lot and fondled him. He'd go to her any time out of my arms.

I hugged him up close and sang him the song Sadie used to get him to sleep by. "Lord Lovell, he stood at the castle gate," I sang and the tears a-running down my face.

"Hush, my pretty," I said, "hush. Sadie's gone, but Mammy's here. Mammy's here with Baby."

He cried, though, for Sadie and wouldn't nothing I could do comfort him. He cried himself hoarse and then he'd keep opening his little mouth but wouldn't no sound come. I felt him and he was hot to the touch. I was feared he'd fret himself into a fever, but there wasn't nothing I could do. I held his arms and legs to the blaze and got him as warm as I could, and then I went off from the fire a little way and laid down with him in my arms.

The Indians kept putting fresh wood to the fire till it blazed up and lit the whole hollow. They squatted around it, talking. After a while half a dozen of them got up and went off in the woods. The light fell far out through the trees. I could see their naked legs moving between the black trunks. Some of them was dragging up down timber for the fire and some kept reaching up and tearing boughs off the trees. They came back trailing the green boughs behind them. Two or three other Indians come over and they all squatted down and begun stripping the leaves off the switches and binding them into hoops. An Indian took one of the scalps off his belt —Sadie's light hair, curling a little at the ends and speckled now all over with blood. I watched it fall across the bough of maple. I watched till they began stretching the scalp on the hoop and then I shut my eyes.

After a while Crowmocker come over and tied me with some rawhide thongs that he took off his belt. He tied me up tight and it felt good to have the keen thongs cutting into me. I strained against them for a while and then I must have dropped off to sleep. I woke myself up hollering. I thought at first it was the Indians hollering, and then I knew it was me. I tried to stop but I couldn't. It would start way down inside me and I would fight to hold it in, but before I knew it my mouth would be wide open and as soon as I'd loose one shriek another would start working its way up and there wasn't nothing I could do to hold it back. I was shaking, too, so hard that the baby rolled out of my arms and started crying.

The old chief got up from where he was sleeping and come over. He stood there looking down at me and then he lighted a torch and went off in the woods a little way. He brought some leaves back with him and he put them to boil in his little kettle. He made me drink some tea from the leaves and he gave the baby some too, and after a while we both went off to sleep.

III

I woke with the old chief shaking me by the arm and telling me it was time to get up. I was still sort of lightheaded and for a minute I didn't know where I was. It was raining hard and so dark you couldn't tell whether it was good day. The Indians had built a fire up under the ledge and were broiling the rest of the venison. I laid there and I saw the light shine on their naked legs and the tomahawks hanging from their belts, and I knew where I was and all that had happened.

The old chief untied the thongs and I stood up with Dinny in my arms. They gave me a little piece of venison and some parched corn. My lips were so swelled I couldn't chew, but I swallowed the corn and I put the meat in my mouth and sucked it till it went away. I felt milk in my breasts and I was glad for the baby. I gave him his dinny but he wouldn't suck. He wouldn't hardly open his eyes. I thought that was from the tea the old Indian had given us and I feared he'd got too much. He was still hot to the touch and I thought he might have got a fever from laying out all night in the rain. I tore off part of my top skirt and I made a sort of sling that I put around my shoulders to carry him in; and I made a cover, too, out of part of the cloth to keep the rain off his little face.

Soon as we had finished eating, the Indians stomped out the fire and scattered the ashes so you couldn't have told there had ever been a camp there, and we started off through the woods.

We hadn't gone far before two of the young Indians left us. I thought they was most likely going back over the trail to watch if anybody was following us. I heard them saying that the folks at the settlement would be sure to send out a party. Some of the Indians thought it wouldn't do no good because the heavy rains had washed out the trail so nobody could find it. But Mad Dog said Tice Harman could follow any trail. I never knew before the Indians was so feared of Harman. They said he was the best hunter among the Long Knives, that he could go as far and stand as much as any Indian, and that they would like for him to come and live with them and be one of their warriors. Mad Dog said now that the only thing was to go so fast and go so far that even Tice Harman couldn't come up with us. He said "O-hi-yo" several times and I judged they meant to make for one of the towns on the river.

It stopped raining after a while but it didn't do much good. It was level ground we was traveling over and the water was standing everywhere, so that half the time you was wading. I knew we was some place high up in the hills, but afterwards I couldn't have told what country I had passed over. I went with my head down most of the time, not seeing anything but the black trunks of the trees going by and the yellow leaves floating in the puddles. Beech woods we must have been in because the leaves was all yellow and little.

We went on like that all day, not stopping to eat anything except some parched corn that the old chief took out of his bag and handed around to us still traveling. Late that evening we come to a water hole. One of the Indians shot a bear and we stopped and built a fire under a cliff. The Indians hadn't no more'n butchered the meat when two scouts come running into camp. They said that white men were following us, on horseback. The Indians all looked scared at this. Crowmocker stood there talking to Mad Dog about what we had best do. I went over and stood by them. Mad Dog said that they ought to kill the child and change the course, that they would have to go faster than ever now and I couldn't keep up, carrying the baby. Crowmocker showed him the sling I had made and said the baby wasn't no burden to me now. He said he had brought me this far and was going to carry me on to his town to teach his women how to weave cloth like the dress I had on.

He told Mad Dog that and then he motioned to me and said, "Go!" I started off, top speed, through the trees. Behind me I could hear the Indians stomping around in the leaves to cover up the signs of the fire. I went on as fast as I could, but every now and then an Indian would shoot past me. Pretty soon they was all ahead except the old chief.

We went down hill towards a hollow that had a little branch running through it. Mad Dog was in the lead, the other Indians right on his heels, jumping over down logs and bushes quick as cats. The old chief stayed by me, and when I'd slow up getting over a log or fall down in the bushes he'd jerk me onto my feet again.

The branch was narrow but running deep with the rains. Mad Dog started wading downstream and the other Indians after him, single file. They hadn't slowed up much and water splashed high. I could see their legs moving through the splashing water. The old chief by my side was breathing hard. I knew he was winded but I thought he would wind quicker than the others. I thought I would keep moving as long as I saw the Indians' legs going on.

The Indian that was in front of me stepped in a hole up to his waist. When he come out of it he took two, three steps and stood still. I knew then that Mad Dog had stopped and I knew he would be coming back down the line. I looked up, but the sides of the gully was too steep. I turned and ran back upstream fast as I could. I heard the breathing close behind me and I knew it was the old chief, and then there was a big splashing. Mad Dog was after me.

I left the water and ran sideways up the gully. The breathing was closer now. I tried to run faster and I caught my foot in a root. They were on me as soon as I went down. Mad Dog grabbed me by both arms. Crowmocker got there a second after, but Mad Dog already had hold of Dinny. I caught at his legs and tried to push them out from under him but he kicked me away. I got up and went at him again but he kicked me down. He kicked me again and then he went on up the side of the gully till he came to a big tree and he held the baby by the feet and dashed his brains out.

I rolled over on my face and I laid there flat on the ground till the old chief come up. He pulled me to my feet and said we would have to run on fast, that the white men were following us on horses. I said no, I wouldn't go, I would stay there with my baby; but he and another Indian took me by the arms and drug me down the stream spite of all I could do.

We went on down the branch a good way. Towards dark we came out on the banks of a river. Water was standing halfway up the trunks of big trees. I saw the current, running fast and covered with black drift, and I didn't believe even an Indian could get across that raging river. But they didn't stop a minute. Crowmocker fell back and two young Indians took hold of my arms and carried me out into the water. The current caught us and swept us off our feet. I couldn't swim much on account of my clothes, but the two young Indians held on to my wrists and carried me on between them. The other Indians come right in after us. They held their guns up high over their heads and swum like boys treading water. I could see their heads bobbing all around me through the black drift and I couldn't see nothing to keep all of us from drowning. They managed to keep out of the drift somehow, though, and all the time they were working towards the other bank till finally we come out in dead water at the mouth of a creek. The Indians that were holding me up stopped swimming all of a sudden, and I knew that we must have got across. It was so dark by that time I couldn't see anything. I got out of the water as best I could and a little way up the creek bank. I fell down there 'mongst some willows. I saw the Indians come up out of the water shaking themselves

like dogs, and I saw them falling down all around me, and then my eyes
went shut.

IV

The old chief woke me up at the first dawn streak. I heard him and I
felt him shaking me, but I didn't get up. As soon as I opened my eyes
the pain in my feet started up. I touched one foot to the ground and it
throbbed worse'n toothache. I knew I couldn't travel any that day and I
didn't care. I turned over on my back and laid there looking up at the sky.
It had cleared off during the night and the stars was shining. The sky was
all a pale gray except for one long sulphur-colored streak where day was
getting ready to break. Behind me the Indians was looking to their guns
and settling their tomahawks in their belts. I watched their heads and
shoulders moving against that yellow light, and I saw one of them take
his tomahawk out and heft it and then try the blade with his finger. I
thought that if I just kept on laying there that maybe he would be the one
to finish me off, and then I thought Mad Dog was quicker and would beat
him to it.

The old chief was still shaking me. "Get up, Jinny. Day come."

"No," I said, "I ain't going to get up."

He took me by the shoulders and tried to pull me to my feet but I
slumped back on the ground. I spoke to him in Shawnee.

"My feet bleed and I cannot travel. Let me die."

He leaned over and looked at my feet and then he called to one of the
young Indians to bring him some white oak bark. When the bark come
he boiled it over the fire and then he took the liquor from the bark and
cooled it with more water and poured it over my feet.

The other Indians had finished scattering the fire and was starting out
through the willows, but Crowmocker just sat there pouring that stuff on
my feet. I could feel the swelling going down and after a while I touched
my feet to the ground. It didn't hurt like it had, and I got up and we
started off. He give me some parched corn and I ate it, walking. He said
we would have to travel fast to catch up with the other Indians. I asked
him if the white people were still following us and he laughed and said no
white men could get across the river. I owned to myself that they couldn't,
and I didn't think any more about them coming after me. I thought the
Indians would probably take me so far away that I'd never again see a
white face.

We caught up with the other Indians towards dark. That night we slept
in a canebrake by a little river. A buffalo was wallowing in the river as
we come up. One of the Indians shot him. They butchered him there in
the water and drug big slabs of the meat up the bank with ropes cut from
the hide. We must have been in Indian country by this time. They didn't
seem to think it made any different how much noise they made. They

made up a big fire to one side of the brake and they were half the night cooking the meat and eating. I went to sleep under a tree with them singing and yelling all around me.

When I woke up the next morning they were having a council. They talked till the sun was high and then they split up into two parties. Mad Dog and three of the young bucks left us and swum across the river. The rest of us kept on up the bank. We traveled all that day through the cane and then we struck a divide and followed it into another valley. We had run out of everything to eat by this time except the strings of jerked meat that they all carried slung around their necks. We stayed two, three days at a buffalo lick, hoping to kill some game, but none came and we went on.

Most of the leaves were off the trees by this time and the nights were cold. I knew it was some time in October that the Indians come and burned our house, but I didn't know how long we'd been on the trail and I didn't have any idea what country we were in.

One morning we come out in some deep narrows just above where two creeks flowed together. A wild-looking place with tumbling falls and big rocks laying around everywhere. I looked up at the cliffs over our heads and I couldn't believe my eyes. They were *painted*: deer and buffalo and turtles big as a man, painted in red and in black on the rock. Some of the young Indians acted like they had never been there before either. They would keep walking around looking at things and sometimes stand and stare at the pictures of wild beasts that were painted everywhere on the smooth rock.

The old chief took a way up the side of the cliffs, the rest of us following. The young Indians went up like deer, but I had to pull myself up by the laurel that grew down in between the rocks. We walked along a narrow ledge and come to a rockhouse. It was the biggest rockhouse ever I saw, run all along one side of the cliff. The old chief uncovered an iron pot from where it was hid in a lot of trash in one corner of the cave and showed me how to set it up on forked sticks. He said that I would have to do all the work around the camp from now on, the way Indian women did, and when the spring rains come and melted the snows he would take me to his town on the Tenassee and I would learn more about Indian ways and be adopted into the tribe in place of his dead daughter.

I thought if he took me there I would never get away and I had it in mind to make a break for it first chance I got. I got hold of two strings of jerked meat and I kept them tied around my waist so I'd be ready when the time came. I thought I would wait, though, and maybe I would find out how far it was to the settlements. I would lie there in my corner of the cave at night, making out I was asleep, and listen to them talking around the fire. I heard them call the names of the creeks that flowed through that valley—Big Paint and Little Mudlick; and further off was another creek, Big Mudlick, where they went sometimes to hunt. The names were strange to me and I never could tell from their talk how far it was to the settlements or even which way to go. I had an idea that the place I was in was secret to the Indians, for it was a wonder to see and yet I had never heard any white body tell of it. I asked Crowmocker what the pictures of deer and buffalo and bear were for and he said they were the Indians' fathers and that I would learn about them when I was adopted into the tribe. Once he pointed some mounds out to me and said they were graves. He said that he and his people always stopped when they come this way to visit the graves of their fathers that was all over the valley.

A spell of fine weather come, late in the fall. Indian summer they call it. We looked out one day and bees were swarming on the cliffside. Crowmocker was mad when he saw them. He said it meant that the white people were coming; that when bees swarmed out of season they were running away from the white people who had scared all the game out of the country and made it so that even bees couldn't live in it. I asked would the white people find their way into this valley and he said they couldn't— that it was a way known only to Indians; that if a white man ever set foot in it the great bear would come down off the wall and crush him in his paws. He said, though, that there would be fighting soon over all the land and a lot of bloodshed.

I knew that was all foolishness about the bear, but I thought likely as not there would be fighting and I wanted to get away worse than ever. One morning I was down in the hollow by myself, gathering wood, and I thought that was the time. Three of the Indians had gone off hunting and I knew the others were laying up in the cave asleep. I didn't think anybody would be following me, for a while, anyhow. I started off, slipping from tree to tree, and I got quite a way up the hollow. I knew nobody was following me, but I would keep looking back over my shoulder all the time. I got to thinking. I didn't have any way to kill game, and nothing to eat but two strings of jerked meat. I didn't even know how far I'd have to go before I came to any settlement. Worst of all, I didn't even know which way to take. Likely as not I'd starve to death in the woods, or freeze if the weather turned. I'd better stay with the Indians, where at least I could sleep warm and eat, if it wasn't anything but parched corn. I picked up my load of wood and got back to camp quick as I could, and didn't none of them ever know I'd been away.

I never tried it again, but sometimes I'd sit there on the edge of the cliff and pick out the way I'd take if I did go. There was a ridge covered with black pines rose up right in front of the rockhouse. I thought if I could once get up there I could get down into the valley easy. I hadn't ever been over there, but I knew what the country would be like. I saw myself slipping along through that divide, around the foot of the mountain and

over some more mountains till I'd come out on a clearing. I'd slip up to
some cabin, towards dark. They'd think I was an Indian at first, maybe,
and then they'd see my eyes was light and they'd take me in and keep
me till I could get back to my own folks again.

We stayed in that rockhouse a long time. The leaves all fell off the
trees, and one or two light snows fell, but the real cold weather was late
coming. The Indians hunted just enough to keep us in meat. They said
the pelts were thin that year and not worth taking. Sometimes they would
take me along to bring in the game, but mostly they left me to work by
myself. When cold weather set in we built big fires in the cave and it was
warm inside like a house. When the Indians weren't hunting they would
lie around on buffalo skins and sleep. The smoke was terrible and the
smell of Indians was all over everything. At first it bothered me, but after
a while I got so I didn't notice it.

I wasn't in the cave much, even in bad weather. I had to gather all the
firewood. The Indians didn't have an axe and I couldn't get anything but
dead branches. There wasn't much down timber on the cliffside; so I'd
mostly go up over the cliffs when I was hunting wood. There was a barren
there, flat as the palm of your hand and covered with a thin kind of grass.
It had plenty of trees on it but they were all twisty and stunted by the
wind. The only sizable tree was a big elm. It was peeled for thirty or forty
feet and had a rattlesnake painted on it—a monster snake coiling up
around the trunk. You could see that snake from everywhere on the barren.
I was feared to look at it. The Indians seemed to think a lot of it. Sometimes they would go up there at night and I would hear them singing and
dancing and calling to the snake.

Somewhere on the barren there were lead mines. The Indians never let
me go to them, but they would go off and stay two, three hours and come
back with big balls of lead. They made me smelt it out for bullets. I had
to have a mighty fire. It would take me days and days to get up enough
wood. I would heap it up in a big pile and then I would kindle the fire
and keep it going for hours. When the lead melted, it ran down through
little ditches into holes that I had dug to form the bullets. It would take
the lead a long time to melt. Sometimes I would be up on the barren from
sunup to sundown.

I would sit there and think about my husband and my children. I would
wonder whether Tom went out in the woods hunting ginseng the way he
used to do, and was he still looking for me or had give me up for dead.
When I thought of Tom the house would be there, too, not burning
down the way it was last time I saw it, but standing with the rooms just
the way they always were. I could see both rooms plain, even to the hole
that was burnt in the floor when a big log fell out one night. The children
would be playing in and out of the house like they did. It was like they
were all living; it was only me that was gone away.

I would think back, too, over things that happened long before ever I was grown and married to Tom Wiley. There was a man named Rayburn stayed at the settlement one winter. Lance Rayburn. A big, strong man and a mighty hunter. We ate bear of his shooting all that fall. He was handy with snares too, and took over a hundred beaver down in the bottom. He courted me some that winter, sitting in front of the fire after the old folks were in bed. I laughed and went on with him, but Tom Wiley had just started a-courting me and all the time my mind was on him more'n it was on the stranger.

Come time for Rayburn to pack up his pelts to take to the station, he saved one out for me. Beaver, and extra fine and soft. He give it to my sister, Sarah, and told her to hand it to me when I come to the house. She made one of the children bring it down to the creek where I was boiling clothes. I laid it there on the grass and I would stop and look at it as I went back and forth with my clothes, and sometimes I would wipe my hands dry and lay them on the soft fur for pleasure in the feel. But all the time I knew I wasn't going to keep it. When Rayburn come towards me through the willows I went to meet him with the pelt in my hands.

"Keep this," I said, "and give it to some girl where you're going."

"Don't you want it?" he asked.

"I ain't taking nothing from you."

He stood there looking at me and all of a sudden his eyes narrowed up like a cat's. "You're full young to be marrying," he said.

"I ain't too young to know my own mind," I told him and before I thought I laughed.

He come towards me, and before I knowed what he was up to he was on me and trying to bear me to the ground. He was a strong man but I was stout, too, and I stood up to him. We was rassling around in the bushes quite some while before he got me down, and then he had to keep both his hands on my chest. I laid there right still, looking up at him.

"What you reckon my pappy'll say when I tell him about this?" I asked.

He laughed, "I ain't a-feared of no Sellards that ever walked," he said, "but that Tom Wiley ain't no manner of man for you," he said.

"You can talk against Tom Wiley and you can hold me here till Dooms-day," I told him, "but it ain't going to do you no good. I ain't going to have none of you no matter what happens."

His face kind of changed. Looked like it hurt him to hear me say it. He got up off me right away and he picked the beaver pelt up from where it lay in the grass and he throwed it hard as he could into the creek.

"It'll git to my girl that way fast as any other," he said.

I watched the pelt floating down the water and onto a rock and then off again. When I turned around he was out of sight and he was gone when I got back to the house. He stayed at the station a while and then he went off in the mountains hunting bear and wasn't ever heard of again.

Some said he was killed by wild beasts. A rifle and a cap that they said was his was found up in the hills. The man that found the rifle kept it, but they give the cap to the Borderses. Wouldn't anybody wear it, and Sally hung it up in the dog alley. I used to look at it every time I passed and wonder whether it had ever been on Lance Rayburn's head and was he dead or still living. And sometimes I'd wonder how it'd been if I'd married him instead of Tom, but I knew all the time I wouldn't ever have married anybody but Tom because he was the one I fancied from the time I was a chap, living neighbor to the Wileys, back in the Roanoke country.

I thought about Lance Rayburn and I thought about a lot of other folks that had come to the settlement and stayed and then gone on and wouldn't anybody know whether they were living still or dead. And I thought about people dead long ago, my old granny back in Carolina, ninety-eight years old and turned simple. She'd sit in the chimney corner all day long, singing the likeliest tunes!

"Pa'tridge in the pea patch," she'd sing and call me to her and fondle me, liking gals, she said, always better than boys.

> "Pa'tridge in the pea patch
> Pickin' up the peas.
> 'Long comes the bell cow
> Kickin' up her heels . . ."

"Oh . . . h, the bell cow," she'd sing and catch me by my little shimmy tail. "O . . . O . . . hh, the bell cow . . ." and hist me up over the arm of her chair. "O . . . O . . . hh, the bell cow, kickin' up her heels. Call the little gal to milk her in the pail."

I used to call those songs to mind when I had to go down to the lick for salt. It was a place I didn't like to go. A deep hollow with three sulphur springs and a lick that covered nigh an acre of ground. The biggest lick ever I saw in my life. The way was white with the bones of beasts, and in between the piled up bones the long furrows that the buffalo made licking the ground for salt. I would walk down those furrows to the spring and fill my bucket with the salty water and go back up the hill to where my kettle was slung between two little birches. Sitting there waiting for the water to boil, I couldn't keep my eyes off the bones. I would take them up in my hand and turn them over and over, wondering what manner of beasts they had belonged to.

Once I made myself a little beast, laying all the bones out on some lacy moss, the front feet stiff like it was galloping off in the woods, the hind legs drawn up under him. A hare it might have been or a little fawn. Or maybe a beast that nobody ever heard of before.

There were beasts come to that lick one time or another not known to man. Bigger'n buffalo they must have been. One thigh-bone, I mind, longer'n I was and twice as big around as two good-sized men.

I thought of a man used to be around the station, Vard Wiley, second cousin to Tom. Folks said he was the biggest liar in the settlements. He would stay off in the woods hunting day after day and never bring in any game except maybe a brace of wild turkeys. And he told tall tales about a lick bigger'n any lick around those parts, where the beasts come up in tens of thousands. He would lay up in a tree all day and watch 'em, he said, and not take a shot for wonder. There were beasts used there, he said, ten times the size of buffalo. He offered to take anybody there and show them the bones, and when they asked him why he didn't bring them back to the settlement he said couldn't no man carry them, nor no two horses.

Folks laughed at him, and the children round the settlement used to sing a song:

> "Vard Wiley's gone west, Vard Wiley's gone east,
> A-huntin' the woods for a monster beast.
>
> "He'll make him a tent out of the wild beast's hide
> And all the king's horses can stable inside.
>
> "He'll make him a wagon out of solid bone
> And it'll take ten oxen to draw it home."

I called that song to mind and I thought how if I ever saw Vard Wiley again I'd go up to him and say I knew him to be a truth-teller, and all the people would laugh at me maybe, the way they did Vard Wiley, but all the time I would be knowing it was the truth.

I thought, too, of other tales he told and of jokes he played. Of the time he borrowed my dress and sunbonnet and shawl and went and sat on the creek bank when the schoolmaster was in swimming. He sat there all evening with the sunbonnet hiding his face and old Mister Daugherty shaking his fist at him. "You hussy! You brazen hussy! Don't you know I'm naked?" and finally when he come up out of the water naked as the day he was born Vard took out after him and run him clean to the house. Old Mister Daugherty went around saying there was a woman ought to be run out of the settlements, and Vard would talk to him and make out it was me. But Old Man Daugherty knew wouldn't none of Hezekiah Sellards' daughters be carrying on like that. He was bound it was a woman from Ab's Valley.

I would think about 'em sitting there and arguing about how the hussy ought to be run out of the settlements, and I would laugh all by myself there in the woods. Throw back my head and laugh and then feel silly when the woods give back the echo.

I did a lot of work while I was with the Indians. It was hard on me at first but I got used to it. It was better after Mad Dog left us. The old chief was like a father to me, and the young ones knew I belonged to him and didn't bother me. I slept off by myself in a far corner of the cave and he would wake me up at daybreak and tell me what there was to do that day. He took pains to show me how to flesh pelts and cure them, and he showed me how to split a deer sinew for thread and how to make a whistle to call deer out of birch bark and sticks. And after I got so I could sew skins good he had me make him a pair of leggings and trim them with porcupine quills—porcupine quills colored with some roots he got out of the woods.

It bothered him the way I looked and he made me paint my face the way the Indians did. Fixed me up some of the red root mixed with bear's grease, and after I'd been putting it on my face for a while you couldn't told me from an Indian woman, except for my light eyes.

He'd stay in the cave with me sometimes all day, his buffalo hide wrapped around him so tight that his knees were up against him like a chair. He'd sit there and rock back and forth on his heels and talk while I worked. Down in the hollow the young braves would be practicing their war whoops. He would listen to them and laugh.

"Our young men give the war whoop loudly to cover up their fear of the enemy. It was not so when I was young. There was joy in the war whoop then."

He said he was a chief but he might have been something better. He might have been a medicine man. He had the gift of it from his grandmother. His own mother died when he was born, he said, and his old granny raised him. He told me about how she would take him into the woods with her looking for yarbs and roots, and how she knew where everything grew and which roots would be good to take and which had no strength in them. He said that after I was adopted into the tribe he would tell some of her secrets to me, but the Spirit would be angry if a white woman knew them.

I asked him wouldn't I still be a white woman after I was adopted into the tribe but he said no, the white blood would go out of me and the Spirit would send Indian blood to take its place, and then I would feel like an Indian and know all the Indian ways and maybe get to be a wise woman like his old granny.

He told me about his youngest daughter and how she come by her death, following what she thought was a fawn bleating. They found her days afterward, three enemy arrows in her. Her death had been paid for with three scalps of warriors, and he would say that he didn't grieve over her, but I knew he did. I got to feeling sorry for him sometimes to have lost his daughter that meant so much to him, and then I would think how

I had lost all my children and my husband and I would cry, dropping tears on the skin I was sewing.

I got so after a while that the Indian way of doing things seemed natural to me. I thought nothing of seeing dark faces around me all the time, but in the night sometimes I would dream of white faces. White faces coming towards me through the trees. Or sometimes I would be in a house again and look up all of a sudden and all the faces in the room would be white.

One white face was always coming to me in my dreams: Tice Harman, the man whose house the Indians thought they were burning the day they burned ours. I always thought that if anybody came to save me it would be Tice Harman. I could see him plain in my dreams. A little man, wouldn't weigh more'n a hundred and twenty pounds, but he had a big head. A big head and a big beak of a nose and long yellow hair down to his shoulders. His eyes were blue and in my dreams they glittered like ice. I would dream about Tice Harman and when I waked I would think what I'd heard said of him—how he could go further and stand more than any man in the settlements, and how he loved to fight Indians better'n eat when he was hungry. I would think, too, of how folks said he would bring trouble on the settlements shooting that Indian down when there warn't really any use in it; and I would think that since it was him that brought all my trouble on me, maybe it would be him that would get me away from the Indians. But time went on and nobody came, and after a while I got so I didn't think much about it.

One evening I was gathering wood on the cliffside and I heard a lot of whooping and hollering down near the mouth of the creek. The Indians come out from where they were sleeping back in the cave and stood looking over the falls. A long whoop came and the old chief put his hands to his mouth and answered it. There was more whooping back and forth, and then Mad Dog came up the trail by the falls with about twenty Indians following him. They were painted for war and marched single file, all except the last six or eight. They were in pairs and in the middle of them a white man, walking with his hands tied behind him. A white man? A boy. Couldn't have been more than eighteen years old.

I had to step out of the path to let them by. The dead branches rustled in my hands. The prisoner turned his head. He looked straight into my eyes. It was like he didn't know I was there. I spoke to him.

"I can't do nothing," I said. "I'm a white woman, but I can't do nothing. Christ!" I said, "there ain't nothing I can do."

He kept on looking at me but he didn't speak. They were hurrying him past. I dropped the branches and run after them. Mad Dog called to one of the young bucks and he caught me and held me. I fought him, but he held me till they had all gone up the path.

I went on to the rockhouse and kindled up the fire. After a while Mad Dog come down and told me to cook up some meat quick as I could. There would be singing and dancing, he said; they would want meat all night long.

I looked at him. "A present," I said. "A present for Kagahye-liske's daughter. Give me this boy. He is not good for anything but to gather wood."

His eyes were fierce. "Boy?" he said. "He has this day killed my brother." Then he laughed and smoothed my hair. "Jinny," he said, "pretty Jinny."

I made out I had to see to the fire and walked away. I put some bear meat on to boil and I told him I would call him when it was done, and he went on back up the path.

There was a moon coming. I sat there waiting for the meat to boil and watched it rise over the pines. Up on the barren the Indians were dragging up all the dead branches they could find into one pile. After a while I looked up over the rockhouse and saw the sky all light and knew they had kindled the fire.

The stamping and yelling went on, and every now and then a gun would go off. Then there was running around the tree. You could hear the feet pounding and the long calls. "Ai . . . yi . . . Ai . . . yi . . . Ai . . . yi . . ." One for each man that had died that day. And the sharp cry for the scalp taking. They would act it all out and the boy standing there watching. He was dazed, though; he wouldn't see it for what it was. He wouldn't know what they were doing, might not know what they were going to do. There on the path he looked at me and didn't know me for a white woman. I ought to have found out his name and where he come from. I ought to have done that much. But he wouldn't have answered. And what good would it do his folks . . . if I ever saw white folks again. Then Mad Dog's hand on my hair. "Pretty Jinny . . . pretty Jinny . . ."

The flames shot up and lit the whole valley. The moon looked cold where it hung over the pines. I kept the fire up under the kettle but I couldn't sit still. I walked back and forth in the rockhouse, back and forth, back and forth, waiting for the shrieks to start.

They were a long time coming. I thought maybe it was already going on. Indians can stand there burning and not make a sound, and there have been white men that could. But this was just a boy . . .

The first shriek was long and then they come short and quick, one right after the other. I got over in a corner of the rockhouse and held on tight to a big rock. After a while I let go of the rock and put both fingers in my ears and then I was feared to take them out, thinking it might not be over yet. The Indians were still yelling and stamping. The young ones kept running down and grabbing up chunks of meat from the boiling pot and carrying them up to the barren. I could see the old chief's shadow where he stood on the edge of the cliff calling to the new moon.

When he came down to the rockhouse Mad Dog was with him. They stood there dipping meat up out of the kettle. Mad Dog talked.

"It is too much. For five hundred brooches I could buy a girl of the Wild-Cats, young and swift, a fine worker in beads. A girl like a moonbeam, daughter of a mighty warrior."

His eyes were black in the circles of paint. His tongue showed bright between his painted lips. The red lines ran from his forehead down the sides of his cheeks to make gouts of blood on his chin.

A devil. A devil come straight from hell to burn and murder. Three white men killed that day and the boy brought back to torture. It was him that killed them, him that yelled loudest when the boy was burning. Him that set fire to my house and burned my children . . .

I saw him running through the woods, white men after him. I saw him fall, a dozen bullets in him. But he wouldn't be dead. He would lie there bleeding and look at me out of his painted eyes, and I would go up and stomp on him, stomp him into the dirt . . .

My hands shook so I dropped the sticks I was carrying. I was near enough now to hear all they were saying. Mad Dog was taking little silver brooches out of a buckskin. He poured them out in a pile on a rock and then counted them. The old chief stood there till he got through counting; then he swept them all up into a bag he took from around his neck.

"Brother," he said, "the woman is yours."

Mad Dog had left the fire and was coming towards me. I ran over and caught hold of the old chief's arm. I called him by his Indian name.

"Kagahye-liske, do not give me to this man. He has killed my children and burned my house."

He looked down at me and it was like he'd never seen me before. His face, not painted, was as cruel as the Cherokee's, the eyes bloodshot and the whole face swollen from the meat he had eaten.

"The war whoop drowns sorrow," he said. "This chief is my brother and a mighty warrior. He has this day killed three white men."

I hung on to his arm. "Keep me for one of the young men of your village," I said. "The Cherokee are old women. You have said so and you have promised. You have promised to take me with you wherever you go."

He shook my hands off. "A promise," he said, "to a white coward! Go to your work."

He turned around like he was going to leave the cave. I run after him and caught hold of his knees, but he broke away. Mad Dog come and tied me up tight with thongs that he cut from buffalo hide, and then they both went on up to the barren where the other Indians was still screeching and stamping.

The screeching and stamping went on far into the night. The fire under the kettle went out and it was dark except for a little light from the moon. I laid there on the floor, listening to the Indians and thinking about how it would be when Mad Dog came down to take me for his wife. I laid there, expecting him to come any minute, but the singing and dancing went on and he didn't come, and after a while I went to sleep.

V

The white boy that they had burned came to me while I was asleep. He came carrying a lamp that was made from the bleached skull of a sheep. The brain hollow was filled with buffalo fat and there was a wick in it burning bright. He came walking between the trees like he didn't have need to look where he was going. His hair was light like I had seen it when he passed me there on the path, but it was long, too, like Tice Harman's. His eyes were the same eyes that had looked at me there on the path.

I said to him what I had said there. "I couldn't do nothing," I said. "There wasn't nothing I could do."

He didn't speak—only made signs for me to follow him. I got up and walked after him. The rawhide thongs were still on me but they didn't bind any more and I moved as easy and as light as he did. He went down by the falls and clomb up over the hill to where the elm tree stood that had the big rattlesnake painted on it. He walked past the elm tree and struck out through the black pines that were all over that ridge. Sometimes he would go so fast that I couldn't keep up with him, and then I would stand still and after a while I would see the light flickering through the trees and I would go on to where he was waiting for me. We went on through the pine woods and started down the side of the ridge. I heard water running somewhere far down below. I thought that would be Mudlick Creek, but when I got to it it was a branch I'd never seen before. We crossed it and went on up a path through a clearing. There were little shrubs all around like the ones up on the barren, and in the middle of them was a house. It was my house and yet it wasn't. White all over and the walls so thin you could see the light from the lamp shining through the logs.

People were walking around in the yard and sitting on the doorstep. They moved to let me go through the door, but they didn't speak to me and I didn't speak to them.

The men that were sitting in front of the fire playing draughts didn't even look up when I came in. I went over to the hearth and tried to dry out my clothes. I stood there holding out my hands but no heat came. I looked at the logs and they were white like the timbers of the house, and the same light came from them. I saw that the men playing didn't have a lamp and yet there was light all around them.

People kept walking in and out of the cabin, men and women and little children. I would go up to them and look in their faces, but there wasn't anybody there I knew. I walked round and round the room. Every now and then the people would move out of the way and I would catch sight of the walls. White, with patches of green on them. I put my hand up and felt one of the logs. It was round and cold to the touch. No log at all, but bleached bone. I knew then that all the house was bone, the floor and the walls and the chimney, even the table that the men were playing on, all made from the big bones down at the lick.

One of the men at the table stretched his arm out and pulled me over to him. He had on a beaver cap and his face under it was pale like he'd been in the woods a long time. He looked at me and I saw it was Lance Rayburn. He sang, pulling me up over the arm of his chair:

"Oh . . . the bell cow, kicking up her heels,
   Call the little gal to milk her in the pail . . ."

Fiddling started up somewhere and all fell to dancing. They danced to one of my old granny's tunes:

"There was an old lord lived in a northern countree,
   Bowee down, bowee down . . ."

There was bowing back and forth and balancing, and there were figures called, but wasn't any women dancing. I would see something going by and think it was a woman's skirt, but when I got up to it it would be fur or feathers dangling from a belt and all the faces around were dark, not like they were at first.

The great flames went leaping up the chimney, and all of a sudden I knew that they had built that fire to burn somebody by. I looked around for the one they were going to burn but he wasn't there. I said, "They will burn me next," and I saw what they would tie me to—the rattlesnake tree, going straight up from the table through the roof.

I went to the door and I saw through the black trunks a light flickering. I run and Mad Dog and the old chief were after me the way they were that day in the hollow. I thought, "They will kill me now when I go down," and I run faster and then they were both gone away and I was walking through pine woods, the light flickering on ahead of me.

I walked on and come to a creek that run along between wide banks of cane. The light shone on the water and made it light as mist. I stepped in, not knowing whether it was water or mist, and I could feel it coming up around my knees, water and yet not water. I moved along through it light as the wind till I come to where the creek forked. I could see the two forks and the white trunks of the sycamores along the bank, but I didn't know which way to go.

The light was all around me. I could see it shining on the reeds and on the little leaves of the cane and on the water where it broke on the rocks. Behind me there were voices talking.

"Jinny Wiley . . . Jinny Wiley, that was stolen and lived with the Indians . . ."

And then it was the old chief talking to the new moon:

"The white people . . . The white people are all over the land. The beaver makes no more dams and the buffalo does not come to the lick. And bees swarm here in the ancient village. Bees swarm on the graves of our fathers . . ."

The light that had been around me was gone. It was shining now through the tree trunks down a fork of the creek. I waded towards it through the light water, the voices following, and then they were gone and I was standing at the foot of a high mountain. I looked up and saw the light flickering at the top and I clomb towards it, pulling myself up by the scrubs and holly bushes.

I got up on the mountaintop but the young man wasn't there. I walked out onto the edge of a cliff and he was by my side. He said, "Look, Jinny!" and the flame of his lamp leaped up and lighted the whole valley and I looked across a river and saw a fort. I saw the roofs of the houses and the stockade and the timber burned back over the rifle range, and I saw men and women walking around inside the stockade.

I said, "I'm a-going over there," but the young man wasn't with me any more, and the dark that was all around was the inside of the rockhouse.

VI

When I woke up the next morning the Indians had a big fire going and were all sitting around eating. I laid there and made out I was still asleep. They had found trace of buffalo down at the lick and were making ready for a big hunt. I thought maybe they would take me along to bring in the game the way they did sometimes, and then I heard Mad Dog say they would leave me tied up in the cave till they got ready to start for their town.

I was laying with my face turned up and I was feared they could tell by my eyes that I wasn't asleep. I give a kind of groan and rolled over on my side. I laid there not moving while the talking went on all around me. Once footsteps come over to the corner where I was laying and I heard something slap down on the ground right by me but I didn't give any sign and the footsteps went away.

I laid there so still that I went to sleep again with the talking and the making ready for the hunt still going on. I was waked up by a kind of roaring sound. At first I thought it was the falls and then I knew the falls wouldn't sound that loud. I opened my eyes. The Indians were all gone and there was a big storm blowing up.

I laid there watching the pine tops lash back and forth in the wind, and the dream I'd had come back into my mind as plain as if it was something that had happened. I thought it was sent to me on purpose to tell me that now was the chance to get away. I knew that if the Indians come back with any game that night they'd feast high again and were more than likely to take me up on the barren and burn me like they done that boy.

I sat up. A piece of meat was lying on the floor right by me. That meant that the Indians would be all gone all day and maybe another day. If I could only get free of the thongs I might get a long way off before they knew I was gone.

There was a knife stuck in a crack of the rock where they laid the meat. If I could only get hold of that! I rolled over and over till I got to the rock and managed to get up on my knees, though the thongs cut into me bad. I could see the handle of the knife sticking up out of the crack and I laid my face down flat on the rock and tried to catch hold of it with my teeth. But it was too far down and all I did was get my mouth full of grit and sand. I gave up and laid down again. The wind wasn't as high as it had been, but the rain was coming down hard. It blew way back into the cave. I laid there with the big drops spattering in my face and a thought came to me. I rolled over to where the rain was pouring down off the roof and I laid there till I was soaked through. All the time I kept straining at the thongs and I could feel them giving a little, the way leather does when it's wet. I kept on, getting them looser and looser till finally I worked my way out of them and stood up free.

I listened and I couldn't hear anything but the roaring of the wind and the beating of the rain on the ledge. I tiptoed to the end of the cave and looked down the path. But I couldn't see any sign of living creature. I dug the knife out from between the rocks and I took the piece of cooked meat and a little kettle that the old chief had left laying around, and went off out of the other end of the cave and along the cliffside.

I kept to the path a little way and then I struck off through the trees down the hillside. The ground was wet and slid from under my feet in big chunks. I caught on to the trees all the way to keep myself from falling. When I got to the bottom I could look back and see where I'd come, as plain as if I'd blazed a trail. I knew I'd have to strike water. I run in among some pines and come to a wet weather branch. I waded right in. It was swift water and full of holes. I would step in one every now and then and go down, but I kept on as fast as I could. I felt all the time like the Indians were after me. I knew they had gone south towards the salt lick and I knew the whole cliffside and the barren was between me and them, but all the time I felt like they were right behind me. When I looked over my shoulder the top boughs of the rattlesnake tree showed from the barren. I was glad when I rounded a bend and it was out of sight.

When I come out to where the branch flowed into the creek I didn't
know which way to go, and then I thought that in my dream I was following water and I struck right down the stream. It was harder going here
than it was in the branch. The snows melting had filled all the dry weather
branches, and muddy water kept running in till you couldn't tell anything
about the depth. It was well I was going downstream, but even then the
current was a hindrance to me, reaching in and sweeping me off my feet
sometimes into a hole that I would have a time getting out of. More than
once I was in danger of drowning.

I kept on like this all day. When it was drawing towards dark I crawled
up on the bank under some cedars and I laid there and I ate a good-
sized piece of the cooked meat I had brought with me. The rain had fallen
off to a light drizzle and there was some color in the sky, sign of a clear
day tomorrow. There was a flight of little birds over the water and then
round and round the tops of the cedars. Some of them lit in the boughs of
the tree I was laying under. I could hear them flying in and out and the
quick cries and then the twittering as they settled down to roost. It was
dark under the trees but the streak of light stayed on the water. I laid
here and watched it fade and I wished I could stay there where the
cedar boughs were like a little house. I wished I could stay there and not
run any more. I thought I would maybe sleep a few minutes and then I
could go on faster. But when I shut my eyes I would think I heard the
Indians coming through the trees and after a little I got up and went
on again.

I tried wading some more but I couldn't make it in the pitch dark. I
got up on the bank of the creek and pushed my way through the bushes
as best I could. Sometimes the undergrowth would be so thick I couldn't
make it, and then I would have to get down in the water again. All the
way I was worrying about losing time following the bending and twisting
of the creek, and then I would think that was the only sure way to get
out of the hill country and I had best stick to water, spite of all the
bending.

Sometime during the night I lost my way from the creek and wandered
in the pitch dark into a marsh that was all along the creek bottom. More
like a bog it was. I couldn't seem to get out of it no matter what I did. I
stood there bogged to the knees and couldn't even hear the creek running
—nothing but the wind soughing in the trees. And I thought what a lone
place it was and if I came on quicksand, as was more than likely, I could
go down and even my bones never be found. And I thought of how
Lance Rayburn's bones might have been laying all this time in some
hollow of the mountain and nothing maybe but squirrels or deer ever
going near the place, and it seemed to me I might better have stayed with
the Indians. But I knew it wouldn't be any use going back now. They
would put the fire to me sure.

I stood there and I heard some wild thing passing. Pit pat pit pat it went; feet falling on dry ground. I pulled out of the muck and made towards the sound, and a deer or something broke through the thicket and went off through the woods.

I followed and come out on high ground, a slope covered with pine needles. I threw myself down flat on my face. I must have gone off to sleep. When I come to myself light was growing through the trees, and all around me I could hear twigs snapping and little rustlings. I got up quick, thinking it was the Indians coming, and then I felt foolish, knowing it was only game stirring at break of day. I saw two deer go by, moving slow over the brown pine needles. The air was so still they didn't get a whiff of me until they were out of the thicket. The buck wheeled so quick he almost knocked the doe over, and then they were both clattering off over the hill.

I went down to the creek bank and washed my face and let the water run over my wrists where they were scratched by the branches. I ate the last of my meat sitting there on a rock. When I got ready to go I found out that one of my strings of jerked meat had slipped off during the night. I couldn't hardly believe it at first. I stood up and felt all over my clothes time and again but it warn't there.

"Well," I said, "it's gone and they ain't no use crying over it, but I wish to God it'd a been the little piece."

I got in the water and started wading again. The creek was shallow for about half a mile and then it run into a bigger creek. The two of them run on before me and I didn't know which way to go. I stood there looking. The sun was up and it shone on the water. I watched the riffles break on the black rocks where the sun caught them, and the place was not the same place I had seen in the dream and yet it was the same because of the light that was over everything.

I remembered the way I took in the dream. "Left I'll go," I said, "like it was in the dream, and if it don't turn out right it's no fault of mine."

I went on, wading half the time. All that day I was thinking about something to eat. Seems like everything good I ever had to eat in my life come back to torment me that day. The smell of herring, cooking, bothered me most. I would see myself, a chap, back in the Roanoke country, broiling herrings over the coals the way children did when their mammy wouldn't give them anything else to eat between meals. I would go over it all, time and again, the herrings hanging in rows in the smokehouse, like tobacco in a barn, and us climbing up on a slab of wood to get at them.

"Three," Dinny, that's my oldest brother, 'd say every time. "Three. You might as well get one apiece while you're at it."

I thought, too, about people wasting things, of a woman I knew used to give all her buttermilk to her pig, and I thought how it was shameful to have no mind for them that might be starving. And I thought how if I could have that pig's dinner one time, or even a moldy piece of bread, the kind I'd thrown away many a time as not good enough for the dogs. And yet I'd been as wasteful as any of them in my day—worse, even, with game. I used to go hunting just for the fun of it. Seemed like there warn't nothing I liked better than sighting down a rifle. Warn't none of the Sellards or Damron boys a better shot than I was, and I could throw a knife with the best of them. That time John and Dick and me and the two Damrons went to Sinking Fork on a big hunt I shot eighteen wild gobblers, and when we loaded up and there were more'n we could carry it was me that said to leave them laying, that there warn't no use in breaking yourself down and the woods full of gobblers. I thought about them gobblers more'n once that day and, Lord, how I wished I could git my hands on a rifle butt just one more time.

I threw my knife once or twice at some small game, mostly rabbits, but it was a rusty old thing and not fitted to the hand the way a knife has to be to turn proper. One rabbit that I hit square in the middle got up and skittered off like nothing had happened, and I saw then it was a waste of time to throw at them.

Late that evening I come on some forward wild greens in a sheltered place on the creek bank. I went down on my knees and gathered every shoot. I found some punk and went up to a rockhouse on the side of the hill and built a little fire way in under the ledge the way I'd seen the Indians do. I knew it was craziness to build a fire, but it might be days before I'd come on any wild greens again. "I'll eat," I said, "varmints or no varmints."

I put my greens on to boil in the little kettle with a piece of the jerked meat and sat there, thinking about how Indians would go up on a cliff to sight over the country and how the least little smoke curling up would be a sign to them. Once I was on the point of putting the fire out but I couldn't bring myself to do it. I feared to feed it much and yet I'd catch myself putting dead twigs to it. It was a long time before the bubbles started rising up in that little old kettle. I sat there rocking on my heels and talking to them.

"Boil," I said, "boil. God's sake, can't you boil no faster'n that? And me setting here starving."

I ate up every mite of the greens and drank the pot liquor and licked the kettle and then I put out down the hill as fast as I could. I could feel my stomach tight under my waistband and strength coming up in me from the vittles and I run faster than I'd ever run before. It was dark under the trees but there was still light down the water courses. I thought how in some cleared place or in a town it wouldn't be dark for two or three hours yet and I saw myself in such a place, moving around and talking to people but staying always in the light. And I said to myself, if I ever got into such a cleared place again it'd be hard to get me to set foot in the woods.

The creek I was following was a master tumbler. Straight down it went over big rocks and the water white everywhere with its dashing. Once I thought I would leave it and strike out through the woods again, and then I thought falling water'd take me out of the hills quicker'n anything else and I'd best stick to it long as I could.

I went on and then all of a sudden I come upon something that froze my guts cold: the print of a foot by the water. I knew it would be a moccasin but I stooped down and looked at it good. I told myself it might be a white man—might be a hunter wearing moccasins like most of 'em did; but I went on a little way and there were three, four footprints in some wet sand and all of them were moccasins. I thought then the game was up or would be directly, but I run on. I run on. I couldn't think of anything else to do.

It was still light when I come out on a big rock by some little falls. I stood there looking and I couldn't believe my eyes. A broad river ran there before me with clearings here and there on the bank and, right across from the rock I was standing on, a fort: a blockhouse with a stockade fence around it and the timber burned back over the rifle range.

I got off the rock and run down towards the water. A woman and some children were walking along outside the stockade. I called to the woman. She give one look at me and turned and run inside the fort, the children after her. I saw the gate swing to behind them and I knew they had shot the bolt.

I tore off my petticoat and waved it over my head and yelled loud as I could:

"Let me in! Let me in, I tell you!"

I could see heads at the upper story and one somebody standing up on a stump to look over the stockade. But nobody answered and there wasn't no sign of the gate opening.

I looked over my shoulder. The woods were dark behind me and there wasn't any sign of Indians, but I knew they'd be coming any minute. I felt like I knew the place in the woods they were at now. I saw them trotting, trotting through the trees, one after another, the way they went.

I thought, "I'll have to do something quick or they'll get me sure, after all my trouble." I started in to swim it but I couldn't make headway against that current. I saw I would be drowning in a minute, and I swum hard and got back to shallow water. It come to me then that the folks in the fort didn't know who I was. I stood up in the water and yelled, loud as I could:

"I'm Jinny Wiley . . . Jinny Wiley that the Indians stole."

The echo come back to me from the woods, but there wasn't any sound from the fort. Then the gate opened a little way and an old man come out with a gun in his hand. He stood there looking at me and he turned around and said something to the folks in the fort and then he started down the path. I watched him coming down over the rifle range, an old man, gray-haired and feeble enough to a been my grandsire. I shouted at him.

"You can't do it. Send some young body over."

He stood on the bank and shouted back at me, his old voice quavering across the water:

"Where'd you come from?"

I jumped up and down and shrieked, top of my voice:

"God's sakes, man, you going to let me die right here before your eyes? I'm white! White, I tell you!"

"All of 'em's gone but me," he said, "and they ain't no canoe."

"Make a raft," I told him.

He nodded his head up and down. I could see his old gray beard a-shaking. "You better be ready to swim for it," he said. "I don't know as I can git across."

He called to the women in the fort and they come and brought an axe. There was a dead mulberry tree on the bank and they went to work felling it. The old man went off in the woods and come back with some grapevine. When the tree fell it split into three logs and he tied them together with a grapevine and then he and the women rolled them down to the water. They handed him two rifles and he laid them on the raft and started poling. The current caught him and he was going downstream. Yelling had started behind me somewhere in the woods. The Indians were coming.

I run down the bank till I got even with the raft and I swum out and clomb aboard. The old man poled hard. We got halfway out in the river and then the vines begun to come loose and the raft was spreading apart. I knelt down and held the logs together with my hands the best I could. The old man fell down on his knees and started praying.

" 'Tain't no use," he said; "we can't make it."

I looked over my shoulder. The Indians were swarming down to the water. I knew they'd be swimming directly. The old man was still praying. I took the pole away from him.

"Go on and pray, you old fool," I said. "I'm a-going to git across this river."

I put all the strength I had into it, and we made some headway. The yelling was closer now. The Indians were in the water. A shot rung out. I hoped to God one of 'em was hit. I poled harder and I saw some willow boughs ahead of me. I reached out and grabbed hold of 'em and we pulled ourselves to shore.

We went up over the rifle range fast as we could. I looked back once. The Indians had left the water and were standing on the bank. I heard Mad Dog calling:

"Whoopee! . . . whoopee! . . . pretty Jinny!"

We went through the gate. I heard the bolt shoot home and I knew I was inside the fort. I fell down on the ground and the women and children come crowding. The Indians were still yelling. I sat up and the high stockade fence was all around me.

"Lord God," I said, "I was lucky to git away from them Indians!"

COMMENT AND QUESTION

1. In one of his poems, Stephen Vincent Benét describes the ghost of Daniel Boone. As Boone goes by at night, phantom deer spring up, and "all lost, wild America is burning in their eyes." Lost, wild America burns in this story, too. It is the lost wilderness of America that Miss Gordon recreates here.

2. The story is also a picture of a lost pioneer culture. In alien surroundings Jinny remains what she is, a pioneer white woman. How does she preserve her identity? How do we learn of the culture from which she comes? (The most appealing picture is probably that of Jinny's granny, "turned simple.")

3. A tale about the American Indian can easily become trite, romantic, sentimental, or sensational. "The Captive" avoids all these dangers and achieves, instead, a sober reality. Emotional and sensational details are toned down, so much so that for a brief space the reader wonders how simple, unassuming Jinny, telling the story in her own forthright first person, will communicate her feelings.

But Jinny is far from passive. Early in the story toward the close of section II, there is evidence of Jinny's strong emotional response to the horror of which she has become a part. Again, in the dream in section V, where Jinny gets outside herself, the reader can respond to the full force of the story. What strong emotional associations stimulate the incidents in Jinny's dream?

The rhythm of the prose communicates feeling also. Read aloud any part of section V. Consider also the heightened style in the passages where Crowmocker, Jinny, and Mad Dog speak in Shawnee. Is there justification for the stately, poetic language?

4. Early in the story someone tells Jinny that she is "brash" and "lucky." Do these two words keynote the actions of Jinny throughout the story?

5. Jinny's dream, in its inception and in its consequences, is the most interesting part of "The Captive." The immediate stimulation for the dream is quite clear. But the secondary impulses are strong, too, and have been building for a long time.

In section VI, are the conditions for flight any more favorable than they were in section IV? What, then, spurs a flight in section VI? The obvious answer is not satisfactory. Jinny has a stronger and more subtle reason than the presence of Mad Dog.

This subtle reason explains, in part, the force of the dream in the story. Are you willing to accept the dream simply as a supernatural presage or omen? Does Jinny use the dream as an explicit guide? Compare the flame of the young man's lamp as it lights the whole valley (end of section V) with the light breaking over everything on the first morning of Jinny's flight. Is not the relationship poetic rather than explicit?

Jinny's dream has a powerful psychological function. When a human being springs into action, he draws deep down upon all his resources. Would you be willing to accept Jinny's dream as the plan of her unconscious?

THE SECOND DEATH

BY GRAHAM GREENE

GRAHAM GREENE (1904–   ) was born in England and educated at Oxford. He has been a film critic for the *Spectator* and wrote the script for two highly successful motion pictures, "The Fallen Idol," and "The Third Man." He has written excellent detective stories. His three novels have established him among the foremost living novelists. These three novels, *The Power and the Glory* (1940), *The Heart of the Matter* (1948), and *The End of the Affair* (1951), are powerful studies of sin, guilt, and redemption. His short stories appear in *Nineteen Stories* (1949).

SHE FOUND me in the evening under trees that grew outside the village. I had never cared for her and would have hidden myself if I'd seen her coming. She was to blame, I'm certain, for her son's vices. If they were vices, but I'm very far from admitting that they were. At any rate he was generous, never mean, like others in the village I could mention if I chose.

I was staring hard at a leaf or she would never have found me. It was dangling from its twig, its stalk torn across by the wind or else by a stone one of the village children had flung. Only the green tough skin of the stalk held it there suspended. I was watching closely, because a caterpillar was crawling across the surface, making the leaf sway to and fro. The caterpillar was aiming at the twig, and I wondered whether it would reach it in safety or whether the leaf would fall with it into the water. There was a pool underneath the trees, and the water always appeared red, because of the heavy clay in the soil.

I never knew whether the caterpillar reached the twig, for, as I've said, the wretched woman found me. The first I knew of her coming was her voice just behind my ear.

"I've been looking in all the pubs for you," she said in her old shrill voice. It was typical of her to say "all the pubs" when there were only two in the place. She always wanted credit for trouble she hadn't really taken.

I was annoyed and I couldn't help speaking a little harshly. "You might have saved yourself the trouble," I said, "you should have known I wouldn't be in a pub on a fine night like this."

The old vixen became quite humble. She was always smooth enough when she wanted anything. "It's for my poor son," she said. That meant that he was ill. When he was well I never heard her say anything better than "that dratted boy." She'd make him be in the house by midnight every day of the week, as if there were any serious mischief a man could get up to in a little village like ours. Of course we soon found a way to cheat her, but it was the principle of the thing I objected to—a grown man of over thirty ordered about by his mother, just because she hadn't a husband to control. But when he was ill, though it might be with only a small chill, it was "my poor son."

"He's dying," she said, "and God knows what I shall do without him."

"Well, I don't see how I can help you," I said. I was angry, because he'd been dying once before and she'd done everything but actually bury him. I imagined it was the same sort of dying this time, the sort a man gets over. I'd seen him about the week before on his way up the hill to see the big-breasted girl at the farm. I'd watched him till he was like a little black dot, which stayed suddenly by a square grey box in a field. That was the barn where they used to meet. I've very good eyes and it amuses me to try how far and how clearly they can see. I met him again some time after midnight and helped him get into the house without his mother knowing, and he was well enough then—only a little sleepy and tired.

The old vixen was at it again. "He's been asking for you," she shrilled at me.

"If he's as ill as you make out," I said, "it would be better for him to ask for a doctor."

"Doctor's there, but he can't do anything." That startled me for a moment, I'll admit it, until I thought, "The old devil's malingering. He's got some plan or other." He was quite clever enough to cheat a doctor. I had seen him throw a fit that would have deceived Moses.

"For God's sake come," she said, "he seems frightened." Her voice broke quite genuinely, for I suppose in her way she was fond of him. I couldn't help pitying her a little, for I knew that he had never cared a mite for her and had never troubled to disguise the fact.

I left the trees and the red pool and the struggling caterpillar, for I knew that she would never leave me alone, now that her "poor boy" was asking for me. Yet a week ago there was nothing she wouldn't have done to keep us apart. She thought me responsible for his ways, as though any mortal man could have kept him off a likely woman when his appetite was up.

I think it must have been the first time I had entered their cottage by the front door since I came to the village ten years ago. I threw an amused glance at his window. I thought I could see the marks on the wall of the ladder we'd used the week before. We'd had a little difficulty in putting it straight, but his mother slept sound. He had brought the ladder down from the barn, and when he'd got safely in, I carried it up there again. But you could never trust his word. He'd lie to his best friend, and when I reached the barn I found the girl had gone. If he couldn't bribe you with his mother's money, he'd bribe you with other people's promises.

I began to feel uneasy directly I got inside the door. It was natural that the house should be quiet, for the pair of them never had any friends to stay, although the old woman had a sister-in-law living only a few miles away. But I didn't like the sound of the doctor's feet as he came downstairs to meet us. He'd twisted his face into a pious solemnity for our benefit, as though there was something holy about death, even about the death of my friend.

"He's conscious," he said, "but he's going. There's nothing I can do. If you want him to die in peace, better let his friend go along up. He's frightened about something."

The doctor was right. I could tell that as soon as I bent under the lintel and entered my friend's room. He was propped up on a pillow, and his eyes were on the door, waiting for me to come. They were very bright and frightened, and his hair lay across his forehead in sticky stripes. I'd never realized before what an ugly fellow he was. He had sly eyes that looked at you too much out of the corners, but when he was in ordinary health, they held a twinkle that made you forget the slyness. There was something pleasant and brazen in the twinkle, as much as to say, "I know I'm sly and ugly. But what does that matter? I've got guts." It was that twinkle, I think, some women found attractive and stimulating. Now when the twinkle was gone, he looked a rogue and nothing else.

I thought it my duty to cheer him up, so I made a small joke out of the fact that he was alone in bed. He didn't seem to relish it, and I was beginning to fear that he too was taking a religious view of his death, when he told me to sit down, speaking quite sharply.

"I'm dying," he said, talking very fast, "and I want to ask you some-thing. That doctor's no good—he'd think me delirious. I'm frightened, old man. I want to be reassured," and then after a long pause, "someone with common sense." He slipped a little farther down in his bed.

"I've only once been badly ill before," he said. "That was before you settled here. I wasn't much more than a boy. People tell me that I was even supposed to be dead. They were carrying me out to burial when a doctor stopped them just in time."

I'd heard plenty of cases like that, and I saw no reason why he should want to tell me about it. And then I thought I saw his point. His mother had not been too anxious once before to see if he were properly dead, though I had little doubt that she made a great show of grief—"My poor boy. I don't know what I shall do without him." And I'm certain that she believed herself then, as she believed herself now. She wasn't a murderess. She was only inclined to be premature.

"Look here, old man," I said, and I propped him a little higher on his pillow, "you needn't be frightened. You aren't going to die, and any-way I'd see that the doctor cut a vein or something before they moved you. But that's all morbid stuff. Why, I'd stake my shirt that you've got plenty more years in front of you. And plenty more girls too," I added to make him smile.

"Can't you cut out all that?" he said, and I knew then that he had turned religious. "Why," he said, "if I lived, I wouldn't touch another girl. I wouldn't, not one."

I tried not to smile at that, but it wasn't easy to keep a straight face. There's always something a bit funny about a sick man's morals. "Any-way," I said, "you needn't be frightened."

"It's not that," he said. "Old man, when I came round that other time, I thought that I'd been dead. It wasn't like sleep at all. Or rest in peace. There was someone there, all round me, who knew everything. Every girl I'd ever had. Even that young one who hadn't understood. It was before your time. She lived a mile down the road, where Rachel lives now, but she and her family went away afterwards. Even the money I'd taken from mother. I don't call that stealing. It's in the family. I never had a chance to explain. Even the thoughts I'd had. A man can't help his thoughts."

"A nightmare," I said.

"Yes, it must have been a dream, mustn't it? The sort of dream people do get when they are ill. And I saw what was coming to me too. I can't bear being hurt. It wasn't fair. And I wanted to faint and I couldn't, because I was dead."

"In the dream," I said. His fear made me nervous. "In the dream," I said again.

"Yes, it must have been a dream—mustn't it?—because I woke up. The curious thing was I felt quite well and strong. I got up and stood in the road, and a little farther down, kicking up the dust, was a small crowd, going off with a man—the doctor who had stopped them burying me."

"Well," I said.

"Old man," he said, "suppose it was true. Suppose I had been dead. I believed it then, you know, and so did my mother. But you can't trust her. I went straight for a couple of years. I thought it might be a sort of second chance. Then things got fogged and somehow . . . It didn't seem really possible. It's not possible. Of course it's not possible. You know it isn't, don't you?"

"Why no," I said. "Miracles of that sort don't happen nowadays. And anyway, they aren't likely to happen to you, are they? And here of all places under the sun."

"It would be so dreadful," he said, "if it had been true, and I'd got to go through all that again. You don't know what things were going to happen to me in that dream. And they'd be worse now." He stopped and then, after a moment, he added as though he were stating a fact, "When one's dead there's no unconsciousness any more for ever."

"Of course it was a dream," I said and squeezed his hand. He was frightening me with his fancies. I wished that he'd die quickly, so that I could get away from his sly, bloodshot and terrified eyes and see something cheerful and amusing, like the Rachel he had mentioned, who lived a mile down the road.

"Why," I said, "if there had been a man about working miracles like that, we should have heard of others, you may be sure. Even poked away in this god-forsaken spot," I said.

"There were some others," he said. "But the stories only went round among the poor, and they'll believe anything, won't they? There were lots of diseased and crippled they said he'd cured. And there was a man, who'd been born blind, and he came and just touched his eyelids and sight came to him. Those were all old wives' tales, weren't they?" he asked me, stammering with fear, and then lying suddenly still and bunched up at the side of the bed.

I began to say, "Of course they were all lies," but I stopped, because there was no need. All I could do was to go downstairs and tell his mother to come up and close his eyes. I wouldn't have touched them for all the money in the world. It was a long time since I'd thought of that day, ages and ages ago, when I felt a cold touch like spittle on my lids and opening my eyes had seen a man like a tree surrounded by other trees walking away.

COMMENT AND QUESTION

1. One incident from "The Second Death" has a parallel in the Gospel of St. Luke 7:11–16. "At that time Jesus went into a city that is called

Naim: and there went with Him His disciples, and a great multitude. And when He came nigh to the gate of the city, behold a dead man was carried out, the only son of his mother; and she was a widow, and a great multitude of the city was with her. Whom when the Lord had seen, being moved with mercy toward her, He said to her: Weep not. And He came near, and touched the bier. (And they that carried it stood still.) And He said: Young man, I say to thee, arise. And he that was dead sat up, and began to speak. And He gave him to his mother."

2. In "The Second Death" neither mother, son, narrator, nor town has a name. The only name mentioned is that of Rachel, a Jewish name. Do these facts indicate a relationship with the Biblical story?

3. The subjects of sin, guilt, repentance, and moral responsibility are recurring themes in the writing of Greene. Have the experiences of the narrator been like those of the son? Whose story is this? The son's or the narrator's?

4. The keen eyesight of the narrator is stressed throughout the story. Why? What connection is there between the open eyes of the dead man in the last paragraph and the "cold touch" on the eyes of the narrator?

5. The people in this story—mother, son, narrator—are decidedly unpleasant. Did the author have a purpose in establishing this quality?

6. Is this story intended to be a parable?

THE SNOWS OF KILIMANJARO

BY ERNEST HEMINGWAY

ERNEST HEMINGWAY (1898–   ) was born in
Oak Park, Illinois. In the first World War he
served in an ambulance unit on the Italian
front and was wounded. After the war he was
a newspaper correspondent in Paris and became a member of the group of American expatriates. He was a correspondent also in the
Spanish Civil War. He has travelled widely.
He is one of the most influential writers of
fiction in America. Among his best known
novels are *The Sun Also Rises* (1926), *A
Farewell to Arms* (1929), *For Whom the Bell
Tolls* (1940), *Across the River and Into the
Trees* (1950), and *The Old Man and the Sea*
(1952) for which he was awarded the Pulitzer
Prize in 1953. In 1954 he won the Nobel
Prize for Literature. His stories are collected
in the volume *The Short Stories of Ernest
·Hemingway* (1953).

Kilimanjaro is a snow covered mountain 19,710 feet high, and
is said to be the highest mountain in Africa. Its western summit is
called the Masai "Ngàje Ngài," the House of God. Close to the
western summit there is the dried and frozen carcass of a leopard.
No one has explained what the leopard was seeking at that altitude.

"THE MARVELLOUS thing is that it's painless," he said. "That's how
you know when it starts."

"Is it really?"

"Absolutely. I'm awfully sorry about the odor though. That must bother
you."

"Don't! Please don't."

"Look at them," he said. "Now is it sight or is it scent that brings them like that?"

The cot the man lay on was in the wide shade of a mimosa tree and as he looked out past the shade onto the glare of the plain there were three of the big birds squatted obscenely, while in the sky a dozen more sailed, making quick-moving shadows as they passed.

"They've been there since the day the truck broke down," he said. "Today's the first time any have lit on the ground. I watched the way they sailed very carefully at first in case I ever wanted to use them in a story. That's funny now."

"I wish you wouldn't," she said.

"I'm only talking," he said. "It's much easier if I talk. But I don't want to bother you."

"You know it doesn't bother me," she said. "It's that I've gotten so very nervous not being able to do anything. I think we might make it as easy as we can until the plane comes."

"Or until the plane doesn't come."

"Please tell me what I can do. There must be something I can do."

"You can take the leg off and that might stop it, though I doubt it. Or you can shoot me. You're a good shot now. I taught you to shoot didn't I?"

"Please don't talk that way. Couldn't I read to you?"

"Read what?"

"Anything in the book bag that we haven't read."

"I can't listen to it," he said. "Talking is the easiest. We quarrel and that makes the time pass."

"I don't quarrel. I never want to quarrel. Let's not quarrel any more. No matter how nervous we get. Maybe they will be back with another truck today. Maybe the plane will come."

"I don't want to move," the man said. "There is no sense in moving now except to make it easier for you."

"That's cowardly."

"Can't you let a man die as comfortably as he can without calling him names? What's the use of slanging me?"

"You're not going to die."

"Don't be silly. I'm dying now. Ask those bastards." He looked over to where the huge, filthy birds sat, their naked heads sunk in the hunched feathers. A fourth planed down, to run quick-legged and then waddle slowly toward the others.

"They are around every camp. You never notice them. You can't die if you don't give up."

"Where did you read that? You're such a bloody fool."

"You might think about some one else."

"For Christ's sake," he said, "That's been my trade."

He lay then and was quiet for a while and looked across the heat shimmer of the plain to the edge of the bush. There were a few Tommies that showed minute and white against the yellow and, far off, he saw a herd of zebra, white against the green of the bush. This was a pleasant camp under big trees against a hill, with good water, and close by, a nearly dry water hole where sand grouse flighted in the mornings.

"Wouldn't you like me to read?" she asked. She was sitting on a canvas chair beside his cot. "There's a breeze coming up."

"No thanks."

"Maybe the truck will come."

"I don't give a damn about the truck."

"I do."

"You give a damn about so many things that I don't."

"Not so many, Harry."

"What about a drink?"

"It's supposed to be bad for you. It said in Black's to avoid all alcohol. You shouldn't drink."

"Molo!" he shouted.

"Yes Bwana."

"Bring whiskey-soda."

"Yes Bwana."

"You shouldn't," she said. "That's what I mean by giving up. It says it's bad for you. I know it's bad for you."

"No," he said. "It's good for me."

So now it was all over, he thought. So now he would never have a chance to finish it. So this was the way it ended in a bickering over a drink. Since the gangrene started in his right leg he had no pain and with the pain the horror had gone and all he felt now was a great tiredness and anger that this was the end of it. For this, that now was coming, he had very little curiosity. For years it had obsessed him; but now it meant nothing in itself. It was strange how easy being tired enough made it.

Now he would never write the things that he had saved to write until he knew enough to write them well. Well, he would not have to fail at trying to write them either. Maybe you could never write them, and that was why you put them off and delayed the starting. Well he would never know, now.

"I wish we'd never come," the woman said. She was looking at him holding the glass and biting her lip. "You never would have gotten anything like this in Paris. You always said you loved Paris. We could have stayed in Paris or gone anywhere. I'd have gone anywhere. I said I'd go anywhere you wanted. If you wanted to shoot we could have gone shooting in Hungary and been comfortable."

"Your bloody money," he said.

"That's not fair," she said. "It was always yours as much as mine. I left everything and I went wherever you wanted to go and I've done what you wanted to do. But I wish we'd never come here."

"You said you loved it."

"I did when you were all right. But now I hate it. I don't see why that had to happen to your leg. What have we done to have that happen to us?"

"I suppose what I did was to forget to put iodine on it when I first scratched it. Then I didn't pay any attention to it because I never infect. Then, later, when it got bad, it was probably using that weak carbolic solution when the other antiseptics ran out that paralyzed the minute blood vessels and started the gangrene." He looked at her, "What else?"

"I don't mean that."

"If we would have hired a good mechanic instead of a half baked kikuyu driver, he would have checked the oil and never burned out that bearing in the truck."

"I don't mean that."

"If you hadn't left your own people, your goddamned Old Westbury, Saratoga, Palm Beach people to take me on——"

"Why, I loved you. That's not fair. I love you now. I'll always love you. Don't you love me?"

"No," said the man. "I don't think so. I never have."

"Harry, what are you saying? You're out of your head."

"No. I haven't any head to go out of."

"Don't drink that," she said. "Darling, please don't drink that. We have to do everything we can."

"You do it," he said. "I'm tired."

Now in his mind he saw a railway station at Karagatch and he was standing with his pack and that was the headlight of the Simplon-Orient cutting the dark now and he was leaving Thrace then after the retreat. That was one of the things he had saved to write, with, in the morning at breakfast, looking out the window and seeing snow on the mountains in Bulgaria and Nansen's Secretary asking the old man if it were snow and the old man looking at it and saying, No, that's not snow. It's too early for snow. And the Secretary repeating to the other girls, No, you see. It's not snow and them all saying, It's not snow we were mistaken. But it was the snow all right and he sent them on into it when he evolved exchange of populations. And it was snow they tramped along in until they died that winter.

It was snow too that fell all Christmas week that year up in the Gauertal, that year they lived in the woodcutter's house with the big square porcelain stove that filled half the room, and they slept on mattresses filled with beech leaves, the time the deserter came with his feet bloody in the snow. He said the police were right behind him and they gave him woolen socks and held the gendarmes talking until the tracks had drifted over.

In Schrunz, on Christmas day, the snow was so bright it hurt your eyes when you looked out from the weinstube and saw every one coming home from church. That was where they walked up the sleigh-smoothed urine-yellowed road along the river with the steep pine hills, skis heavy on the shoulder, and where they ran that great run down the glacier above the Madlener-haus, the snow as smooth to see as cake frosting and as light as powder and he remembered the noiseless rush the speed made as you dropped down like a bird.

They were snow-bound a week in the Madlener-haus that time in the blizzard playing cards in the smoke by the lantern light and the stakes were higher all the time as Herr Lent lost more. Finally he lost it all. Everything, the skischule money and all the season's profit and then his capital. He could see him with his long nose, picking up the cards and then opening, "Sans Voir." There was always gambling then. When there was no snow you gambled and when there was too much you gambled. He thought of all the time in his life he had spent gambling.

But he had never written a line of that, nor of that cold, bright Christmas day with the mountains showing across the plain that Barker had flown across the lines to bomb the Austrian officers' leave train, machine-gunning them as they scattered and ran. He remembered Barker afterwards coming into the mess and starting to tell about it. And how quiet it got and then somebody saying, "You bloody murderous bastard."

Those were the same Austrians they killed then that he skied with later. No not the same. Hans, that he skied with all that year, had been in the Kaiser-Jägers and when they went hunting hares together up the little valley above the saw-mill they had talked of the fighting on Pasubio and of the attack on Pertica and Asalone and he had never written a word of that. Nor of Monte Corno, nor the Siete Commum, nor of Arsiedo.

How many winters had he lived in the Voralberg and the Arlberg? It was four and then he remembered the man who had the fox to sell when they had walked into Bludenz, that time to buy presents, and the cherry-pit taste of good kirsch, the fast-slipping rush of running powder-snow on crust, singing "Hi! Ho! said Rolly!" as you ran down the last stretch to the steep drop, taking it straight, then running the orchard in three turns and out across the ditch and onto the icy road behind the inn. Knocking your bindings loose, kicking the skis free and leaning them up against the wooden wall of the inn, the lamplight coming from the window, where inside, in the smoky new-wine smelling warmth, they were playing the accordion.

"Where did we stay in Paris?" he asked the woman who was sitting by him in a canvas chair, now, in Africa.

"At the Crillon. You know that."

"Why do I know that?"

"That's where we always stayed."

"No. Not always."

"There and at the Pavillion Henri-Quatre in St. Germain. You said you loved it there."

"Love is a dunghill," said Harry. "And I'm the cock that gets on it to crow."

"If you have to go away," she said, "is it absolutely necessary to kill off everything you leave behind? I mean do you have to take away everything? Do you have to kill your horse, and your wife and burn your saddle and your armour?"

"Yes," he said. "Your damned money was my armour. My Swift and my Armour."

"Don't."

"All right. I'll stop that. I don't want to hurt you."

"It's a little bit late now."

"All right then. I'll go on hurting you. It's more amusing. The only thing I ever really liked to do with you I can't do now."

"No, that's not true. You liked to do many things and everything you wanted to do I did."

"Oh, for Christ sake stop bragging, will you?"

He looked at her and saw her crying.

"Listen," he said. "Do you think that it is fun to do this? I don't know why I'm doing it. It's trying to kill to keep yourself alive, I imagine. I was all right when we started talking. I didn't mean to start this, and now I'm crazy as a coot and being as cruel to you as I can be. Don't pay any attention, darling, to what I say. I love you, really. You know I love you. I've never loved any one else the way I love you."

He slipped into the familiar lie he made his bread and butter by.

"You're sweet to me."

"You bitch," he said. "You rich bitch. That's poetry. I'm full of poetry now. Rot and poetry. Rotten poetry."

"Stop it, Harry, why do you have to turn into a devil now?"

"I don't like to leave anything," the man said. "I don't like to leave things behind."

       ❊   ❊   ❊

It was evening now and he had been asleep. The sun was gone behind the hill and there was a shadow all across the plain and the small animals were feeding close to camp; quick dropping heads and switching tails, he watched them keeping well out away from the bush now. The birds no longer waited on the ground. They were all perched heavily in a tree.

There were many more of them. His personal boy was sitting by the bed. "Memsahib's gone to shoot," the boy said. "Does Bwana want?"

"Nothing."

She had gone to kill a piece of meat and, knowing how he liked to watch the game, she had gone well away so she would not disturb this little pocket of the plain that he could see. She was always thoughtful, he thought. On anything she knew about, or had read, or that she had ever heard.

It was not her fault that when he went to her he was already over. How could a woman know that you meant nothing that you said; that you spoke only from habit and to be comfortable? After he no longer meant what he said, his lies were more successful with women than when he had told them the truth.

It was not so much that he lied as that there was no truth to tell. He had had his life and it was over and then he went on living it again with different people and more money, with the best of the same places, and some new ones.

You kept from thinking and it was all marvellous. You were equipped with good insides so that you did not go to pieces that way, the way most of them had, and you made an attitude that you cared nothing for the work you used to do, now that you could no longer do it. But, in yourself, you said that you would write about these people; about the very rich; that you were really not of them but a spy in their country; that you would leave it and write of it and for once it would be written by some one who knew what he was writing of. But he would never do it, because each day of not writing, of comfort, of being that which he despised, dulled his ability and softened his will to work so that, finally, he did no work at all. The people he knew now were all much more comfortable when he did not work. Africa was where he had been happiest in the good time of his life, so he had come out here to start again. They had made this safari with the minimum of comfort. There was no hardship; but there was no luxury and he had thought that he could get back into training that way. That in some way he could work the fat off his soul the way a fighter went into the mountains to work and train in order to burn it out of his body.

She had liked it. She said she loved it. She loved anything that was exciting, that involved a change of scene, where there were new people and where things were pleasant. And he had felt the illusion of returning strength of will to work. Now if this was how it ended, and he knew it was, he must not turn like some snake biting itself because its back was broken. It wasn't this woman's fault. If it had not been she it would have been another. If he lived by a lie he should try to die by it. He heard a shot beyond the hill.

She shot very well this good, this rich bitch, this kindly caretaker and destroyer of his talent. Nonsense. He had destroyed his talent himself. Why should he blame this woman because she kept him well? He had destroyed his talent by not using it, by betrayals of himself and what he believed in, by drinking so much that he blunted the edge of his perceptions, by laziness, by sloth, and by snobbery, by pride and by prejudice, by hook and by crook. What was this? A catalogue of old books? What was his talent anyway? It was a talent all right but instead of using it, he had traded on it. It was never what he had done, but always what he could do. And he had chosen to make his living with something else instead of a pen or a pencil. It was strange, too, wasn't it, that when he fell in love with another woman, that woman should always have more money than the last one? But when he no longer was in love, when he was only lying, as to this woman, now, who had the most money of all, who had all the money there was, who had had a husband and children, who had taken lovers and been dissatisfied with them, and who loved him dearly as a writer, as a man, as a companion and as a proud possession; it was strange that when he did not love her at all and was lying, that he should be able to give her more for her money than when he had really loved.

We must all be cut out for what we do, he thought. However you make your living is where your talent lies. He had sold vitality, in one form or another, all his life and when your affections are not too involved you give much better value for the money. He had found that out but he would never write that, now, either. No, he would not write that, although it was well worth writing.

Now she came in sight, walking across the open toward the camp. She was wearing jodhpurs and carrying her rifle. The two boys had a Tommie slung and they were coming along behind her. She was still a good-looking woman, he thought, and she had a pleasant body. She had a great talent and appreciation for the bed, she was not pretty, but he liked her face, she read enormously, liked to ride and shoot and, certainly, she drank too much. Her husband had died when she was still a comparatively young woman and for a while she had devoted herself to her two just-grown children, who did not need her and were embarrassed at having her about, to her stable of horses, to books, and to bottles. She liked to read in the evening before dinner, and she drank Scotch and soda while she read. By dinner she was fairly drunk and after a bottle of wine at dinner she was usually drunk enough to sleep.

That was before the lovers. After she had the lovers she did not drink so much because she did not have to be drunk to sleep. But the lovers bored her. She had been married to a man who had never bored her and these people bored her very much.

Then one of her two children was killed in a plane crash and after that was over she did not want the lovers, and drink being no anæsthetic she had to make another life. Suddenly, she had been acutely frightened of being alone. But she wanted some one that she respected with her.

It had begun very simply. She liked what he wrote and she had always envied the life he led. She thought he did exactly what he wanted to. The steps by which she had acquired him and the way in which she had finally fallen in love with him were all part of a regular progression in which she had built herself a new life and he had traded away what remained of his old life.

He had traded it for security, for comfort too, there was no denying that, and for what else? He did not know. She would have bought him anything he wanted. He knew that. She was a damned nice woman too. He would as soon be in bed with her as any one; rather with her, because she was richer, because she was very pleasant and appreciative and because she never made scenes. And now this life that she had built again was coming to a term because he had not used iodine two weeks ago when a thorn had scratched his knee as they moved forward trying to photograph a herd of waterbuck standing, their heads up, peering while their nostrils searched the air, their ears spread wide to hear the first noise that would send them rushing into the bush. They had bolted, too, before he got the picture.

Here she came now.

He turned his head on the cot to look toward her. "Hello," he said.

"I shot a Tommy ram," she told him. "He'll make you good broth and I'll have them mash some potatoes with the Klim. How do you feel?"

"Much better."

"Isn't that lovely? You know I thought perhaps you would. You were sleeping when I left."

"I had a good sleep. Did you walk far?"

"No. Just around behind the hill. I made quite a good shot on the Tommy."

"You shoot marvellously, you know."

"I love it. I've loved Africa. Really, If *you're* all right it's the most fun that I've ever had. You don't know the fun it's been to shoot with you. I've loved the country."

"I love it too."

"Darling, you don't know how marvellous it is to see you feeling better. I couldn't stand it when you felt that way. You won't talk to me like that again, will you? Promise me?"

"No," he said. "I don't remember what I said."

"You don't have to destroy me. Do you? I'm only a middle-aged woman who loves you and wants to do what you want to do. I've been destroyed two or three times already. You wouldn't want to destroy me again, would you?"

"I'd like to destroy you a few times in bed," he said.

"Yes. That's the good destruction. That's the way we're made to be destroyed. The plane will be here tomorrow."

"How do you know?"

"I'm sure. It's bound to come. The boys have the wood all ready and the grass to make the smudge. I went down and looked at it again today. There's plenty of room to land and we have the smudges ready at both ends."

"What makes you think it will come tomorrow?"

"I'm sure it will. It's overdue now. Then, in town, they will fix up your leg and then we will have some good destruction. Not that dreadful talking kind."

"Should we have a drink? The sun is down."

"Do you think you should?"

"I'm having one."

"We'll have one together. *Molo, letti dui whiskey-soda!*" she called.

"You'd better put on your mosquito boots," he told her.

"I'll wait till I bathe . . ."

While it grew dark they drank and just before it was dark and there was no longer enough light to shoot, a hyena crossed the open on his way around the hill.

"That bastard crosses there every night," the man said. "Every night for two weeks."

"He's the one makes the noise at night. I don't mind it. They're a filthy animal though."

Drinking together, with no pain now except the discomfort of lying in the one position, the boys lighting a fire, its shadow jumping on the tents, he could feel the return of acquiescence in this life of pleasant surrender. She *was* very good to him. He had been cruel and unjust in the afternoon. She was a fine woman, marvellous really. And just then it occurred to him that he was going to die.

It came with a rush; not as a rush of water nor of wind; but of a sudden evil-smelling emptiness and the odd thing was that the hyena slipped lightly along the edge of it.

"What is it, Harry?" she asked him.

"Nothing," he said. "You had better move over to the other side. To windward."

"Did Molo change the dressing?"

"Yes. I'm just using the boric now."

"How do you feel?"

"A little wobbly."

"I'm going in to bathe," she said. "I'll be right out. I'll eat with you and then we'll put the cot in."

So, he said to himself, we did well to stop the quarrelling. He had never quarrelled much with this woman, while with the women that he loved he had quarrelled so much they had finally, always, with the corrosion of the quarrelling, killed what they had together. He had loved too much, demanded too much, and he wore it all out.

He thought about alone in Constantinople that time, having quarrelled in Paris before he had gone out. He had whored the whole time and then, when that was over, and he had failed to kill his loneliness, but only made it worse, he had written her, the first one, the one who left him, a letter telling her how he had never been able to kill it. . . . How when he thought he saw her outside the Regence one time it made him go all faint and sick inside, and that he would follow a woman who looked like her in some way, along the Boulevard, afraid to see it was not she, afraid to lose the feeling it gave him. How every one he had slept with had only made him miss her more. How what she had done could never matter since he knew he could not cure himself of loving her. He wrote this letter at the Club, cold sober, and mailed it to New York asking her to write him at the office in Paris. That seemed safe. And that night missing her so much it made him feel hollow sick inside, he wandered up past Taxim's, picked a girl up and took her out to supper. He had gone to a place to dance with her afterward, she danced badly, and left her for a hot Armenian slut, that swung her belly against him so it almost scalded. He took her away from a British gunner subaltern after a row. The gunner asked him outside and they fought in the street on the cobbles in the dark. He'd hit him twice, hard, on the side of the jaw and when he didn't go down he knew he was in for a fight. The gunner hit him in the body, then beside his eye. He swung with his left again and landed and the gunner fell on him and grabbed his coat and tore the sleeve off and he clubbed him twice behind the ear and then smashed him with his right as he pushed him away. When the gunner went down his head hit first and he ran with the girl because they heard the M. P.'s coming. They got into a taxi and drove out to Rimmily Hissa along the Bosphorus, and around, and back in the cool night and went to bed and she felt as over-ripe as she looked but smooth, rose-petal, syrupy, smooth-bellied, big-breasted and needed no pillow under her buttocks, and he left her before she was awake looking blousy enough in the first daylight and turned up at the Pera Palace with a black eye, carrying his coat because one sleeve was missing.

That same night he left for Anatolia and he remembered, later on that trip, riding all day through fields of the poppies that they raised for opium and how strange it made you feel, finally, and all the distances seemed wrong, to where they had made the attack with the newly arrived Constantine officers, that did not know a god-damned thing, and the artillery had fired into the troops and the British observer had cried like a child.

That was the day he'd first seen dead men wearing white ballet skirts

*and upturned shoes with pompons on them. The Turks had come steadily
and lumpily and he had seen the skirted men running and the officers
shooting into them and running then themselves and he and the British
observer had run too until his lungs ached and his mouth was full of the
taste of pennies and they stopped behind some rocks and there were the
Turks coming as lumpily as ever. Later he had seen the things that he
could never think of and later still he had seen much worse. So when he
got back to Paris that time he could not talk about it or stand to have it
mentioned. And there in the café as he passed was that American poet
with a pile of saucers in front of him and a stupid look on his potato face
talking about the Dada movement with a Roumanian who said his name
was Tristan Tzara, who always wore a monocle and had a headache, and,
back at the apartment with his wife that now he loved again, the quarrel
all over, the madness all over, glad to be home, the office sent his mail up
to the flat. So then the letter in answer to the one he'd written came in on
a platter one morning and when he saw the handwriting he went cold all
over and tried to slip the letter underneath another. But his wife said,
"Who is that letter from, dear?" and that was the end of the beginning
of that.*

*He remembered the good times with them all, and the quarrels. They
always picked the finest places to have the quarrels. And why had they
always quarrelled when he was feeling best? He had never written any of
that because, at first, he never wanted to hurt any one and then it seemed
as though there was enough to write without it. But he had always thought
that he would write it finally. There was so much to write. He had seen
the world change; not just the events; although he had seen many of them
and had watched the people, but he had seen the subtler change and he
could remember how the people were at different times. He had been in
it and he had watched it and it was his duty to write of it; but now he
never would.*

"How do you feel?" she said. She had come out from the tent now after
her bath.

"All right."

"Could you eat now?" He saw Molo behind her with the folding table
and the other boy with the dishes.

"I want to write," he said.

"You ought to take some broth to keep your strength up."

"I'm going to die tonight," he said. "I don't need my strength up."

"Don't be melodramatic, Harry, please," she said.

"Why don't you use your nose? I'm rotted half way up my thigh now.
What the hell should I fool with broth for? Molo bring whiskey-soda."

"Please take the broth," she said gently.

"All right."

The broth was too hot. He had to hold it in the cup until it cooled enough to take it and then he just got it down without gagging.

"You're a fine woman," he said. "Don't pay any attention to me."

She looked at him with her well-known, well-loved face from *Spur* and *Town and Country*, only a little the worse for drink, only a little the worse for bed, but *Town and Country* never showed those good breasts and those useful thighs and those lightly small-of-back-caressing hands, and as he looked and saw her well known pleasant smile, he felt death come again. This time there was no rush. It was a puff, as of a wind that makes a candle flicker and the flame go tall.

"They can bring my net out later and hang it from the tree and build the fire up. I'm not going in the tent tonight. It's not worth moving. It's a clear night. There won't be any rain."

So this was how you died, in whispers that you did not hear. Well, there would be no more quarrelling. He could promise that. The one experience that he had never had he was not going to spoil now. He probably would. You spoiled everything. But perhaps he wouldn't.

"You can't take dictation, can you?"

"I never learned," she told him.

"That's all right."

There wasn't time, of course, although it seemed as though it telescoped so that you might put it all into one paragraph if you could get it right.

There was a log house, chinked white with mortar, on a hill above the lake. There was a bell on a pole by the door to call the people in to meals. Behind the house were fields and behind the fields was the timber. A line of lombardy poplars ran from the house to the dock. Other poplars ran along the point. A road went up to the hills along the edge of the timber and along that road he picked blackberries. Then that log house was burned down and all the guns that had been on deer foot racks above the open fire place were burned and afterwards their barrels, with the lead melted in the magazines, and the stocks burned away, lay out on the heap of ashes that were used to make lye for the big iron soap kettles, and you asked Grandfather if you could have them to play with, and he said, no. You see they were his guns still and he never bought any others. Nor did he hunt any more. The house was rebuilt in the same place out of lumber now and painted white and from its porch you saw the poplars and the lake beyond; but there were never any more guns. The barrels of the guns that had hung on the deer feet on the wall of the log house lay out there on the heap of ashes and no one ever touched them.

In the Black Forest, after the war, we rented a trout stream and there were two ways to walk to it. One was down the valley from Triberg and around the valley road in the shade of the trees that bordered the white road, and then up a side road that went up through the hills past many small farms, with the big Schwarzwald houses, until that road crossed the stream. That was where our fishing began.

The other way was to climb steeply up to the edge of the woods and then go across the top of the hills through the pine woods, and then out to the edge of a meadow and down across this meadow to the bridge. There were birches along the stream and it was not big, but narrow, clear and fast, with pools where it had cut under the roots of the birches. At the Hotel in Triberg the proprietor had a fine season. It was very pleasant and we were all great friends. The next year came the inflation and the money he had made the year before was not enough to buy supplies to open the hotel and he hanged himself.

You could dictate that, but you could not dictate the Place Contrescarpe where the flower sellers dyed their flowers in the street and the dye ran over the paving where the autobus started and the old men and the women, always drunk on wine and bad marc; and the children with their noses running in the cold; the smell of dirty sweat and poverty and drunkenness at the Café des Amateurs and the whores at the Bal Musette they lived above. The Concierge who entertained the trooper of the Garde Republicaine in her loge, his horse-hair-plumed helmet on a chair. The locataire across the hall whose husband was a bicycle racer and her joy that morning at the Cremerie when she had opened L'Auto and seen where he placed third in Paris-Tours, his first big race. She had blushed and laughed and then gone upstairs crying with the yellow sporting paper in her hand. The husband of the woman who ran the Bal Musette drove a taxi and when he, Harry, had to take an early plane the husband knocked upon the door to wake him and they each drank a glass of white wine at the zinc of the bar before they started. He knew his neighbors in that quarter then because they all were poor.

Around that Place there were two kinds; the drunkards and the sportifs. The drunkards killed their poverty that way; the sportifs took it out in exercise. They were the descendants of the Communards and it was no struggle for them to know their politics. They knew who had shot their fathers, their relatives, their brothers, and their friends when the Versailles troops came in and took the town after the Commune and executed any one they could catch with calloused hands, or who wore a cap, or carried any other sign he was a working man. And in that poverty, and in that quarter across the street from a Boucherie Chevaline and a wine co-operative he had written the start of all he was to do. There never was another part of Paris that he loved like that, the sprawling trees, the old white plastered houses painted brown below, the long green of the autobus in that round square, the purple flower dye upon the paving, the sudden drop down the hill of the rue Cardinal Lemoine to the River, and the other way the narrow crowded world of the rue Mouffetard. The street

*that ran up toward the Pantheon and the other that he always took with
the bicycle, the only asphalted street in all that quarter, smooth under the
tires, with the high narrow houses and the cheap tall hotel where Paul
Verlaine had died. There were only two rooms in the apartments where
they lived and he had a room on the top floor of that hotel that cost him
sixty francs a month where he did his writing, and from it he could see
the roofs and chimney pots and all the hills of Paris.*

*From the apartment you could only see the wood and coal man's place.
He sold wine too, bad wine. The golden horse's head outside the Boucherie
Chevaline where the carcasses hung yellow gold and red in the open window, and the green painted co-operative where they bought their wine;
good wine and cheap. The rest was plaster walls and the windows of the
neighbors. The neighbors who, at night, when some one lay drunk in the
street, moaning and groaning in that typical French ivresse that you were
propaganded to believe did not exist, would open their windows and
then the murmur of talk.*

*"Where is the policeman? When you don't want him the bugger is
always there. He's sleeping with some concierge. Get the Agent." Till
some one threw a bucket of water from a window and the moaning
stopped. "What's that? Water. Ah, that's intelligent." And the windows
shutting. Marie, his femme de menage, protesting against the eight-hour
day saying, "If a husband works until six he gets only a little drunk on the
way home and does not waste too much. If he works only until five he is
drunk every night and one has no money. It is the wife of the working
man who suffers from this shortening of hours."*

"Wouldn't you like some more broth?" the woman asked him now.
"No, thank you very much. It is awfully good."
"Try just a little."
"I would like a whiskey-soda."
"It's not good for you."
"No. It's bad for me. Cole Porter wrote the words and the music. This
knowledge that you're going mad for me."
"You know I like you to drink."
"Oh yes. Only it's bad for me."
When she goes, he thought. I'll have all I want. Not all I want but all
there is. Ayee he was tired. Too tired. He was going to sleep a little while.
He lay still and death was not there. It must have gone around another
street. It went in pairs, on bicycles, and moved absolutely silently on the
pavements.

*No, he had never written about Paris. Not the Paris that he cared about.
But what about the rest that he had never written?*

What about the ranch and the silvered gray of the sage brush, the quick, clear water in the irrigation ditches, and the heavy green of the alfalfa. The trail went up into the hills and the cattle in the summer were shy as deer. The bawling and the steady noise and slow moving mass raising a dust as you brought them down in the fall. And behind the mountains, the clear sharpness of the peak in the evening light and, riding down along the trail in the moonlight, bright across the valley. Now he remembered coming down through the timber in the dark holding the horse's tail when you could not see and all the stories that he meant to write.

About the half-wit chore boy who was left at the ranch that time and told not to let any one get any hay, and that old bastard from the Forks who had beaten the boy when he had worked for him stopping to get some feed. The boy refusing and the old man saying he would beat him again. The boy got the rifle from the kitchen and shot him when he tried to come into the barn and when they came back to the ranch he'd been dead a week, frozen in the corral, and the dogs had eaten part of him. But what was left you packed on a sled wrapped in a blanket and roped on and you got the boy to help you haul it, and the two of you took it out over the road on skis, and sixty miles down to town to turn the boy over. He having no idea that he would be arrested. Thinking he had done his duty and that you were his friend and he would be rewarded. He'd helped to haul the old man in so everybody could know how bad the old man had been and how he'd tried to steal some feed that didn't belong to him, and when the sheriff put the handcuffs on the boy he couldn't believe it. Then he'd started to cry. That was one story he had saved to write. He knew at least twenty good stories from out there and he had never written one. Why?

"You tell them why," he said.

"Why what, dear?"

"Why nothing."

She didn't drink so much, now, since she had him. But if he lived he would never write about her, he knew that now. Nor about any of them. The rich were dull and they drank too much, or they played too much backgammon. They were dull and they were repetitious. He remembered poor Julian and his romantic awe of them and how he had started a story once that began, "The very rich are different from you and me." And how some one had said to Julian, Yes, they have more money. But that was not humorous to Julian. He thought they were a special glamourous race and when he found they weren't it wrecked him just as much as any other thing that wrecked him.

He had been contemptuous of those who wrecked. You did not have to like it because you understood it. He could beat anything, he thought, because no thing could hurt him if he did not care.

All right. Now he would not care for death. One thing he had always dreaded was the pain. He could stand pain as well as any man, until it went on too long, and wore him out, but here he had something that had hurt frightfully and just when he had felt it breaking him, the pain had stopped.

He remembered long ago when Williamson, the bombing officer, had been hit by a stick bomb some one in a German patrol had thrown as he was coming in through the wire that night and, screaming, had begged every one to kill him. He was a fat man, very brave, and a good officer, although addicted to fantastic shows. But that night he was caught in the wire, with a flare lighting him up and his bowels spilled out into the wire, so when they brought him in, alive, they had to cut him loose. Shoot me, Harry. For Christ sake shoot me. They had had an argument one time about our Lord never sending you anything you could not bear and some one's theory had been that meant that at a certain time the pain passed you out automatically. But he had always remembered Williamson, that night. Nothing passed out Williamson until he gave him all his morphine tablets that he had always saved to use himself and then they did not work right away.

Still this now, that he had, was very easy; and if it was no worse as it went on there was nothing to worry about. Except that he would rather be in better company.

He thought a little about the company that he would like to have.

No, he thought, when everything you do, you do too long, and do too late, you can't expect to find the people still there. The people all are gone. The party's over and you are with your hostess now.

I'm getting as bored with dying as with everything else, he thought.

"It's a bore," he said out loud.

"What is, my dear?"

"Anything you do too bloody long."

He looked at her face between him and the fire. She was leaning back in the chair and the firelight shone on her pleasantly lined face and he could see that she was sleepy. He heard the hyena make a noise just outside the range of the fire.

"I've been writing," he said. "But I got tired."

"Do you think you will be able to sleep?"

"Pretty sure. Why don't you turn in?"

"I like to sit here with you."

"Do you feel anything strange?" he asked her.

"No. Just a little sleepy."

"I do," he said.

He had just felt death come by again.

"You know the only thing I've never lost is curiosity," he said to her.

"You've never lost anything. You're the most complete man I've ever known."

"Christ," he said. "How little a woman knows. What is that? Your intuition?"

Because, just then, death had come and rested its head on the foot of the cot and he could smell its breath.

"Never believe any of that about a scythe and a skull," he told her. "It can be two bicycle policemen as easily, or be a bird. Or it can have a wide snout like a hyena."

It had moved up on him now, but it had no shape any more. It simply occupied space.

"Tell it to go away."

It did not go away but moved a little closer.

"You've got a hell of a breath," he told it. "You stinking bastard."

It moved up closer to him still and now he could not speak to it, and when it saw he could not speak it came a little closer, and now he tried to send it away without speaking, but it moved in on him so its weight was all upon his chest, and while it crouched there and he could not move, or speak, he heard the woman say, "Bwana is asleep now. Take the cot up very gently and carry it into the tent."

He could not speak to tell her to make it go away and it crouched now, heavier, so he could not breathe. And then, while they lifted the cot, suddenly it was all right and the weight went from his chest.

It was morning and had been morning for some time and he heard the plane. It showed very tiny and then made a wide circle and the boys ran out and lit the fires, using kerosene, and piled on grass so there were two big smudges at each end of the level place and the morning breeze blew them toward the camp and the plane circled twice more, low this time, and then glided down and levelled off and landed smoothly and, coming walking toward him, was old Compton in slacks, a tweed jacket and a brown felt hat.

"What's the matter, old cock?" Compton said.

"Bad leg," he told him. "Will you have some breakfast?"

"Thanks. I'll just have some tea. It's the Puss Moth you know. I won't be able to take the Memsahib. There's only room for one. Your lorry is on the way."

Helen had taken Compton aside and was speaking to him. Compton came back more cheery than ever.

"We'll get you right in," he said. "I'll be back for the Mem. Now I'm afraid I'll have to stop at Arusha to refuel. We'd better get going."

"What about the tea?"

"I don't really care about it you know."

The boys had picked up the cot and carried it around the green tents and down along the rock and out onto the plain and along past the smudges that were burning brightly now, the grass all consumed, and the wind fanning the fire, to the little plane. It was difficult getting him in, but once in he lay back in the leather seat, and the leg was stuck straight out to one side of the seat where Compton sat. Compton started the motor and got in. He waved to Helen and to the boys and, as the clatter moved into the old familiar roar, they swung around with Compie watching for wart-hog holes and roared, bumping, along the stretch between the fires and with the last bump rose and he saw them all standing below, waving, and the camp beside the hill, flattening now, and the plain spreading, clumps of trees, and the bush flattening, while the game trails ran now smoothly to the dry waterholes, and there was a new water that he had never known of. The zebra, small rounded backs now, and the wildebeeste, big-headed dots seeming to climb as they moved in long fingers across the plain, now scattering as the shadow came toward them, they were tiny now, and the movement had no gallop, and the plain as far as you could see, gray-yellow now and ahead old Compie's tweed back and the brown felt hat. Then they were over the first hills and the wildebeeste were trailing up them, and then they were over mountains with sudden depths of green-rising forest and the solid bamboo slopes, and then the heavy forest again, sculptured into peaks and hollows until they crossed, and hills sloped down and then another plain, hot now, and purple brown, bumpy with heat and Compie looking back to see how he was riding. Then there were other mountains dark ahead.

And then instead of going on to Arusha they turned left, he evidently figured that they had the gas, and looking down he saw a pink sifting cloud, moving over the ground, and in the air, like the first snow in a blizzard, that comes from nowhere, and he knew the locusts were coming up from the South. Then they began to climb and they were going to the East it seemed, and then it darkened and they were in a storm, the rain so thick it seemed like flying through a waterfall, and then they were out and Compie turned his head and grinned and pointed and there, ahead, all he could see, as wide as all the world, great, high, and unbelievably white in the sun, was the square top of Kilimanjaro. And then he knew that there was where he was going.

Just then the hyena stopped whimpering in the night and started to make a strange, human, almost crying sound. The woman heard it and stirred uneasily. She did not wake. In her dream she was at the house on Long Island and it was the night before her daughter's début. Somehow her father was there and he had been very rude. Then the noise the hyena made was so loud she woke and for a moment she did not know where she was and she was very afraid. Then she took the flashlight and shone it on the other cot that they had carried in after Harry had gone to sleep. She could see his bulk under the mosquito bar but somehow he had gotten his leg out and it hung down alongside the cot. The dressings had all come down and she could not look at it.

"Molo," she called, "Molo! Molo!"

Then she said, "Harry, Harry!" Then her voice rising, "Harry! Please, Oh Harry!"

There was no answer and she could not hear him breathing.

Outside the tent the hyena made the same strange noise that had awakened her. But she did not hear him for the beating of her heart.

COMMENT AND QUESTION

1. *The attitude of defeat.* A Hemingway character can usually express his attitude toward life in the simple phrase: "You can't win." The more admirable Hemingway character usually adds: "But you can be brave." These two phrases constitute a Hemingway code. Is this code apparent in this story? Is Harry brave? Or is defeat dominant here?

When "The Snows of Kilimanjaro" opens, the chips are down for Harry. He is engaged in a final judgment of his life.

a. *Harry and Helen.* Does Harry love his wife? Has he ever loved her? Perhaps one should ask: Has he ever loved her as a "wife"? Although Harry and Helen are married, the reader knows that Helen is not Harry's "wife" in any true sense. Do you think that Harry recognizes this truth clearly enough for it to add to his personal tragedy? Or does he seem unaware of this particular defeat?

b. *Harry's talent.* What part did Helen play in the loss of Harry's talent? Does Harry blame Helen completely? Does Harry seem deeply disturbed about the loss of his talent?

c. *Harry's attitude toward defeat.* Harry thinks: "You spoiled everything." The "you" refers to himself. Is Harry's reflection correct? Or does he have a code that ultimately gives some meaning to his life?

The reader should withhold final judgment on the defeat in Harry's life until he has considered the story as a whole.

2. *The importance of physical sensations.* A Hemingway character usually finds that truth and reality are limited to his sense experiences. To think is not to live, at least not to live realistically.

Notice the contrast between the italicized portions and the rest of the story. The italicized portions emphasize physical sensations. What, then, does the rest of the story emphasize? Why are these two activities so sharply divided in this story? Is it significant that Harry's illness is painless?

What is the range of Harry's sense experience? He comments that death is the only experience he has never had. If so, has his range of sense experience been limited?

3. *The death.* Is the death in this story inglorious, grotesque, and filthy? Consider the following:

a. The trivial accidents which lead to the infection.

b. The three or four shapes or forms in which death or the thought of death becomes tangible, beginning with the buzzards.

c. The physical characteristics of Harry's malady. Is the death in this story ironic? Could big game hunting be part of an italicized section?

4. *Spoiling the last experience.* Stoicism in the face of death is a virtue Hemingway grants to many of his characters. Does Harry succeed in his desire to keep from spoiling the last experience? Does he display any stoicism? Any kindliness and courage? What of his wife?

Since Harry had fulfilled himself once in life (as the italicized portions show), the most important statement here is: "I've been writing." Properly related to Harry's defeat and to the italicized portions, this statement gives some dignity and significance to the death.

5. *The italicized portions.* Read aloud, these portions of the story reveal the cadence and rhythm of Hemingway's best prose, his skill in poetic repetition and variation of a theme. The first italicized portion speaks of snow like a theme in music. Why should snow come to Harry's mind? How does the second italicized portion grow out of Harry's quarreling with Helen? What stimulates the last italicized reflection? All of these portions are closely integrated with the main story although they could exist independently.

Do these portions merely represent stories that Harry wants to write? Or is a dying man fulfilling himself in them as he had done once before in his life? If so, is the fulfillment limited to physical sensations gained through love, sports, nature, fighting? Or are there other values? Does Harry have conceptions of courage, defeat, violence, cruelty, and injustice? In other words, does he have a code? Which seems dominant, however, the code or the physical sensations?

Violence, which is characteristic of Hemingway's writing, occurs here in the italicized portions. Would violence be a natural part of Hemingway's attitude toward life?

An Analysis of the Scene in the Airplane

The most interesting problem in "The Snows of Kilimanjaro" is reflected in the following questions: Does the story have spiritual values? Does Hemingway give spiritual significance to a defeated man in the episode where the airplane is flying toward Kilimanjaro, also known **as** the House of God? Is the scene in the airplane intended to be a mystical experience? Some critics have answered "Yes" to all these questions.

But the scene in the airplane disturbs many readers, including the critics who find spiritual values in the story. One critic feels that Hemingway "muffed" what was intended to be a mystical experience because he did not prepare the reader properly nor develop a lofty tone. Another critic feels that a snow-capped mountain as a symbol of the House of God is too trite and conventional to have much force.

Actually the scene does not seem to be intended to be a mystical experience. A more believable explanation is that the scene in the airplane is an hallucination. Much in this scene is dependent upon the sense impressions which have stimulated Harry in the story. Notice that the death occurs when the cot is lifted (p. 264). This lifting sensation is part of the hallucination of the airplane, for the boys pick up the cot and carry it. It is difficult to get Harry into the airplane because of the position of his leg, and this position is explained in the final scene (p. 266). The coming of the airplane had been discussed by Helen and Harry. And the rain that falls during the flight had been a matter of dispute also (p. 259).

The gradual diminution of Harry's powers is one of the effective parts of this story. Notice how his powers fail from the first sentence through the "whispers" (p. 259), to statements by Harry which Helen does not hear (p. 264). Harry's whirling sensations end in an hallucination, and the scene in the airplane is made up of a series of physical sensations and a series of thoughts that he can no longer logically piece together.

The grotesque details of the hallucination are also in keeping with the grotesque details of the death, like the reference to the bicycle policemen. Compie's grin as he indicates Kilimanjaro is the final grotesque touch. The reader should note also that the description of Kilimanjaro preceding the story has ironic overtones. The fantastic detail of the leopard in a description of the House of God supports the irony. If no one can explain what the leopard was seeking, no one can explain what the two men in the airplane are seeking. Furthermore, without thought mysticism does not exist, and Harry's reflections do not rise far above physical sensation.

Nothing in the story prepares the reader for a belief in a spiritual home. Little in the scene in the airplane supports the belief. The conclusion is that the scene can hardly be called a mystical experience and that Hemingway did not intend to give spiritual significance to a dying, defeated man in "The Snows of Kilimanjaro."

In "The Second Death" Greene tries to achieve a mystical experience. Compare these two stories. Study the development of tone in both and you will come to a clearer understanding of the purpose of Greene and the purpose of Hemingway.

THE BENCH OF DESOLATION

BY HENRY JAMES

HENRY JAMES (1843–1916) is the most distinguished member of a distinguished American family. His father was Henry James, the
philosopher, and his brother was William
James, the philosopher and psychologist. Born
in America, he travelled a good deal in England and Europe, and finally settled in
England when he was thirty-two. He became
a British subject in 1915. In spite of this background, he is usually considered an American
writer. Americans figure prominently in many
of his better known novels like *The Ambas-
sadors* (1903), *The American* (1877), *Daisy
Miller* (1879), *Portrait of a Lady* (1881),
and *The Golden Bowl* (1904). A penetrating
psychological and moral insight pervades his
numerous stories and novels. James is the
author, also, of a good deal of criticism, collected in *The Art of the Novel* (1934). To-
day James is being acclaimed not only as the
classic critic of the technique of fiction but
also as the foremost American writer of fiction.

SHE HAD practically, he believed, conveyed the intimation, the horrid,
brutal, vulgar menace, in the course of their last dreadful conversation,
when, for whatever was left him of pluck or confidence—confidence in
what he would fain have called a little more confidently the strength of
his position—he had judged best not to take it up. But this time there was
no question of not understanding, or of pretending he didn't; the ugly, the

awful words, ruthlessly formed by her lips, were like the fingers of a hand that she might have thrust into her pocket for extraction of the monstrous object that would serve best for—what should he call it?—a gage of battle.

"If I haven't a very different answer from you within the next three days I shall put the matter into the hands of my solicitor, whom it may interest you to know I've already seen. I shall bring an action for 'breach' against you, Herbert Dodd, as sure as my name's Kate Cookham."

There it was, straight and strong—yet he felt he could say for himself, when once it had come, or even, already, just as it was coming, that it turned on, as if she had moved an electric switch, the very brightest light of his own very reasons. There *she* was, in all the grossness of her native indelicacy, in all her essential excess of will and destitution of scruple; and it was the woman capable of that ignoble threat who, his sharper sense of her quality having become so quite deterrent, was now making for him a crime of it that he shouldn't wish to tie himself to her for life. The vivid, lurid thing was the reality, all unmistakable, of her purpose; she had thought her case well out; had measured its odious, specious present-ability; had taken, he might be sure, the very best advice obtainable at Properley, where there was always a first-rate promptitude of everything fourth-rate; it was disgustingly certain, in short, that she'd proceed. She was sharp and adroit, moreover—distinctly in certain ways a masterhand; how otherwise, with her so limited mere attractiveness, should she have entangled him? He couldn't shut his eyes to the very probable truth that if she should try it she'd pull it off. She *knew* she would—precisely; and her assurance was thus the very proof of her cruelty. That she had pretended she loved him was comparatively nothing; other women had pretended it, and other women too had really done it; but that she had pretended he could possibly have been right and safe and blest in loving *her*, a creature of the kind who could sniff that squalor of the law-court, of claimed dam-ages and brazen lies and published kisses, of love-letters read amid obscene guffaws, as a positive tonic to resentment, as a high incentive to her course —this was what put him so beautifully in the right. It was what it meant in a woman all through, he said to himself, the mere imagination of such machinery. Truly what a devilish conception and what an appalling nature!

But there was no doubt, luckily, either, that he *could* plant his feet the firmer for his now intensified sense of these things. He was to live, it appeared, abominably worried, he was to live consciously rueful, he was to live perhaps even what a scoffing world would call abjectly exposed; but at least he was to live saved. In spite of his clutch of which steadying truth, however, and in spite of his declaring to her, with many other angry protests and pleas, that the line of conduct she announced was worthy of a vindictive barmaid, a lurking fear in him, too deep to counsel mere defiance, made him appear to keep open a little, till he could somehow turn round again, the door of possible composition. He had scoffed at her claim, at her threat, at her thinking she could hustle and bully him—"Such away, my eye, to call back to life a dead love!"—yet his instinct was ever, prudentially but helplessly, for gaining time, even if time only more woefully to quake, and he gained it now by not absolutely giving for his ultimatum that he wouldn't think of coming round. He didn't in the smallest degree mean to come round, but it was characteristic of him that he could for three or four days breathe a little easier by having left her under the impression that he perhaps might. At the same time he could not have said—what had conduced to bring out, in retort, her own last word, the word on which they had parted—"Do you mean to say you yourself would now be *willing* to marry and live with a man of whom you could feel, the thing done, that he'd be all the while thinking of you in the light of a hideous coercion?" "Never you mind about *my* willingness," Kate answered; "you've known what that has been for the last six months. Leave that to me, my willingness—I'll take care of it all right; and just see what conclusion you can come to about your own."

He was to remember afterwards how he had wondered whether, turned upon her in silence while her odious lucidity reigned unchecked, his face had shown her anything like the quantity of hate he felt. Probably not at all; no man's face *could* express that immense amount; especially the fair, refined, intellectual, gentlemanlike face which had had—and by her own more than once repeated avowal—so much to do with the enormous fancy she had originally taken to him. "Which—frankly now—would you personally *rather* I should do," he had at any rate asked her with an intention of supreme irony: "just sordidly marry you on top of this, or leave you the pleasure of your lovely appearance in court and of your so assured (since that's how you feel it) big haul of damages? Shan't you be awfully disappointed, in fact, if I don't let you get something better out of me than a poor, plain, ten-shilling gold ring and the rest of the blasphemous rubbish, as we should make it between us, pronounced at the altar? I take it, of course," he had swaggered on, "that your pretention wouldn't be for a moment that I should—after the act of profanity—take up my life with you."

"It's just as much my dream as it ever was, Herbert Dodd, to take up mine with *you*! Remember for me that I can do with it, my dear, that my idea is for even as much as that of you!" she had cried; "remember that for me, Herbert Dodd; remember, remember!"

It was on this she had left him—left him frankly under a mortal chill. There might have been the last ring of an appeal or a show of persistent and perverse tenderness in it, however preposterous any such matter; but in point of fact her large, clean, plain brown face—so much too big for her head, he now more than ever felt it to be, just as her head was so much too big for her body, and just as her hats had an irritating way of appearing to decline choice and conformity in respect to *any* of her dimensions—presented itself with about as much expression as his own shop-window when the broad, blank, sallow blind was down. He was fond of his shop-window with some good show on; he had a fancy for a good show and was master of twenty different schemes of taking arrangement for the old books and prints, "high-class rarities" his modest catalogue called them, in which he dealt and which his maternal uncle, David Geddes, had, as he liked to say, "handed down" to him (his widowed mother had screwed the whole thing, the stock and the connection and the rather bad little house in the rather bad little street, out of the ancient worthy, shortly before his death, in the name of the youngest and most interesting, the "delicate" one and the literary, of her five scattered and struggling children); he could enjoy his happiest collocations and contrasts and effects, his harmonies and varieties of toned and faded leather and cloth, his sought color-notes and the high clearnesses, here and there, of his white and beautifully figured price-labels, they could please him enough in themselves almost to console him for not oftener having to break, on a customer's insistence, into the balanced composition; but the dropped expanse of time-soiled canvas, the thing of Sundays and holidays, with just his name, "Herbert Dodd, Successor," painted on below his uncle's antique style, the feeble penlike flourishes already quite archaic, this ugly vacant mask, which might so easily be taken for the mask of failure, somehow always gave him a chill.

That had been just the sort of chill—the analogy was complete—of Kate Cookham's last look. He supposed people doing an awfully good and sure and steady business, in whatever line, could see a whole front turned to vacancy that way, and merely think of the hours off represented by it. Only for this—nervously to bear it, in other words, and Herbert Dodd, quite with the literary temperament himself, was capable of that amount of play of fancy, or even of morbid analysis—you had to be on some footing, you had to feel some confidence, pretty different from his own up to now. He had never *not* enjoyed passing his show on the other side of the street and taking it in thence with a casual obliquity; but he had never held optical commerce with the drawn blind for a moment longer than he could help. It *always* looked horribly final and as if it never would come up again. Big and bare, with his name staring at him from the middle, it thus offered in its grimness a turn of comparison for Miss Cookham's ominous visage. She never wore pretty, dotty, transparent veils, as Nan Drury did, and the words "Herbert Dodd"—save that she had sounded them at him there two or three times more like a Meg Merrilies or the bold bad woman in one of the melodramas of high life given during the fine season in the pavilion at the end of Properley Pier—were dreadfully, were permanently seated on her lips. *She* was grim, no mistake.

That evening, alone in the back room above his shop, he saw so little what he could do that, consciously demoralised for the hour, he gave way to tears about it. Her taking a stand so incredibly "low," that was what he couldn't get over. The particular bitterness of his cup was his having let himself in for a struggle on such terms—the use, on her side, of the vulgarest process known to the law: the vulgarest, the vulgarest, he kept repeating that, clinging to the help rendered him by this imputation to his terrorist of the vice he sincerely believed he had ever, among difficulties (for oh he recognized the difficulties!) sought to keep most alien to him. He knew what he was, in a dismal, downtrodden sphere enough— the lean young proprietor of an old business that had itself rather shrivelled with age than ever grown fat, the purchase and sale of second-hand books and prints, with the back street of a long-fronted south-coast watering-place (Old Town by good luck) for the dusky field of his life. But he had gone in for all the education he could get—his educated customers would often hang about for more talk by the half-hour at a time, he actually feeling himself, and almost with a scruple, hold them there; which meant that he had had (he couldn't be blind to that) natural taste and had lovingly cultivated and formed it. Thus, from as far back as he could remember, there had been things all round him that he suffered from when other people didn't; and he had kept most of his sufferings to himself— which had taught him, in a manner, *how* to suffer, and how almost to like to.

So, at any rate, he had never let go his sense of certain differences, he had done everything he could to keep it up—whereby everything that was vulgar was on the wrong side of his line. He had believed, for a series of strange, oppressed months, that Kate Cookham's manners and tone were on the right side; she had been governess—for young children—in two very good private families, and now had classes in literature and history for bigger girls who were sometimes brought by their mammas; in fact, coming in one day to look over his collection of students' manuals, and drawing it out, as so many did, for the evident sake of his conversation, she had appealed to him that very first time by her apparently pronounced intellectual side—goodness knew she didn't even then by the physical!— which she had artfully kept in view till she had entangled him past undoing. And it had all been but the cheapest of traps—when he came to take the pieces apart a bit—laid over a brazen avidity. What he now collapsed for, none the less—what he sank down on a chair at a table and nursed his weak, scared sobs in his resting arms for—was the fact that, whatever the trap, it held him as with the grip of sharp murderous steel. There he was, there he was; alone in the brown summer dusk—brown through *his* windows—he cried and he cried. He shouldn't get out without losing a limb. The only question was which of his limbs it should be.

Before he went out, later on—for he at last felt the need to—he could, however, but seek to remove from his face and his betraying eyes, over his washing-stand the traces of his want of fortitude. He brushed himself up; with which, catching his stricken image a bit spectrally, in an old dim toilet-glass, he knew again, in a flash, the glow of righteous resentment. Who should be assured against coarse usage if a man of his really elegant, perhaps in fact a trifle over-refined appearance, his absolutely gentleman-like type, couldn't be? He never went so far as to rate himself, with exaggeration, a gentleman; but he would have maintained against all comers, with perfect candor and as claiming a high advantage, that he was, in spite of that liability to blubber, "like" one; which he *was* no doubt, for that matter, at several points. Like what lady then, who could ever possibly have been taken for one, was Kate Cookham, and therefore how could one have anything—anything of the intimate and private order—out with her fairly and on the plane, the only possible one, of common equality? He might find himself crippled for life; he believed, verily, the more he thought, that that was what was before him. But he ended by seeing this doom in the almost redeeming light of the fact that it would all have been because he was, comparatively, too gentlemanlike. Yes, a man in his station couldn't afford to carry that so far—it must sooner or later, in one way or another, spell ruin. Never mind—it was the only thing he could be. Of course he should exquisitely suffer—but when hadn't he exquisitely suffered? How was he going to get through life by *any* arrangement without that? No wonder such a woman as Kate Cookham had been keen to annex so rare a value. The right thing would have been that the highest price should be paid for it—by such a different sort of logic from this nightmare of *his* having to pay.

II

Which was the way, of course, he talked to Nan Drury—as he had felt the immediate wild need to do; for he should perhaps be able to bear it all somehow or other with *her*—while they sat together, when time and freedom served, on one of the very last, the far westward benches of the interminable sea-front. It wasn't every one who walked so far, especially at that flat season—the only ghost of a bustle now, save for the gregarious, the obstreperous haunters of the fluttering, far-shining Pier, being reserved for the sunny Parade of midwinter. It wasn't everyone who cared for the sunsets (which you got awfully well from there and which were a particular strong point of the lower, the more "sympathetic" as Herbert Dodd liked to call it, Properley horizon) as he had always intensely cared, and as he had found Nan Drury cared; to say nothing of his having also observed how little they directly spoke to Miss Cookham. He had taught this oppressive companion to notice them a bit, as he had taught her plenty of other things, but that was a different matter; for the reason that the "land's end" (stretching a point it carried off that name) had been, and had had to be, by their lack of more sequestered resorts and conveniences, the scene of so much of what she styled their wooing-time—or, to put it more properly, of the time during which she had made the straightest and most unabashed love to *him*: just as it could henceforth but render possible, under an equal rigor, that he should enjoy there periods of consolation from beautiful, gentle, tender-souled Nan, to whom he was now at last, after the wonderful way they had helped each other to behave, going to make love, absolutely unreserved and abandoned, absolutely reckless and romantic love, a refuge from poisonous reality, as hard as ever he might.

The league-long, paved, lighted, garden-plotted, seated and refuged Marina renounced its more or less celebrated attractions to break off short here; and an inward curve of the kindly westward shore almost made a wide-armed bay, with all the ugliness between town and country, and the further casual fringe of the coast, turning, as the day waned, to rich afternoon blooms of gray and brown and distant—it might fairly have been beautiful Hampshire—blue. Here it was that all that blighted summer, with Nan—from the dreadful Mayday on—he gave himself up to the reaction of intimacy with the *kind* of woman, at least, that he liked; even if of everything else that might make life possible he was to be, by what he could make out, forever starved. Here it was that—as well as on whatever other scraps of occasions they could manage—Nan began to take off and fold up and put away in her pocket her pretty, dotty, becoming veil; as under the logic of his having so tremendously ceased, in the shake of his dark storm-gust, to be engaged to another woman. Her removal of that obstacle to a trusted friend's assuring himself whether the peachlike bloom of her finer facial curves bore the test of such further inquiry into their cool sweetness as might reinforce a mere baffled gaze—her momentous, complete surrender of so much of her charm, let us say, both marked the change in the situation of the pair and established the record of their perfect observance of every propriety for so long before. They afterwards in fact could have dated it, their full clutch of their freedom and the bliss of their having so little henceforth to consider save their impotence, their poverty, their ruin; dated it from the hour of his recital to her of the—at the first blush—quite appalling upshot of his second and conclusive "scene of violence" with the mistress of his fortune, when the dire terms of his release had to be formally, and oh! so abjectly, acceded to. She "compromised," the cruel brute, for Four Hundred Pounds down—for not a farthing less would she stay her strength fom "proceedings." No jury in the land but would give her six, on the nail ("Oh she knew quite where she was, thank you") and he might feel lucky to get off with so whole a skin. This was the sum, then, for which he had grovellingly compounded —under an agreement sealed by a supreme exchange of remarks.

" 'Where in the name of lifelong ruin are you to *find* Four Hundred?' " Miss Cookham had mockingly repeated after him, while he gasped as from the twist of her grip on his collar. "That's *your* look-out, and I should have thought you'd have made sure you knew before you decided on your base perfidy." And then she mouthed and minced, with ever so false a gentility, her consistent, her sickening conclusion, "Of course—I may mention again—if you too distinctly object to the trouble of looking, you know where to find *me*."

"I had rather starve to death than ever go within a mile of you!" Herbert described himself as having sweetly answered; and that was accordingly where *they* devotedly but desperately were—he and she, penniless Nan Drury. Her father, of Drury & Dean, was, like so far too many other of the anxious characters who peered through the dull window-glass of dusty offices at Properley, an Estate and House Agent, Surveyor, and Auctioneer; she was the prettiest Valuer of six, with two brothers, neither of the least use, but, thanks to the manner in which their main natural protector appeared to languish under the accumulation of his attributes, they couldn't be said very particularly or positively to live. Their continued collective existence was a good deal of a miracle even to themselves, though they had fallen into the way of not unnecessarily, or too nervously, exchanging remarks upon it, and had even in a sort, from year to year, got used to it. Nan's brooding pinkness when he talked to her, her so very parted lips, considering her pretty teeth, her so very parted eyelids, considering her pretty eyes, all of which might have been those of some waxen image of uncritical faith, cooled the heat of his helplessness very much as if he were laying his head on a tense silk pillow. She had, it was true, forms of speech, familiar watchwords, that affected him as small scratchy perforations of the smooth surface from within; but his pleasure in her and need of her were independent of such things and really almost altogether determined by the fact of the happy, even if all so lonely, forms and instincts in her which claimed kinship with his own. With her natural elegance stamped on her as by a die, with her dim and disinherited individual refinement of grace, which would have made any one wonder who she was anywhere—hat and veil and feather-boa and smart umbrella—knob and all —with her regular God-given distinction of type, in fine, she couldn't abide vulgarity much more than he could.

Therefore, it didn't seem to him, under his stress, to matter particularly, for instance, if she *would* keep on referring so many things to the time, as she called it, when she came into his life—his own great insistence and contention being that she hadn't in the least entered there till his mind was wholly made up to eliminate his other friend. What that methodical fury was so fierce to bring home to him was the falsity to herself involved in the later acquaintance; whereas just his precious right to hold up his head to everything—before himself at least—sprang from the fact that she couldn't make dates fit anyhow. He hadn't so much as heard of his true beauty's existence (she had come back but a few weeks before from her two years with her terribly trying deceased aunt at Swindon, previous to which absence she had been an unnoticeable chit) till days and days, ever so many, upon his honor, after he had struck for freedom by his great first backing-out letter—the precious document, the treat for a British jury, in which, by itself, Miss Cookham's firm instructed her to recognize the prospect of a fortune. The way the ruffians had been "her" ruffians, it appeared as if she had posted them behind her from the first of her beginning her game, and the way "instructions" bounced out, with it, at a touch, larger than life, as if she had arrived with her pocket full of them! The date of the letter, taken with its other connections, and the date of *her* first give-away for himself, his seeing her get out of the Brighton train with Bill Frankle that day he had gone to make the row at the Station parcels' office about the miscarriage of the box from Wales—those were the facts it sufficed him to point to, as he had pointed to them for Nan Drury's benefit, goodness knew, often and often enough. If he didn't seek occasion to do so for anyone else's—in open court as they said—that was his own affair, or at least his and Nan's.

It little mattered, meanwhile, if on their bench of desolation, all that summer—and it may be added for summers and summers, to say nothing of winters, there and elsewhere, to come—she did give way to her artless habit of not contradicting him enough, which led to her often trailing up and down before him, too complacently, the untimely shreds and patches of his own glooms and desperations. "Well, I'm glad I *am* in your life, terrible as it is, however or whenever I did come in!" and "*Of course* you'd rather have starved—and it seems pretty well as if we shall, doesn't it?—than have bought her off by a false abhorrent love, wouldn't you?" and "It isn't as if she hadn't made up to you the way she did before you had so much as looked at her, is it? or as if you hadn't shown her what you felt her really to be before you had so much as looked at *me*, is it either?" and "Yes, how on earth, pawning the shoes on your feet, you're going to raise another shilling—*that*'s what you want to know, poor darling, don't you?"

III

His creditor, at the hour it suited her, transferred her base of operations to town, to which impenetrable scene she had also herself retired; and his raising of the first Two Hundred, during five exasperated and miserable months, and then of another Seventy piecemeal, bleedingly, after long delays and under the epistolary whiplash cracked by the London solicitor in his wretched ear even to an effect of the very report of Miss Cookham's tongue—these melancholy efforts formed a scramble up an arduous steep where steps were planted and missed, and bared knees were excoriated, and clutches at wayside tufts succeeded and failed, on a system to which poor Nan could have intelligently entered only if she had been somehow less ladylike. She kept putting into his mouth the sick quaver of where he should find the rest, the always inextinguishable rest, long after he had in silent rage fallen away from any further payment at all—at first, he had but too blackly felt, for himself, to the still quite possible non-exclusion of some penetrating ray of "exposure." He didn't care a two-penny damn now, and in point of fact, after he had by hook and by crook succeeded in being able to unload to the tune of Two-Hundred-and-Seventy, and then simply returned the newest reminder of his outstanding obligation unopened, this latter belated but real sign of fight, the first he had risked, remarkably caused nothing at all to happen; nothing at least but his being moved to quite tragically rueful wonder as to whether exactly some such demonstration mightn't have served his turn at an earlier stage.

He could by this time at any rate measure his ruin—with three fantastic mortgages on his house, his shop, his stock, and a burden of interest to carry under which his business simply stretched itself inanimate, without strength for a protesting kick, without breath for an appealing groan. Customers lingering for further enjoyment of the tasteful remarks he had cultivated the unobstrusive art of throwing in, would at this crisis have found plenty to repay them, might his wit have strayed a little more widely still, toward a circuitous egotistical outbreak, from the immediate question of the merits of this and that author or of the condition of this and that volume. He had come to be conscious through it all of strangely glaring at people when they tried to haggle—and not, as formerly, with the glare of derisive comment on their overdone humor, but with that of fairly idiotized surrender—as if they were much mistaken in supposing, for the sake of conversation, that he might take himself for savable by the difference between sevenpence and ninepence. He watched everything impossible and deplorable happen, as in an endless prolongation of his nightmare; watched himself proceed, that is, with the finest, richest incoherence, to the due preparation of his catastrophe. Everything came to seem *equally* part of this—in complete defiance of proportion; even his final command of detachment, on the bench of desolation (where each successive fact of his dire case regularly cut itself out black, yet of senseless outline, against the red west) in respect to poor Nan's flat infelicities, which for the most part kept no pace with the years or with change, but only shook like hard peas in a child's rattle, the same peas always, of course, so long as the rattle didn't split open with usage or from somebody's act of irritation. They represented, or they had long done so, her contribution to the more superficial of the two branches of intimacy—the intellectual alternative, the one that didn't merely consist in her preparing herself for his putting his arm round her waist.

There were to have been moments, nevertheless, all the first couple of years, when she did touch in him, though to his actively dissimulating it, a more or less sensitive nerve—moments as they were too, to do her justice, when she treated him not to his own wisdom, or even folly, served up cold, but to a certain small bitter fruit of her personal, her unnatural, plucking. "I wonder that since *she* took legal advice so freely, to come down on you, you didn't take it yourself, a little, before being so sure you stood no chance. Perhaps *your* people would have been sure of something quite different—*perhaps*, I only say, you know." She "only" said it, but she said it, none the less, in the early time, about once a fortnight. In the later, and especially after their marriage, it had a way of coming up again to the exclusion, as it seemed to him, of almost everything else; in fact during the most dismal years, the three of the loss of their two children, the long stretch of sordid embarrassment ending in her death, he was afterwards to think of her as having generally said it several times a day. He was then also to remember that his answer, before she had learnt to discount it, had been inveterately at hand: "What would any solicitor have done or wanted to do but drag me just into the hideous public arena"—he had always so put it—"that it has been at any rate my pride and my honor, the one rag of self-respect covering my nakedness, to have loathed and avoided from every point of view?"

That had disposed of it so long as he cared, and by the time he had ceased to care for anything it had also lost itself in the rest of the vain babble of home. After his wife's death, during his year of mortal solitude, it awoke again as an echo of far-off things—far-off, very far-off, because he felt then not ten but twenty years older. That was by reason simply of the dead weight with which his load of debt had settled—the persistence of his misery dragging itself out. With all that had come and gone the bench of desolation was still there, just as the immortal flush of the westward sky kept hanging its indestructible curtain. He had never got away—everything had left him, but he himself had been able to turn his back on nothing—and now, his day's labor before a dirty desk at the Gas Works ended, he more often than not, almost any season at temperate Properley serving his turn, took his slow straight way to the Land's End and, collapsing there to rest, sat often for an hour at a time staring before him. He might in these sessions, with his eyes on the gray-green sea, have been counting again and still recounting the beads, almost all worn smooth of his rosary of pain—which had for the fingers of memory and the recurrences of wonder the same felt break of the smaller ones by the larger that would have aided a pious mumble in some dusky altar-chapel.

If it has been said of him that when once full submersion, as from far back, had visibly begun to await him, he watched himself, in a cold lucidity, *do* punctually and necessarily each of the deplorable things that were inconsistent with his keeping afloat, so at present again he might have been held agaze just by the presented grotesqueness of that vigil. Such ghosts of dead seasons were all he *had* now to watch—such a recap-

tured sense for instance as that of the dismal unavailing awareness that
had attended his act of marriage. He had let submersion final and absolute
become the signal for it—a mere minor determinant having been the more
or less contemporaneously unfavorable effect on the business of Drury &
Dean of the sudden disappearance of Mr. Dean with the single small tin
box into which the certificates of the firm's credit had been found to be
compressible. That had been his only form—or had at any rate seemed his
only one. He couldn't not have married, no doubt, just as he couldn't not
have suffered the last degree of humiliation and almost of want, or just as
his wife and children couldn't not have died of the little he was able,
under dire reiterated pinches, to do for them; but it *was* "rum," for final
solitary brooding, that he hadn't appeared to see his way definitely to undertake the support of a family till the last scrap of his little low-browed,
high-toned business and the last figment of "property" in the old tiled and
timbered shell that housed it, had been sacrificed to creditors mustering
six rows deep.

Of course what had counted too in the odd order was that even at the
end of the two or three years he had "allowed" her, Kate Cookham,
gorged with his unholy tribute, had become the subject of no successful
siege on the part either of Bill Frankle or, by what he could make out,
of anyone else. She had judged decent—he could do her that justice—to
take herself personally out of his world, as he called it, for good and all,
as soon as he had begun regularly to bleed; and, to whatever lucrative
practice she might be devoting her great talents in London or elsewhere,
he felt his conscious curiosity about her as cold, with time, as the passion
of vain protest that she had originally left him to. He could recall but two
direct echoes of her in all the bitter years—both communicated by Bill
Frankle, disappointed and exposed and at last quite remarkable ingenuous
sneak, who had also, from far back, taken to roaming the world, but who,
during a period, used fitfully and ruefully to reappear. Herbert Dodd had
quickly seen, at their first meeting—everyone met everyone sooner or later
at Properley, if meeting it could always be called, either in the glare or
the gloom of the explodedly attractive Embankment—that no silver stream
of which he himself had been the remoter source could have played over
the career of this all but repudiated acquaintance. That hadn't fitted with
his first, his quite primitive raw vision of the probabilities, and he had
further been puzzled when, much later on, it had come to him in a round-
about way that Miss Cookham was supposed to be, or to have been,
among them for a few days "on the quiet," and that Frankle, who had
seen her and who claimed to know more about it than he said, was cited
as authority for the fact. But he hadn't himself at this juncture seen
Frankle; he had only wondered, and a degree of mystification had even
remained.

That memory referred itself to the dark days of old Drury's smash, the few weeks between his partner's dastardly flight and Herbert's own comment on it in the form of his standing up with Nan for the nuptial benediction of the Vicar of St. Bernards on a very cold, bleak December morning and amid a circle of seven or eight long-faced, red-nosed and altogether dowdy persons. Poor Nan herself had struck him as red-nosed and dowdy by that time, but this only added, in his then, and indeed in his lasting view, to his general and his particular morbid bravery. He had cultivated ignorance, there were small inward immaterial luxuries he could scrappily cherish even among other, and the harshest destitutions; and one of them was represented by this easy refusal of his mind to render to certain passages of his experience, to various ugly images, names, associations, the homage of continued attention. That served him, that helped him; but what happened when, a dozen dismal years having worn themselves away, he sat single and scraped bare again, as if his long wave of misfortune had washed him far beyond everything and then conspicuously retreated, was that, thus stranded by tidal action, deposited in the lonely hollow of his fate, he felt even sustaining pride turn to nought and heard no challenge from it when old mystifications, stealing forth in the dusk of the day's work done, scratched at the door of speculation and hung about, through the idle hours, for irritated notice.

The evenings of his squalid clerkship were all leisure now, but there was nothing at all near home on the other hand, for his imagination, numb and stiff from its long chill, to begin to play with. Voices from far off would quaver to him therefore in the stillness; where he knew for the most recurrent, little by little, the faint wail of his wife. He had become deaf to it in life, but at present, after so great an interval, he listened again, listened and listened, and seemed to hear it sound as by the pressure of some weak broken spring. It phrased for his ear her perpetual question, the one she had come to at the last as under the obsession of a discovered and resented wrong, a wrong withal that had its source much more in his own action than anywhere else. "That you didn't make *sure* she could have done anything, that you didn't make sure and that you were too afraid!"—this commemoration had ended by playing such a part in Nan's finally quite contracted consciousness as to exclude everything else.

At the time, somehow, he had made his terms with it; he had then more urgent questions to meet than that of the poor creature's taste in worrying pain; but actually it struck him—not the question but the fact itself of the taste—as the one thing left over from all that had come and gone. So it was; nothing remained to him in the world, on the bench of desolation, but the option of taking up that echo—together with an abundance of free time for doing so. That he hadn't made sure of what might and what mightn't have been done to him, that he had been too afraid—had the proposition a possible bearing on his present apprehension of things? To reply indeed he would have had to be able to say what his present appre-

hension of things, left to itself, amounted to; an uninspiring effort indeed
he judged it, sunk to so poor a pitch was his material of thought—though
it might at last have been the feat he sought to perform as he stared at
the gray-green sea.

IV

It was seldom Herbert Dodd was disturbed in any form of sequestered
speculation, or that at his times of predilection, especially that of the long
autumn blankness between the season of trippers and the season of Bath-
chairs, there were westward stragglers enough to jar upon his settled sense
of priority. For himself his seat, the term of his walk, was consecrated; it
had figured to him for years as the last (though there were others, not
immediately near it, and differently disposed, that might have aspired to
the title); so that he could invidiously distinguish as he approached, make
out from a distance any accident of occupation, and never draw nearer
while that unpleasantness lasted. What he disliked was to compromise on
his tradition, whether for a man, a woman, or a connoodling couple; it was
to idiots of this last composition he most objected, he having sat there, in
the past, alone, having sat there interminably with Nan, having sat there
with—well, with other women when women, at hours of ease, could still
care or count for him, but having never shared the place with any shuffling
or snuffling stranger.

It was a world of fidgets and starts, however, the world of his present
dreariness—he alone possessed in it, he seemed to make out, of the secret
of the dignity of sitting still with one's fate; so that if he took a turn about
or rested briefly elsewhere even foolish philanderers (though this would
never have been his and Nan's way) ended soon by some adjournment as
visibly pointless as their sprawl. Then, their backs turned, he would drop
down on it, the bench of desolation—which was what he, and he only,
made it, by sad adoption; where, for that matter, moreover, once he had
settled at his end, it was marked that nobody else ever came to sit. He saw
people, along the Marina, take this liberty with other resting presences;
but his own struck them perhaps in general as either of too grim or just of
too dingy a vicinage. He might have affected the fellow-lounger as a man
evil, unsociable, possibly engaged in working out the idea of a crime; or
otherwise, more probably—for on the whole he surely looked harmless—
devoted to the worship of some absolutely unpractical remorse.

On a certain October Saturday he had got off, as usual, early; but the
afternoon light, his pilgrimage drawing to its aim, could still show him, at
long range, the rare case of an established usurper. His impulse was then,
as by custom, to deviate a little and wait, all the more that the occupant
of the bench was a lady, and that ladies, when alone, were—at that austere
end of the varied frontal stretch—markedly discontinuous; but he kept on
at sight of this person's rising, while he was still fifty yards off, and pro-

ceeding, her back turned, to the edge of the broad terrace, the outer line of which followed the interspaced succession of seats and was guarded by an iron rail from the abruptly lower level of the beach. Here she stood before the sea, while our friend on his side, recognizing no reason to the contrary, sank into the place she had quitted. There were other benches, eastward and off by the course of the drive, for vague ladies. The lady indeed thus thrust upon Herbert's vision might have struck an observer either as not quite vague or as vague with a perverse intensity suggesting design.

Not that our own observer at once thought of these things; he only took in, and with no great interest, that the obtruded presence was a "real" lady; that she was dressed (he noticed such matters) with a certain elegance of propriety or intention of harmony; and that she remained perfectly still for a good many minutes; so many in fact that he presently ceased to heed her, and that as she wasn't straight before him, but as far to the left as was consistent with his missing her profile, he had turned himself to one of his sunsets again (though it wasn't quite one of his best) and let it hold him for a time that enabled her to alter her attitude and present a fuller view. Without other movement, but her back now to the sea and her face to the odd person who had appropriated her corner, she had taken a sustained look at him before he was aware she had stirred. On that apprehension, however, he became also promptly aware of her direct, her applied observation. As his sense of this quickly increased he wondered who she was and what she wanted—what, as it were, was the matter with her; it suggested to him, the next thing, that she had, under some strange idea, actually been waiting for him. Any idea about him to-day on the part of anyone could only *be* strange.

Yes, she stood there with the ample width of the Marina between them, but turned to him, for all the world, as to show frankly that she was concerned with him. And she *was*—oh yes—a real lady: a middle-aged person of good appearance and of the best condition, in quiet but "handsome" black, save for very fresh white kid gloves, and with a pretty, dotty, becoming veil, predominantly white, adjusted to her countenance; which through it somehow, even to his imperfect sight, showed strong fine black brows and what he would have called on the spot character. But she was pale; her black brows were the blacker behind the flattering tissue; she still kept a hand, for support, on the terrace-rail, while the other, at the end of an extended arm that had an effect of rigidity, clearly pressed hard on the knob of a small and shining umbrella, the lower extremity of whose stick was equally, was sustainingly firm, on the walk. So this mature, qualified, important person stood and looked at the limp, undistinguished (oh his values of aspect now!), shabby man on the bench.

It was extraordinary, but the fact of her interest, by immensely surprising, by immediately agitating him, blinded him at first to her identity and, for the space of his long stare, diverted him from it; with which even then, when recognition did break, the sense of the shock, striking inward, simply consumed itself in gaping stillness. He sat here motionless and weak, fairly faint with surprise, and there was no instant, in all the succession of so many, at which Kate Cookham could have caught the special sign of his intelligence. Yet that she did catch something he saw—for he saw her steady herself, by her two supported hands, to meet it; while, after she had done so, a very wonderful thing happened, of which he could scarce, later on, have made a clear statement, though he was to think it over again and again. She moved toward him, she reached him, she stood there, she sat down near him, he merely passive and wonder-struck, unresentfully "impressed," gaping and taking it in—and all as with an open allowance on the part of each, so that they positively and quite intimately met in it, of the impertinence for their case, this case that brought them again, after horrible years, face to face, of the vanity, the profanity, the impossibility, of anything between them but silence.

Nearer to him, beside him at a considerable interval (oh she was immensely considerate!) she presented him, in the sharp terms of her transformed state—but thus the more amply, formally, ceremoniously—with the reasons that would serve him best for not having precipitately known her. She was simply another and a totally different person, and the exhibition of it to which she had proceeded, with this solemn anxiety was all, obviously, for his benefit—once he had, as he appeared to be doing, provisionally accepted her approach. He had remembered her as inclined to the massive and cut off from the graceful; but this was a spare, fine, worn, almost wasted lady—who had repaired waste, it was true, however, with something he could only appreciate as a rich accumulation of manner. She was strangely older, so far as that went—marked by experience and as if many things had happened to her; her face had suffered to its improvement, contraction and concentration; and if he had granted, of old and from the first, that her eyes were remarkable, had they yet ever had for him this sombre glow? Withal, something said, she had flourished—he felt it, wincing at it, as that; she had had a life, a career, a history—something that her present waiting air and nervous consciousness couldn't prevent his noting there as a deeply latent assurance. She had flourished, she had flourished—though to learn it after this fashion was somehow at the same time not to feel she flaunted it. It wasn't thus execration that she revived in him; she made in fact, exhibitively, as he could only have put it, the matter of long ago irrelevant and these extraordinary minutes of their reconstituted relation—how many? how few?—addressed themselves altogether to new possibilities.

Still it after a little awoke in him as with the throb of a touched nerve that his very own attitude was supplying a connection; he knew presently that he wouldn't have had her go, *couldn't* have made a sign to her for it (which was what she had been uncertain of) without speaking to him; and that therefore he was, as at the other, the hideous time, passive to whatever she might do. She was even yet, she was always, in possession of him; she had known how and where to find him and had appointed that he should see her, and, though he had never dreamed it was again to happen to him, he was meeting it already as if it might have been the only thing that the least humanly *could*. Yes, he had come back there to flop, by long custom, upon the bench of desolation *as* the man in the whole place, precisely to whom nothing worth more than tuppence could happen; whereupon, in the gray desert of his consciousness, the very earth had suddenly opened and flamed. With this, further, it came over him that he hadn't been prepared and that his wretched appearance must show it. He wasn't fit to receive a visit—any visit; a flush for his felt misery, in the light of her opulence, broke out in his lean cheeks. But if he colored he sat as he was—she should at least, as a visitor, be satisfied. His eyes only, at last, turned from her and resumed a little their gaze at the sea. That, however, didn't relieve him, and he perpetrated in the course of another moment the odd desperate gesture of raising both his hands to his face and letting them, while he pressed it to them, cover and guard it. It was as he held them there that she at last spoke.

"I'll go away if you wish me to." And then she waited a moment. "I mean now—now that you've seen I'm here. I wanted you to know it, and I thought of writing—I was afraid of our meeting accidentally. Then I was afraid that if I wrote you might refuse. So I thought of this way—as I knew you must come out here." She went on with pauses, giving him a chance to make a sign. "I've waited several days. But I'll do what you wish. Only I should like in that case to come back." Again she stopped; but strange was it to him that he wouldn't have made her break off. She held him in boundless wonder. "I came down—I mean I came from town— on purpose. I'm staying on still, and I've a great patience and will give you time. Only may I say it's important? Now that I do see you," she brought out in the same way, "I see how inevitable it was—I mean that I should have wanted to come. But you must feel about it as you can," she wound up—"till you get used to the idea."

She spoke so for accommodation, for discretion, for some ulterior view already expressed in her manner, that, after taking well in, from behind his hands, that this was her very voice—oh ladylike!—heard, and heard in deprecation of displeasure, after long years again, he uncovered his face and freshly met her eyes. More than ever he couldn't have known her. Less and less remained of the figure, all the facts of which had long ago so hardened for him. She was a handsome, grave, authoritative, but refined and as it were, physically rearranged person—she, the outrageous vulgarity of whose prime assault had kept him shuddering so long as a shudder was in him. That atrocity in her was what everything had been built on, but somehow, all strangely, it was slipping from him; so that, after the oddest fashion conceivable, when he felt he mustn't let her go, it was as if he were putting out his hand to *save* the past, the hideous real unalterable past, exactly as she had been the cause of its being and the cause of his undergoing it. He should have been too awfully "sold" if he wasn't going to have been right about her.

"I don't mind," he heard himself at last say. Not to mind had seemed for the instant the length he was prepared to go; but he was afterward aware of how soon he must have added: "You've come on purpose to see me?" He was on the point of putting to her further: "What then do you want of me?" But he would keep—yes, in time—from appearing to show he cared. If he showed he cared, where then would be his revenge? So he was already, within five minutes, thinking his revenge uncomfortably over instead of just comfortably knowing it. What came to him, at any rate, as they actually fell to talk was that, with such precautions, considerations, reduplications of consciousness, almost avowed feelings of her way on her own part, and light fingerings of his chords of sensibility, she was understanding, she *had* understood, more things than all the years, up to this strange eventide, had given him an inkling of. They talked, they went on—he hadn't let her retreat, to whatever it committed him and however abjectly it did so; yet keeping off and off, dealing with such surface facts as involved ancient acquaintance but kept abominations at bay. The recognition, the attestation that she *had* come down for him, that there would be reasons, that she had even hovered and watched, assured herself a little of his habits (which she managed to speak of as if, on their present ampler development, they were much to be deferred to), held them long enough to make vivid how, listen as stiffly or as serenely as he might, she sat there in fear, just as she had so stood there at first, and that her fear had really to do with her calculation of some sort of chance with him. What chance could it possibly be? Whatever it might have done, on this prodigious showing, with Kate Cookham, it made the present witness to the state of his fortunes simply exquisite: he ground his teeth secretly together as he saw he should have to take *that*. For what did it mean but that she would have liked to pity him if she could have done it with safety? Ah, however, he must give her no measure of safety!

By the time he had remarked, with that idea, that she probably saw few changes about them there that weren't for the worse—the place was going down, down and down, so fast that goodness knew where it would stop—and had also mentioned that in spite of this he himself remained faithful, with all its faults loving it still; by the time he had, after that fashion, superficially indulged her, adding a few further light and just sufficiently dry reflections on local matters, the disappearance of landmarks and important persons, the frequency of gales, the low policy of the town-council in playing down to cheap excursionists: by the time he had so acquitted himself, and she had observed, of her own motion, that she was staying at the Royal, which he knew for the time-honored, the conservative and exclusive hotel, he had made out for himself one thing at least, the amazing fact that he had been landed by his troubles, at the end of time, in a "social relation," of all things in the world, and that of that luxury he was now having unprecedented experience. He had but once in his life had his nose in the Royal, on the occasion of his himself delivering a parcel during some hiatus in his succession of impossible small boys, and meeting in the hall the lady who had bought of him, in the morning, a set of Crabbe, largely, he flattered himself, under the artful persuasion of his acute remarks on that author, gracefully associated by him, in this colloquy, he remembered, with a glance at Charles Lamb as well, and who went off, in a day or two, without settling, though he received her cheque from London three or four months later.

That hadn't been a social relation; and truly, deep within his appeal to himself to be remarkable, to be imperturbable and impenetrable, to be in fact quite incomparable now, throbbed the intense vision of his drawing out and draining dry the sensation he had begun to taste. He would do it, moreover—that would be the refinement of his art—not only without the betrayed anxiety of a single question, but just even by seeing her flounder (since she must, in a vagueness deeply disconcerting to her) as to her real effect on him. She was distinctly floundering by the time he had brought her—it had taken ten minutes—down to a consciousness of absurd and twaddling topics, to the reported precarious state, for instance, of the syndicate running the Bijou Theatre at the Pier-head—all as an admonition that she might want him to want to know why she was thus waiting on him, might want it for all she was worth, before he had ceased to be so remarkable as not to ask her. He didn't—and this assuredly was wondrous enough—want to do anything worse to her than let her flounder; but he was willing to do that so long as it mightn't prevent his seeing at least where *he* was. He seemed still to see where he was even at the minute that followed her final break-off, clearly intended to be resolute, from make-believe talk.

"I wonder if I might prevail on you to come to tea with me to-morrow at five."

He didn't so much as answer it—though he could scarcely believe his ears. To-morrow was Sunday, and the proposal referred, clearly, to the custom of "five-o'clock" tea, known to him only by the contemporary novel of manners and the catchy advertisement of table-linen. He had never in his life been present at any such luxurious rite, but he was offering practical indifference to it as a false mark of his sense that his social relation had already risen to his chin. "I gave up my very modest, but rather interesting little old book-business, perhaps you know, ever so long ago."

She floundered so that she could say nothing—meet *that* with no pos-

sible word; all the less too that his tone, casual and colorless, wholly
defied any apprehension of it as a reverse. Silence only came; but after
a moment she returned to her effort. "If you *can* come I shall be at home.
To see you otherwise than this was in fact what, as I tell you, I came down
for. But I leave it," she returned, "to your feeling."

He had at this, it struck him, an inspiration; which he required however a minute or two to decide to carry out; a minute or two during
which the shake of his foot over his knee became an intensity of fidget.
"Of course I know I still owe you a large sum of money. If it's about *that*
you wish to see me," he went on, "I may as well tell you just here that I
shall be able to meet my full obligation in the future as little as I've met
in the past. I can never," said Herbert Dodd, "pay up that balance."

He had looked at her while he spoke, but on finishing looked off at the
sea again and continued to agitate his foot. He knew now what he had
done and why; and the sense of her fixed dark eyes on him during his
speech and after didn't alter his small contentment. Yet even when she
still said nothing he didn't turn round; he simply kept his corner as if *that*
were his point made, should it even be the last word between them. It
might have been, for that matter, from the way in which she presently
rose, gathering herself, her fine umbrella and her very small smart reticule, in the construction of which shining gilt much figured, well together,
and, after standing another instant, moved across to the rail of the terrace
as she had done before and remained, as before, with her back to him,
though this time, it well might be, under a different fear. A quarter of an
hour ago she hadn't tried him, and had had that anxiety; now that she had
tried him it wasn't easier—but she was thinking what she still could do.
He left her to think—nothing in fact more interesting than the way she
might decide had ever happened to him; but it was a part of this also
that as she turned round and came nearer again he didn't rise, he gave
her no help. If she got any, at least, from his looking up at her only, meeting her fixed eyes once more in silence, that was her own affair. "You must
think," she said—"you must take all your time, but I shall be at home."
She left it to him thus—she insisted, with her idea, on leaving him something too. And on her side as well she showed an art—which resulted,
after another instant, in his having to rise to his feet. He flushed afresh
as he did it—it exposed him so shabbily the more; and now if she took
him in, with each of his seedy items from head to foot, he didn't and
couldn't and wouldn't know it, attaching his eyes hard and straight to
something quite away from them.

It stuck in his throat to say he'd come, but she had so curious a way
with her that he still less could say he wouldn't, and in a moment had
taken refuge in something that was neither. "Are you married?"—he put
it to her with that plainness, though it had seemed before he said it to do
more for him than while she waited before replying.

"No, I'm not married," she said: and then had another wait that might have amounted to a question of what this had to do with it.

He surely couldn't have told her; so that he had recourse, a little poorly as he felt, but to an "Oh!" that still left them opposed. He turned away for it—that is for the poorness, which, lingering in the air, had almost a vulgar platitude; and when, he presently again wheeled about she had fallen off as for quitting him, only with a pause once more, for a last look. It was all a bit awkward, but he had another happy thought, which consisted in his silently raising his hat as for a sign of dignified dismissal. He had cultivated of old, for the occasions of life, the right, the discriminated bow, and now, out of the gray limbo of the time when he could care for such things, this flicker of propriety leaped and worked. She might, for that matter, herself have liked it; since, receding further, only with her white face toward him, she paid it the homage of submission. He remained dignified, and she almost humbly went.

V

Nothing in the world, on the Sunday afternoon, could have prevented him from going; he was not after all destitute of three or four such articles of clothing as, if they wouldn't particularly grace the occasion, wouldn't positively dishonor it. That deficiency might have kept him away, but no voice of the spirit, no consideration of pride. It sweetened his impatience in fact—for he fairly felt it a long time to wait—that his pride would really most find its account in his acceptance of these conciliatory steps. From the moment he could put it in that way—that he couldn't refuse to hear what she might have, so very elaborately, to say for herself—he ought certainly to be at his ease; in illustration of which he whistled odd snatches to himself as he hung about on that cloud-dappled autumn Sunday, a mild private minstrelsy that his lips hadn't known since when? The interval of the twenty-four hours, made longer by a night of many more revivals than oblivions, had in fact dragged not a little; in spite of which, however, our extremely brushed-up and trimmed and polished friend knew an unprecedented flutter as he was ushered, at the Royal Hotel, into Miss Cookham's sitting-room. Yes, it was an adventure, and he had never had an adventure in his life; the term, for him, was essentially a term of high appreciation—such as disqualified for that figure, under due criticism, every single passage of his past career.

What struck him at the moment as qualifying in the highest degree this actual passage was the fact that at no great distance from his hostess in the luxurious room, as he apprehended it, in which the close of day had begun to hang a few shadows, sat a gentleman who rose as she rose, and whose name she at once mentioned to him. He had for Herbert Dodd all the air of a swell, the gentleman—rather red-faced and bald-headed, but moustachioed, waistcoated, neck-tied, to the highest pitch, with an effect

of chains and rings, of shining teeth in a glassily monocular smile; a wondrous apparition to have been asked to "meet" him, as in contemporary
fiction, or for him to have been asked to meet. "Captain Roper, Mr. Herbert Dodd"—their entertainer introduced them, yes; but with a sequel
immediately afterwards more disconcerting apparently to Captain Roper
himself even than to her second and more breathless visitor; a "Well then,
good-bye till the next time," with a hand thrust straight out, which allowed
the personage so addressed no alternative but to lay aside his tea-cup,
even though Herbert saw there was a good deal left in it, and glare about
him for his hat. Miss Cookham had had her tea-tray on a small table
before her, she had served Captain Roper while waiting for Mr. Dodd;
but she simply dismissed him now, with a high sweet unmistakable decision, a knowledge of what she was about, as our hero would have called
it, which enlarged at a stroke the latter's view of the number of different
things and sorts of things, in the sphere of the manners and ways of those
living at their ease, that a social relation would put before one. Captain
Roper would have liked to remain, would have liked more tea, but Kate
signified in this direct fashion that she had had enough of him. Herbert
had seen things, in his walk of life—rough things, plenty; but never things
smoothed with that especial smoothness, carried out as it were by the
fine form of Captain Roper's own retreat, which included even a bright
convulsed leave-taking cognizance of the plain, vague individual, of no
lustre at all and with the very low-class guard of an old silver watch
buttoned away under an ill-made coat, to whom he was sacrificed.

It came to Herbert as he left the place a shade less remarkable—though
there was still wonder enough and to spare—that he had been even publicly and designedly sacrificed; exactly so that, as the door closed behind
him, Kate Cookham, standing there to wait for it, could seem to say, across
the room, to the friend of her youth, only by the expression of her fine
eyes: "There—see what I do for you!" "For" him—that was the extraordinary thing, and not less so that he was already, within three minutes,
after this fashion, taking it in as by the intensity of a new light; a light
that was one somehow with this rich inner air of the plush-draped and
much-mirrored hotel, where the firelight and the approach of evening
confirmed together the privacy, and the loose curtains at the wide window
were parted for a command of his old lifelong Parade—the field of life so
familiar to him from below and in the wind and the wet, but which he
had never in all the long years hung over at this vantage.

"He's an acquaintance, but a bore," his hostess explained in respect to
Captain Roper. "He turned up yesterday, but I didn't invite him, and I
had said to him before you came in that I was expecting a gentleman with
whom I should wish to be alone. I go quite straight at my idea that way,
as a rule; but you know," she now strikingly went on, "how straight I go.
And he had had," she added, "his tea."

Dodd had been looking all round—had taken in, with the rest, the brightness, the distinguished elegance, as he supposed it, of the tea-service with which she was dealing and the variously tinted appeal of certain savory edibles on plates. "Oh but he *hadn't* had his tea!" he heard himself the next moment earnestly reply; which speech had at once betrayed, he was then quickly aware, the candor of his interest, the unsophisticated state that had survived so many troubles. If he was so interested how could he be proud, and if he was proud how could he be so interested?

He had made her at any rate laugh outright, and was further conscious, for this, both that it was the first time of that since their new meeting, and that it didn't affect him as harsh. It affected him, however, as free, for she replied at once, still smiling and as a part of it: "Oh, I think we shall get on!"

This told him he had made some difference for her, shown her the way, or something like it, that she hadn't been sure of yesterday; which moreover wasn't what he had intended—he had come armed for showing her nothing; so that after she had gone on with the same gain of gaiety, "You must at any rate comfortably have yours," there was but one answer for him to make.

His eyes played again over the tea-things—they seemed strangely to help him; but he didn't sit down. "I've come, as you see—but I've come, please, to understand; and if you require to be alone with me, and if I break bread with you, it seems to me I should first know exactly where I am and to what you suppose I so commit myself." He had thought it out and over and over, particularly the turn about breaking bread; though perhaps he didn't give it, in her presence—this was impossible, her presence altered so many things—quite the full sound or the weight he had planned.

But it had none the less come to his aid—it had made her perfectly grave. "You commit yourself to nothing. You're perfectly free. It's only I who commit myself."

On which, while she stood there as if all handsomely and deferentially waiting for him to consider and decide, he would have been naturally moved to ask her what she committed herself then *to*—so moved, that is, if he hadn't, before saying it, thought more sharply still of something better. "Oh, that's another thing."

"Yes, that's another thing," Kate Cookham returned. To which she added "So *now* won't you sit down?" He sank with deliberation into the seat from which Captain Roper had risen; she went back to her own and while she did so spoke again. "I'm *not* free. At least," she said over her tea-tray, "I'm free only for this."

Everything was there before them and around them, everything massive and shining, so that he had instinctively fallen back in his chair as for the wondering, the resigned acceptance of it; where her last words stirred in him a sense of odd depreciation. Only for "that"? "That" was everything, at this moment, to his long inanition, and the effect, as if she had suddenly and perversely mocked him, was to press the spring of a protest. "Isn't 'this' then riches?"

"Riches?" she smiled over, handing him his cup—for she had triumphed in having struck from him a question.

"I mean haven't you a lot of money?" He didn't care now that it was out; his cup was in his hand, and what was that but proved interest? He had succumbed to the social relation.

"Yes, I've money. Of course you wonder—but I've wanted you to wonder. It was to make you take that in that I came. So now you know," she said, leaning back where she faced him, but in a straighter chair and with her arms closely folded, after a fashion characteristic of her, as for some control of her nerves.

"You came to show you've money?"

"That's one of the things. Not a lot—not even very much. But enough," said Kate Cookham.

"Enough? I should think so!" he again couldn't help a bit crudely exhaling.

"Enough for what I wanted. I don't always live like this—not at all. But I came to the best hotel on purpose. I wanted to show you I could. Now," she asked, "do you understand?"

"Understand?" He only gaped.

She threw up her loosed arms which dropped again beside her. "I did it for you—I did it for you!"

" 'For' me——?"

"What I did—what I did here of old."

He stared, trying to see it. "When you made me pay you?"

"The Two Hundred and Seventy—all I could get from you, as you reminded me yesterday, so that I had to give up the rest. It was my idea," she went on—"it was my idea."

"To bleed me quite to death?" Oh, his ice was broken now!

"To make you raise money—since you could, you *could*. You did, you did—so what better proof?"

His hands fell from what he had touched; he could only stare—her own manner for it was different now too. "I did. I did indeed—!" And the woeful weak simplicity of it, which seemed somehow all that was left him, fell even on his own ear.

"Well then, here it is—it isn't lost!" she returned with a graver face.

" 'Here' it is," he gasped, "my poor old money—my blood?"

"Oh, it's *my* blood too, you must know now!" She held up her head as not before—as for her right to speak of the thing to-day most precious to her. "I took it, but this—my being here this way—is what I've made of it! That was the idea I had!"

Her "ideas," as things to boast of, staggered him. "To have everything in the world, like this, at my wretched expense?"

She had folded her arms back again—grasping each elbow she sat firm; she knew he could see, and had known well from the first, what she had wanted to say, difficult, monstrous though it might be. "No more than at my own—but to do something with your money that you'd never do yourself."

"Myself, myself?" he wonderingly wailed. "Do you know—or don't you? —what my life has been?"

She waited, and for an instant, though the light in the room had failed a little more and would soon be mainly that of the flaring lamps on the windy Parade, he caught from her dark eye a silver gleam of impatience. "You've suffered and you've worked—which, God knows, is what I've done! *Of course* you've suffered," she said—"you inevitably had to! We have to," she went on, "to do or to be or to get anything."

"And pray what have I done or been or got?" Herbert Dodd found it almost desolately natural to demand.

It made her cover him again as with all she was thinking of. "Can you imagine nothing, or can't you conceive—?" And then as her challenge struck deeper in, deeper down than it had yet reached, and with the effect of a rush of the blood to his face, "It was *for* you, it was *for* you!" she again broke out—"and for what or whom else could it have been?"

He saw things to a tune now that made him answer straight: "I thought at one time it might be for Bill Frankle."

"Yes—that was the way you treated me," Miss Cookham as plainly replied.

But he let this pass; his thought had already got away from it. "What good then—it's having been for me—has that ever done me?"

"Doesn't it do you any good *now*?" his friend returned. To which she added, with another dim play of her tormented brightness, before he could speak: "But if you won't even have your tea——!"

He had in fact touched nothing and, if he could have explained, would have pleaded very veraciously that his appetite, keen when he came in, had somehow suddenly failed. It was beyond eating or drinking, what she seemed to want him to take from her. So if he looked, before him, over the array, it was to say, very grave and graceless: "Am I to understand that you offer to repay me?"

"I offer to repay you with interest, Herbert Dodd"—and her emphasis of the great word was wonderful.

It held him in his place a minute, and held his eyes upon her; after which, agitated too sharply to sit still, he pushed back his chair and stood

up. It was as if mere distress or dismay at first worked in him, and was
in fact a wave of deep and irresistible emotion which made him, on his
feet, sway as in a great trouble and then, to correct it, throw himself
stiffly toward the window, where he stood and looked out unseeing. The
road, the wide terrace beyond, the seats, the eternal sea beyond that, the
lighted lamps now flaring in the October night-wind, with the few dis-
persed people abroad at the tea-hour; these things, meeting and melting
into the firelit hospitality at his elbow—or was it that portentous amenity
that melted into *them*?—seemed to form round him and to put before him,
all together, the strangest of circles and the newest of experiences, in
which the unforgettable and the unimaginable were confoundingly mixed.
"Oh, oh, oh!"—he could only almost howl for it.

And then, while a thick blur for some moments mantled everything,
he knew she had got up, that she stood watching him, allowing for everything, he knew she had got up, that she stood watching him, allowing for
everything again all "cleverly" patient with him, and he heard her speak
again as with studied quietness and clearness. "I wanted to take care of
you—it was what I first wanted—and what you first consented to. I'd have
done it, oh I'd have done it, I'd have loved you and helped you and
guarded you, and you'd have had no trouble, no bad blighting ruin, in all
your easy, yes, just your quite jolly and comfortable life. I showed you and
proved to you this—I brought it home to you, as I fondly fancied, and it
made me briefly happy. You swore you cared for me, you wrote it and
made me believe it—you pledged me your honor and your faith. Then
you turned and changed suddenly from one day to another; everything
altered, you broke your vows, you as good as told me you only wanted it
off. You faced me with dislike, and in fact tried not to face me at all;
you behaved as if you hated me—you had seen a girl, of great beauty, I
admit, who made me a fright and a bore."

This brought him straight round. "No, Kate Cookham."

"Yes, Herbert Dodd." She but shook her head, calmly and nobly, in the
now gathered dusk, and her memories and her cause and her character—
or was it only her arch-subtlety, her line and her "idea"?—gave her an
extraordinary large assurance.

She had touched, however, the treasure of his own case—his terrible
own case that began to live again at once by the force of her talking of
hers, and which could always all cluster about his great asseveration.
"No, no, never, never; I had never seen her then and didn't dream of her;
so that when you yourself began to be harsh and sharp with me, and
to seem to want to quarrel, I could have but one idea—which was an
appearance you didn't in the least, as I saw it then, account for or dis-
prove."

"An appearance—?" Kate desired, as with high astonishment, to know
which one.

"How *shouldn't* I have supposed you really to care for Bill Frankle?—as, thoroughly believing the motive of your claim for my money to be its help to your marrying him, since you couldn't marry me. I was only surprised when, time passing, I made out that that hadn't happened; and perhaps," he added the next instant with something of a conscious lapse from the finer style, "hadn't been in question."

She had listened to this only staring, and she was silent after he had said it, so silent for some instants that while he considered her something seemed to fail him, much as if he had thrown out his foot for a step and not found the place to rest it. He jerked round to the window again, and then she answered, but without passion unless it was that of her weariness for something stupid and forgiven in him, "Oh, the blind, the pitiful folly!" —to which, as it might perfectly have applied to her own behavior, he returned nothing. She had moreover at once gone on. "Put it then that there wasn't much to do—between your finding that you loathed me for another woman, or discovering only, when it came to the point, that you loathed me quite enough for myself."

Which, as she put it in that immensely effective fashion, he recognized that he must just unprotestingly and not so very awkwardly—not so *very*!—take from her; since, whatever he had thus come to her for, it wasn't to perjure himself with any pretence that, "another woman" or no other woman, he hadn't, for years and years, abhorred her. Now he was taking tea with her—or rather, literally, seemed not to be; but this made no difference, and he let her express it as she would while he distinguished a man he knew, Charley Coote, outside on the Parade, under favor of the empty hour and one of the flaring lamps, making up to a young woman with whom (it stuck out grotesquely in his manner) he had never before conversed. Dodd's own position was that of acquiescing in this recall of what had so bitterly been—but he hadn't come back to her, of himself, to stir up, to recall or to recriminate, and for *her* it could but be the very lesson of her whole present act that if she touched anything she touched everything. Soon enough she *was* indeed, and all overwhelmingly, touching everything—with a hand of which the boldness grew.

"But I didn't let *that*, even, make a difference in what I wanted—which was all," she said, "and had only and passionately been, to take care of you. I had *no* money whatever—nothing then of my own, not a penny to come by anyhow; so it wasn't with mine I could do it. But I could do it with yours," she amazingly wound up—"if I could once get yours out of you."

He faced straight about again—his eyebrows higher than they had ever been in his life. "Mine? What penny of it was mine? What scrap beyond a living had I ever pretended to have?"

She held herself still a minute, visibly with force; only her eyes consciously attached to the seat of a chair the back of which her hands,

making it tilt toward her a little, grasped as for support. "You pretended
to have enough to marry me—and that was all I afterwards claimed of you
when you wouldn't." He was on the point of retorting that he had absolutely pretended to nothing—least of all to the primary desire that such a
way of putting it fastened on him; he was on the point for ten seconds of
giving her full in the face: "I never *had* any such dream till you yourself—
infatuated with me as, frankly, you on the whole appeared to be—got
round me and muddled me up and made me behave as if in a way that
went against the evidence of my senses." But he was to feel as quickly
that, whatever the ugly, the spent, the irrecoverable truth, he might better
have bitten his tongue off: there beat on him there this strange and other,
this so prodigiously different beautiful and dreadful truth that no far
remembrance and no abiding ache of his own could wholly falsify, and
that was indeed all out with her next words. "That—*using* it for you and
using you yourself for your own future—was my motive. I've led my life,
which has been an affair, I assure you; and, as I've told you without your
quite seeming to understand—I've brought everything fivefold back to
you."

The perspiration broke out on his forehead. "Everything's mine?" he
quavered as for the deep piercing pain of it.

"Everything!" said Kate Cookham.

So it told him how she had loved him—but with the tremendous effect
at once of its only glaring out at him from the whole thing that it was
verily she, a thousand times over, who, in the exposure of his youth and
his vanity, had, on the bench of desolation, the scene of yesterday's own
renewal, left for him no forward steps to take. It hung there for him
tragically vivid again, the hour she had first found him sequestered and
accessible after making his acquaintance at his shop. And from this, by a
succession of links that fairly clicked to his ear as with their perfect fitting,
the fate and the pain and the payment of others stood together in a great
grim order. Everything there then was *his*—to make him ask what had
been Nan's, poor Nan's of the constant question of whether he need have
collapsed. She was before him, she was between them, his little dead dissatisfied wife; across all whose final woe and whose lowly grave he was to
reach out, it appeared, to take gifts. He saw them too, the gifts; saw
them—she bristled with them—in his actual companion's brave and sincere
and authoritative figure, her strangest of demonstrations. But the other
appearance was intenser, as if their ghost had waved wild arms; so that
half a minute hadn't passed before the one poor thing that remained of
Nan, and that yet thus became a quite mighty and momentous poor thing,
was sitting on his lips as for its sole opportunity.

"Can you give me your word of honor that I mightn't, under decent
advice, have defied you?"

It made her turn very white; but now that she had said what she *had* said she could still hold up her head. "Certainly you might have defied me, Herbert Dodd."

"They would have told me you had no legal case?"

Well, if she was pale she was bold. "You talk of decent advice—!" She broke off, there was too much to say, and all needless. What she said instead was: "They would have told you I had nothing."

"I didn't so much as ask," her sad visitor remarked.

"Of course you didn't so much as ask."

"I couldn't be so outrageously vulgar," he went on.

"I could, by God's help!" said Kate Cookham.

"Thank you." He had found at his command a tone that made him feel more gentlemanlike than he had ever felt in his life or should doubtless ever feel again. It might have been enough—but somehow as they stood there with this immense clearance between them it wasn't. The clearance was like a sudden gap or great bleak opening through which there blew upon them a deadly chill. Too many things had fallen away, too many new rolled up and over him, and they made something within shake him to his base. It upset the full vessel, and though she kept her eyes on him he let that consequence come, bursting into tears, weakly crying there before her even as he had cried to himself in the hour of his youth when she had made him groundlessly fear. She turned away then—*that* she couldn't watch, and had presently flung herself on the sofa and, all responsively wailing, buried her own face on the cushioned arm. So for a minute their smothered sobs only filled the room. But he made out, through this disorder, where he had put down his hat; his stick and his new tan-colored gloves—they had cost two-and-thruppence and would have represented sacrifices—were on the chair beside it. He picked these articles up and all silently and softly-gasping, that is, but quite on tiptoe—reached the door and let himself out.

VI

Off there on the bench of desolation a week later she made him a more particular statement, which it had taken the remarkably tense interval to render possible. After leaving her at the hotel that last Sunday he had gone forth in his re-aggravated trouble and walked straight before him, in the teeth of the west wind, close to the iron rails of the stretched Marina and with his telltale face turned from persons occasionally met, and toward the surging sea. At the land's end, even in the confirmed darkness and the perhaps imminent big blow, his immemorial nook, small shelter as it yielded had again received him; and it was in the course of this heedless session, no doubt, where the agitated air had nothing to add to the commotion within him, that he began to look his extraordinary fortune a bit straighter in the face and see it confess itself at once a fairy-tale and a nightmare. That, visibly, confoundingly, she was still attached to him (attached in fact was a mild word!) and that the unquestionable proof of it was in this offered pecuniary salve, of the thickest composition, for his wounds and sores and shames—these things were the fantastic fable, the tale of money in handfuls, that he seemed to have only to stand there and swallow and digest and feel himself full-fed by; but the whole of the rest was nightmare, and most of all nightmare his having thus to thank one through whom Nan and his little girls had known torture.

He didn't care for himself now, and this unextinguished, and apparently inextinguishable, charm by which he had held her was a fact incredibly romantic; but he gazed with a longer face than he had ever had for anything in the world at his potential acceptance of a great bouncing benefit from the person he intimately, if even in a manner indirectly, associated with the conditions to which his lovely wife and his little girls (who would have been so lovely too) had pitifully succumbed. He had accepted the social relation—which meant he had taken even that on trial—without knowing what it so dazzlingly masked; for a social relation it had become with a vengeance when it drove him about the place as now at his hours of freedom (and he actually and recklessly took, all demoralised and unstrung and unfit either for work or for anything else, other liberties that would get him into trouble) under this queer torment of irreconcilable things, a bewildered consciousness of tenderness and patience and cruelty, of great evident mystifying facts that were as little to be questioned as to be conceived or explained, and that were yet least, withal, to be lost sight of.

On that Sunday night he had wandered wild, incoherently ranging and throbbing, but this became the law of his next days as well, since he lacked more than ever all other resort or refuge and had nowhere to carry, to deposit or contractedly let loose and lock up, as it were, his swollen consciousness, which fairly split in twain the raw shell of his sordid little boarding-place. The arch of the sky and the spread of sea and shore alone gave him space; he could roam with himself anywhere, in short, far or near—he could only never take himself back. That certitude—that this was impossible to him even should she wait there among her plushes and bronzes ten years—was the thing he kept closest clutch of: it did wonders for what he would have called his self-respect. Exactly as he had left her so he would stand off—even though at moments when he pulled up sharp somewhere to put himself an intensest question his heart almost stood still. The days of the week went by, and as he had left her she stayed; to the extent, that is, of his having neither sight nor sound of her, and of the failure of every sign. It took nerve, he said, not to return to her, even for curiosity—since how, after all, in the name of wonder, had she invested the fruits of her extortion to such advantage, there being no chapter of all the obscurity of the years to beat that for queerness? But he dropped, tired to death, on benches, half-a-dozen times an evening—exactly on purpose to recognize that the nerve required was just the nerve he had.

As the days without a token from her multiplied he came in as well for hours—and these indeed mainly on the bench of desolation—of sitting stiff and stark in presence of the probability that he had lost everything forever. When he passed the Royal he never turned an eyelash, and when he met Captain Roper on the Front, three days after having been introduced to him, he "cut him dead"—another privileged consequence of a social relation—rather than seem to himself to make the remotest approach to the question of whether Miss Cookham had left Properley. He had cut people in the days of his life before, just as he had come to being himself cut—since there had been no time for him wholly without one or other face of that necessity—but had never effected such a severance as of this rare connection, which helped to give him thus the measure of his really precious sincerity. If he had lost what had hovered before him he had lost it, his only tribute to which proposition was to grind his teeth with one of those "scrunches," as he would have said, of which the violence fairly reached his ear. It wouldn't make him lift a finger, and in fact if Kate had simply taken herself off on the Tuesday or the Wednesday she would have reabsorbed again into the darkness from which she had emerged—and no lifting of fingers, the unspeakable chapter closed, would evermore avail. That at any rate was the kind of man he still was—even after all that had come and gone, and even if for a few dazed hours certain things had seemed pleasant. The dazed hours had passed, the surge of the old bitterness had dished him (shouldn't he have been shamed if it hadn't?) and he might sit there as before, as always, with nothing at all on earth to look to. He had therefore wrongfully believed himself to be degraded; and the last word about him would be that he *couldn't* then, it appeared, sink to vulgarity as he had tried to let his miseries make him.

And yet on the next Sunday morning, face to face with him again at the land's end, what she very soon came to was: "As if I believed you didn't *know* by what cord you hold me!" Absolutely too, and just that morning in fact, above all, he wouldn't, he quite couldn't have taken his solemn oath that he hadn't a sneaking remnant, as he might have put it to himself—a remnant of faith in tremendous things still to come of their interview. The day was sunny and breezy, the sea of a cold purple; he wouldn't go to church as he mostly went of Sunday mornings, that being, in its way too a social relation—and not least when two-and-thruppenny tan-colored gloves were new; which indeed he had the art of keeping them for ages. Yet he would dress himself as he scarce mustered resources for even to figure on the fringe of Society, local and transient, at St. Bernard's, and in this trim he took his way westward; occupied largely, as he went, it might have seemed to any person pursuing the same course and happening to observe him, in a fascinated study of the motions of his shadow, the more or less grotesque shape projected, in front of him and mostly a bit to the right, over the blanched asphalt of the Parade and dangling and dancing at such a rate, shooting out and then contracting, that, viewed in themselves, its eccentricities might have formed the basis of an interesting challenge: "Find the state of mind, guess the nature of the agitation, possessing the person so remarkably represented!" Herbert Dodd, for that matter, might have been himself attempting to make by the sun's sharp aid some approach to his immediate horoscope.

It had at any rate been thus put before him that the dandling and dancing of his image occasionally gave way to perfect immobility, when he stopped and kept his eyes on it. "Suppose she should come, suppose she *should!*" it is revealed at least to ourselves that he had at these moments breathed to himself with the intensity of an arrest between hope and fear. It had glimmered upon him from early, with the look of the day, that, given all else that could happen, this would be rather, as he put it, in her line; and the possibility lived for him, as he proceeded, to the tune of a suspense almost sickening. It was, from one small stage of his pilgrimage to another, the "Forever, never!" of the sentimental case the playmates of his youth used to pretend to settle by plucking the petals of a daisy. But it came to his truly turning faint—so "queer" he felt—when, at the gained point of the long stretch from which he could always tell, he arrived within positive sight of his immemorial goal. His seat was taken and she was keeping it for him—it could only be *she* there in possession; whereby it shone out for Herbert Dodd that if he hadn't been quite sure of her recurrence she had at least been quite sure of his. *That* pulled him up to some purpose, where recognition began for them—or to the effect, in other words, of his pausing to judge if he could bear, for the sharpest note of their intercourse, this inveterate demonstration of her making him do what she liked. What settled the question for him then—and just while they avowedly watched each other, over the long interval, before closing, as if, on either side, for the major advantage—what settled it was this very fact that what she liked she liked so terribly. If it were simply to "use" him, as she had said the last time, and no matter to the profit of which of them she called it, one might let it go for that; since it could make her wait over, day after day, in that fashion, and with such a spending of money, on the hazard of their meeting again. How could she be the least sure he would ever again consent to it after the proved action on him, a week ago, of her last monstrous honesty? It was indeed positively as if he were now himself putting this influence—and for their common edification —to the supreme, to the finest test. He had a sublime, an ideal flight, which lasted about a minute. "Suppose, now that I see her there and what she has taken so characteristically for granted, suppose I just show her that she *hasn't* only confidently to wait or whistle for me, and that the length of my leash is greater than she measures, and that everything's impossible always?—show it by turning my back on her now and walking straight away. She won't be able not to understand *that!*"

Nothing had passed, across their distance, but the mute apprehension of each on the part of each; the whole expanse, at the church hour, was void of other life (he had scarce met a creature on his way from end to end), and the sun-seasoned gusts kept brushing the air and all the larger prospect clean. It was through this beautiful lucidity that he watched her watch him, as it were—watch him for what he would do. Neither moved at this high tension; Kate Cookham, her face fixed on him, only waited with a stiff appearance of leaving him, not for dignity but (to an effect of even deeper perversity) for kindness, free to choose. It yet somehow affected him at present, this attitude, as a gage of her *knowing too*—knowing, that is, that he wasn't really free, that this was the thinnest of vain parades, the poorest of hollow heroics, that his need, his solitude, his suffered wrong, his exhausted rancor, his foredoomed submission to any shown interest, all hung together too heavy on him to let the weak wings of his pride do more than vaguely tremble. They couldn't, they didn't carry him a single beat further away; according to which he stood rooted, neither retreating nor advancing, but presently correcting his own share of their bleak exchange by looking off at the sea. Deeply conscious of the awkwardness this posture gave him, he yet clung to it as the last shred of his honor, to the clear argument that it was one thing for him to have felt beneath all others, the previous days, that she was to be counted on, but quite a different for her to have felt that *he* was. His checked approach, arriving thus at no term, could in these odd conditions have established that he wasn't only if Kate Cookham had, as either of them might have said, taken it so—if she had given up the game at last by rising, by walking away and adding to the distance between them, and he had then definitely let her vanish into space. It became a fact that when she did finally rise— though after how long our record scarce takes on itself to say—it was not to confirm their separation but to put an end to it; and this by slowly approaching him till she had come within earshot. He had wondered, once aware of it in spite of his averted face, what she would say and on what note, as it were, she would break their week's silence; so that he had to recognise anew, her voice reaching him, that remarkable quality in her which again and again came up for him as her art.

"There are twelve hundred and sixty pounds, to be definite, but I have it all down for you—and you've only to draw."

They lost themselves, these words, rare and exquisite, in the wide bright genial medium and the Sunday stillness, but even while that occurred and he was gaping for it she was herself there, in her battered lady-like truth, to answer for them, to represent them, and, if a further grace than their simple syllabled beauty were conceivable, almost embarrassingly to cause them to materialise. Yes, she let her smart and tight little reticule hang as if it bulged, beneath its clasp, with the whole portentous sum, and he felt himself glare again at this vividest of her attested claims. She might have been ready, on the spot, to open the store to the plunge of his hand, or with the situation otherwise conceived, to impose on his pauperized state an acceptance of alms on a scale unprecedented in the annals of street-charity. Nothing so much counted for him, however, neither grave numeral nor elegant fraction, as the short, rich, rounded word that the breeze had picked up as it dropped and seemed now to blow about between them. "To draw—to draw?" Yes, he gaped it as if it had no sense; the fact being that even while he did so he was reading into her use of the term more romance than any word in the language had ever had for him. He, Herbert Dodd, was to live to "draw," like people, scarce hampered by the conditions of earth, whom he had remotely and circuitously heard about, and in fact when he walked back with her to where she had been sitting it was very much, for his strained nerves, as if the very bench of desolation itself were to be the scene of that exploit and he mightn't really live till he reached it.

When they had sat down together she did press the spring of her reticule, from which she drew, not a handful of gold nor a packet of crisp notes, but an oblong sealed letter, which she had thus waited on him she remarked, on purpose to deliver, and which would certify, with sundry particulars, to the credit she had opened for him at a London bank. He took it from her without looking at it, and held it, in the same manner, conspicuous and unassimilated, for most of the rest of the immediate time, appearing embarrassed with it, nervously twisting and flapping it, yet thus publicly retaining it even while aware, beneath everything, of the strange, the quite dreadful, wouldn't it be? engagement that such inaction practically stood for. He could accept money to that amount, yes—but not for nothing in return. For what then in return? He kept asking himself for what while she said other things and made above all, in her high, shrewd, successful way the point that, no, he needn't pretend that his conviction of her continued personal interest in him wouldn't have tided him over any question besetting him since their separation. She put it to him that the deep instinct of where he should at last find her must confidently have worked for him, since she confessed to her instinct of where she should find *him*; which meant—oh it came home to him as he fingered his sealed treasure!—neither more nor less than that she had now created between them an equality of experience. He wasn't to have done all the suffering, *she* was to have "been through" things he couldn't even guess at; and, since he was bargaining away his right ever again to allude to the unforgettable, so much there was of it, what her tacit proposition came to was that they were "square" and might start afresh.

He didn't take up her charge, as his so compromised "pride" yet in a manner prompted him, that he had enjoyed all the week all those elements of ease about her; the most he achieved for that was to declare, with an ingenuity contributing to float him no small distance further, that of course he had turned up at their old place of tryst, which had been, all the years, the haunt of his solitude and the goal of his walk any Sunday morning that seemed too beautiful for church; but that he hadn't in the least built on her presence there—since that supposition gave him, she would understand, wouldn't she? the air, disagreeable to him, of having come in search of her. Her quest of himself, once he had been seated there, would have been another matter—but in short "Of course after all you did come to me, just now, didn't you?" He felt himself, too, lamely and gracelessly grin, as for the final kick of his honor, in confirmation of the record that he had then yielded but to her humility. Her humility became for him at this hour and to this tune, on the bench of desolation, a quantity more prodigious and even more mysterious than that other guaranteed quantity the finger-tips of his left hand could feel the tap of by the action of his right; though what was in especial extraordinary was the manner in which she could keep making him such allowances and yet meet him again, at some turn, as with her residuum for her clever self so great.

"Come to you, Herbert Dodd?" She imperturbably echoed. "I've been coming to you for the last ten years!"

There had been for him, just before this, sixty supreme seconds of intensest aspiration—a minute of his keeping his certificate poised for a sharp thrust back at her, the thrust of the wild freedom of his saying: "No, no, I *can't* give them up; I can't simply sink them deep down in my soul forever, with no cross in all my future to mark *that* burial; so that if this is what our arrangement means I must decline to have anything to do with it." The words none the less hadn't come, and when she had herself, a couple of minutes later, spoken those others, the blood rose to his face as if, given his stiffness and her extravagance, he had just indeed saved himself.

Everything in fact stopped, even his fidget with his paper; she imposed a hush, she imposed at any rate the conscious decent form of one, and he couldn't afterwards have told how long, at this juncture, he must have sat simply gazing before him. It was so long, at any rate, that Kate herself got up—and quite indeed, presently, as if her own forms were now at an end. He had returned her nothing—so what was she waiting for? She had been on the two other occasions momentarily at a loss, but never so much so, no doubt, as was thus testified to by her leaving the bench and moving over once more to the rail of the terrace. She could carry it off, in a manner, with her resources, that she was waiting with so little to wait for; she could face him again, after looking off at the sea, as if this slightly stiff delay, not wholly exempt from awkwardness, had been but a fine scruple of her courtesy. She had gathered herself in; after giving him time to appeal she could take it that he had decided and that nothing was left for her to do. "Well then," she clearly launched at him across the broad walk—"well then, good-bye."

She had come nearer with it, as if he might rise for some show of express separation; but he only leaned back motionless, his eyes on her now —he kept her a moment before him. "Do you mean that we don't—that we don't—?" But he broke down.

"Do I 'mean'—?" She remained as for questions he might ask, but it was well-nigh as if there played through her dotty veil an irrepressible irony for that particular one. "I've meant, for long years, I think, all I'm capable of meaning. I've meant so much that I can't mean more. So there it is."

"But if you go," he appealed—and with a sense as of final flatness, however he arranged it, for his own attitude—"but if you go sha'n't I see you again?"

She waited a little, and it was strangely for him now as if—though at last so much more gorged with her tribute than she had ever been with his—something still depended on her. "Do you *like* to see me?" she very simply asked.

At this he did get up; that was easier than to say—at least with responsive simplicity; and again for a little he looked hard and in silence at his letter; which at last, however, raising his eyes to her own for the act, while he masked their conscious ruefulness, to his utmost, in some air of assurance, he slipped into the inner pocket of his coat, letting it settle there securely. "You're too wonderful." But he frowned at her with it as never in his life. "Where does it all come from?"

"The wonder of poor me?" Kate Cookham said. "It comes from *you*."

He shook his head slowly—feeling, with his letter there against his heart, such a new agility, almost such a new range of interest. "I mean so *much* money—so extraordinarily much."

Well, she held him a while blank. "Does it seem to you extraordinarily much—twelve-hundred-and-sixty? Because, you know," she added, "it's all."

"It's enough!" he returned with a slight thoughtful droop of his head to the right and his eyes attached to the far horizon as through a shade of shyness for what he was saying. He felt all her own lingering nearness somehow on his cheek.

"It's enough? Thank you then!" she rather oddly went on.

He shifted a little his posture. "It was more than a hundred a year—for you to get together."

"Yes," she assented, "that was what year by year I tried for."

"But that you could live all the while and save that—!" Yes, he was at liberty, as he hadn't been, quite pleasantly to marvel. All his wonderments in life had been hitherto unanswered—and didn't the change mean that here again was the social relation?

"Ah, I didn't live as you saw me the other day."

"Yes," he answered—and didn't he the next instant feel he must fairly have smiled with it?—"the other day you *were* going it!"

"For once in my life," said Kate Cookham. "I've left the hotel," she after a moment added.

"Ah, you're in—a—lodgings?" he found himself inquiring as for positive sociability.

She had apparently a slight shade of hesitation, but in an instant it was all right; as what he showed he wanted to know she seemed mostly to give him. "Yes—but far of course from here. Up on the hill." To which, after another instant, "At The Mount, Castle Terrace," she subjoined.

"Oh, I know The Mount. And Castle Terrace is awfully sunny and nice."

"Awfully sunny and nice," Kate Cookham took from him.

"So that if it isn't," he pursued, "like the Royal, why you're at least comfortable."

"I shall be comfortable anywhere now," she replied with a certain dryness.

It was astonishing, however, what had become of his own. "Because I've accepted——?"

"Call it that!" she dimly smiled.

"I hope then at any rate," he returned, "you can now thoroughly rest." He spoke as for a cheerful conclusion and moved again also to smile, though as with a poor grimace, no doubt; since what he seemed most clearly to feel was that since he "accepted" he mustn't, for his last note, have accepted in sulkiness or gloom. With that, at the same time, he couldn't but know, in all his fibres, that with such a still-watching face as the dotty veil didn't disguise for him there was no possible concluding, at least on his part. On hers, on hers it was—as he had so often for a week had reflectively to pronounce things—another affair. Ah, somehow, both formidably and helpfully, her face concluded—yet in a sense so strangely enshrouded in things she didn't tell him. What *must* she, what mustn't she, have done? What she had said—and she had really told him nothing— was no account of her life; in the midst of which conflict of opposed recognitions, at any rate, it was as if, for all he could do, he himself now considerably floundered. "But I can't think—I can't think——!"

"You can't think I can have made so much money in the time and been honest?"

"Oh, you've been *honest!*" Herbert Dodd distinctly allowed.

It moved her stillness to a gesture—which, however, she had as promptly checked; and she went on the next instant as for further generosity to his failure of thought. "Everything was possible, under my stress, with my hatred."

"Your hatred—?" For she had paused as if it were after all too diffi· cult.

"Of what I should for so long have been doing to you."

With this, for all his failures, a greater light than any yet shone upon him. "It made you think of ways——?"

"It made me think of everything. It made me work," said Kate Cookham. She added, however, the next moment: "But that's my story."

"And I mayn't hear it?"

"No—because I mayn't hear yours."

"Oh, mine—!" he said with the strangest, saddest, yet after all most resigned sense of surrender of it; which he tried to make sound as if he couldn't have told it, for its splendor of sacrifice and of misery, even if he would.

It seemed to move in her a little, exactly, that sense of the invidious. "Ah, mine too, I assure you——!"

He rallied at once to the interest. "Oh, we *can* talk then?"

"Never," she all oddly replied. "Never," said Kate Cookham.

They remained so, face to face; the effect of which for him was that he had after a little understood why. That was fundamental. "Well, I see."

Thus confronted they stayed; and then, as he saw with a contentment that came up from deeper still, it was indeed she who, with her worn fine face, would conclude. "But I can take care of you."

"You *have!*" he said as with nothing left of him but a beautiful appreciative candor.

"Oh, but you'll want it now in a way—!" she responsibly answered.

He waited a moment, dropping again on the seat. So, while she still stood, he looked up at her; with the sense somehow that there were too many things and that they were all together, terribly, irresistibly, doubtless blessedly, in her eyes and her whole person; which thus affected him for the moment as more than he could bear. He leaned forward, dropping his elbows to his knees and pressing his head on his hands. So he stayed, saying nothing; only, with the sense of her own sustained, renewed and wonderful action, knowing that an arm had passed round him and that he was held. She was beside him on the bench of desolation.

COMMENT AND QUESTION

1. *The story.* "The Bench of Desolation" should be read first for the story alone. If plot and character motivation are carefully followed, much of the underlying intention of James will become clear even upon the first reading. The reader must understand the importance of such details as the following: the cause of the suit, the Four Hundred pounds, the Two Hundred and Seventy pounds, the failure of Mr. Drury, Herbert's pride in his shop, Nan's reproaches, Herbert's visit to the Royal, the acceptance of a bank draft. These and other details constitute the plot level. Successive

readings will reveal the full intention of James on other levels of interest. With successive readings the story becomes more moving and powerful.

2. *The intent of James.* "The Bench of Desolation" is the story of a man's moral growth and of his self-fulfillment. It is the story of a love between a man and a woman. It is the story of love itself.

The most significant statement in the story is the following: "Yes, Dodd had come back there to flop, by long custom, upon the bench of desolation *as* the man in the whole place, precisely to whom nothing worth more than tuppence could happen. . . ."

The man to whom nothing worthwhile happens does not live a secure and comfortable, if sterile existence. His life is the life of Herbert Dodd.

3. *The life of Dodd.*

a. *The climate in which Dodd moves.* One clue to the life of Dodd is a statement he makes about himself: "He knew what he was, in a dismal, downtrodden sphere enough—the lean young proprietor of an old business that had itself rather shrivelled with age than ever grown fat, the purchase and sale of second-hand books and prints, with the back street of a long-fronted south-coast watering-place (Old Town by good luck) for the dusky field of his life."

As the story develops, the reader begins to understand the importance here of such words and phrases as "dismal," "downtrodden," "old," "second-hand," "back back street."

b. *The frustrations of Dodd.* Fear, loneliness, and regret—these three devastating emotions encompass Dodd as he sits on his bench of desolation. Is Dodd responsible for his frustrations? Is there a major defect in his character and personality? Consider his fears. What happens when Dodd shows his first sign of fight about paying damages? What would have happened if he had shown signs of fight in the first few pages? Consider his regrets. How does Dodd himself insure that his regret will be ever-present, ever fresh and keen?

c. *Dodd and vulgarity.* To James, vulgarity, in the sense of commonness, is a sin. Vulgar motives, vulgar aspirations build a mean existence. Dodd thinks he is a gentleman. He claims to be "like" a gentleman. He abhors vulgarity. Does he not protest too much?

Did Dodd inherit his shop in a vulgar way? Did he marry a vulgar woman? Did he use his gentlemanly aspirations as a shield?

In section V, a significant exchange occurs between Dodd and Kate:
"'I couldn't be so outrageously vulgar,' he went on."
"'I could, by God's help!' said Kate Cookham."

Find this passage in its context and reconcile it with the picture of Kate as a lady (section IV) and with the failure of Dodd's life.

4. *The life of Kate.*

a. *The climate in which Kate moves.* This story exists entirely in the consciousness of Herbert Dodd. It is the more remarkable, then, that we get such a very clear portrait of Kate, who has a more powerful personality than has Dodd.

The most significant statement in this story, quoted earlier, includes Kate: "Yes, he had come back there to flop, by long custom, upon the bench of desolation _as_ the man in the whole place, precisely to whom nothing worth more than tuppence could happen; _whereupon, in the grey desert of his consciousness, the very earth had suddenly opened and flamed._" The last part of this sentence refers to Kate. The italics are not James'. They have been used to emphasize the effect of Kate's return and the climate in which she moves.

Study the visit of Dodd to the Royal. The man who "had never had an adventure in his life" is keenly aware of the atmosphere surrounding Kate in the Royal. Find the paragraph in section V, which begins "It came to Herbert . . ." and notice the concluding lines, which contrast Herbert's sphere with Kate's: ". . . the loose curtains at the wide window were parted for a command of his old lifelong Parade—the field of life so familiar to him from below and in the wind and the wet, but which he had never in all the long years hung over at this vantage." The wind and the wet were Herbert's. The warm, secure vantage of the Royal was Kate's.

b. _The "out-going" principle in Kate._ When Kate and Dodd meet after a lapse of years, the contrast between them is startling. Can you explain why Kate has changed even more for the better than Dodd seems to have changed for the worse? Dodd recognizes that Kate "had had a life, a career, a history." Can you explain why Kate has lived and Dodd has not?

Who first made love to the other, Kate or Dodd? Who makes love throughout the story? Does Kate require any positive action from Dodd? What of the Four Hundred pounds? In the last scene in the story, does Dodd use his own free will?

How do Kate and Herbert react each to his own suffering?

c. _Kate and love._ Kate loves, and her love is patient, is kind; is not puffed up; is not ambitious; seeketh not her own; beareth all things, believeth all things, hopeth all things, endureth all things. This truly remarkable love, fully described in the Thirteenth Corinthians, is amply illustrated in the motives and actions of Kate. It is the crown of Kate's life and the crown of this story. It explains the atmosphere in which she moves; it explains her energy and her final victory. Yet, for long stretches in his life, Dodd abhors her. Why?

Can you explain the following statements in their reference to Kate's love?

     (1) " 'I'm _not_ free. . . . I'm free only for this.' " P. 291.

     (2) " 'As if I believed you didn't _know_ by what cord you hold me!' " P. 299.

     (3) " 'I've been coming to you for the last ten years.' " P. 303.

5. *The final choice of Dodd.* In section VI, is the indecision of Dodd due to pride? To the accumulated habit of years? Is it due to the nightmarish thought of "his having to thank one through whom Nan and his little girls had known torture"? Is there justification for his indecision?

How does Dodd finally attain self-fulfillment? Why is the following passage important? " 'The wonder of poor me?' Kate Cookham said. 'It comes from *you.*'" P. 304.

James has been criticized for what often seems to be deliberate ambiguity in his plots and in his characterizations. Can you be sure that you understand precisely the motives of Dodd in the last scene in the story?

6. *Metaphors.* "The Bench of Desolation" is itself a metaphor developed in detail. But it is rich also in its separate metaphors, which help to explain the intention of the author. Some of the most important are the following:

a. *The name of the town, Properley.* Remember that Dodd admits that there "was always a first-rate promptitude of everything fourth-rate" in Properley.

b. *The drawn blind of Dodd's shop.*

c. *The money.* The meaning of the money is partially revealed in the following statements:

(1) " 'Oh, it's *my* blood too, you must know now.'" P. 292.

(2) " 'You pretended to have enough money to marry me—and that was all I afterwards claimed of you when you wouldn't.'" P. 296.

(3) " '. . . using it for you and using you yourself for your own future—was my motive.'" P. 296.

d. *The bench of desolation.* Notice the setting for the bench. Notice that the bench is as inevitable as the recurring sunset. Remember that fear, loneliness, poverty, and regret sit with Dodd on his bench of desolation. Do strangers ever share it with him? Has anyone but a woman ever sat there with Dodd? Is it significant that Kate looks for Dodd on the bench, that she knows just where to find him? In her scenes with Dodd, notice how Kate constantly rises, leaves the bench, and then comes back to it.

7. *Theme and style.* "The Bench of Desolation" is quite characteristic of James, for much of his writing is concerned with principles of conduct and with a search for moral certitude. James developed a theme very similar to the theme of "The Bench of Desolation" in his well-known "The Beast in the Jungle," where Marcher is "*the* man, to whom nothing on earth was to have happened." But "The Bench of Desolation" is a more hopeful story than "The Beast in the Jungle." Because of the power of Kate's love, Dodd escapes from the usual Jamesian stricture of "too late."

"The Bench of Desolation" was published first in 1909 and it reflects what has been called James' "later style." The reader will be aware of sentences of circuitous involvement, baffling to the keenest mind. Notice the opening sentence of the story. Notice the sentence on p. 284, beginning "She moved toward him, she reached him. . . ." But the reader will also be aware of passages of subtle but lucid prose, expressing perfectly the subtlety of the ideas of James.

CLAY

BY JAMES JOYCE

JAMES JOYCE (1882–1941) is generally regarded by leading critics as the most influential novelist of the twentieth century. His
short stories, collected in *Dubliners* (1914),
foreshadow the material but not the technique of his novel *Ulysses* (1922). His experiments in language and his exploration of
the subconscious are reflected in *Ulysses* and
also in *A Portrait of the Artist as a Young Man*
(1916) and *Finnegan's Wake* (1939). Born
in Dublin, Joyce lived most of his adult life
in Paris, but Ireland and its people are the
theme of all his writing.

THE MATRON had given her leave to go out as soon as the women's tea
was over and Maria looked forward to her evening out. The kitchen was
spick and span: the cook said you could see yourself in the big copper
boilers. The fire was nice and bright and on one of the side-tables were
four very big barmbracks. These barmbracks seemed uncut; but if you
went closer you would see that they had been cut into long thick even
slices and were ready to be handed round at tea. Maria had cut them
herself.

Maria was a very, very small person indeed but she had a very long
nose and a very long chin. She talked a little through her nose, always
soothingly: "Yes, my dear," and "No, my dear." She was always sent for
when the women quarreled over their tubs and always succeeded in making peace. One day the matron had said to her:

"Maria, you are a veritable peace-maker!"

CLAY From *Dubliners*, included in *The Portable James Joyce*. Copyright 1946,
1947 by The Viking Press, Inc. Reprinted by permission of The Viking Press,
Inc., New York.

And the sub-matron and two of the Board ladies had heard the compliment. And Ginger Mooney was always saying what she wouldn't do to
the dummy who had charge of the irons if it wasn't for Maria. Everyone
was so fond of Maria.

The women would have their tea at six o'clock and she would be able
to get away before seven. From Ballsbridge to the Pillar, twenty minutes; from the Pillar to Drumcondra, twenty minutes; and twenty minutes to buy the things. She would be there before eight. She took out her
purse with the silver clasps and read again the words *A Present from
Belfast*. She was very fond of that purse because Joe had brought it to her
five years before when he and Alphy had gone to Belfast on a Whit-
Monday trip. In the purse were two half-crowns and some coppers. She
would have five shillings clear after paying tram fare. What a nice evening they would have, all the children singing! Only she hoped that Joe
wouldn't come in drunk. He was so different when he took any drink.

Often he had wanted her to go and live with them; but she would have
felt herself in the way (though Joe's wife was ever so nice with her) and
she had become accustomed to the life of the laundry. Joe was a good
fellow. She had nursed him and Alphy too; and Joe used often say:

"Mamma is mamma but Maria is my proper mother."

After the break-up at home the boys had got her that position in the
Dublin by Lamplight laundry, and she liked it. She used to have such a
bad opinion of Protestants but now she thought they were very nice
people, a little quiet and serious, but still very nice people to live with.
Then she had her plants in the conservatory and she liked looking after
them. She had lovely ferns and wax-plants and, whenever anyone came
to visit her, she always gave the visitor one or two slips from her conservatory. There was one thing she didn't like and that was the tracts on
the walls; but the matron was such a nice person to deal with, so gen-
teel.

When the cook told her everything was ready she went into the
women's room and began to pull the big bell. In a few minutes the
women began to come in by twos and threes, wiping their steaming
hands in their petticoats and pulling down the sleeves of their blouses
over their red steaming arms. They settled down before their huge mugs
which the cook and the dummy filled up with hot tea, already mixed with
milk and sugar in huge tin cans. Maria superintended the distribution of
the barmbrack and saw that every woman got her four slices. There was
a great deal of laughing and joking during the meal. Lizzie Fleming said
Maria was sure to get the ring and, though Fleming had said that for so
many Hallow Eves, Maria had to laugh and say she didn't want any ring
or man either; and when she laughed her gray-green eyes sparkled with
disappointed shyness and the tip of her nose nearly met the tip of her
chin. Then Ginger Mooney lifted up her mug of tea and proposed Maria's

health while all the other women clattered with their mugs on the table, and said she was sorry she hadn't a sup of porter to drink it in. And Maria laughed again till the tip of her nose nearly met the tip of her chin and till her minute body nearly shook itself asunder because she knew that Mooney meant well though, of course, she had the notions of a common woman.

But wasn't Maria glad when the women had finished their tea and the cook and the dummy had begun to clear away the tea-things! She went into her little bedroom and, remembering that the next morning was a mass morning, changed the hand of the alarm from seven to six. Then she took off her working skirt and her house-boots and laid her best skirt out on the bed and her tiny dress-boots beside the foot of the bed. She changed her blouse too and, as she stood before the mirror, she thought of how she used to dress for mass on Sunday morning when she was a young girl; and she looked with quaint affection at the diminutive body which she had so often adorned. In spite of its years she found it a nice tidy little body.

When she got outside the streets were shining with rain and she was glad of her old brown waterproof. The tram was full and she had to sit on the little stool at the end of the car, facing all the people, with her toes barely touching the floor. She arranged in her mind all she was going to do and thought how much better it was to be independent and to have your own money in your pocket. She hoped they would have a nice evening. She was sure they would but she could not help thinking what a pity it was Alphy and Joe were not speaking. They were always falling out now but when they were boys together they used to be the best of friends: but such was life.

She got out of her tram at the Pillar and ferreted her way quickly among the crowds. She went into Downes's cake-shop but the shop was so full of people that it was a long time before she could get herself attended to. She bought a dozen of mixed penny cakes, and at last came out of the shop laden with a big bag. Then she thought what else would she buy: she wanted to buy something really nice. They would be sure to have plenty of apples and nuts. It was hard to know what to buy and all she could think of was cake. She decided to buy some plumcake but Downes's plumcake had not enough almond icing on top of it so she went over to a shop in Henry Street. Here she was a long time in suiting herself and the stylish young lady behind the counter, who was evidently a little annoyed by her, asked her was it wedding-cake she wanted to buy. That made Maria blush and smile at the young lady; but the young lady took it all very seriously and finally cut a thick slice of plumcake, parceled it up and said:

"Two-and-four, please."

She thought she would have to stand in the Drumcondra tram because none of the young men seemed to notice her but an elderly gentleman made room for her. He was a stout gentleman and he wore a brown hard hat; he had a square red face and a grayish mustache. Maria thought he was a colonel-looking gentleman and she reflected how much more polite he was than the young men who simply stared straight before them. The gentleman began to chat with her about Hallow Eve and the rainy weather. He supposed the bag was full of good things for the little ones and said it was only right that the youngsters should enjoy themselves while they were young. Maria agreed with him and favored him with demure nods and hems. He was very nice with her, and when she was getting out at the Canal Bridge she thanked him and bowed, and he bowed to her and raised his hat and smiled agreeably; and while she was going up along the terrace, bending her tiny head under the rain, she thought how easy it was to know a gentleman even when he has a drop taken.

Everybody said: *"O, here's Maria!"* when she came to Joe's house. Joe was there, having come home from business, and all the children had their Sunday dresses on. There were two big girls in from next door and games were going on. Maria gave the bag of cakes to the eldest boy, Alphy, to divide and Mrs. Donnelly said it was too good of her to bring such a big bag of cakes and made all the children say:

"Thanks, Maria."

But Maria said she had brought something special for papa and mamma, something they would be sure to like, and she began to look for her plumcake. She tried in Downes's bag and then in the pockets of her waterproof and then on the hallstand but nowhere could she find it. Then she asked all the children had any of them eaten it—by mistake, of course—but the children all said no and looked as if they did not like to eat cakes if they were to be accused of stealing. Everybody had a solution for the mystery and Mrs. Donnelly said it was plain that Maria had left it behind her in the tram. Maria, remembering how confused the gentleman with the grayish mustache had made her, colored with shame and vexation and disappointment. At the thought of the failure of her little surprise and of the two and four-pence she had thrown away for nothing she nearly cried outright.

But Joe said it didn't matter and made her sit down by the fire. He was very nice with her. He told her all that went on in his office, repeating for her a smart answer which he had made to the manager. Maria did not understand why Joe laughed so much over the answer he had made but she said that the manager must have been a very overbearing person to deal with. Joe said he wasn't so bad when you knew how to take him, that he was a decent sort so long as you didn't rub him the wrong way. Mrs. Donnelly played the piano for the children and they danced and sang. Then the two next-door girls handed round the nuts. Nobody could find the nutcrackers and Joe was nearly getting cross over it and asked how did they expect Maria to crack nuts without a nutcracker. But Maria said she didn't like nuts and that they weren't to bother about her. Then Joe asked would she take a bottle of stout and Mrs. Donnelly said there was port wine too in the house if she would prefer that. Maria said she would rather they didn't ask her to take anything: but Joe insisted.

So Maria let him have his way and they sat by the fire talking over old times and Maria thought she would put in a good word for Alphy. But Joe cried that God might strike him stone dead if ever he spoke a word to his brother again and Maria said she was sorry she had mentioned the matter. Mrs. Donnelly told her husband it was a great shame for him to speak that way of his own flesh and blood but Joe said that Alphy was no brother of his and there was nearly being a row on the head of it. But Joe said he would not lose his temper on account of the night it was and asked his wife to open some more stout. The two next-door girls had arranged some Hallow Eve games and soon everything was merry again. Maria was delighted to see the children so merry and Joe and his wife in such good spirits. The next-door girls put some saucers on the table and then led the children up to the table, blindfold. One got the prayer-book and the other three got the water; and when one of the next-door girls got the ring Mrs. Donnelly shook her finger at the blushing girl as much as to say: *O, I know all about it!* They insisted then on blindfolding Maria and leading her up to the table to see what she would get; and, while they were putting on the bandage, Maria laughed and laughed again till the tip of her nose nearly met the tip of her chin.

They led her up to the table amid laughing and joking and she put her hand out in the air as she was told to do. She moved her hand about here and there in the air and descended on one of the saucers. She felt a soft wet substance with her fingers and was surprised that nobody spoke or took off her bandage. There was a pause for a few seconds; and then a great deal of scuffling and whispering. Somebody said something about the garden, and at last Mrs. Donnelly said something very cross to one of the next-door girls and told her to throw it out at once: that was no play. Maria understood that it was wrong that time and so she had to do it over again: and this time she got the prayer-book.

After that Mrs. Donnelly played Miss McCloud's Reel for the children and Joe made Maria take a glass of wine. Soon they were all quite merry again and Mrs. Donnelly said Maria would enter a convent before the year was out because she had got the prayer-book. Maria had never seen Joe so nice to her as he was that night, so full of pleasant talk and reminiscences. She said they were all very good to her.

At last the children grew tired and sleepy and Joe asked Maria would she not sing some little song before she went, one of the old songs. Mrs. Donnelly said: *"Do, please, Maria!"* and so Maria had to get up and stand beside the piano. Mrs. Donnelly bade the children be quiet and listen to Maria's song. Then she played the prelude and said *"Now, Maria!"* and Maria, blushing very much, began to sing in a tiny quavering voice. She sang *I Dreamt that I Dwelt,* and when she came to the second verse she sang again:

> *I dreamt that I dwelt in marble halls*
> *With vassals and serfs at my side*
> *And of all who assembled within those walls*
> *That I was the hope and the pride.*

> *I had riches too great to count, could boast*
> *Of a high ancestral name,*
> *But I also dreamt, which pleased me most,*
> *That you loved me still the same.*

But no one tried to show her her mistake; and when she had ended her song Joe was very much moved. He said that there was no time like the long ago and no music for him like poor old Balfe, whatever other people might say; and his eyes filled up so much with tears that he could not find what he was looking for and in the end he had to ask his wife to tell him where the corkscrew was.

COMMENT AND QUESTION

1. "Clay" is taken from Joyce's collection of short stories, *Dubliners,* which, according to Joyce, presents episodes in the moral history of a community. Mr. Harry Levin has commented that the recurring situation in these short stories is entrapment. Is Maria trapped in "Clay"?

2. Does Maria seem to live in a kind of psychological paralysis? Is her emotional life as diminutive as her body? Does she perform any successful acts of willing? What happens to the plumcake? What happens to her overture about Alphy? Is she the peacemaker she is said to be?

3. Maria's character can be traced through two separate but intertwining series of events. The first concerns her daily life. Trace the frustrations of Maria's life, beginning with her living (as a devout Catholic) among Protestants, through her treatment by clerks, to the climax of the clay. Is clay as a symbol necessarily restricted to the idea of death?

4. The second series of details emphasizes Maria's spinsterhood. This series begins with the ring at the laundry tea, is developed through half a dozen allusions, and ends with the song.

5. Maria's most common remark is "I don't want it." Is there a psychological connection between this attitude and her failure to sing the second stanza of the song? The omitted stanza reads as follows:

I dreamt that suitors sought my hand,
 That knights upon bended knee,
And with vows no maiden heart could withstand,
 They pledged their faith to me.

And I dreamt that one of that noble host
 Came forth my hand to claim,
But I also dreamt, which charmed me most,
 That you loved me still the same.

6. Maria does not know that she has omitted part of the song. Does Maria know what her life is like? Does the fact make her more pitiful or less pitiful?

7. What do the ring, the prayerbook, and the clay symbolize? Why are the games being played?

8. What does Maria look like when she laughs? Why is this picture important?

9. Although the style of *Dubliners* does not in any way foreshadow Joyce's brilliant performance in *Ulysses*, "Clay" reveals a technique very popular today among short story writers. As Mr. Levin has remarked, the structure is so casual, so "loose" that nothing seems to happen. But the casual structure permits a "dense" texture; that is, the story is really "told" through a number of close observations which reveal character and meaning.

AN OLD PAGE[1]

BY FRANZ KAFKA

FRANZ KAFKA (1883–1924) was born in
Prague of Jewish ancestry. He fought in the
first World War, ruined his health, suffered
through the poverty which was the aftermath of the war, and died of tuberculosis.
Most of his work was published after his
death, including his three unfinished novels,
The Castle (1930), *The Trial* (1937), and
Amerika (1940). Complete agreement on
the interpretation of Kafka's writing has not
been reached. But in general readers seem to
feel that Kafka gives a picture of a confused
and troubled age, a despairing picture of a
universe which man seems unable to understand or interpret. Besides his three novels,
the following works of Kafka are available in
English: *The Great Wall of China* (1933),
Metamorphosis (1937), and *A Franz Kafka
Miscellany* (1940).

IT LOOKS as if much had been neglected in our country's system of
defense. We have not concerned ourselves with it until now and have
gone about our daily work; but things that have been happening recently
begin to trouble us.

I have a cobbler's workshop in the square that lies before the Emperor's palace. Scarcely have I taken my shutters down, at the first glim-
mer of dawn, when I see armed soldiers already posted in the mouth of

---

AN OLD PAGE   Reprinted from *The Penal Colony* under the title "An Old Manuscript" by Franz Kafka, by permission of Schocken Books, New York. Copyright
1948 by Schocken Books, New York.

[1] The title of this story is translated as "An Old Manuscript" in *The Penal
Colony*, the volume in which this story occurs.

every street opening on the square. But these soldiers are not ours, they are obviously nomads from the North. In some way that is incomprehensible to me they have pushed right into the capital, although it is a long way from the frontier. At any rate, here they are; it seems that every morning there are more of them.

As is their nature, they camp under the open sky, for they abominate dwelling houses. They busy themselves sharpening swords, whittling arrows and practicing horsemanship. This peaceful square, which was always kept so scrupulously clean, they have made literally into a stable. We do try every now and then to run out of our shops and clear away at least the worst of the filth, but this happens less and less often, for the labor is in vain and brings us besides into danger of falling under the hoofs of the wild horses or of being crippled with lashes from the whips.

Speech with the nomads is impossible. They do not know our language, indeed they hardly have a language of their own. They communicate with each other much as jackdaws do. A screeching as of jackdaws is always in our ears. Our way of living and our institutions they neither understand nor care to understand. And so they are unwilling to make sense even out of our sign language. You can gesture at them till you dislocate your jaws and your wrists and still they will not have understood you and will never understand. They often make grimaces; then the whites of their eyes turn up and foam gathers on their lips, but they do not mean anything by that, not even a threat; they do it because it is their nature to do it. Whatever they need, they take. You cannot call it taking by force. They grab at something and you simply stand aside and leave them to it.

From my stock, too, they have taken many good articles. But I cannot complain when I see how the butcher, for instance, suffers across the street. As soon as he brings in any meat the nomads snatch it all from him and gobble it up. Even their horses devour flesh; often enough a horseman and his horse are lying side by side, both of them gnawing at the same joint, one at either end. The butcher is nervous and does not dare to stop his deliveries of meat. We understand that, however, and subscribe money to keep him going. If the nomads got no meat, who knows what they might think of doing; who knows anyhow what they may think of, even though they get meat every day.

Not long ago the butcher thought he might at least spare himself the trouble of slaughtering, and so one morning he brought along a live ox. But he will never dare to do that again. I lay for a whole hour flat on the floor at the back of my workshop with my head muffled in all the clothes and rugs and pillows I had, simply to keep from hearing the bellowing of that ox, which the nomads were leaping on from all sides, tearing morsels out of its living flesh with their teeth. It had been quiet for a long time before I risked coming out; they were lying overcome round the remains of the carcass like drunkards round a wine cask.

This was the occasion when I fancied I actually saw the Emperor himself at a window of the palace; usually he never enters these outer rooms but spends all his time in the innermost garden; yet on this occasion he was standing, or so at least it seemed to me, at one of the windows, watching with bent head the ongoings before his residence.

"What is going to happen?" we all ask ourselves. "How long can we endure this burden and torment? The Emperor's palace has drawn the nomads here but does not know how to drive them away again. The gate stays shut; the guards, who used to be always marching out and in with ceremony, keep close behind barred windows. It is left to us artisans and tradesmen to save our country; but we are not equal to such a task; nor have we ever claimed to be capable of it. This is a misunderstanding of some kind; and it will be the ruin of us."

COMMENT AND QUESTION

1. *Kafka and Existentialism.* Both Kafka and the Existentialist movement, of which he is a part, are a troubled sea for critics, a wide and troubled sea. It seems best, therefore, to limit the discussion here to those details which will help most in understanding "An Old Page."

First, a definition of Existentialism: "There are many 'existentialisms,' including several Christian brands, and most of them have not found literary expression. The essential fact is the sense of cosmic chaos, induced by the social chaos in which we are living. This sense was keenly felt by Céline, who is no philosopher, and by Kafka, who died in 1924. The tendency of the group is better expressed in *The Myth of Sisyphus*, by Albert Camus, than in the formidable treatise of Sartre. Camus' keyword is: The Absurd. The world was not created according to the norms of human reason, nor is it governed for the special benefit of the human race. From the point of view of man, it is absurd and unconsciously hostile. But man, by the mere fact of conceiving and naming the Absurd, transcends and conquers it. He does not need to capitulate to the dark forces of chaos. He can create, within himself, and around himself, an area of precarious but luminous order." Professor Albert Guérard, "The Leading French Novelists of the Present Moment," *College English*, Vol. 12 (April, 1951), p. 368.

The optimistic note at the close of this definition should not obscure the fact that Existentialism is, in general, an attitude of despair. The degree of despair depends upon the sensitivity of the individual man in his struggle with the "dark forces of chaos."

The reader of "An Old Page" will find the definition of Professor Guérard valuable, especially the sentence referring to cosmic and social chaos.

2. *Interpretations of "An Old Page."* Kafka works with symbols and often manipulates them to create two or three levels of meaning in a given story. Consequently, most of his novels and stories have received two or three different interpretations. Sometimes the varying interpretations can co-exist logically. Sometimes they are directly contradictory. Some interpretations of "An Old Page" are given below.

a. "For a suggestion regarding the futility of expecting the proletariat to stamp out evil, see the story, 'An Old Page.'" F. J. Hoffman, "Escape from Father," *The Kafka Problem*, ed. by Angel Flores (New Directions, 1946), footnote, p. 244.

b. ". . . how fragile is the crust of civilization and reason which separates us from the atrocious, from the barbarous, from the unthinkable. . . . Kafka has strongly the sense that human life is entirely bordered by the inhuman. That is what 'An Old Page' expresses, the fragment of an anonymous account, jotted down on a fluttering leaf of paper which floats as the last trace of a civilization." Claude-Edmonde Magny, "The Objective Depiction of Absurdity," *The Kafka Problem*, ed. by Angel Flores (New Directions, 1946), p. 95.

c. "'An Old Page' is a poetic imagistic portrayal of disorder and barbarism in a world lacking in faith and brotherhood. It purports to be about the distant, feudal past but is, of course, about the present." Charles Neider, *Kafka: His Mind and Art* (London, 1949), p. 81.

If the reader accepts one of these interpretations, he should find a coherent set of details in the story to support his view.

3. *Social and cosmic chaos.* If the reader regards the story as a picture of social or cosmic chaos, he will find the last paragraph important. He should also consider the following:

a. Is there lack of communication? Is it widespread?

b. Is it significant that the men in the square are nomads? Is not a nomadic life lawless, chaotic, subject to no settled rules or fixed standards? Are these nomads seeking something? What keeps them from storming the palace?

c. What do the wild horses and whips signify?

4. *Kafka as a man of religion.* One group of critics favors a religious or theological interpretation of Kafka. This interpretation is closely connected with "the sense of cosmic chaos." As a man of religion Kafka recognizes that man's primary purpose in life is his search for his relationship with God. But for Kafka there is no intelligible definition of this relationship and no rational guide to this relationship. According to Kafka, man finds himself in the position of being accountable to a God whose ways and whose justice are incomprehensible to man.

If the reader wishes to interpret "An Old Page" in a religious light, he might consider the palace as the church, the emperor as the minister of the church, and the artisans as lay people. The symbols then fall into a pattern revealing Kafka's view that the relations of God and humanity are in-commensurable. The following details will have special significance:

  a. The emperor has withdrawn to his innermost gardens.

  b. The emperor's palace drew the nomads.

  c. The emperor's palace does not know how to drive the nomads away.

  d. The ceremony (or ritual) of the guards has been stopped.

5. *The psychiatric interpretation of Kafka.* A second group of critics favors the psycho-analytical approach to Kafka. According to them, Kafka's writing is a revelation of the unconscious of a disordered personality. Born a Jew in Austria-dominated Bohemia, attracted and repelled by his father, stricken by tuberculosis, Kafka presumably developed severe psychoses—chiefly sexual—which motivated his work. There seems to be little justifica-tion, however, for a psychiatric interpretation of "An Old Page."

6. *Kafka's style.* This story is typical of Kafka in its nightmare atmos-phere, in its sadism, and in the way in which the story shifts without warn-ing from a realistic or naturalistic level to a fantastic level. Mr. Claude-Edmonde Magny has explained Kafka's style by saying that only by a fantastic tale can Kafka express his conception of the turmoil and irration-ality of the world.

Kafka's literary technique can also be described as one of "significant obscurity." After studying this story, do you think such a technique is valid? In spite of Kafka's "significant obscurity"—or because of it—he has achieved a wide following. This statement is true whether Kafka is said to be expressing a disordered personality, a disordered society, or a dis-ordered cosmos.

ZONE OF QUIET

BY RING W. LARDNER

RING W. LARDNER (1885–1933) was born in
Michigan and educated at the Armour Insti-
tute of Technology at Chicago. He became a
newspaper reporter, but left sports writing for
literary work. At the time of his death, he was
one of America's best-loved humorists. If his
humor survives, it will doubtless do so because of his satire, which exposes vulgar motives and attitudes. Among his collections of
stories are *You Know Me, Al* (1915), *Gul-
lible's Travels* (1917), *How to Write Short
Stories* (1924), *The Love Nest* (1926), and
Round-Up (1929).

"WELL," said the Doctor briskly, "how do you feel?"

"Oh, I guess I'm all right," replied the man in bed. "I'm still kind of
drowsy, that's all."

"You were under the anesthetic an hour and a half. It's no wonder you
aren't wide awake yet. But you'll be better after a good night's rest, and
I've left something with Miss Lyons that'll make you sleep. I'm going along
now. Miss Lyons will take good care of you."

"I'm off at seven o'clock," said Miss Lyons. "I'm going to a show with
my G. F. but Miss Halsey's all right. She's the night floor nurse. Anything
you want, she'll get it for you. What can I give him to eat, Doctor?"

"Nothing at all; not till after I've been here tomorrow. He'll be better
off without anything. Just see that he's kept quiet. Don't let him talk, and
don't talk to him; that is, if you can help it."

"Help it!" said Miss Lyons. "Say, I can be old lady Sphinx herself when I want to! Sometimes I sit for hours—not alone, neither—and never say a word. Just think and think. And dream.

"I had a G. F. in Baltimore, where I took my training; she used to call me Dummy. Not because I'm dumb like some people—you know—but because I'd sit there and not say nothing. She'd say, 'A penny for your thoughts, Eleanor.' That's my first name—Eleanor."

"Well, I must run along. I'll see you in the morning."

"Good-by, Doctor," said the man in bed, as he went out.

"Good-by, Doctor Cox," said Miss Lyons as the door closed.

"He seems like an awful nice fella," said Miss Lyons. "And a good doctor, too. This is the first time I've been on a case with him. He gives a girl credit for having some sense. Most of these doctors treat us like they thought we were Mormons or something. Like Doctor Holland. I was on a case with him last week. He treated me like I was a Mormon or something. Finally, I told him, I said, 'I'm not as dumb as I look.' She died Friday night."

"Who?" asked the man in bed.

"The woman; the case I was on," said Miss Lyons.

"And what did the doctor say when you told him you weren't as dumb as you look?"

"I don't remember," said Miss Lyons. "He said, 'I hope not,' or something. What *could* he say? Gee! It's quarter to seven. I hadn't no idear it was so late. I must get busy and fix you up for the night. And I'll tell Miss Halsey to take good care of you. We're going to see 'What Price Glory?' I'm going with my G. F. Her B. F. gave her the tickets and he's going to meet us after the show and take us to supper.

"Marian—that's my G. F.—she's crazy wild about him. And he's crazy about her, to hear her tell it. But I said to her this noon—she called me up on the phone—I said to her, 'If he's so crazy about you, why don't he propose? He's got plenty of money and no strings tied to him, and as far as I can see there's no reason why he shouldn't marry you if he wants you as bad as you say he does.' So she said maybe he was going to ask her to-night. I told her, 'Don't be silly! Would he drag me along if he was going to ask you?'

"That about him having plenty of money, though, that's a joke. He told her he had and she believes him. I haven't met him yet, but he looks in his picture like he's lucky if he's getting twenty-five dollars a week. She thinks he must be rich because he's in Wall Street. I told her, I said, 'That being in Wall Street don't mean nothing. What does he do there? is the question. You know they have to have janitors in those buildings just the same like anywhere else.' But she thinks he's God or somebody.

"She keeps asking me if I don't think he's the best looking thing I ever saw. I tell her yes, sure, but between you and I, I don't believe anybody'd ever mistake him for Richard Barthelmess.

"Oh, say! I saw him the other day, coming out of the Algonquin! He's the best looking thing! Even better looking than on the screen. Roy Stewart."

"What about Roy Stewart?" asked the man in bed.

"Oh, he's the fella I was telling you about," said Miss Lyons. "He's my G. F.'s B. F."

"Maybe I'm a D. F. not to know, but would you tell me what a B. F. and G. F. are?"

"Well, you *are* dumb, aren't you!" said Miss Lyons. "A G. F., that's a girl friend, and a B. F. is a boy friend. I thought everybody knew that.

"I'm going out now and find Miss Halsey and tell her to be nice to you. But maybe I better not."

"Why not?" asked the man in bed.

"Oh, nothing. I was just thinking of something funny that happened last time I was on a case in this hospital. It was the day the man had been operated on and he was the best looking somebody you ever saw. So when I went off duty I told Miss Halsey to be nice to him, like I was going to tell her about you. And when I came back in the morning he was dead. Isn't that funny?"

"Very!"

"Well," said Miss Lyons, "did you have a good night? You look a lot better, anyway. How'd you like Miss Halsey? Did you notice her ankles? She's got pretty near the smallest ankles I ever saw. Cute. I remember one day Tyler—that's one of the internes—he said if he could just see our ankles, mine and Miss Halsey's, he wouldn't know which was which. Of course we don't look anything alike other ways. She's pretty close to thirty and—well, nobody'd ever take her for Julia Hoyt. Helen."

"Who's Helen?" asked the man in bed.

"Helen Halsey. Helen; that's her first name. She was engaged to a man in Boston. He was going to Tufts College. He was going to be a doctor. But he died. She still carries his picture with her. I tell her she's silly to mope about a man that's been dead four years. And besides a girl's a fool to marry a doctor. They've got too many alibis.

"When I marry somebody, he's got to be a somebody that has regular office hours like he's in Wall Street or somewhere. Then when he don't come home, he'll have to think up something better than being 'on a case.' I used to use that on my sister when we were living together. When I happened to be out late, I'd tell her I was on a case. She never knew the difference. Poor sis! She married a terrible oil can! But she didn't have the looks to get a real somebody. I'm making this for her. It's a bridge table cover for her birthday. She'll be twenty-nine. Don't that seem old?"

"Maybe to you; not to me," said the man in bed.

"You're about forty, aren't you?" said Miss Lyons.

"Just about."

"And how old would you say I am?"

"Twenty-three."

"I'm twenty-five," said Miss Lyons. "Twenty-five and forty. That's fifteen years' difference. But I know a married couple that the husband is forty-five and she's only twenty-four, and they get along fine."

"I'm married myself," said the man in bed.

"You would be!" said Miss Lyons. "The last four cases I've been on was all married men. But at that, I'd rather have any kind of a man than a woman. I hate women! I mean sick ones. They treat a nurse like a dog, especially a pretty nurse. What's that you're reading?"

" 'Vanity Fair,' " replied the man in bed.

" 'Vanity Fair.' I thought that was a magazine."

"Well, there's a magazine *and* a book. This is the book."

"Is it about a girl?"

"Yes."

"I haven't read it yet. I've been busy making this thing for my sister's birthday. She'll be twenty-nine. It's a bridge table cover. When you get that old, about all there is left is bridge or cross-word puzzles. Are you a puzzle fan? I did them religiously for a while, but I got sick of them. They put in such crazy words. Like one day they had a word with only three letters and it said 'A e-longated fish' and the first letter had to be an *e*. And only three letters. That *couldn't* be right. So I said if they put things wrong like that, what's the use? Life's too short. And we only live once. When you're dead, you stay a long time dead.

"That's what a B. F. of mine used to say. He was a caution! But he was crazy about me. I might of married him only for a G. F. telling him lies about me. And called herself my friend! Charley Pierce."

"Who's Charley Pierce?"

"That was my B. F. that the other girl lied to him about me. I told him, I said, 'Well, if you believe all them stories about me, maybe we better part once and for all. I don't want to be tied up to a somebody that believes all the dirt they hear about me.' So he said he didn't really believe it and if I would take him back he wouldn't quarrel with me no more. But I said I thought it was best for us to part. I got their announcement two years ago, while I was still in training in Baltimore."

"Did he marry the girl that lied to him about you?"

"Yes, the poor fish! And I bet he's satisfied! They're a match for each other! He was all right, though, at that, till he fell for her. He used to be so thoughtful of me, like I was his sister or something.

"I like a man to respect me. Most fellas wants to kiss you before they know your name.

"Golly! I'm sleepy this morning! And got a right to be, too. Do you know what time I got home last night, or this morning, rather? Well, it was half past three. What would mama say if she could see her little girl now! But we did have a good time. First we went to the show—'What Price Glory?'—I and my G. F.—and afterwards her B. F. met us and took us in a taxi down to Barney Gallant's. Peewee Byers has got the orchestra there now. Used to be with Whiteman's. Gee! How he can dance! I mean Roy."

"Your G. F.'s B. F.?"

"Yes, but I don't believe he's as crazy about her as she thinks he is. Anyway—but this is a secret—he took down the phone number of the hospital while Marian was out powdering her nose, and he said he'd give me a ring about noon. Gee! I'm sleepy! Roy Stewart!"

"Well," said Miss Lyons, "how's my patient? I'm twenty minutes late, but honest, it's a wonder I got up at all! Two nights in succession is too much for this child!"

"Barney Gallant's again?" asked the man in bed.

"No, but it was dancing, and pretty near as late. It'll be different tonight. I'm going to bed just the minute I get home. But I did have a dandy time. And I'm crazy about a certain somebody."

"Roy Stewart?"

"How'd you guess it? But honest, he's wonderful! And so different than most of the fellas I've met. He says the craziest things, just keeps you in hysterics. We were talking about books and reading, and he asked me if I liked poetry—only he called it 'poultry'—and I said I was wild about it and Edgar M. Guest was just about my favorite, and then I asked him if he liked Kipling and what do you think he said? He said he didn't know; he'd never kipled.

"He's a scream! We just sat there in the house till half past eleven and didn't do nothing but just talk and the time went like we was at a show. He's better than a show. But finally I noticed how late it was and I asked him didn't he think he better be going and he said he'd go if I'd go with him, so I asked him where could we go at that hour of night, and he said he knew a roadhouse just a little ways away, and I didn't want to go, but he said we wouldn't stay for only just one dance, so I went with him. To the Jericho Inn.

"I don't know what the woman thought of me where I stay, going out that time of night. But he *is* such a wonderful dancer and such a perfect gentleman! Of course we had more than one dance and it was after two o'clock before I knew it. We had some gin, too, but he just kissed me once and that was when we said good night."

"What about your G. F., Marian? Does she know?"

"About Roy and I? No. I always say that what a person don't know don't hurt them. Besides, there's nothing *for* her to know—yet. But listen: If there was a chance in the world for her, if I thought he cared anything about her, I'd be the last one in the world to accept his intentions. I hope I'm not that kind! But as far as anything serious between them is concerned, well, it's cold. I happen to *know* that! She's not the girl for him.

"In the first place, while she's pretty in a way, her complexion's bad and her hair's scraggy and her figure, well, it's like some woman in the funny pictures. And she's not peppy enough for Roy. She'd rather stay home than do anything. Stay home! It'll be time enough for that when you can't get anybody to take you out.

"She'd never make a wife for him. He'll be a rich man in another year; that is, if things go right for him in Wall Street like he expects. And a man as rich as he'll be wants a wife that can live up to it and entertain and step out once in a while. He don't want a wife that's a drag on him. And he's too good-looking for Marian. A fella as good-looking as him needs a pretty wife or the first thing you know some girl that is pretty will steal him off of you. But it's silly to talk about them marrying each other. He'd have to ask her first, and he's not going to. I know! So I don't feel at all like I'm trespassing.

"Anyway, you know the old saying, everything goes in love. And I—— But I'm keeping you from reading your book. Oh, yes; I almost forgot a T. L. that Miss Halsey said about you. Do you know what a T. L. is?"

"Yes."

"Well, then, you give me one and I'll give you this one."

"But I haven't talked to anybody but the Doctor. I can give you one from myself. He asked me how I liked you and I said all right."

"Well, that's better than nothing. Here's what Miss Halsey said: She said if you were shaved and fixed up, you wouldn't be bad. And now I'm going out and see if there's any mail for me. Most of my mail goes to where I live, but some of it comes here sometimes. What I'm looking for is a letter from the state board telling me if I passed my state examination. They ask you the craziest questions. Like 'Is ice a disinfectant?' Who cares! Nobody's going to waste ice to kill germs when there's so much of it needed in high-balls. Do you like high-balls? Roy says it spoils whisky to mix it with water. He takes it straight. He's a terror! But maybe you want to read."

"Good morning," said Miss Lyons. "Did you sleep good?"

"Not so good," said the man in bed. "I——"

"I bet you got more sleep than I did," said Miss Lyons. "He's the most persistent somebody I ever knew! I asked him last night, I said, 'Don't you never get tired of dancing?' So he said, well, he did get tired of dancing with some people, but there was others who he never got tired of dancing with them. So I said, 'Yes, Mr. Jollier, but I wasn't born yesterday and I know apple sauce when I hear it and I bet you've told that to fifty girls.' I guess he really did mean it, though.

"Of course most anybody'd rather dance with slender girls than stout girls. I remember a B. F. I had one time in Washington. He said dancing with me was just like dancing with nothing. That sounds like he was insulting me, but it was really a compliment. He meant it wasn't any effort to dance with me like with some girls. You take Marian, for instance, and while I'm crazy about her, still that don't make her a good dancer and dancing with her must be a good deal like moving the piano or something.

"I'd die if I was fat! People are always making jokes about fat people. And there's the old saying, 'Nobody loves a fat man.' And it's even worse with a girl. Besides people making jokes about them and don't want to dance with them and so forth, besides that they're always trying to reduce and can't eat what they want to. I bet, though, if I was fat, I'd eat everything in sight. Though I guess not, either. Because I hardly eat anything as it is. But they do make jokes about them.

"I'll never forget one day last winter, I was on a case in Great Neck and the man's wife was the fattest thing! So they had a radio in the house and one day she saw in the paper where Bugs Baer was going to talk on the radio and it would probably be awfully funny because he writes so crazy. Do you ever read his articles? But this woman, she was awfully sensitive about being fat and I nearly died sitting there with her listening to Bugs Baer, because his whole talk was all about some fat woman and he said the craziest things, but I couldn't laugh on account of she being there in the room with me. One thing he said was that the woman, this woman he was talking about, he said she was so fat that she wore a wrist watch on her thumb. Henry J. Belden."

"Who is Henry J. Belden? Is that the name of Bugs Baer's fat lady?"

"No, you crazy!" said Miss Lyons. "Mr. Belden was the case I was on in Great Neck. He died."

"It seems to me a good many of your cases die."

"Isn't it a scream!" said Miss Lyons. "But it's true; that is, it's been true lately. The last five cases I've been on has all died. Of course it's just luck, but the girls have been kidding me about it and calling me a jinx, and when Miss Halsey saw me here the evening of the day you was operated, she said, 'God help him!' That's the night floor nurse's name. But you're going to be mean and live through it and spoil my record, aren't you? I'm just kidding. Of course I want you to get all right.

"But it *is* queer, the way things have happened, and it's made me feel kind of creepy. And besides, I'm not like some of the girls and don't care.

I get awfully fond of some of my cases and I hate to see them die, especially if they're men and not very sick and treat you half-way decent and don't yell for you the minute you go out of the room. There's only one case I was ever on where I didn't mind her dying and that was a woman. She had nephritis. Mrs. Judson.

"Do you want some gum? I chew it just when I'm nervous. And I always get nervous when I don't have enough sleep. You can bet I'll stay home tonight, B. F. or no B. F. But anyway he's got an engagement tonight, some directors' meeting or something. He's the busiest somebody in the world. And I told him last night, I said, 'I should think you'd need sleep, too, even more than I do because you have to have all your wits about you in your business or those big bankers would take advantage and rob you. You can't afford to be sleepy,' I told him.

"So he said, 'No, but of course it's all right for you, because if you go to sleep on your job, there's no danger of you doing any damage except maybe give one of your patients a bichloride of mercury tablet instead of an alcohol rub.' He's terrible! But you can't help from laughing.

"There was four of us in the party last night. He brought along his B. F. and another girl. She was just blah, but the B. F. wasn't so bad, only he insisted on me helping him drink a half a bottle of Scotch, and on top of gin, too. I guess I was the life of the party; that is, at first. Afterwards I got sick and it wasn't so good.

"But at first I was certainly going strong. And I guess I made quite a hit with Roy's B. F. He knows Marian, too, but he won't say anything, and if he does, I don't care. If she don't want to lose her beaus, she ought to know better than to introduce them to all the pretty girls in the world. I don't mean that I'm any Norma Talmadge, but at least—well—but I sure was sick when I *was* sick!

"I must give Marian a ring this noon. I haven't talked to her since the night she introduced me to him. I've been kind of scared. But I've got to find out what she knows. Or if she's sore at me. Though I don't see how she can be, do you? But maybe you want to read."

"I called Marian up, but I didn't get her. She's out of town but she'll be back tonight. She's been out on a case. Hudson, New York. That's where she went. The message was waiting for her when she got home the other night, the night she introduced me to Roy."

"Good morning," said Miss Lyons.

"Good morning," said the man in bed. "Did you sleep enough?"

"Yes," said Miss Lyons. "I mean no, not enough."

"Your eyes look bad. They almost look as if you'd been crying."

"Who? Me? It'd take more than—I mean, I'm not a baby! But go on and read your book."

"Well, good morning," said Miss Lyons. "And how's my patient? And this is the last morning I can call you that, isn't it? I think you're mean to get well so quick and leave me out of a job. I'm just kidding. I'm glad you're all right again, and I can use a little rest myself."

"Another big night?" asked the man in bed.

"Pretty big," said Miss Lyons. "And another one coming. But tomorrow I won't ever get up. Honest, I danced so much last night that I thought my feet would drop off. But he certainly is a dancing fool! And the nicest somebody to talk to that I've met since I came to this town. Not a smart Alex and not always trying to be funny like some people, but just nice. He understands. He seems to know just what you're thinking. George Morse."

"George Morse!" exclaimed the man in bed.

"Why yes," said Miss Lyons. "Do you know him?"

"No. But I thought you were talking about this Stewart, this Roy."

"Oh, him!" said Miss Lyons. "I should say not! He's private property; other people's property, not mine. He's engaged to my G. F. Marian. It happened day before yesterday, after she got home from Hudson. She was on a case up there. She told me about it night before last. I told her congratulations. Because I wouldn't hurt her feelings for the world! But heavens! what a mess she's going to be in, married to that dumb-bell. But of course some people can't be choosey. And I doubt if they ever get married unless some friend loans him the price of a license.

"He's got her believing he's in Wall Street, but I bet if he ever goes there at all, it's to sweep it. He's one of these kind of fellas that's got a great line for a little while, but you don't want to live with a clown. And I'd hate to marry a man that all he thinks about is to step out every night and dance and drink.

"I had a notion to tell her what I really thought. But that'd only of made her sore, or she'd of thought I was jealous or something. As if I couldn't of had him myself! Though even if he wasn't so awful, if I'd liked him instead of loathed him, I wouldn't of taken him from her on account of she being my G. F. And especially while she was out of town.

"He's the kind of a fella that'd marry a nurse in the hopes that some day he'd be an invalid. You know, that kind.

"But say—did you ever hear of J. P. Morgan and Company? That's where my B. F. works, and he don't claim to own it neither. George Morse.

"Haven't you finished that book yet?"

COMMENT AND QUESTION

1. Eleanor is having trouble getting married. What are her reasons? What are the real reasons?

2. Does Eleanor seem fitted to be a nurse?

3. How does Eleanor regard women? Men? What conditions her frequent reversal of opinion?

4. How many times did Roy Stewart "date Eleanor? Why did Roy "date" her in the first place?

5. Why did Roy fly so swiftly into Marian's arms and the security of an engagement?

6. In the Comment and Question section following the story "First Confession" by Frank O'Connor, you will find a brief discussion of various types of humor.

7. To which type of humor does "Zone of Quiet" belong?

8. Is the humor in this story developed in words and in phrasing as well as in character and incident?

MARIO AND THE MAGICIAN

BY THOMAS MANN

THOMAS MANN (1875–   ) is a major literary
figure not only of Germany but of the world.
He was born in Lübeck, Germany. He became
an exile from his country during the Nazi re-
gime and since 1938 has lived with his family
in the United States. The volume *Stories of
Three Decades* (1936) is an American edition
of his shorter fiction. His novels available in
English include *Buddenbrooks* (1916), *The
Magic Mountain* (1924), *Joseph and His
Brothers* (1934), *Young Joseph* (1935), *Joseph in Egypt* (1938), *The Beloved Returns*
(1940), *Joseph the Provider* (1944), and
Doctor Faustus (1948).

THE ATMOSPHERE of Torre di Venere remains unpleasant in the memory.
From the first moment the air of the place made us uneasy, we felt irritable, on edge; then at the end came the shocking business of Cipolla, that
dreadful being who seemed to incorporate, in so fateful and so humanly
impressive a way, all the peculiar evilness of the situation as a whole.
Looking back, we had the feeling that the horrible end of the affair had
been preordained and lay in the nature of things; that the children had to
be present at it was an added impropriety, due to the false colours in
which the weird creature presented himself. Luckily for them, they did
not know where the comedy left off and the tragedy began; and we let
them remain in their happy belief that the whole thing had been a play up
till the end.

MARIO AND THE MAGICIAN   From *Stories of Three Decades* by Thomas Mann.
Reprinted by permission of Alfred A. Knopf, Inc. Copyright 1931, 1936 by
Alfred A. Knopf, Inc.

Torre di Venere lies some fifteen kilometres from Portoclemente, one of the most popular summer resorts on the Tyrrhenian Sea. Portoclemente is urban and elegant and full to overflowing for months on end. Its gay and busy main street of shops and hotels runs down to a wide sandy beach covered with tents and pennanted sand-castles and sunburnt humanity, where at all times a lively social bustle reigns, and much noise. But this same spacious and inviting fine-sanded beach, this same border of pine grove and near, presiding mountains, continues all the way along the coast. No wonder then that some competition of a quiet kind should have sprung up further on. Torre di Venere—the tower that gave the town its name is gone long since, one looks for it in vain—is an offshoot of the larger resort, and for some years remained an idyll for the few, a refuge for more un-worldly spirits. But the usual history of such places repeated itself: peace has had to retire further along the coast, to Marina Petriera and dear knows where else. We all know how the world at once seeks peace and puts her to flight—rushing upon her in the fond idea that they two will wed, and where she is, there it can be at home. It will even set up its Vanity Fair in a spot and be capable of thinking that peace is still by its side. Thus Torre—though its atmosphere so far is more modest and con-templative than that of Portoclemente—has been quite taken up, by both Italians and foreigners. It is no longer the thing to go to Portoclemente—though still so much the thing that it is as noisy and crowded as ever. One goes next door, so to speak: to Torre. So much more refined, even, and cheaper to boot. And the attractiveness of these qualities persists, though the qualities themselves long ago ceased to be evident. Torre has got a Grand Hotel. Numerous pensions have sprung up, some modest, some pretentious. The people who own or rent the villas and pinetas overlook-ing the sea no longer have it all their own way on the beach. In July and August it looks just like the beach at Portoclemente: it swarms with a screaming, squabbling, merrymaking crowd, and the sun, blazing down like mad, peels the skin off their necks. Garish little flat-bottomed boats rock on the glittering blue, manned by children, whose mothers hover afar and fill the air with anxious cries of Nino! and Sandro! and Bice! and Maria! Pedlars step across the legs of recumbent sun-bathers, selling flowers and corals, oysters, lemonade, and *cornetti al burro*, and crying their wares in the breathy, full-throated southern voice.

Such was the scene that greeted our arrival in Torre: pleasant enough, but after all, we thought, we had come too soon. It was the middle of August, the Italian season was still at its height, scarcely the moment for strangers to learn to love the special charms of the place. What an after-noon crowd in the cafés on the front! For instance, in the Esquisito, where we sometimes sat and were served by Mario, that very Mario of whom I shall have presently to tell. It is well-nigh impossible to find a table; and the various orchestras contend together in the midst of one's conversation with bewildering effect. Of course, it is in the afternoon that people come over from Portoclemente. The excursion is a favourite one for the restless denizens of that pleasure resort, and a Fiat motor-bus plies to and fro, coating inch-thick with dust the oleander and laurel hedges along the highroad—a notable if repulsive sight.

Yes, decidedly one should go to Torre in September, when the great public has left. Or else in May, before the water is warm enough to tempt the Southerner to bathe. Even in the before and after seasons Torre is not empty, but life is less national and more subdued. English, French, and German prevail under the tent-awnings and in the pension dining-rooms; whereas in August—in the Grand Hotel, at least, where, in default of private addresses, we had engaged rooms—the stranger finds the field so occupied by Florentine and Roman society that he feels quite isolated and even temporarily *déclassé*.

We had, rather to our annoyance, this experience on the evening we arrived, when we went in to dinner and were shown to our table by the waiter in charge. As a table, it had nothing against it, save that we had already fixed our eyes upon those on the veranda beyond, built out over the water, where little red-shaded lamps glowed—and there were still some tables empty, though it was as full as the dining-room within. The children went into raptures at the festive sight, and without more ado we announced our intention to take our meals by preference in the veranda. Our words, it appeared, were prompted by ignorance; for we were informed, with somewhat embarrassed politeness, that the cosy nook outside was reserved for the clients of the hotel: *ai nostri clienti*. Their clients? But we were their clients. We were not tourists or trippers, but boarders for a stay of some three or four weeks. However, we forbore to press for an explanation of the difference between the likes of us and that clientèle to whom it was vouchsafed to eat out there in the glow of the red lamps, and took our dinner by the prosaic common light of the dining-room chandelier—a thoroughly ordinary and monotonous hotel bill of fare, be it said In Pensione Eleonora, a few steps landward, the table, as we were to discover, was much better.

And thither it was that we moved, three or four days later, before we had had time to settle in properly at the Grand Hotel. Not on account of the veranda and the lamps. The children, straightway on the best of terms with waiters and pages, absorbed in the joys of life on the beach, promptly forgot those colourful seductions. But now there arose, between ourselves and the veranda clientèle—or perhaps more correctly with the compliant management—one of those little unpleasantnesses which can quite spoil the pleasure of a holiday. Among the guests were some high Roman aristocracy, a Principe X and his family. These grand folk occupied rooms close to our own, and the Principessa, a great and a passionately maternal lady, was thrown into a panic by the vestiges of a whooping-cough which our little ones had lately got over, but which now and then still faintly troubled the unshatterable slumbers of our youngest-born. The nature of this illness is not clear, leaving some play for the imagination. So we took no offence at our elegant neighbour for clinging to the widely held view that whooping-cough is acoustically contagious and quite simply fearing lest her children yield to the bad example set by ours. In the fullness of her feminine self-confidence she protested to the management, which then, in the person of the proverbial frock-coated manager, hastened to represent to us, with many expressions of regret, that under the circumstances they were obliged to transfer us to the annexe. We did our best to assure him that the disease was in its very last stages, that it was actually over, and presented no danger of infection to anybody. All that we gained was permission to bring the case before the hotel physician—not one chosen by us—by whose verdict we must then abide. We agreed, convinced that thus we should at once pacify the Princess and escape the trouble of moving. The doctor appeared, and behaved like a faithful and honest servant of science. He examined the child and gave his opinion: the disease was quite over, no danger of contagion was present. We drew a long breath and considered the incident closed—until the manager announced that despite the doctor's verdict it would still be necessary for us to give up our rooms and retire to the *dépendance*. Byzantinism like this outraged us. It is not likely that the Principessa was responsible for the wilful breach of faith. Very likely the fawning management had not even dared to tell her what the physician said. Anyhow, we made it clear to his understanding that we preferred to leave the hotel altogether and at once—and packed our trunks. We could do so with a light heart, having already set up casual friendly relations with Casa Eleonora. We had noticed its pleasant exterior and formed the acquaintance of its proprietor, Signora Angiolieri, and her husband: she slender and black-haired, Tuscan in type, probably at the beginning of the thirties, with the dead ivory complexion of the southern woman, he quiet and bald and carefully dressed. They owned a larger establishment in Florence and presided only in summer and early autumn over the branch in Torre di Venere. But earlier, before her marriage, our new landlady had been companion, fellow-traveller, wardrobe mistress, yes, friend, of Eleonora Duse and manifestly regarded that period as the crown of her career. Even at our first visit she spoke of it with animation. Numerous photographs of the great actress, with affectionate inscriptions, were displayed about the drawing-room, and other souvenirs of their life together adorned the little tables and étagères. This cult of a so interesting past was calculated, of course, to heighten the advantages of the signora's present business. Nevertheless our pleasure and interest were quite genuine as we were conducted through the house by its owner and listened to her sonorous and staccato Tuscan voice relating anecdotes of that immortal mistress, depicting her suffering saintliness, her genius, her profound delicacy of feeling.

Thither, then, we moved our effects, to the dismay of the staff of the Grand Hotel, who, like all Italians, were very good to children. Our new quarters were retired and pleasant, we were within easy reach of the sea through the avenue of young plane trees that ran down to the esplanade. In the clean, cool dining-room Signora Angiolieri daily served the soup with her own hands, the service was attentive and good, the table capital. We even discovered some Viennese acquaintances, and enjoyed chatting with them after luncheon, in front of the house. They, in their turn, were the means of our finding others—in short, all seemed for the best, and we were heartily glad of the change we had made. Nothing was now wanting to a holiday of the most gratifying kind.

And yet no proper gratification ensued. Perhaps the stupid occasion of our change of quarters pursued us to the new ones we had found. Personally, I admit that I do not easily forget these collisions with ordinary humanity, the naïve misuse of power, the injustice, the sycophantic corruption. I dwelt upon the incident too much, it irritated me in retrospect—quite futilely, of course, since such phenomena are only all too natural and all too much the rule. And we had not broken off relations with the Grand Hotel. The children were as friendly as ever there, the porter mended their toys, and we sometimes took tea in the garden. We even saw the Principessa. She would come out, with her firm and delicate tread, her lips emphatically corallined, to look after her children, playing under the supervision of their English governess. She did not dream that we were anywhere near, for so soon as she appeared in the offing we sternly forbade our little one even to clear his throat.

The heat—if I may bring it in evidence—was extreme. It was African. The power of the sun, directly one left the border of the indigo-blue wave, was so frightful, so relentless, that the mere thought of the few steps between the beach and luncheon was a burden, clad though one might be only in pyjamas. Do you care for that sort of thing? Weeks on end? Yes, of course, it is proper to the south, it is classic weather, the sun of Homer, the climate wherein human culture came to flower—and all the rest of it. But after a while it is too much for me, I reach a point where I begin to find it dull. The burning void of the sky, day after day, weighs one down; the high coloration, the enormous naïveté of the unrefracted light—they do, I dare say, induce light-heartedness, a carefree mood born of immunity from downpours and other meteorological caprices. But slowly, slowly, there makes itself felt a lack: the deeper, more complex needs of the northern soul remain unsatisfied. You are left barren—even, it may be, in time, a little contemptuous. True, without that stupid business of the whooping-cough I might not have been feeling these things. I was annoyed, very likely I wanted to feel them and so half-unconsciously seized upon an idea lying ready to hand to induce, or if not to induce, at least to justify and strengthen, my attitude. Up to this point, then, if you like, let us grant some ill will on our part. But the sea; and the mornings spent extended upon the fine sand in face of its eternal splendours—no, the sea could not conceivably induce such feelings. Yet it was none the less true that, despite all previous experience, we were not at home on the beach, we were not happy.

It was too soon, too soon. The beach, as I have said, was still in the hands of the middle-class native. It is a pleasing breed to look at, and among the young we saw much shapeliness and charm. Still, we were necessarily surrounded by a great deal of very average humanity—a middle-class mob, which, you will admit, is not more charming under this sun than under one's own native sky. The voices these women have! It was sometimes hard to believe that we were in the land which is the western cradle of the art of song. "*Fuggièro!*" I can still hear that cry, as for twenty mornings long I heard it close behind me, breathy, full-throated, hideously stressed, with a harsh open *e*, uttered in accents of mechanical despair. "*Fuggièro! Rispondi almeno!*" Answer when I call you! The *sp* in *rispondi* was pronounced like *shp*, as Germans pronounce it; and this, on top of what I felt already, vexed my sensitive soul. The cry was addressed to a repulsive youngster whose sunburn had made disgusting raw sores on his shoulders. He outdid anything I have ever seen for ill-breeding, refractoriness, and temper and was a great coward to boot, putting the whole beach in an uproar, one day, because of his outrageous sensitiveness to the slightest pain. A sand-crab had pinched his toe in the water, and the minute injury made him set up a cry of heroic proportions—the shout of an antique hero in his agony—that pierced one to the marrow and called up visions of some frightful tragedy. Evidently he considered himself not only wounded, but poisoned as well; he crawled out on the sand and lay in apparently intolerable anguish, groaning "*Ohi!*" and "*Ohimè!*" and threshing about with arms and legs to ward off his mother's tragic appeals and the questions of the bystanders. An audience gathered round. A doctor was fetched—the same who had pronounced objective judgment on our whooping-cough—and here again acquitted himself like a man of science. Good-naturedly he reassured the boy, telling him that he was not hurt at all, he should simply go into the water again to relieve the smart. Instead of which, Fuggièro was borne off the beach, followed by a concourse of people. But he did not fail to appear next morning, nor did he leave off spoiling our children's sand-castles. Of course, always by accident. In short, a perfect terror.

And this twelve-year-old lad was prominent among the influences that, imperceptibly at first, combined to spoil our holiday and render it unwholesome. Somehow or other, there was a stiffness, a lack of innocent enjoyment. These people stood on their dignity—just why, and in what spirit, it was not easy at first to tell. They displayed much self-respectingness; towards each other and towards the foreigner their bearing was that of a person newly conscious of a sense of honour. And wherefore? Gradually we realized the political implications and understood that we were in the presence of a national ideal. The beach, in fact, was alive with patriotic children—a phenomenon as unnatural as it was depressing. Children are a human species and a society apart, a nation of their own, so to speak. On the basis of their common form of life, they find each other out with the greatest ease, no matter how different their small vocabularies. Ours soon played with natives and foreigners alike. Yet they were plainly both puzzled and disappointed at times. There were wounded sensibilities, displays of assertiveness—or rather hardly assertiveness, for it was too self-conscious and too didactic to deserve the name. There were quarrels over flags, disputes about authority and precedence. Grown-ups joined in, not so much to pacify as to render judgment and enunciate principles. Phrases were dropped about the greatness and dignity of Italy, solemn phrases that spoilt the fun. We saw our two little ones retreat, puzzled and hurt, and were put to it to explain the situation. These people, we told them, were just passing through a certain stage, something rather like an illness, perhaps; not very pleasant, but probably unavoidable.

We had only our own carelessness to thank that we came to blows in the end with this "stage"—which, after all, we had seen and sized up long before now. Yes, it came to another "cross-purposes," so evidently the earlier ones had not been sheer accident. In a word, we became an offence to the public morals. Our small daughter—eight years old, but in physical development a good year younger and thin as a chicken—had had a good long bathe and gone playing in the warm sun in her wet costume. We told her that she might take off her bathing-suit, which was stiff with sand, rinse it in the sea, and put it on again, after which she must take care to keep it cleaner. Off goes the costume and she runs down naked to the sea, rinses her little jersey, and comes back. Ought we to have foreseen the outburst of anger and resentment which her conduct, and thus our conduct, called forth? Without delivering a homily on the subject, I may say that in the last decade our attitude towards the nude body and our feelings regarding it have undergone, all over the world, a fundamental change. There are things we "never think about" any more, and among them is the freedom we had permitted to this by no means provocative little childish body. But in these parts it was taken as a challenge. The patriotic children hooted. Fuggièro whistled on his fingers. The sudden buzz of conversation among the grown people in our neighbourhood boded no good. A gentleman in city togs, with a not very apropos bowler hat on the back of his head, was assuring his outraged womenfolk that he proposed to take punitive measures; he stepped up to us, and a philippic descended on our unworthy heads, in which all the emotionalism of the sense-loving south spoke in the service of morality and discipline. The offence against decency of which we had been guilty was, he said, the more to be condemned because it was also a gross ingratitude and an insulting breach of his country's hospitality. We had criminally injured not only the letter and spirit of the public bathing regulations, but also the honour of Italy; he, the gentleman in the city togs, knew how to defend that honour and proposed to see to it that our offence against the national dignity should not go unpunished.

We did our best, bowing respectfully, to give ear to this eloquence. To contradict the man, overheated as he was, would probably be to fall from one error into another. On the tips of our tongues we had various answers: as, that the word "hospitality," in its strictest sense, was not quite the right one, taking all the circumstances into consideration. We were not literally the guests of Italy, but of Signora Angiolieri, who had assumed the rôle of dispenser of hospitality some years ago on laying down that of familiar friend to Eleonora Duse. We longed to say that surely this beautiful country had not sunk so low as to be reduced to a state of hypersensitive prudishness. But we confined ourselves to assuring the gentleman that any lack of respect, any provocation on our parts, had been the furthest from our thoughts. And as a mitigating circumstance we pointed out the tender age and physical slightness of the little culprit. In vain. Our protests were waved away, he did not believe in them; our defence would not hold water. We must be made an example of. The authorities were notified, by telephone, I believe, and their representative appeared on the beach. He said the case was "*molto grave.*" We had to go with him to the Municipio up in the Piazza, where a higher official confirmed the previous verdict of "*molto grave,*" launched into a stream of the usual didactic phrases—the selfsame tune and words as the man in the bowler hat—and levied a fine and ransom of fifty lire. We felt that the adventure must willy-nilly be worth to us this much of a contribution to the economy of the Italian government; paid, and left. Ought we not at this point to have left Torre as well?

If we only had! We should thus have escaped that fatal Cipolla. But circumstances combined to prevent us from making up our minds to a change. A certain poet says that it is indolence that makes us endure uncomfortable situations. The *aperçu* may serve as an explanation for our inaction. Anyhow, one dislikes voiding the field immediately upon such an event. Especially if sympathy from other quarters encourages one to defy it. And in the Villa Eleonora they pronounced as with one voice upon the injustice of our punishment. Some Italian after-dinner acquaintances found that the episode put their country in a very bad light, and proposed taking the man in the bowler hat to task, as one fellow-citizen to another. But the next day he and his party had vanished from the beach. Not on our account, of course. Though it might be that the consciousness of his impending departure had added energy to his rebuke; in any case his going was a relief. And, furthermore, we stayed because our stay had by now become remarkable in our own eyes, which is worth something in itself, quite apart from the comfort or discomfort involved. Shall we strike sail, avoid a certain experience so soon as it seems not expressly calculated to increase our enjoyment or our self-esteem? Shall we go away whenever life looks like turning in the slightest uncanny, or not quite normal, or even rather painful and mortifying? No, surely not. Rather stay and look matters in the face, brave them out; perhaps precisely in so doing lies a lesson for us to learn. We stayed on and reaped as the awful reward of our constancy the unholy and staggering experience with Cipolla.

I have not mentioned that the after season had begun, almost on the very day we were disciplined by the city authorities. The worshipful gentleman in the bowler hat, our denouncer, was not the only person to leave the resort. There was a regular exodus, on every hand you saw luggage-carts on their way to the station. The beach denationalized itself. Life in Torre, in the cafés and the pinetas, became more homelike and more European. Very likely we might even have eaten at a table in the glass veranda, but we refrained, being content at Signora Angiolieri's—as content, that is, as our evil star would let us be. But at the same time with this turn for the better came a change in the weather: almost to an hour it showed itself in harmony with the holiday calendar of the general public. The sky was overcast; not that it grew any cooler, but the un-clouded heat of the entire eighteen days since our arrival, and probably long before that, gave place to a stifling sirocco air, while from time to time a little ineffectual rain sprinkled the velvety surface of the beach. Add to which, that two-thirds of our intended stay at Torre had passed. The colourless, lazy sea, with sluggish jellyfish floating in its shallows, was at least a change. And it would have been silly to feel retrospective longings after a sun that had caused us so many sighs when it burned down in all its arrogant power.

At this juncture, then, it was that Cipolla announced himself. Cavaliere Cipolla he was called on the posters that appeared one day stuck up every-where, even in the dining-room of Pensione Eleonora. A travelling vir-tuoso, an entertainer, *"forzatore, illusionista, prestidigatore,"* as he called himself, who proposed to wait upon the highly respectable population of Torre di Venere with a display of extraordinary phenomena of a mys-terious and staggering kind. A conjuror! The bare announcement was enough to turn our children's heads. They had never seen anything of the sort, and now our present holiday was to afford them this new excitement. From that moment on they besieged us with prayers to take tickets for the performance. We had doubts, from the first, on the score of the late-ness of the hour, nine o'clock; but gave way, in the idea that we might see a little of what Cipolla had to offer, probably no great matter, and then go home. Besides, of course, the children could sleep late next day. We bought four tickets of Signora Angiolieri herself, she having taken a number of the stalls on commission to sell them to her guests. She could not vouch for the man's performance, and we had no great expectations. But we were conscious of a need for diversion, and the children's violent curiosity proved catching.

The Cavaliere's performance was to take place in a hall where during the season there had been a cinema with a weekly programme. We had never been there. You reached it by following the main street under the wall of the *"palazzo,"* a ruin with a "For sale" sign, that suggested a castle and had obviously been built in lordlier days. In the same street were the chemist, the hairdresser, and all the better shops; it led, so to speak, from the feudal past the bourgeois into the proletarian, for it ended off between two rows of poor fishing-huts, where old women sat mending nets before the doors. And here, among the proletariat, was the hall, not much more, actually, than a wooden shed, though a large one, with a turreted entrance, plastered on either side with layers of gay placards. Some while after dinner, then, on the appointed evening, we wended our way thither in the dark, the children dressed in their best and blissful with the sense of so much irregularity. It was sultry, as it had been for days; there was heat lightning now and then, and a little rain; we proceeded under umbrellas. It took us a quarter of an hour.

Our tickets were collected at the entrance, our places we had to find ourselves. They were in the third row left, and as we sat down we saw that, late though the hour was for the performance, it was to be interpreted with even more laxity. Only very slowly did an audience—who seemed to be relied upon to come late—begin to fill the stalls. These comprised the whole auditorium; there were no boxes. This tardiness gave us some concern. The children's cheeks were already flushed as much with fatigue as with excitement. But even when we entered, the standing-room at the back and in the side aisles was already well occupied. There stood the manhood of Torre di Venere, all and sundry, fisherfolk, rough-and-ready youths with bare forearms crossed over their striped jerseys. We were well pleased with the presence of this native assemblage, which always adds colour and animation to occasions like the present; and the children were frankly delighted. For they had friends among these people —acquaintances picked up on afternoon strolls to the further ends of the beach. We would be turning homeward, at the hour when the sun dropped into the sea, spent with the huge effort it had made and gilding with reddish gold the oncoming surf; and we would come upon bare-legged fisherfolk standing in rows, bracing and hauling with long-drawn cries as they drew in the nets and harvested in dripping baskets their catch, often so scanty, of *frutta di mare*. The children looked on, helped to pull, brought out their little stock of Italian words, made friends. So now they exchanged nods with the "standing-room" clientèle; there was Guiscardo, there Antonio, they knew them by name and waved and called across in half-whispers, getting answering nods and smiles that displayed rows of healthy white teeth. Look, there is even Mario, Mario from the Esquisito, who brings us the chocolate. He wants to see the conjuror, too, and he must have come early, for he is almost in front; but he does not see us, he is not paying attention; that is a way he has, even though he is a waiter. So we wave instead to the man who lets out the little boats on the beach; he is there too, standing at the back.

It had got to a quarter past nine, it got to almost half past. It was natural that we should be nervous. When would the children get to bed? It had been a mistake to bring them, for now it would be very hard to suggest breaking off their enjoyment before it had got well under way. The stalls had filled in time; all Torre, apparently, was there: the guests of the Grand Hotel, the guests of Villa Eleanora, familiar faces from the beach. We heard English and German and the sort of French that Rumanians speak with Italians. Madame Angiolieri herself sat two rows behind us, with her quiet, bald-headed spouse, who kept stroking his moustache with the two middle fingers of his right hand. Everybody had come late, but nobody too late. Cipolla made us wait for him.

He made us wait. That is probably the way to put it. He heightened the suspense by his delay in appearing. And we could see the point of this, too—only not when it was carried to extremes. Towards half past nine the audience began to clap—an amiable way of expressing justifiable impatience, evincing as it does an eagerness to applaud. For the little ones, this was a joy in itself—all children love to clap. From the popular sphere came loud cries of *"Pronti!" "Cominciamo!"* And lo, it seemed now as easy to begin as before it had been hard. A gong sounded, greeted by the standing rows with a many-voiced "Ah-h!" and the curtains parted. They revealed a platform furnished more like a schoolroom than like the theatre of a conjuring performance—largely because of the blackboard in the left foreground. There was a common yellow hat-stand, a few ordinary straw-bottomed chairs, and further back a little round table holding a water carafe and glass, also a tray with a liqueur glass and a flask of pale yellow liquid. We had still a few seconds of time to let these things sink in. Then, with no darkening of the house, Cavaliere Cipolla made his entry.

He came forward with a rapid step that expressed his eagerness to appear before his public and gave rise to the illusion that he had already come a long way to put himself at their service—whereas, of course, he had only been standing in the wings. His costume supported the fiction. A man of an age hard to determine, but by no means young; with a sharp, ravaged face, piercing eyes, compressed lips, small black waxed moustache, and a so-called imperial in the curve between mouth and chin. He was dressed for the street with a sort of complicated evening elegance, in a wide black pelerine with velvet collar and satin lining; which, in the hampered state of his arms, he held together in front with his white-gloved hands. He had a white scarf round his neck; a top hat with a curving brim sat far back on his head. Perhaps more than anywhere else the eighteenth century is still alive in Italy, and with it the charlatan and mountebank type so characteristic of the period. Only there, at any rate, does one still encounter really well-preserved specimens. Cipolla had in his whole appearance much of the historic type; his very clothes helped to conjure up the traditional figure with its blatantly, fantastically foppish air. His pretentious costume sat upon him, or rather hung upon him, most curiously, being in one place drawn too tight, in another a mass of awkward folds. There was something not quite in order about his figure, both front and back—that was plain later on. But I must emphasize the fact that there was not a trace of personal jocularity or clownishness in his pose, manner, or behaviour. On the contrary, there was complete serious-ness, an absence of any humorous appeal; occasionally even a cross-grained pride, along with that curious, self-satisfied air so characteristic of the deformed. None of all this, however, prevented his appearance from being greeted with laughter from more than one quarter of the hall.

All the eagerness had left his manner. The swift entry had been merely an expression of energy, not of zeal. Standing at the footlights he negli-gently drew off his gloves, to display long yellow hands, one of them adorned with a seal ring with a lapis-lazuli in a high setting. As he stood there, his small hard eyes, with flabby pouches beneath them, roved ap-praisingly about the hall, not quickly, rather in a considered examination, pausing here and there upon a face with his lips clipped together, not speaking a word. Then with a display of skill as surprising as it was casual, he rolled his gloves into a ball and tossed them across a considerable dis-tance into the glass on the table. Next from an inner pocket he drew forth a packet of cigarettes; you could see by the wrapper that they were the cheapest sort the government sells. With his fingertips he pulled out a cigarette and lighted it, without looking, from a quick-firing benzine lighter. He drew the smoke deep into his lungs and let it out again, tapping his foot, with both lips drawn in an arrogant grimace and the grey smoke streaming out between broken and saw-edged teeth.

With a keenness equal to his own his audience eyed him. The youths at the rear scowled as they peered at this cocksure creature to search out his secret weaknesses. He betrayed none. In fetching out and putting back the cigarettes his clothes got in his way. He had to turn back his pelerine, and in so doing revealed a riding-whip with a silver claw-handle that hung by a leather thong from his left forearm and looked decidely out of place. You could see that he had on not evening clothes but a frock-coat, and under this, as he lifted it to get at his pocket, could be seen a striped sash worn about the body. Somebody behind me whispered that this sash went with his title of Cavaliere. I give the information for what it may be worth

—personally, I never heard that the title carried such insignia with it. Perhaps the sash was sheer pose, like the way he stood there, without a word, casually and arrogantly puffing smoke into his audience's face.

People laughed, as I said. The merriment had become almost general when somebody in the "standing seats," in a loud, dry voice, remarked: "*Buona sera.*"

Cipolla cocked his head. "Who was that?" asked he, as though he had been dared. "Who was that just spoke? Well? First so bold and now so modest? *Paura*, eh?" He spoke with a rather high, asthmatic voice, which yet had a metallic quality. He waited.

"That was me," a youth at the rear broke into the stillness, seeing himself thus challenged. He was not far from us, a handsome fellow in a woollen shirt, with his coat hanging over one shoulder. He wore his curly, wiry hair in a high, dishevelled mop, the style affected by the youth of the awakened Fatherland; it gave him an African appearance that rather spoiled his looks. "*Bè!* That was me. It was your business to say it first, but I was trying to be friendly."

More laughter. The chap had a tongue in his head. "*Ha sciolto la scilinguágnolo*," I heard near me. After all, the retort was deserved.

"Ah, bravo!" answered Cipolla. "I like you, *giovanotto*. Trust me, I've had my eye on you for some time. People like you are just in my line. I can use them. And you are the pick of the lot, that's plain to see. You do what you like. Or is it possible you have ever not done what you liked—or even, maybe, what you didn't like? What somebody else liked, in short? Hark ye, my friend, that might be a pleasant change for you, to divide up the willing and the doing and stop tackling both jobs at once. Division of labour, *sistema americano, sa'!* For instance, suppose you were to show your tongue to this select and honourable audience here—your whole tongue, right down to the roots?"

"No, I won't," said the youth, hostilely. "Sticking out your tongue shows a bad bringing-up."

"Nothing of the sort," retorted Cipolla. "You would only be *doing* it. With all due respect to your bringing-up, I suggest that before I count ten, you will perform a right turn and stick out your tongue at the company here further than you knew yourself that you could stick it out."

He gazed at the youth, and his piercing eyes seemed to sink deeper into their sockets. "*Uno!*" said he. He had let his riding-whip slide down his arm and made it whistle once through the air. The boy faced about and put out his tongue, so long, so extendedly, that you could see it was the very uttermost in tongue which he had to offer. Then turned back, stony-faced, to his former position.

"That was me," mocked Cipolla, with a jerk of his head towards the youth. "*Bè!* That was me." Leaving the audience to enjoy its sensations, he turned towards the little round table, lifted the bottle, poured out a

small glass of what was obviously cognac, and tipped it up with a practised hand.

The children laughed with all their hearts. They had understood practically nothing of what had been said, but it pleased them hugely that
something so funny should happen, straightaway, between that queer man
up there and somebody out of the audience. They had no preconception
of what an "evening" would be like and were quite ready to find this a
priceless beginning. As for us, we exchanged a glance and I remember
that involuntarily I made with my lips the sound that Cipolla's whip had
made when it cut the air. For the rest, it was plain that people did not
know what to make of a preposterous beginning like this to a sleight-of-
hand performance. They could not see why the *giovanotto*, who after all
in a way had been their spokesman, should suddenly have turned on
them to vent his incivility. They felt that he had behaved like a silly
ass and withdrew their countenances from him in favour of the artist,
who now came back from his refreshment table and addressed them as
follows:

"Ladies and gentlemen," said he, in his wheezing, metallic voice, "you
saw just now that I was rather sensitive on the score of the rebuke this
hopeful young linguist saw fit to give me"—"*questo linguista di belle
speranze*" was what he said, and we all laughed at the pun. "I am a man
who sets some store by himself, you may take it from me. And I see no
point in being wished a good-evening unless it is done courteously and
in all seriousness. For anything else there is no occasion. When a man
wishes me a good-evening and he wishes himself one, for the audience
will have one only if I do. So this lady-killer of Torre di Venere" (another thrust) "did well to testify that I have one tonight and that I can
dispense with any wishes of his in the matter. I can boast of having good
evenings almost without exception. One not so good does come my way
now and again, but very seldom. My calling is hard and my health not of
the best. I have a little physical defect which prevented me from doing
my bit in the war for the greater glory of the Fatherland. It is perforce
with my mental and spiritual parts that I conquer life—which after all only
means conquering oneself. And I flatter myself that my achievements have
aroused interest and respect among the educated public. The leading
newspapers have lauded me, the *Corriere della Sera* did me the courtesy
of calling me a phenomenon, and in Rome the brother of the *Duce*
honoured me by his presence at one of my evenings. I should not have
thought that in a relatively less important place" (laughter here, at the
expense of poor little Torre) "I should have to give up the small personal
habits which brilliant and elevated audiences had been ready to overlook.
Nor did I think I had to stand being heckled by a person who seems to
have been rather spoilt by the favours of the fair sex." All this of course at
the expense of the youth whom Cipolla never tired of presenting in the

guise of *donnaiuolo* and rustic Don Juan. His persistent thin-skinnedness and animosity were in striking contrast to the self-confidence and the worldly success he boasted of. One might have assumed that the *giovan-otto* was merely the chosen butt of Cipolla's customary professional sallies, had not the very pointed witticisms betrayed a genuine antagonism. No one looking at the physical parts of the two men need have been at a loss for the explanation, even if the deformed man had not constantly played on the other's supposed success with the fair sex. "Well," Cipolla went on, "before beginning our entertainment this evening, perhaps you will permit me to make myself comfortable."

And he went towards the hat-stand to take off his things.

"*Parla benissimo*," asserted somebody in our neighbourhood. So far, the man had done nothing; but what he had said was accepted as an achievement, by means of that he had made an impression. Among southern peoples speech is a constituent part of the pleasure of living, it enjoys far livelier social esteem than in the north. That national cement, the mother tongue, is paid symbolic honours down here, and there is something blithely symbolical in the pleasure people take in their respect for its forms and phonetics. They enjoy speaking, they enjoy listening; and they listen with discrimination. For the way a man speaks serves as a measure of his personal rank; carelessness and clumsiness are greeted with scorn, elegance and mastery are rewarded with social *éclat*. Wherefore the small man too, where it is a question of getting his effect, chooses his phrase nicely and turns it with care. On this count, then, at least, Cipolla had won his audience; though he by no means belonged to the class of men which the Italian, in a singular mixture of moral and æsthetic judg-ments, labels "*simpatico.*"

After removing his hat, scarf, and mantle he came to the front of the stage, settling his coat, pulling down his cuffs with their large cuff-buttons, adjusting his absurd sash. He had very ugly hair; the top of his head, that is, was almost bald, while a narrow, black-varnished frizz of curls ran from front to back as though stuck on; the side hair, likewise blackened, was brushed forward to the corners of the eyes—it was, in short, the hair-dressing of an old-fashioned circus-director, fantastic, but entirely suited to his outmoded personal type and worn with so much assurance as to take the edge off the public's sense of humour. The little physical defect of which he had warned us was now all too visible, though the nature of it was even now not very clear: the chest was too high, as is usual in such cases; but the corresponding malformation of the back did not sit between the shoulders, it took the form of a sort of hips or buttocks hump, which did not indeed hinder his movements but gave him a grotesque and dip-ping stride at every step he took. However, by mentioning his deformity beforehand he had broken the shock of it, and a delicate propriety of feel-ing appeared to reign throughout the hall.

"At your service," said Cipolla. "With your kind permission, we will begin the evening with some arithmetical tests."

Arithmetic? That did not sound much like sleight-of-hand. We began to have our suspicions that the man was sailing under a false flag, only we did not yet know which was the right one. I felt sorry on the children's account; but for the moment they were content simply to be there.

The numerical test which Cipolla now introduced was as simple as it was baffling. He began by fastening a piece of paper to the upper right-hand corner of the blackboard; then lifting it up, he wrote something underneath. He talked all the while, relieving the dryness of his offering by a constant flow of words, and showed himself a practised speaker, never at a loss for conversational turns of phrase. It was in keeping with the nature of his performance, and at the same time vastly entertained the children, that he went on to eliminate the gap between stage and audience, which had already been bridged over by the curious skirmish with the fisher lad: he had representatives from the audience mount the stage, and himself descended the wooden steps to seek personal contact with his public. And again, with individuals, he fell into his former taunting tone. I do not know how far that was a deliberate feature of his system; he preserved a serious, even a peevish air, but his audience, at least the more popular section, seemed convinced that that was all part of the game. So then, after he had written something and covered the writing by the paper, he desired that two persons should come up on the platform and help to perform the calculations. They would not be difficult, even for people not clever at figures. As usual, nobody volunteered, and Cipolla took care not to molest the more select portion of his audience. He kept to the populace. Turning to two sturdy young louts standing behind us, he beckoned them to the front, encouraging and scolding by turns. They should not stand there gaping, he said, unwilling to oblige the company. Actually, he got them in motion; with clumsy tread they came down the middle aisle, climbed the steps, and stood in front of the blackboard, grinning sheepishly at their comrades' shouts and applause. Cipolla joked with them for a few minutes, praised their heroic firmness of limb and the size of their hands, so well calculated to do this service for the public. Then he handed one of them the chalk and told him to write down the numbers as they were called out. But now the creature declared that he could not write! *"Non so scrivere,"* said he in his gruff voice, and his companion added that neither did he.

God knows whether they told the truth or whether they wanted to make game of Cipolla. Anyhow, the latter was far from sharing the general merriment which their confession aroused. He was insulted and disgusted. He sat there on a straw-bottomed chair in the centre of the stage with his legs crossed, smoking a fresh cigarette out of his cheap packet; obviously it tasted the better for the cognac he had indulged in while the yokels were stumping up the steps. Again he inhaled the smoke and let it stream out between curling lips. Swinging his leg, with his gaze sternly averted from the two shamelessly chuckling creatures and from the audience as well, he stared into space as one who withdraws himself and his dignity from the contemplation of an utterly despicable phenomenon.

"Scandalous," said he, in a sort of icy snarl. "Go back to your places! In Italy everybody can write—in all her greatness there is no room for ignorance and unenlightenment. To accuse her of them, in the hearing of this international company, is a cheap joke, in which you yourselves cut a very poor figure and humiliate the government and the whole country as well. If it is true that Torre di Venere is indeed the last refuge of such ignorance, then I must blush to have visited the place—being, as I already was, aware of its inferiority to Rome in more than one respect—"

Here Cipolla was interrupted by the youth with the Nubian coiffure and his jacket across his shoulder. His fighting spirit, as we now saw, had only abdicated temporarily, and he now flung himself into the breach in defence of his native heath. "That will do," said he loudly. "That's enough jokes about Torre. We all come from the place and we won't stand strangers making fun of it. These two chaps are our friends. Maybe they are no scholars, but even so they may be straighter than some folks in the room who are so free with their boasts about Rome, though they did not build it either."

That was capital. The young man had certainly cut his eye-teeth. And this sort of spectacle was good fun, even though it still further delayed the regular performance. It is always fascinating to listen to an altercation. Some people it simply amuses, they take a sort of kill-joy pleasure in not being principals. Others feel upset and uneasy, and my sympathies are with these latter, although on the present occasion I was under the impression that all this was part of the show—the analphabetic yokels no less than the *giovanotto* with the jacket. The children listened well pleased. They understood not at all, but the sound of the voices made them hold their breath. So this was a "magic evening"—at least it was the kind they have in Italy. They expressly found it "lovely."

Cipolla had stood up and with two of his scooping strides was at the footlights.

"Well, well, see who's here!" said he with grim cordiality. "An old acquaintance! A young man with his heart at the end of his tongue" (he used the word *linguaccia*, which means a coated tongue, and gave rise to much hilarity). "That will do, my friends," he turned to the yokels. "I do not need you now, I have business with this deserving young man here, *con questo torregiano di Venere*, this tower of Venus, who no doubt expects the gratitude of the fair as a reward for his prowess—"

"*Ah, non scherziamo!* We're talking earnest," cried out the youth. His eyes flashed, and he actually made as though to pull off his jacket and proceed to direct methods of settlement.

Cipolla did not take him too seriously. We had exchanged apprehensive glances; but he was dealing with a fellow-countryman and had his native soil beneath his feet. He kept quite cool and showed complete mastery of the situation. He looked at his audience, smiled, and made a sideways motion of the head towards the young cockerel as though calling the public to witness how the man's bumptiousness only served to betray the simplicity of his mind. And then, for the second time, something strange happened, which set Cipolla's calm superiority in an uncanny light, and in some mysterious and irritating way turned all the explosiveness latent in the air into matter for laughter.

Cipolla drew still nearer to the fellow, looking him in the eye with a peculiar gaze. He even came half-way down the steps that led into the auditorium on our left, so that he stood directly in front of the trouble-maker, on slightly higher ground. The riding-whip hung from his arm.

"My son, you do not feel much like joking," he said. "It is only too natural, for anyone can see that you are not feeling too well. Even your tongue, which leaves something to be desired on the score of cleanliness, indicates acute disorder of the gastric system. An evening entertainment is no place for people in your state; you yourself, I can tell, were of several minds whether you would not do better to put on a flannel bandage and go to bed. It was not good judgment to drink so much of that very sour white wine this afternoon. Now you have such a colic you would like to double up with the pain. Go ahead, don't be embarrassed. There is a distinct relief that comes from bending over, in cases of intestinal cramp."

He spoke thus, word for word, with quiet impressiveness and a kind of stern sympathy, and his eyes, plunged the while deep in the young man's, seemed to grow very tired and at the same time burning above their enlarged tear-ducts—they were the strangest eyes, you could tell that not manly pride alone was preventing the young adversary from withdrawing his gaze. And presently, indeed, all trace of its former arrogance was gone from the bronzed young face. He looked open-mouthed at the Cavaliere and the open mouth was drawn in a rueful smile.

"Double over," repeated Cipolla. "What else can you do? With a colic like that you *must* bend. Surely you will not struggle against the performance of a perfectly natural action just because somebody suggests it to you?"

Slowly the youth lifted his forearms, folded and squeezed them across his body; it turned a little sideways, then bent, lower and lower, the feet shifted, the knees turned inward, until he had become a picture of writhing pain, until he all but grovelled upon the ground. Cipolla let him stand for some seconds thus, then made a short cut through the air with his whip and went with his scooping stride back to the little table, where he poured himself out a cognac.

"*Il boit beaucoup*," asserted a lady behind us. Was that the only thing that struck her? We could not tell how far the audience grasped the situation. The fellow was standing upright again, with a sheepish grin—he looked as though he scarcely knew how it had all happened. The scene had been followed with tense interest and applauded at the end; there were shouts of "*Bravo, Cipolla!*" and "*Bravo, giovanotto!*" Apparently the issue of the duel was not looked upon as a personal defeat for the young man. Rather the audience encouraged him as one does an actor who succeeds in an unsympathetic rôle. Certainly his way of screwing himself up with cramp had been highly picturesque, its appeal was directly calculated to impress the gallery—in short, a fine dramatic performance. But I am not sure how far the audience were moved by that natural tactfulness in which the south excels, or how far it penetrated into the nature of what was going on.

The Cavaliere, refreshed, had lighted another cigarette. The numerical tests might now proceed. A young man was easily found in the back row who was willing to write down on the blackboard the numbers as they were dictated to him. Him too we knew; the whole entertainment had taken on an intimate character through our acquaintance with so many of the actors. This was the man who worked at the greengrocer's in the main street; he had served us several times, with neatness and dispatch. He wielded the chalk with clerkly confidence, while Cipolla descended to our level and walked with his deformed gait through the audience, collecting numbers as they were given, in two, three, and four places, and calling them out to the grocer's assistant, who wrote them down in a column. In all this, everything on both sides was calculated to amuse, with its jokes and its oratorical asides. The artist could not fail to hit on foreigners, who were not ready with their figures, and with them he was elaborately patient and chivalrous, to the great amusement of the natives, whom he reduced to confusion in their turn, by making them translate numbers that were given in English or French. Some people gave dates concerned with great events in Italian history. Cipolla took them up at once and made patriotic comments. Somebody shouted "Number one!" The Cavaliere, incensed at this as at every attempt to make game of him, retorted over his shoulder that he could not take less than two-place figures. Whereupon another joker cried out "Number two!" and was greeted with the applause and laughter which every reference to natural functions is sure to win among southerners.

When fifteen numbers stood in a long straggling row on the board, Cipolla called for a general adding-match. Ready reckoners might add in their heads, but pencil and paper were not forbidden. Cipolla, while the work went on, sat on his chair near the blackboard, smoked and grimaced, with the complacent, pompous air cripples so often have. The five-place addition was soon done. Somebody announced the answer, somebody else confirmed it, a third had arrived at a slightly different result, but the fourth agreed with the first and second. Cipolla got up, tapped some ash from his coat, and lifted the paper at the upper right-hand corner of the board to display the writing. The correct answer, a sum close on a million, stood there; he had written it down beforehand.

Astonishment, and loud applause. The children were overwhelmed. How had he done that, they wanted to know. We told them it was a trick, not easily explainable offhand. In short, the man was a conjuror. This was what a sleight-of-hand evening was like, so now they knew. First the fisherman had cramp, and then the right answer was written down beforehand—it was all simply glorious, and we saw with dismay that despite the hot eyes and the hand of the clock at almost half past ten, it would be very hard to get them away. There would be tears. And yet it was plain that this magician did not "magick"—at least not in the accepted sense, of manual dexterity—and that the entertainment was not at all suitable for children. Again, I do not know, either, what the audience really thought. Obviously there was grave doubt whether its answers had been given of "free choice"; here and there an individual might have answered of his own motion, but on the whole Cipolla certainly selected his people and thus kept the whole procedure in his own hands and directed it towards the given result. Even so, one had to admire the quickness of his calculations, however much one felt disinclined to admire anything else about the performance. Then his patriotism, his irritable sense of dignity— the Cavaliere's own countrymen might feel in their element with all that and continue in a laughing mood; but the combination certainly gave us outsiders food for thought.

Cipolla himself saw to it—though without giving them a name—that the nature of his powers should be clear beyond a doubt to even the least-instructed person. He alluded to them, of course, in his talk—and he talked without stopping—but only in vague, boastful, self-advertising phrases. He went on awhile with experiments on the same lines as the first, merely making them more complicated by introducing operations in multiplying, subtracting, and dividing; then he simplified them to the last degree in order to bring out the method. He simply had numbers "guessed" which were previously written under the paper; and the guess was nearly always right. One guesser admitted that he had had in mind to give a certain number, when Cipolla's whip went whistling through the air, and a quite different one slipped out, which proved to be the "right" one. Cipolla's shoulders shook. He pretended admiration for the powers of the people he questioned. But in all his compliments there was something fleering and derogatory; the victims could scarcely have relished them much, although they smiled, and although they might easily have set down some part of the applause to their own credit. Moreover, I had not the impression that the artist was popular with his public. A certain ill will and reluctance were in the air, but courtesy kept such feelings in check, as did Cipolla's competency and his stern self-confidence. Even the riding-whip, I think, did much to keep rebellion from becoming overt.

From tricks with numbers he passed to tricks with cards. There were two packs, which he drew out of his pockets, and so much I still remember, that the basis of the tricks he played with them was as follows: from the first pack he drew three cards and thrust them without looking at them inside his coat. Another person then drew three out of the second pack, and these turned out to be the same as the first three—not invariably all the three, for it did happen that only two were the same. But in the majority of cases Cipolla triumphed, showing his three cards with a little bow in acknowledgment of the applause with which his audience conceded his possession of strange powers—strange whether for good or evil. A young man in the front row, to our right, an Italian, with proud, finely chiselled features, rose up and said that he intended to assert his own will in his choice and consciously to resist any influence, of whatever sort. Under these circumstances, what did Cipolla think would be the result? "You will," answered the Cavaliere, "make my task somewhat more difficult thereby. As for the result, your resistance will not alter it in the least. Freedom exists, and also the will exists; but freedom of the will does not exist, for a will that aims at its own freedom aims at the unknown. You are free to draw or not to draw. But if you draw, you will draw the right cards—the more certainly, the more wilfully obstinate your behaviour."

One must admit that he could not have chosen his words better, to trouble the waters and confuse the mind. The refractory youth hesitated before drawing. Then he pulled out a card and at once demanded to see if it was among the chosen three. "But why?" queried Cipolla. "Why do things by halves?" Then, as the other defiantly insisted, *"E servito,"* said the juggler, with a gesture of exaggerated servility; and held out the three cards fanwise, without looking at them himself. The left-hand card was the one drawn.

Amid general applause, the apostle of freedom sat down. How far Cipolla employed small tricks and manual dexterity to help out his natural talents, the deuce only knew. But even without them the result would have been the same: the curiosity of the entire audience was unbounded and universal, everybody both enjoyed the amazing character of the entertainment and unanimously conceded the professional skill of the performer. *"Lavora bene,"* we heard, here and there in our neighbourhood; it signified the triumph of objective judgment over antipathy and repressed resentment.

After his last, incomplete, yet so much the more telling success, Cipolla had at once fortified himself with another cognac. Truly he did "drink a lot," and the fact made a bad impression. But obviously he needed the liquor and the cigarettes for the replenishment of his energy, upon which, as he himself said, heavy demands were made in all directions. Certainly in the intervals he looked very ill, exhausted and hollow-eyed. Then the little glassful would redress the balance, and the flow of lively, self-confident chatter run on, while the smoke he inhaled gushed out grey from his lungs. I clearly recall that he passed from the card-tricks to parlour games—the kind based on certain powers which in human nature are higher or else lower than human reason: on intuition and "magnetic" transmission; in short, upon a low type of manifestation. What I do not remember is the precise order things came in. And I will not bore you with a description of these experiments; everybody knows them, everybody has at one time or another taken part in this finding of hidden articles, this blind carrying out of a series of acts, directed by a force that proceeds from organism to organism by unexplored paths. Everybody has had his little glimpse into the equivocal, impure, inexplicable nature of the occult, has been conscious of both curiosity and contempt, has shaken his head over the human tendency of those who deal in it to help themselves out with humbuggery, though, after all, the humbuggery is no disproof whatever of the genuineness of the other elements in the dubious amalgam. I can only say here that each single circumstance gains in weight and the whole greatly in impressiveness when it is a man like Cipolla who is the chief actor and guiding spirit in the sinister business. He sat smoking at the rear of the stage, his back to the audience while they conferred. The object passed from hand to hand which it was his task to find, with which he was to perform some action agreed upon beforehand. Then he would start to move zigzag through the hall, with his head thrown back and one hand outstretched, the other clasped in that of a guide who was in the secret but enjoined to keep himself perfectly passive, with his thoughts directed upon the agreed goal. Cipolla moved with the bearing typical in these experiments: now groping upon a false start, now with a quick forward thrust, now pausing as though to listen and by sudden inspiration correcting his course. The rôles seemed reversed, the stream of influence was moving in the contrary direction, as the artist himself pointed out, in his ceaseless flow of discourse. The suffering, receptive, performing part was now his, the will he had before imposed on others was shut out, he acted in obedience to a voiceless common will which was in the air. But he made it perfectly clear that it all came to the same thing. The capacity for self-surrender, he said, for becoming a tool, for the most unconditional and utter self-abnegation, was but the reverse side of that other power to will and to command. Commanding and obeying formed together one single principle, one indissoluble unity; he who knew how to obey knew also how to command, and conversely; the one idea was comprehended in the other, as people and leader were comprehended in one another. But that which was *done*, the highly exacting and exhausting performance, was in every case his, the leader's and mover's, in whom the will became obedience, the obedience will, whose person was the cradle and womb of both, and who thus suffered enormous hardship. Repeatedly he emphasized the fact that his lot was a hard one—presumably to account for his need of stimulant and his frequent recourse to the little glass.

Thus he groped his way forward, like a blind seer, led and sustained by the mysterious common will. He drew a pin set with a stone out of its hiding-place in an Englishwoman's shoe, carried it, halting and pressing on by turns, to another lady—Signora Angiolieri—and handed it to her on bended knee, with the words it had been agreed he was to utter. "I present you with this in token of my respect," was the sentence. Their sense was obvious, but the words themselves not easy to hit upon, for the reason that they had been agreed on in French; the language complication seemed to us a little malicious, implying as it did a conflict between the audience's natural interest in the success of the miracle, and their desire to witness the humiliation of this presumptuous man. It was a strange sight: Cipolla on his knees before the signora, wrestling, amid efforts at speech, after knowledge of the preordained words. "I must say something," he said, "and I feel clearly what it is I must say. But I also feel that if it passed my lips it would be wrong. Be careful not to help me unintentionally!" he cried out, though very likely that was precisely what he was hoping for. "*Pensez très fort,*" he cried all at once, in bad French, and then burst out with the required words—in Italian, indeed, but with the final substantive pronounced in the sister tongue, in which he was probably far from fluent: he said *vénération* instead of *venerazione*, with an impossible nasal. And this partial success, after the complete success before it, the finding of the pin, the presentation of it on his knees to the right person—was almost more impressive than if he had got the sentence exactly right, and evoked bursts of admiring applause.

Cipolla got up from his knees and wiped the perspiration from his brow. You understand that this experiment with the pin was a single case, which I describe because it sticks in my memory. But he changed his method several times and improvised a number of variations suggested by his contact with his audience; a good deal of time thus went by. He seemed to get particular inspiration from the person of our landlady; she drew him on to the most extraordinary displays of clairvoyance. "It does not escape me, madame," he said to her, "that there is something unusual about you, some special and honourable distinction. He who has eyes to see decries about your lovely brow an aureola—if I mistake not, it once was stronger than now—a slowly paling radiance . . . hush, not a word! Don't help me. Beside you sits your husband—yes?" He turned towards the silent Signor Angiolieri. "You are the husband of this lady, and your happiness is complete. But in the midst of this happiness memories rise

. . . the past, signora, so it seems to me, plays an important part in your present. You knew a king . . . has not a king crossed your path in bygone days?"

"No," breathed the dispenser of our midday soup, her golden-brown eyes gleaming in the noble pallor of her face.

"No? No, not a king; I meant that generally, I did not mean literally a king. Not a king, not a prince, and a prince after all, a king of a loftier realm; it was a great artist, at whose side you once—you would contradict me, and yet I am not wholly wrong. Well, then! It was a woman, a great, a world-renowned woman artist, whose friendship you enjoyed in your tender years, whose sacred memory overshadows and transfigures your whole existence. Her name? Need I utter it, whose fame has long been bound up with the Fatherland's immortal as its own? Eleonora Duse," he finished, softly and with much solemnity.

The little woman bowed her head, overcome. The applause was like a patriotic demonstration. Nearly everyone there knew about Signora Angiolieri's wonderful past; they were all able to confirm the Cavaliere's intuition—not least the present guests of Casa Eleonora. But we wondered how much of the truth he had learned as the result of professional inquiries made on his arrival. Yet I see no reason at all to cast doubt, on rational grounds, upon powers which, before our very eyes, became fatal to their possessor.

At this point there was an intermission. Our lord and master withdrew. Now I confess that almost ever since the beginning of my tale I have looked forward with dread to this moment in it. The thoughts of men are mostly not hard to read; in this case they are very easy. You are sure to ask why we did not choose this moment to go away—and I must continue to owe you an answer. I do not know why. I cannot defend myself. By this time it was certainly eleven, probably later. The children were asleep. The last series of tests had been too long, nature had had her way. They were sleeping in our laps, the little one on mine, the boy on his mother's. That was, in a way, a consolation; but at the same time it was also ground for compassion and a clear leading to take them home to bed. And I give you my word that we wanted to obey this touching admonition, we seriously wanted to. We roused the poor things and told them it was now high time to go. But they were no sooner conscious than they began to resist and implore—you know how horrified children are at the thought of leaving before the end of a thing. No cajoling has any effect, you have to use force. It was so lovely, they wailed. How did we know what was coming next? Surely we could not leave until after the intermission; they liked a little nap now and again—only not go home, only not go to bed, while the beautiful evening was still going on!

We yielded, but only for the moment, of course—so far as we knew—only for a little while, just a few minutes longer. I cannot excuse our staying, scarcely can I even understand it. Did we think, having once said A, we had to say B—having once brought the children hither we had to let them stay? No, it is not good enough. Were we ourselves so highly entertained? Yes, and no. Our feelings for Cavaliere Cipolla were of a very mixed kind, but so were the feelings of the whole audience, if I mistake not, and nobody left. Were we under the sway of a fascination which emanated from this man who took so strange a way to earn his bread; a fascination which he gave out independently of the programme and even between the tricks and which paralysed our resolve? Again, sheer curiosity may account for something. One was curious to know how such an evening turned out; Cipolla in his remarks having all along hinted that he had tricks in his bag stranger than any he had yet produced.

But all that is not it—or at least it is not all of it. More correct it would be to answer the first question with another. Why had we not left Torre di Venere itself before now? To me the two questions are one and the same, and in order to get out of the impasse I might simply say that I had answered it already. For, as things had been in Torre in general: queer, uncomfortable, troublesome, tense, oppressive, so precisely they were here in this hall tonight. Yes, more than precisely. For it seemed to be the fountainhead of all the uncanniness and all the strained feelings which had oppressed the atmosphere of our holiday. This man whose return to the stage we were awaiting was the personification of all that; and, as we had not gone away in general, so to speak, it would have been inconsistent to do it in the particular case. You may call this an explanation, you may call it inertia, as you see fit. Any argument more to the purpose I simply do not know how to adduce.

Well, there was an interval of ten minutes, which grew into nearly twenty. The children remained awake. They were enchanted by our compliance, and filled the break to their own satisfaction by renewing relations with the popular sphere, with Antonio, Guiscardo, and the canoe man. They put their hands to their mouths and called messages across, appealing to us for the Italian words. "Hope you have a good catch tomorrow, a whole netful!" They called to Mario, Esquisito Mario: *"Mario, una cioccolata e biscotti!"* And this time he heeded and answered with a smile: *"Subito, signorini!"* Later we had reason to recall this kindly, if rather absent and pensive smile.

Thus the interval passed, the gong sounded. The audience, which had scattered in conversation, took their places again, the children sat up straight in their chairs with their hands in their laps. The curtain had not been dropped. Cipolla came forward again, with his dipping stride, and began to introduce the second half of the programme with a lecture.

Let me state once for all that this self-confident cripple was the most powerful hypnotist I have ever seen in my life. It was pretty plain now that he threw dust in the public eye and advertised himself as a prestidigitator on account of police regulations which would have prevented him from making his living by the exercise of his powers. Perhaps this eye-wash is the usual thing in Italy; it may be permitted or even connived at by the authorities. Certainly the man had from the beginning made little concealment of the actual nature of his operations; and this second half of the programme was quite frankly and exclusively devoted to one sort of experiment. While he still practised some rhetorical circumlocutions, the tests themselves were one long series of attacks upon the will-power, the loss or compulsion of volition. Comic, exciting, amazing by turns, by midnight they were still in full swing; we ran the gamut of all the phe-nomena this natural-unnatural field has to show, from the unimpressive at one end of the scale to the monstrous at the other. The audience laughed and applauded as they followed the grotesque details; shook their heads, clapped their knees, fell very frankly under the spell of this stern, self-assured personality. At the same time I saw signs that they were not quite complacent, not quite unconscious of the peculiar ignominy which lay, for the individual and for the general, in Cipolla's triumphs.

Two main features were constant in all the experiments: the liquor glass and the claw-handled riding-whip. The first was always invoked to add fuel to his demoniac fires; without it, apparently, they might have burned out. On this score we might even have felt pity for the man; but the whistle of his scourge, the insulting symbol of his domination, before which we all cowered, drowned out every sensation save a dazed and out-braved submission to his power. Did he then lay claim to our sympathy to boot? I was struck by a remark he made—it suggested no less. At the climax of his experiments, by stroking and breathing upon a certain young man who had offered himself as a subject and already proved himself a particularly susceptible one, he had not only put him into the condition known as deep trance and extended his insensible body by neck and feet across the backs of two chairs, but had actually sat down on the rigid form as on a bench, without making it yield. The sight of this unholy figure in a frock-coat squatted on the stiff body was horrible and incredible; the audience, convinced that the victim of this scientific diversion must be suffering, expressed its sympathy: "*Ah, poveretto!*" Poor soul, poor soul! "*Poor soul!*" Cipolla mocked them, with some bitterness. "Ladies and gentlemen, you are barking up the wrong tree. *Sono io il poveretto.* I am the person who is suffering, I am the one to be pitied." We pocketed the information. Very good. Maybe the experiment was at his expense, maybe it was he who had suffered the cramp when the *giovanotto* over there had made the faces. But appearances were all against it; and one does not feel like saying *poveretto* to a man who is suffering to bring about the humili-ation of others.

I have got ahead of my story and lost sight of the sequence of events. To this day my mind is full of the Cavaliere's feats of endurance; only I do not recall them in their order—which does not matter. So much I do know: that the longer and more circumstantial tests, which got the most applause, impressed me less than some of the small ones which passed quickly over. I remember the young man whose body Cipolla converted into a board, only because of the accompanying remarks which I have quoted. An elderly lady in a cane-seated chair was lulled by Cipolla in the delusion that she was on a voyage to India and gave a voluble account of her adventures by land and sea. But I found this phenomenon less impressive than one which followed immediately after the intermission. A tall, well-built, soldierly man was unable to lift his arm, after the hunchback had told him that he could not and given a cut through the air with his whip. I can still see the face of that stately, mustachioed colonel smiling and clenching his teeth as he struggled to regain his lost freedom of action. A staggering performance! He seemed to be exerting his will, and in vain; the trouble, however, was probably simply that he could not will. There was involved here that recoil of the will upon itself which paralyses choice —as our tyrant had previously explained to the Roman gentleman.

Still less can I forget the touching scene, at once comic and horrible, with Signora Angiolieri. The Cavaliere, probably in his first bold survey of the room, had spied out her ethereal lack of resistance to his power. For actually he bewitched her, literally drew her out of her seat, out of her row, and away with him whither he willed. And in order to enhance his effect, he bade Signor Angiolieri call upon his wife by her name, to throw, as it were, all the weight of his existence and his rights in her into the scale, to rouse by the voice of her husband everything in his spouse's soul which could shield her virtue against the evil assaults of magic. And how vain it all was! Cipolla was standing at some distance from the couple, when he made a single cut with his whip through the air. It caused our landlady to shudder violently and turn her face towards him. "Sofronia!" cried Signor Angiolieri—we had not known that Signora Angiolieri's name was Sofronia. And he did well to call, everybody saw that there was no time to lose. His wife kept her face turned in the direction of the diabolical Cavaliere, who with his ten long yellow fingers was making passes at his victim, moving backwards as he did so, step by step. Then Signora Angiolieri, her pale face gleaming, rose up from her seat, turned right round, and began to glide after him. Fatal and forbidding sight! Her face as though moonstruck, stiff-armed, her lovely hands lifted a little at the wrists, the feet as it were together, she seemed to float slowly out of her row and after the tempter. "Call her, sir, keep on calling," prompted the redoubtable man. And Signor Angiolieri, in a weak voice, called: "Sofronia!" Ah, again and again he called; as his wife went further off he even curved one hand round his lips and beckoned with the other as he called. But the poor voice of love and duty echoed unheard, in vain, behind the lost one's back; the signora swayed along, moonstruck, deaf,

enslaved; she glided into the middle aisle and down it towards the fingering hunchback, towards the door. We were convinced, we were driven to
the conviction, that she would have followed her master, had he so willed
it, to the ends of the earth.

"*Accidente!*" cried out Signor Angiolieri, in genuine affright, springing
up as the exit was reached. But at the same moment the Cavaliere put
aside, as it were, the triumphal crown and broke off. "Enough, signora, I
thank you," he said, and offered his arm to lead her back to her husband.
"Signor," he greeted the latter, "here is your wife. Unharmed, with my
compliments, I give her into your hands. Cherish with all the strength of
your manhood a treasure which is so wholly yours, and let your zeal be
quickened by knowing that there are powers stronger than reason or
virtue, and not always so magnanimously ready to relinquish their
prey!"

Poor Signor Angiolieri, so quiet, so bald! He did not look as though he
would know how to defend his happiness, even against powers much less
demoniac than these which were now adding mockery to frightfulness.
Solemnly and pompously the Cavaliere retired to the stage, amid applause
to which his eloquence gave double strength. It was this particular
episode, I feel sure, that set the seal upon his ascendancy. For now he
made them dance, yes, literally; and the dancing lent a dissolute, abandoned, topsy-turvy air to the scene, a drunken abdication of the critical
spirit which had so long resisted the spell of this man. Yes, he had had
to fight to get the upper hand—for instance against the animosity of the
young Roman gentleman, whose rebellious spirit threatened to serve others
as a rallying-point. But it was precisely upon the importance of example
that the Cavaliere was so strong. He had the wit to make his attack at the
weakest point and to choose as his first victim that feeble, ecstatic youth
whom he had previously made into a board. The master had but to look
at him, when this young man would fling himself back as though struck
by lightning, place his hands rigidly at his sides, and fall into a state of
military somnambulism, in which it was plain to any eye that he was open
to the most absurd suggestion that might be made to him. He seemed
quite content in his abject state, quite pleased to be relieved of the burden
of voluntary choice. Again and again he offered himself as a subject and
gloried in the model facility he had in losing consciousness. So now he
mounted the platform, and a single cut of the whip was enough to make
him dance to the Cavaliere's orders, in a kind of complacent ecstasy, eyes
closed, head nodding, lank limbs flying in all directions.

It looked unmistakably like enjoyment, and other recruits were not long
in coming forward: two other young men, one humbly and one well
dressed, were soon jigging alongside the first. But now the gentleman
from Rome bobbed up again, asking defiantly if the Cavaliere would
engage to make him dance too, even against his will.

"Even against your will," answered Cipolla, in unforgettable accents. That frightful *"anche se non vuole"* still rings in my ears. The struggle began. After Cipolla had taken another little glass and lighted a fresh cigarette he stationed the Roman at a point in the middle aisle and himself took up a position some distance behind him, making his whip whistle through the air as he gave the order: *"Balla!"* His opponent did not stir. *"Balla!"* repeated the Cavaliere incisively, and snapped his whip. You saw the young man move his neck round in his collar; at the same time one hand lifted slightly at the wrist, one ankle turned outward. But that was all, for the time at least; merely a tendency to twitch, now sternly repressed, now seeming about to get the upper hand. It escaped nobody that here a heroic obstinacy, a fixed resolve to resist, must needs be conquered; we were beholding a gallant effort to strike out and save the honour of the human race. He twitched but danced not; and the struggle was so prolonged that the Cavaliere had to divide his attention between it and the stage, turning now and then to make his riding-whip whistle in the direction of the dancers, as it were to keep them in leash. At the same time he advised the audience that no fatigue was involved in such activities, however long they went on, since it was not the automatons up there who danced, but himself. Then once more his eye would bore itself into the back of the Roman's neck and lay siege to the strength of purpose which defied him.

One saw it waver, that strength of purpose, beneath the repeated summons and whip-crackings. Saw with an objective interest which yet was not quite free from traces of sympathetic emotion—from pity, even from a cruel kind of pleasure. If I understand what was going on, it was the negative character of the young man's fighting position which was his undoing. It is likely that *not* willing is not a practicable state of mind; *not* to want to do something may be in the long run a mental content impossible to subsist on. Between not willing a certain thing and not willing at all— in other words, yielding to another person's will—there may lie too small a space for the idea of freedom to squeeze into. Again, there were the Cavaliere's persuasive words, woven in among the whip-crackings and commands, as he mingled effects that were his own secret with others of a bewilderingly psychological kind. *"Balla!"* said he. "Who wants to torture himself like that? Is forcing yourself your idea of freedom? *Una ballatina!* Why, your arms and legs are aching for it. What a relief to give way to them—there, you are dancing already! That is no struggle any more, it is a pleasure!" And so it was. The jerking and twitching of the refractory youth's limbs had at last got the upper hand; he lifted his arms, then his knees, his joints quite suddenly relaxed, he flung his legs and danced, and amid bursts of applause the Cavaliere led him to join the row of puppets on the stage. Up there we could see his face as he "enjoyed" himself; it was clothed in a broad grin and the eyes were half-shut. In a way, it was consoling to see that he was having a better time than he had had in the hour of his pride.

His "fall" was, I may say, an epoch. The ice was completely broken, Cipolla's triumph had reached its height. The Circe's wand, that whistling leather whip with the claw handle, held absolute sway. At one time—it must have been well after midnight—not only were there eight or ten persons dancing on the little stage, but in the hall below a varied animation reigned, and a long-toothed Anglo-Saxoness in a pince-nez left her seat of her own motion to perform a tarantella in the centre aisle. Cipolla was lounging in a cane-seated chair at the left of the stage, gulping down the smoke of a cigarette and breathing it impudently out through his bad teeth. He tapped his foot and shrugged his shoulders, looking down upon the abandoned scene in the hall; now and then he snapped his whip backwards at a laggard upon the stage. The children were awake at the moment. With shame I speak of them. For it was not good to be here, least of all for them; that we had not taken them away can only be explained by saying that we had caught the general devil-may-careness of the hour. By that time it was all one. Anyhow, thank goodness, they lacked understanding for the disreputable side of the entertainment, and in their innocence were perpetually charmed by the unheard-of indulgence which permitted them to be present at such a thing as a magician's "evening." Whole quarter-hours at a time they drowsed on our laps, waking refreshed and rosy-cheeked, with sleep-drunk eyes, to laugh to bursting at the leaps and jumps the magician made those people up there make. They had not thought it would be so jolly; they joined with their clumsy little hands in every round of applause. And jumped for joy upon their chairs, as was their wont, when Cipolla beckoned to their friend Mario from the Esquisito, beckoned to him just like a picture in a book, holding his hand in front of his nose and bending and straightening the forefinger by turns.

Mario obeyed. I can see him now going up the stairs to Cipolla, who continued to beckon him, in that droll, picture-book sort of way. He hesitated for a moment at first; that, too, I recall quite clearly. During the whole evening he had lounged against a wooden pillar at the side entrance, with his arms folded, or else with his hands thrust into his jacket pockets. He was on our left, near the youth with the militant hair, and had followed the performance attentively, so far as we had seen, if with no particular animation and God knows how much comprehension. He could not much relish being summoned thus, at the end of the evening. But it was only too easy to see why he obeyed. After all, obedience was his calling in life; and then, how should a simple lad like him find it within his human capacity to refuse compliance to a man so throned and crowned as Cipolla at that hour? Willy-nilly he left his column and with a word of thanks to those making way for him he mounted the steps with a doubtful smile on his full lips.

Picture a thickset youth of twenty years, with clipt hair, a low forehead, and heavy-lidded eyes of an indefinite grey, shot with green and yellow. These things I knew from having spoken with him, as we often had. There was a saddle of freckles on the flat nose, the whole upper half of the face retreated behind the lower, and that again was dominated by thick lips that parted to show the salivated teeth. These thick lips and the veiled look of the eyes lent the whole face a primitive melancholy—it was that which had drawn us to him from the first. In it was not the faintest trace of brutality—indeed, his hands would have given the lie to such an idea, being unusually slender and delicate even for a southerner. They were hands by which one liked being served.

We knew him humanly without knowing him personally, if I may make that distinction. We saw him nearly every day, and felt a certain kindness for his dreamy ways, which might at times be actual inattentiveness, suddenly transformed into a redeeming zeal to serve. His mien was serious, only the children could bring a smile to his face. It was not sulky, but uningratiating, without intentional effort to please—or, rather, it seemed to give up being pleasant in the conviction that it could not succeed. We should have remembered Mario in any case, as one of those homely recollections of travel which often stick in the mind better than more important ones. But of his circumstances we knew no more than that his father was a petty clerk in the Municipio and his mother took in washing.

His white waiter's coat became him better than the faded striped suit he wore, with a gay coloured scarf instead of a collar, the ends tucked into his jacket. He neared Cipolla, who however did not leave off that motion of his finger before his nose, so that Mario had to come still closer, right up to the chair-seat and the master's legs. Whereupon the latter spread out his elbows and seized the lad, turning him so that we had a view of his face. Then gazed him briskly up and down, with a careless, commanding eye.

"Well, *ragazzo mio*, how comes it we make acquaintance so late in the day? But believe me, I made yours long ago. Yes, yes, I've had you in my eye this long while and known what good stuff you were made of. How could I go and forget you again? Well, I've had a good deal to think about. . . . Now tell me, what is your name? The first name, that's all I want."

"My name is Mario," the young man answered, in a low voice.

"Ah, Mario. Very good. Yes, yes, there is such a name, quite a common name, a classic name too, one of those which preserve the heroic traditions of the Fatherland. *Bravo! Salve!*" And he flung up his arm slantingly above his crooked shoulder, palm outward, in the Roman salute. He may have been slightly tipsy by now, and no wonder; but he spoke as before, clearly, fluently, and with emphasis. Though about this time there had crept into his voice a gross, autocratic note, and a kind of arrogance was in his sprawl.

"Well, now, Mario *mio*," he went on, "it's a good thing you came this evening, and that's a pretty scarf you've got on; it is becoming to your style of beauty. It must stand you in good stead with the girls, the pretty pretty girls of Torre—"

From the row of youths, close by the place where Mario had been standing, sounded a laugh. It came from the youth with the militant hair. He stood there, his jacket over his shoulder, and laughed outright, rudely and scornfully.

Mario gave a start. I think it was a shrug, but he may have started and then hastened to cover the movement by shrugging his shoulders, as much as to say that the neckerchief and the fair sex were matters of equal indifference to him.

The Cavaliere gave a downward glance.

"We needn't trouble about him," he said. "He is jealous, because your scarf is so popular with the girls, maybe partly because you and I are so friendly up here. Perhaps he'd like me to put him in mind of his colic—I could do it free of charge. Tell me, Mario. You've come here this evening for a bit of fun—and in the daytime you work in an ironmonger's shop?"

"In a café," corrected the youth.

"Oh, in a café. That's where Cipolla nearly came a cropper! What you are is a cup-bearer, a Ganymede—I like that, it is another classical allusion —*Salvietta!*" Again the Cavaliere saluted, to the huge gratification of his audience.

Mario smiled too. "But before that," he interpolated, in the interest of accuracy, "I worked for a while in a shop in Portoclemente." He seemed visited by a natural desire to assist the prophecy by dredging out its essential features.

"There, didn't I say so? in an ironmonger's shop?"

"They kept combs and brushes," Mario got round it.

"Didn't I say that you were not always a Ganymede? Not always at the sign of the serviette? Even when Cipolla makes a mistake, it is a kind that makes you believe in him. Now tell me: Do you believe in me?"

An indefinite gesture.

"A half-way answer," commented the Cavaliere. "Probably it is not easy to win your confidence. Even for me, I can see, it is not so easy. I see in your features a reserve, a sadness, *un tratto di malinconia* . . . tell me" (he seized Mario's hand persuasively) "have you troubles?"

"*Nossignore*," answered Mario, promptly and decidedly.

"You *have* troubles," insisted the Cavaliere, bearing down the denial by the weight of his authority. "Can't I see? Trying to pull the wool over Cipolla's eyes, are you? Of course, about the girls—it is a girl, isn't it? You have love troubles?"

Mario gave a vigorous head-shake. And again the *giovanotto's* brutal laugh rang out. The Cavaliere gave heed. His eyes were roving about somewhere in the air; but he cocked an ear to the sound, then swung his whip backwards, as he had once or twice before in his conversation with Mario, that none of his puppets might flag in their zeal. The gesture had nearly cost him his new prey: Mario gave a sudden start in the direction of the steps. But Cipolla had him in his clutch.

"Not so fast," said he. "That would be fine, wouldn't it? So you want to skip, do you, Ganymede, right in the middle of the fun, or, rather, when it is just beginning? Stay with me, I'll show you something nice, I'll convince you. You have no reason to worry, I promise you. This girl— you know her and others know her too—what's her name? Wait! I read the name in your eyes, it is on the tip of my tongue and yours too—"

"Silvestra!" shouted the *giovanotto* from below.

The Cavaliere's face did not change.

"Aren't there the forward people?" he asked, not looking down, more as in undisturbed converse with Mario. "Aren't there the young fighting-cocks that crow in season and out? Takes the word out of your mouth, the conceited fool, and seems to think he has some special right to it. Let him be. But Silvestra, your Silvestra—ah, what a girl that is! What a prize! Brings your heart into your mouth to see her walk or laugh or breathe, she is so lovely. And her round arms when she washes, and tosses her head back to get the hair out of her eyes! An angel from paradise!"

Mario stared at him, his head thrust forward. He seemed to have forgotten the audience, forgotten where he was. The red rings round his eyes had got larger, they looked as though they were painted on. His thick lips parted.

"And she makes you suffer, this angel," went on Cipolla, "or, rather, you make yourself suffer for her—there is a difference, my lad, a most important difference, let me tell you. There are misunderstandings in love, maybe nowhere else in the world are there so many. I know what you are thinking: what does this Cipolla, with his little physical defect, know about love? Wrong, all wrong, he knows a lot. He has a wide and power-ful understanding of its workings, and it pays to listen to his advice. But let's leave Cipolla out, cut him out altogether and think only of Silvestra, your peerless Silvestra! What! Is she to give any young gamecock the preference, so that he can laugh while you cry? To prefer him to a chap like you, so full of feeling and so sympathetic? Not very likely, is it? It is impossible—we know better, Cipolla and she. If I were to put myself in her place and choose between the two of you, a tarry lout like that—a codfish, a sea-urchin—and a Mario, a knight of the serviette, who moves among gentlefolk and hands round refreshments with an air—my word, but my heart would speak in no uncertain tones—it knows to whom I gave it long ago. It is time that he should see and understand, my chosen one! It is time that you see me and recognize me, Mario, my beloved! Tell me, who am I?"

It was grisly, the way the betrayer made himself irresistible, wreathed and coquetted with his crooked shoulder, languished with the puffy eyes, and showed his splintered teeth in a sickly smile. And alas, at his beguiling words, what was come of our Mario? It is hard for me to tell, hard as it was for me to see; for here was nothing less than an utter abandonment of the inmost soul, a public exposure of timid and deluded passion and rapture. He put his hands across his mouth, his shoulders rose and fell with his pantings. He could not, it was plain, trust his eyes and ears for joy, and the one thing he forgot was precisely that he could not trust them. "Silvestra!" he breathed, from the very depths of his vanquished heart.

"Kiss me!" said the hunchback. "Trust me, I love thee. Kiss me here." And with the tip of his index finger, hand, arm, and little finger outspread, he pointed to his cheek, near the mouth. And Mario bent and kissed him.

It had grown very still in the room. That was a monstrous moment, grotesque and thrilling, the moment of Mario's bliss. In that evil span of time, crowded with a sense of the illusiveness of all joy, one sound became audible, and that not quite at once, but on the instant of the melancholy and ribald meeting between Mario's lips and the repulsive flesh which thrust itself forward for his caress. It was the sound of a laugh, from the *giovanotto* on our left. It broke into the dramatic suspense of the moment, coarse, mocking, and yet—or I must have been grossly mistaken—with an undertone of compassion for the poor bewildered, victimized creature. It had a faint ring of that *"Poveretto"* which Cipolla had declared was wasted on the wrong person, when he claimed the pity for his own.

The laugh still rang in the air when the recipient of the caress gave his whip a little swish, low down, close to his chair-leg, and Mario started up and flung himself back. He stood in that posture staring, his hands one over the other on those desecrated lips. Then he beat his temples with his clenched fists, over and over; turned and staggered down the steps, while the audience applauded, and Cipolla sat there with his hands in his lap, his shoulders shaking. Once below, and even while in full retreat, Mario hurled himself round with legs flung wide apart; one arm flew up, and two flat shattering detonations crashed through applause and laughter

There was instant silence. Even the dancers came to a full stop and stared about, struck dumb. Cipolla bounded from his seat. He stood with his arms spread out, slanting as though to ward everybody off, as though next moment he would cry out: "Stop! Keep back! Silence! What was that?" Then, in that instant, he sank back in his seat, his head rolling on his chest; in the next he had fallen sideways to the floor, where he lay motionless, a huddled heap of clothing, with limbs awry.

The commotion was indescribable. Ladies hid their faces, shuddering, on the breasts of their escorts. There were shouts for a doctor, for the police. People flung themselves on Mario in a mob, to disarm him, to take away the weapon that hung from his fingers—that small, dull-metal, scarcely pistol-shaped tool with hardly any barrel—in how strange and unexpected a direction had fate levelled it!

And now—now finally, at last—we took the children and led them towards the exit, past the pair of *carabinieri* just entering. Was that the end, they wanted to know, that they might go in peace? Yes, we assured them, that was the end. An end of horror, a fatal end. And yet a liberation—for I could not, and I cannot, but find it so!

COMMENT AND QUESTION

"Mario and the Magician" appeared in 1929, when Mussolini was established in Italy as a dictator. The story is a political allegory describing fascism, but the allegory could reflect any totalitarian government. In the totalitarian governments of modern times, nationalism has been both a means and an end. In "Mario and the Magician," the reader will become aware of incidents illustrating national purity, national honor, national pride in past glories, national prestige in art, national health, and the exploitation of young men in national military service.

But the story is more than a political allegory. In the preface to his *Stories of Three Decades*, Mann remarks that the story has moral as well as political implications. The moral allegory lies in the action which liberates the audience from its subjugation to the will of Cipolla. Mario's act is a moral act which finds its authority in the teaching of Schopenhauer.

THE POLITICAL IMPLICATIONS

1. *The children and the opening incidents.* In the first four incidents of the story we see an evil situation obscurely. We are once-removed from the evil itself. We see an effect, not the cause. The four opening incidents —the hotel table, the whooping cough, Fuggièro, and the bathing suit— expose us to the hysterical nationalism of Mussolini's Italy. During the episode of the bathing suit, for example, the "patriotic children" hoot, and an adult delivers a "philippic" in "the service of morality and discipline."

The major part of the story, Cipolla and his magic, reveals the evil source of fascist power. We now see a people tricked, deluded, coerced, but responsible in part themselves because of their spiritual and moral poverty. The four opening incidents of the story concern children, who, in their innocence and ignorance, are also once-removed from the evil surrounding them. But Cipolla is supported by adults. The children, who are present, see only a "show." The adults are initiated into evil.

2. *The show of Cipolla.* In order to study the meaning of Cipolla and his feats, the reader should notice the following:

a. *The location of the hall.* Find the paragraph which describes the location of the hall where Cipolla performs. What history of totalitarian government is given there?

b. *Cipolla, the magician.* Cipolla means "onion" or "a bulbous shape." The name carries several meanings for the story, the most obvious one being a reference to Cipolla's own bulbous deformity. Why is Cipolla thus deformed? What relation do the following have to fascism or totalitarianism—Cipolla's title *Cavaliere?* His whip? His drinking? His likeness to a charlatan or mountebank?

c. *Cipolla's feats*

(1) *The progression of Cipolla's feats.* The order in which Cipolla performs his feats is important. At first Cipolla took care "not to molest the more select portion of his audience. He kept to the populace." He begins with the fishing folk but is forced to pass on to a grocer's clerk and later to a "mustachioed colonel" and to a tourist, an Englishwoman. What development of fascism is seen here? (Mario, it is true, climaxes the incidents, but Mario's chief importance is moral, not political.)

(2) *The powers of the populace.* If Cipolla wishes to perform all his tricks, he cannot confine his attention to the populace. As his tricks become more difficult, he chooses subjects elsewhere than from the proletariat. Why? At this point the incident of the two young men who cannot write is most revealing. Cipolla praises the two young men "for their heroic firmness of limb and the size of their hands, so well calculated to do this service for the public." Then he finds that they cannot write. What qualities of the proletariat are most useful to a dictator? Why is it significant that the feats of the fisherman are mere vulgarity?

(3) *The dancing and its military significance.* The dancing is the climax of the political parallels. Why is the dancing more revolting and terrifying than the merely vulgar episodes at the beginning?

Much of the dancing is military. What criticism of a nationally exploited military service is seen in the young man who "would fling himself back as though struck by lightning, place his hands rigidly at his sides, and fall into a state of military somnambulism, in which it was plain to any eye that he was open to the most absurd suggestion that might be made to him"? What is the significance of "military somnambulism"? What absurd suggestions might the young man follow? What criticism of modern humanity is seen in the fact that the young man was "pleased to be relieved of the burden of voluntary choice"? What is the significance in the fact that the young man's dancing looks "unmistakably like enjoyment" and that other "recruits" join him from the hall?

The powerful appeal of military life in a fascist state is seen in the rebellious young man who offers most resistance to Cipolla but who succumbs finally to the lure of the dancing. The subjugation of this defiant young man is due in part to the barrenness of his life. The reader should find the passage beginning "If I understand what was going on, it was the negative character of the young man's fighting position which was his undoing. It is likely that *not* willing . . ." etc. A spiritually and morally impoverished people falls easy prey to a dictator.

(4) *The subjugation of the will to the will of a dictator.* This matter is properly discussed under the moral implications of the story. But a few incidents reveal either literally or ironically the methods and snares of a dictatorship.

(a) What is the fascist motive behind the inducement of dividing up "the willing and the doing"?

(b) In the arithmetic game what trick of a totalitarian government is seen in the revelation that Cipolla knew the answers beforehand? During the game the following incident occurs: "One guesser admitted that he had in mind to give a certain number, when Cipolla's whip went whistling through the air, and a quite different one slipped out, which proved to be the right one." This admission amuses Cipolla. Since the whip symbolizes force, he has reason to be amused.

(c) During the game of finding an object, Cipolla acts "in obedience to a voiceless common will which was in the air." What reflection of fascism is here?

(d) What contributes to the subjugation of Signora Angiolieri?

AN ANALYSIS OF THE MORAL IMPLICATIONS OF
"MARIO AND THE MAGICIAN"

At the end of "Mario and the Magician," Mario breaks the spell of Cipolla. He frees not only himself but the entire audience from the evil dominance of Cipolla's will. But why does Mario succeed when everyone else has failed? What spiritual or moral strength does this slow, passive, gentle boy possess? The answer lies in the moral philosophy of Schopenhauer, for in this incident various theories of Schopenhauer come to life. According to Schopenhauer, liberation from the blind forces of the

Will does not come through the resistance of the individual will. Witness the futile rebellion of the Roman youth in the story. Liberation comes, instead, through complete resignation of the will, which, as will be shown later, has been Mario's lot in life.

It should be mentioned at the outset that Mann's interest in Schopenhauer is deep-seated. Mann's essay on Schopenhauer is a clue to the influence of Schopenhauer in Mann's writing. The influence is reflected also in the preface to Mann's *Stories of Three Decades* and in the illuminating leading article in *The London Times Literary Supplement* for January 5, 1951.

A brief résumé of Mann's interpretation of Schopenhauer in *Essays of Three Decades* will reveal parallels with the final incident in the story. In Schopenhauer's philosophy the world is nothing but the objective manifestation of the Will, the life forces, the will to life. When the will objectifies itself, it produces individual existences. It produces mind and body. In short, it produces a suffering world. The Will or will to life is a blind, senseless, causeless force, and the individual existences, the objectivations of the Will, are constantly struggling and constantly frustrated. The world becomes a place where the Will, divided into multiple existences, struggles against itself.

But mind or knowledge can alleviate this suffering. Although mind is a product of the Will, it is at the same time the highest objectivation of the Will. Mind can break loose from its master, the Will, and can free man in two ways: through art or the aesthetic state and through morality or the moral state. Both the artist and the good man achieve this liberation through abnegation of their own will. "There is a state," writes Mann in his essay on Schopenhauer, "where the miracle comes to pass, that knowledge wrenches itself free from will, the subject ceases to be merely individual and becomes the pure, will-less subject of knowledge. We may call it the aesthetic state."

The aesthetic state, however, is prior to the moral state; the artist is subordinate to the saint. The moral state is more enduring than the aesthetic state, its insight more penetrating. The abnegation of the individual will in the good man, or saint, comes through a profound recognition of the worthlessness of the world, the worthlessness of the will to life. Through supreme knowledge the will to life comes to "understand itself as something to be definitely and absolutely rejected."

The good man attains the resignation of his will partly through sympathy with other men. The good man knows that he and all men are alike because they exist in and by the Will, that is, in and by "the will to life, which embodies itself in everything, animals as well as all nature. . . ." Therefore the good man "will not even misuse a beast." The moral state, in which the miracle of liberation occurs, requires selflessness, sympathy, and a recognition of the will to life as worthless.

1. *Mario and his actions.* Of all the people in the hall, Mario, at first glance, seems the least likely to shatter the evil domination of Cipolla. Mario seems destined to be a passive, pliable subject. He is a waiter—"obedience was his calling in life." He has a "zeal to serve." His hands are "hands by which one liked being served." He is so subservient that he makes no "intentional effort to please." He shows no will in his response to Cipolla's questions.

But if liberation from the Will is to take place through the complete abnegation of individual will, then Mario, far from being the least likely person to defy Cipolla becomes the likeliest. Mario, in his subserviency, has already ceased to be individual and is the "will-less subject of knowledge." Even though he has no troubles, his face is sad. The "primitive melancholy" in Mario's face, which even Cipolla notices, may be the result of Mario's transcendent knowledge, his insight into evil.

Mario "wrenches" himself free from Cipolla just as knowledge wrenches itself free from Will. He tears himself free from Cipolla's control at the precise moment that Cipolla swishes his whip. And the last sentence of the story announces a "liberation."

2. *Mario, Cipolla, and sex.* In his essay on Schopenhauer, Mann makes the following statement: "Sex is to Schopenhauer the focal point of the will; in its physical objectivation the opposite pole of the brain, which represented knowledge." Cipolla thus assaults Mario in a crucial objectivation of the will to life, a response to sex. But Mario, if we are to believe his characterization, has achieved abnegation of the will to live. He exists in the will-less state of knowledge where he can reject as worthless the will to life, especially the will to life objectified in the travesty of the sex impulse offered by Cipolla. Cipolla, as a dictator, offers only a hideous parody of the will to life. And so, "the will to life comes to understand itself as something to be definitely and absolutely rejected." Mario wrenches free from the Will with explosive force.

Mann emphasizes the motif of sex throughout the story. The setting of the story is an Italian town called Tower of Venus. Cipolla's performance begins and ends with references to sex. Cipolla develops a "genuine antagonism" toward the handsome youth who first challenges him. Cipolla calls him this "lady-killer," this "Tower of Venus" who has "been rather spoilt by the favors of the fair sex." The narrator observes: "No one looking at the physical parts of the two men need have been at a loss for the explanation" of the antagonism. Because of his deformity and his isolation from women, Cipolla's trick with Mario is clearly rooted in the plot. The horror on the plot level is easily transferred to the allegorical level. The handsome young man who is a favorite of the ladies is the same man who laughs brutally and derisively at the spectacle of Mario and Cipolla. His discernment, on the plot level, may be translated into the knowledge, on the philosophical level, which causes Mario to break away from Cipolla.

3. *The argument on will.* Running through Cipolla's performance is an argument on will, which is also related to theories of Schopenhauer. To the youth who twice tries boldly to assert his own will, Cipolla remarks: ". . . freedom of the will does not exist, for a will that aims at its own freedom aims at the unknown." True. Only in the unknown, in the transcendent state, is the will free. In the empiric world, will is determined. The soldierly gentleman in the story, like the rebellious youth, has no free will. He illustrates "that recoil of the will upon itself which paralyzes choice." Only in the transcendent state, to which Mario's abnegation of the will has led him, is Mario free. It is not through the resistance of the individual will but through resignation of the individual will that evil like Cipolla will be conquered.

In a totalitarian government, people give their wills over to the leader, a fearful, unnatural bondage since will is the essence of their existence. They merely *do,* they do not *will,* as Cipolla demonstrates to the first hardy youth who resists him. Cipolla's comment, "That was me," indicates the young man's miserable bondage.

4. *Fascism as objectivation of the Will.* Mann seems to be saying that fascism or the totalitarian state is a frightful objectivation of the Schopenhauerian Will. Superimposed upon the primary objectivations of Will, it paralyzes humanity. Mann, speaking for Schopenhauer, writes: "Evil is that man who, as soon as no other outer power prevents him, inflicts evil. I mean a man who, not content with affirming the will to life as manifested in his own body, also denies the will manifest in other individuals. . . ." Cipolla is precisely this type of man. Liberation from crippling totalitarianism will come about through morality. And the human being who values his liberty can ponder the thoughts of the narrator in "Mario and the Magician," who watches the hardiest of men crack under the attacks of Cipolla: "It is likely that *not* willing is not a practicable state of mind; *not* to want to do something may be in the long run a mental content impossible to subsist on. Between not willing a certain thing and not willing at all—in other words, yielding to another person's will—there may lie too small a space for the idea of freedom to squeeze into." If Cipolla's audience had had positive goals, if the audience had not been negative and barren, Cipolla would have found his subjects less tractable.

5. *The value of the moral allegory.* The reader who goes outside the framework of Schopenhauer's philosophy is likely to find that the moral allegory of "Mario and the Magician" is ambiguous. Schopenhauer's liberators, both artist and saint, reject the world. But people and governments exist *in* the world, not in the "nothingness" of Schopenhauer's artists and saints. Within the framework of Schopenhauer, however, Mann's story is powerful. Mann shows that a people enslaved to a totalitarian government can free itself only through the moral knowledge that

a dictator offers a base parody of life. "Mario and the Magician" engenders a moral revulsion which an intellectual perception of fascism does not produce.

THE MEANING OF MARIO'S ACTIONS

The following explanation of Mario's actions in "Mario and the Magician" was made by an advisory editor after reading the analysis based on Schopenhauer. It is valuable because it offers a different view.

"Hating fascism and embodying his hatred in his masterly portrait of Cipolla, Mann seems to have tried to suggest that ultimately fascism meets its doom by outraging or betraying a fundamental sense of decency, a basic natural idealism, in the common man. Mario is this man of the people, dedicated to service and to obedience, but possessing a capacity for idealization of which Cipolla tries to take extreme advantage. Mario's idealism is symbolized by his fixation on Silvestra. Everybody knows that Mario is hopelessly enamored of Silvestra: the giovanotto shouts the information. To Mario this idealization is enough in itself: he has no love troubles. But since there is something sacred to him about Silvestra, she is his weakness; when Cipolla pretends that he is Silvestra, he goes too far in his manipulation. Cipolla's own perverse, homosexual passion leads him to hypnotize Mario into a betrayal of his love. Thinking, under Cipolla's spell, that Cipolla is Silvestra, Mario kisses him and is then horrified at the sacrilege, at his mistake. The swish of the whip reminds Mario that he has surrendered himself, not to the love that Silvestra represents, but to the power represented in the whip. "He stood in that posture staring, his hands one over the other on those desecrated lips." Consciousness of his betrayal, of his having been fooled by Cipolla, of having kissed monstrous amoral force under the illusion that it was spiritual grace—this is what leads Mario to destroy the mountebank. Fascism will ultimately destroy itself by trying to appear to the common man as a form of salvation; his natural religious sense, his natural piety, will be outraged. That fascism will fall when it tries to set itself up as an ersatz religion may be wishful thinking on the part of Mann. But this idea is what he seems to be trying to get across in his treatment of Mario."

BLISS

BY KATHERINE MANSFIELD

KATHERINE MANSFIELD (1888–1923) was born in New Zealand. She settled permanently in England in 1909 and published her first volume of stories, *In a German Pension* in 1911. In 1913 she married John Middleton Murry, the critic. The qualities of her work —her irony, her psychological subtlety, her perception of symbolic values—reflect the influence of Chekhov, of whom she was an ardent student. Her short stories are collected in the following volumes: *Bliss* (1921), *The Garden Party* (1922), *The Dove's Nest* (1923), and *The Short Stories of Katherine Mansfield* (1950). The *Journal of Katherine Mansfield* (1927) and *The Letters of Katherine Mansfield* (1928) reveal her literary development.

Aᴌᴛʜᴏᴜɢʜ Bertha Young was thirty she still had moments like this when she wanted to run instead of walk, to take dancing steps on and off the pavement, to bowl a hoop, to throw something up in the air and catch it again, or to stand still and laugh at—nothing—at nothing, simply.

What can you do if you are thirty and, turning the corner of your own street, you are overcome, suddenly, by a feeling of bliss—absolute bliss!— as though you'd suddenly swallowed a bright piece of that late afternoon sun and it burned in your bosom, sending out a little shower of sparks into every particle, into every finger and toe? . . .

Oh, is there no way you can express it without being "drunk and disorderly"? How idiotic civilization is! Why be given a body if you have to keep it shut up in a case like a rare, rare fiddle?

"No, that about the fiddle is not quite what I mean," she thought, running up the steps and feeling in her bag for the key—she'd forgotten it, as usual—and rattling the letter-box. "It's not what I mean, because—Thank you, Mary"—she went into the hall. "Is nurse back?"

"Yes, M'm."

"And has the fruit come?"

"Yes, M'm. Everything's come."

"Bring the fruit up to the dining-room, will you? I'll arrange it before I go upstairs."

It was dusky in the dining-room and quite chilly. But all the same Bertha threw off her coat; she could not bear the tight clasp of it another moment, and the cold air fell on her arms.

But in her bosom there was still that bright glowing place—that shower of little sparks coming from it. It was almost unbearable. She hardly dared to breathe for fear of fanning it higher, and yet she breathed deeply, deeply. She hardly dared to look into the cold mirror—but she did look, and it gave her back a woman, radiant, with smiling, trembling lips, with big, dark eyes and an air of listening, waiting for something . . . divine to happen . . . that she knew must happen . . . infallibly.

Mary brought in the fruit on a tray and with it a glass bowl, and a blue dish, very lovely, with a strange sheen on it as though it had been dipped in milk.

"Shall I turn on the light, M'm?"

"No, thank you. I can see quite well."

There were tangerines and apples stained with strawberry pink. Some yellow pears, smooth as silk, some white grapes covered with a silver bloom and a big cluster of purple ones. These last she had bought to tone in with the new dining-room carpet. Yes, that did sound rather far-fetched and absurd, but it was really why she had bought them. She had thought in the shop: "I must have some purple ones to bring the carpet up to the table." And it had seemed quite sense at the time.

When she had finished with them and had made two pyramids of these bright round shapes, she stood away from the table to get the effect—and it really was most curious. For the dark table seemed to melt into the dusky light and the glass dish and the blue bowl to float in the air. This, of course in her present mood, was so incredibly beautiful. . . . She began to laugh.

"No, no. I'm getting hysterical." And she seized her bag and coat and ran upstairs to the nursery.

Nurse sat at a low table giving Little B her supper after her bath. The baby had on a white flannel gown and a blue woollen jacket, and her dark, fine hair was brushed up into a funny little peak. She looked up when she saw her mother and began to jump.

"Now, my lovey, eat it up like a good girl," said Nurse, setting her lips in a way that Bertha knew, and that meant she had come into the nursery at another wrong moment.

"Has she been good, Nanny?"

"She's been a little sweet all the afternoon," whispered Nanny. "We went to the park and I sat down on a chair and took her out of the pram and a big dog came along and put its head on my knee and she clutched its ear, tugged it. Oh, you should have seen her."

Bertha wanted to ask if it wasn't rather dangerous to let her clutch at a strange dog's ear. But she did not dare to. She stood watching them, her hands by her side, like the poor little girl in front of the rich little girl with the doll.

The baby looked up at her again, stared, and then smiled so charmingly that Bertha couldn't help crying:

"Oh, Nanny, do let me finish giving her her supper while you put the bath things away."

"Well, M'm, she oughtn't to be changed hands while she's eating," said Nanny, still whispering. "It unsettles her; it's very likely to upset her."

How absurd it was. Why have a baby if it has to be kept—not in a case like a rare, rare fiddle—but in another woman's arms?

"Oh, I must!" said she.

Very offended, Nanny handed her over.

"Now, don't excite her after her supper. You know you do, M'm. And I have such a time with her after!"

Thank heaven! Nanny went out of the room with the bath towels.

"Now I've got you to myself, my little precious," said Bertha, as the baby leaned against her.

She ate delightfully, holding up her lips for the spoon and then waving her hands. Sometimes she wouldn't let the spoon go; and sometimes, just as Bertha had filled it, she waved it away to the four winds.

When the soup was finished Bertha turned round to the fire.

"You're nice—you're very nice!" said she, kissing her warm baby. "I'm fond of you. I like you."

And, indeed, she loved Little B so much—her neck as she bent forward, her exquisite toes as they shone transparent in the firelight—that all her feeling of bliss came back again, and again she didn't know how to express it—what to do with it.

"You're wanted on the telephone," said Nanny, coming back in triumph and seizing *her* Little B.

Down she flew. It was Harry.

"Oh, is that you, Ber? Look here. I'll be late. I'll take a taxi and come

along as quickly as I can, but get dinner put back ten minutes—will you?
All right?"

"Yes, perfectly. Oh, Harry!"

"Yes?"

What had she to say? She'd nothing to say. She only wanted to get in
touch with him for a moment. She couldn't absurdly cry: "Hasn't it been
a divine day!"

"What is it?" rapped out the little voice.

"Nothing. *Entendu*," said Bertha, and hung up the receiver, thinking
how more than idiotic civilization was.

They had people coming to dinner. The Norman Knights—a very
sound couple—he was about to start a theatre, and she was awfully keen
on interior decoration, a young man, Eddie Warren, who had just published a little book of poems and whom everybody was asking to dine, and
a "find" of Bertha's called Pearl Fulton. What Miss Fulton did, Bertha
didn't know. They had met at the club and Bertha had fallen in love with
her, as she always did fall in love with beautiful women who had something strange about them.

The provoking thing was that, though they had been about together
and met a number of times and really talked, Bertha couldn't yet make
her out. Up to a certain point Miss Fulton was rarely, wonderfully frank,
but the certain point was there, and beyond that she would not go.

Was there anything beyond it? Harry said "No." Voted her dullish,
and "cold like all blond women, with a touch, perhaps, of anæmia of the
brain." But Bertha wouldn't agree with him; not yet, at any rate.

"No, the way she has of sitting with her head a little on one side, and
smiling, has something behind it, Harry, and I must find out what that
something is."

"Most likely it's a good stomach," answered Harry.

He made a point of catching Bertha's heels with replies of that kind
. . . "liver frozen, my dear girl," or "pure flatulence," or "kidney disease,"
. . . and so on. For some strange reason Bertha liked this, and almost
admired it in him very much.

She went into the drawing-room and lighted the fire; then, picking up
the cushions, one by one, that Mary had disposed so carefully, she threw
them back on to the chairs and the couches. That made all the difference;
the room came alive at once. As she was about to throw the last one she
surprised herself by suddenly hugging it to her, passionately, passionately.
But it did not put out the fire in her bosom. Oh, on the contrary!

The windows of the drawing-room opened on to a balcony over-
looking the garden. At the far end, against the wall, there was a tall,
slender pear tree in fullest, richest bloom; it stood perfect, as though be-
calmed against the jade-green sky. Bertha couldn't help feeling, even

from this distance, that it had not a single bud or a faded petal. Down below, in the garden beds, the red and yellow tulips, heavy with flowers, seemed to lean upon the dusk. A grey cat, dragging its belly, crept across the lawn, and a black one, its shadow, trailed after. The sight of them, so intent and so quick, gave Bertha a curious shiver.

"What creepy things cats are!" she stammered, and she turned away from the window and began walking up and down. . . .

How strong the jonquils smelled in the warm room. Too strong? Oh, no. And yet, as though overcome, she flung down on a couch and pressed her hands to her eyes.

"I'm too happy—too happy!" she murmured.

And she seemed to see on her eyelids the lovely pear tree with its wide open blossoms as a symbol of her own life.

Really—really—she had everything. She was young. Harry and she were as much in love as ever, and they got on together splendidly and were really good pals. She had an adorable baby. They didn't have to worry about money. They had this absolutely satisfactory house and garden. And friends—modern, thrilling friends, writers and painters and poets or people keen on social questions—just the kind of friends they wanted. And then there were books, and there was music, and she had found a wonderful little dressmaker, and they were going abroad in the summer, and their new cook made the most superb omelettes. . . .

"I'm absurd. Absurd!" She sat up; but she felt quite dizzy, quite drunk. It must have been the spring.

Yes, it was the spring. Now she was so tired she could not drag herself upstairs to dress.

A white dress, a string of jade beads, green shoes and stockings. It wasn't intentional. She had thought of this scheme hours before she stood at the drawing-room window.

Her petals rustled softly into the hall, and she kissed Mrs. Norman Knight, who was taking off the most amusing orange coat with a procession of black monkeys round the hem and up the fronts.

". . . Why! Why! Why is the middle-class so stodgy—so utterly without a sense of humour! My dear, it's only by a fluke that I am here at all—Norman being the protective fluke. For my darling monkeys so upset the train that it rose to a man and simply ate me with its eyes. Didn't laugh—wasn't amused—that I should have loved. No, just stared—and bored me through and through."

"But the cream of it was," said Norman, pressing a large tortoiseshell-rimmed monocle into his eye, "you don't mind me telling this, Face, do you?" (In their home and among their friends they called each other Face and Mug.) "The cream of it was when she, being full fed, turned to the woman beside her and said: 'Haven't you ever seen a monkey before?' "

"Oh, yes!" Mrs. Norman Knight joined in the laughter. "Wasn't that too absolutely creamy?"

And a funnier thing still was that now her coat was off she did look like a very intelligent monkey—who had even made that yellow silk dress out of scraped banana skins. And her amber ear-rings; they were like little dangling nuts.

"This is a sad, sad fall!" said Mug, pausing in front of Little B's perambulator. "When the perambulator comes into the hall—" and he waved the rest of the quotation away.

The bell rang. It was lean, pale Eddie Warren (as usual) in a state of acute distress.

"It *is* the right house, *isn't* it?" he pleaded

"Oh, I think so—I hope so," said Bertha brightly.

"I have had such a *dreadful* experience with a taxi-man; he was *most* sinister. I couldn't get him to *stop*. The *more* I knocked and called the *faster* he went. And *in* the moonlight this *bizarre* figure with the *flattened* head *crouching* over the *lit-tle* wheel. . . ."

He shuddered, taking off an immense white silk scarf. Bertha noticed that his socks were white, too—most charming.

"But how dreadful!" she cried.

"Yes, it really was," said Eddie, following her into the drawing-room. "I saw myself *driving* through Eternity in a *timeless* taxi."

He knew the Norman Knights. In fact, he was going to write a play for N. K. when the theatre scheme came off.

"Well, Warren, how's the play?" said Norman Knight, dropping his monocle and giving his eye a moment in which to rise to the surface before it was screwed down again.

And Mrs. Norman Knight: "Oh, Mr. Warren, what happy socks!"

"I *am* so glad you like them," said he, staring at his feet. "They seem to have got so *much* whiter since the moon rose." And he turned his lean sorrowful young face to Bertha. "There *is* a moon, you know."

She wanted to cry: "I am sure there is—often—often!"

He really was a most attractive person. But so was Face, crouched before the fire in her banana skins, and so was Mug, smoking a cigarette and saying as he flicked the ash: "Why doth the bridegroom tarry?"

"There he is, now."

Bang went the front door open and shut. Harry shouted: "Hullo, you people. Down in five minutes." And they heard him swarm up the stairs. Bertha couldn't help smiling; she knew how he loved doing things at high pressure. What, after all, did an extra five minutes matter? But he would pretend to himself that they mattered beyond measure. And then he would make a great point of coming into the drawing-room, extravagantly cool and collected.

Harry had such a zest for life. Oh, how she appreciated it in him. And his passion for fighting—for seeking in everything that came up against him another test of his power and of his courage—that, too, she understood. Even when it made him just occasionally, to other people, who didn't know him well, a little ridiculous perhaps. . . . For there were moments when he rushed into battle where no battle was. . . . She talked and laughed and positively forgot until he had come in (just as she had imagined) that Pearl Fulton had not turned up.

"I wonder if Miss Fulton has forgotten?"

"I expect so," said Harry. "Is she on the 'phone?"

"Ah! There's a taxi, now." And Bertha smiled with that little air of proprietorship that she always assumed while her women finds were new and mysterious. "She lives in taxis." •

"She'll run to fat if she does," said Harry coolly, ringing the bell for dinner. "Frightful danger for blond women."

"Harry—don't," warned Bertha, laughing up at him.

Came another tiny moment, while they waited, laughing and talking, just a trifle too much at their ease, a trifle too unaware. And then Miss Fulton, all in silver, with a silver fillet binding her pale blond hair, came in smiling, her head a little on one side.

"Am I late?"

"No, not at all," said Bertha. "Come along." And she took her arm and they moved into the dining-room.

What was there in the touch of that cool arm that could fan—fan—start blazing—blazing—the fire of bliss that Bertha did not know what to do with?

Miss Fulton did not look at her; but then she seldom did look at people directly. Her heavy eyelids lay upon her eyes and the strange half smile came and went upon her lips as though she lived by listening rather than seeing. But Bertha knew, suddenly, as if the longest, most intimate look had passed between them—as if they had said to each other: "You, too?"—that Pearl Fulton, stirring the beautiful red soup in the grey plate, was feeling just what she was feeling.

And the others? Face and Mug, Eddie and Harry, their spoons rising and falling—dabbing their lips with their napkins, crumbling bread, fiddling with the forks and glasses and talking.

"I met her at the Alpha show—the weirdest little person. She'd not only cut off her hair, but she seemed to have taken a dreadfully good snip off her legs and arms and her neck and her poor little nose as well."

"Isn't she very *liée* with Michael Oat?"

"The man who wrote *Love in False Teeth*?"

"He wants to write a play for me. One act. One man. Decides to commit suicide. Gives all the reasons why he should and why he shouldn't. And just as he has made up his mind either to do it or not to do it—curtain. Not half a bad idea."

"What's he going to call it—'Stomach Trouble'?"

"I *think* I've come across the *same* idea in a lit-tle French review, *quite* unknown in England."

No, they didn't share it. They were dears—dears—and she loved having them there, at her table, and giving them delicious food and wine. In fact, she longed to tell them how delightful they were, and what a decorative group they made, how they seemed to set one another off and how they reminded her of a play by Tchekof!

Harry was enjoying his dinner. It was part of his—well, not his nature, exactly, and certainly not his pose—his—something or other—to talk about food and to glory in his "shameless passion for the white flesh of the lobster" and "the green of pistachio ices—green and cold like the eyelids of Egyptian dancers."

When he looked up at her and said: "Bertha, this is a very admirable *soufflée!*" she almost could have wept with child-like pleasure.

Oh, why did she feel so tender towards the whole world tonight? Everything was good—was right. All that happened seemed to fill again her brimming cup of bliss.

And still, in the back of her mind, there was the pear tree. It would be silver now, in the light of poor dear Eddie's moon, silver as Miss Fulton, who sat there turning a tangerine in her slender fingers that were so pale a light seemed to come from them.

What she simply couldn't make out—what was miraculous—was how she should have guessed Miss Fulton's mood so exactly and so instantly. For she never doubted for a moment that she was right, and yet what had she to go on? Less than nothing.

"I believe this does happen very, very rarely between women. Never between men," thought Bertha. "But while I am making the coffee in the drawing-room perhaps she will 'give a sign.'"

What she meant by that she did not know, and what would happen after that she could not imagine.

While she thought like this she saw herself talking and laughing. She had to talk because of her desire to laugh.

"I must laugh or die."

But when she noticed Face's funny little habit of tucking something down the front of her bodice—as if she kept a tiny, secret hoard of nuts there, too—Bertha had to dig her nails into her hands—so as not to laugh too much.

It was over at last. And: "Come and see my new coffee machine," said Bertha.

"We only have a new coffee machine once a fortnight," said Harry. Face took her arm this time; Miss Fulton bent her head and followed after.

The fire had died down in the drawing-room to a red, flickering "nest of baby phoenixes," said Face.

"Don't turn up the light for a moment. It is so lovely." And down she crouched by the fire again. She was always cold . . . "without her little red flannel jacket, of course," thought Bertha.

At that moment Miss Fulton "gave the sign."

"Have you a garden?" said the cool, sleepy voice.

This was so exquisite on her part that all Bertha could do was to obey. She crossed the room, pulled the curtains apart, and opened those long windows.

"There!" she breathed.

And the two women stood side by side looking at the slender, flowering tree. Although it was so still it seemed, like the flame of a candle, to stretch up, to point, to quiver in the bright air, to grow taller and taller as they gazed—almost to touch the rim of the round, silver moon.

How long did they stand there? Both, as it were, caught in that circle of unearthly light, understanding each other perfectly, creatures of another world, and wondering what they were to do in this one with all this blissful treasure that burned in their bosoms and dropped, in silver flowers, from their hair and hands?

For ever—for a moment? And did Miss Fulton murmur: "Yes. Just *that*." Or did Bertha dream it?

Then the light was snapped on and Face made the coffee and Harry said: "My dear Mrs. Knight, don't ask me about my baby. I never see her. I shan't feel the slightest interest in her until she has a lover," and Mug took his eye out of the conservatory for a moment and then put it under glass again and Eddie Warren drank his coffee and set down the cup with a face of anguish as though he had drunk and seen the spider.

"What I want to do is to give the young men a show. I believe London is simply teeming with first-chop, unwritten plays. What I want to say to 'em is: 'Here's the theatre. Fire ahead.' "

"You know, my dear, I am going to decorate a room for the Jacob Nathans. Oh, I am so tempted to do a fried-fish scheme, with the backs of the chairs shaped like frying pans and lovely chip potatoes embroidered all over the curtains."

"The trouble with our young writing men is that they are still too romantic. You can't put out to sea without being seasick and wanting a basin. Well, why won't they have the courage of those basins?"

"A *dreadful* poem about a *girl* who was *violated* by a beggar *without* a a nose in a lit-tle wood. . . ."

Miss Fulton sank into the lowest, deepest chair and Harry handed round the cigarettes.

From the way he stood in front of her shaking the silver box and saying abruptly: "Egyptian? Turkish? Virginian? They're all mixed up," Bertha realized that she not only bored him; he really disliked her. And she decided from the way Miss Fulton said: "No, thank you, I won't smoke," that she felt it, too, and was hurt.

"Oh, Harry, don't dislike her. You are quite wrong about her. She's wonderful, wonderful. And, besides, how can you feel so differently about someone who means so much to me. I shall try to tell you when we are in bed to-night what has been happening. What she and I have shared."

At those last words something strange and almost terrifying darted into Bertha's mind. And this something blind and smiling whispered to her: "Soon these people will go. The house will be quiet—quiet. The lights will be out. And you and he will be alone together in the dark room—the warm bed. . . ."

She jumped up from her chair and ran over to the piano.

"What a pity someone does not play!" she cried. "What a pity somebody does not play."

For the first time in her life Bertha Young desired her husband.

Oh, she'd loved him—she'd been in love with him, of course, in every other way, but just not in that way. And, equally, of course, she'd understood that he was different. They'd discussed it so often. It had worried her dreadfully at first to find that she was so cold, but after a time it had not seemed to matter. They were so frank with each other—such good pals. That was the best of being modern.

But now—ardently! ardently! The word ached in her ardent body! Was this what that feeling of bliss had been leading up to? But then then—

"My dear," said Mrs. Norman Knight, "you know our shame. We are the victims of time and train. We live in Hampstead. It's been so nice."

"I'll come with you into the hall," said Bertha. "I loved having you. But you must not miss the last train. That's so awful, isn't it?"

"Have a whisky, Knight, before you go?" called Harry.

"No, thanks, old chap."

Bertha squeezed his hand for that as she shook it.

"Good night, good-bye," she cried from the top step, feeling that this self of hers was taking leave of them for ever.

When she got back into the drawing-room the others were on the move.

". . . Then you can come part of the way in my taxi."

"I shall be *so* thankful *not* to have to face *another* drive *alone* after my *dreadful* experience."

"You can get a taxi at the rank just at the end of the street. You won't have to walk more than a few yards."

"That's a comfort. I'll go and put on my coat."

Miss Fulton moved towards the hall and Bertha was following when Harry almost pushed past.

"Let me help you."

Bertha knew that he was repenting his rudeness—she let him go. What a boy he was in some ways—so impulsive—so—simple.

And Eddie and she were left by the fire.

"I *wonder* if you have seen Bilks' *new* poem called *Table d'Hôte*," said Eddie softly. "It's *so* wonderful. In the last Anthology. Have you got a copy? I'd *so* like to *show* it to you. It begins with an *incredibly* beautiful line: 'Why Must it Always be Tomato Soup?'"

"Yes," said Bertha. And she moved noiselessly to a table opposite the drawing-room door and Eddie glided noiselessly after her. She picked up the little book and gave it to him; they had not made a sound.

While he looked it up she turned her head towards the hall. And she saw . . . Harry with Miss Fulton's coat in his arms and Miss Fulton with her back turned to him and her head bent. He tossed the coat away, put his hands on her shoulders and turned her violently to him. His lips said: "I adore you," and Miss Fulton laid her moonbeam fingers on his cheeks and smiled her sleepy smile. Harry's nostrils quivered; his lips curled back in a hideous grin while he whispered: "To-morrow," and with her eyelids Miss Fulton said: "Yes."

"Here it is," said Eddie. "'Why Must it Always be Tomato Soup?' It's so *deeply* true, don't you feel? Tomato soup is so *dreadfully* eternal."

"If you prefer," said Harry's voice, very loud, from the hall, "I can phone you a cab to come to the door."

"Oh, no. It's not necessary," said Miss Fulton, and she came up to Bertha and gave her the slender fingers to hold.

"Good-bye. Thank you so much."

"Good-bye," said Bertha.

Miss Fulton held her hand a moment longer.

"Your lovely pear tree!" she murmured.

And then she was gone, with Eddie following, like the black cat following the grey cat.

"I'll shut up shop," said Harry, extravagantly cool and collected.

"Your lovely pear tree—pear tree—pear tree!"

Bertha simply ran over to the long windows.

"Oh, what is going to happen now?" she cried.

But the pear tree was as lovely as ever and as full of flower and as still.

COMMENT AND QUESTION

1. Early in the story Bertha reflects that she has everything: Harry, her baby, her friends. As the story proceeds, the reader should keep this statement always in mind.

    a. Is Harry the paragon to the reader that he is to his wife? Does he have any unpleasant qualities? Does he make any comments which seem crude or lacking in sensitivity?

b. Who in the story possesses the baby, controls the baby, has a chance to love the baby?

c. Are Bertha's "thrilling" friends artistic or "arty"?

2. Certain symbols occur in this story.

a. The colors of green and white occur several times. For Bertha the colors are poetic. But Harry glories in his "shameless passion for the white flesh of the lobster" and "the green of pistachio ices—green and cold like the eyelids of Egyptian dancers." Miss Mansfield tells as much through the various objects invested with green and white (the colors of spring) as she does perhaps in all the rest of the story.

b. A second symbol is the two cats, mentioned twice.

c. A third is the pear tree (which is white against a jade-green sky). Is the pear tree more than a symbol of spring? The reader should remember that the pear tree has a profound meaning for Pearl as well as for Bertha. Does it mean for Bertha what it means for Pearl? At the close of the story, why had Bertha expected the tree to change?

3. It is no accident that "Bliss" takes place in the spring. Neither is it an accident that Pearl fans the "fire of bliss" in Bertha. What indication is there that Pearl and Harry had probably been together before each arrives for the dinner?

4. There is an important repeated theme. Under the influence of a spring day, Bertha reflects: "Why be given a body if you have to keep it shut up in a case like a rare, rare fiddle?" Under the influence of the baby, she reflects: "Why have a baby if it has to be kept—not in a case like a rare, rare fiddle—but in another woman's arms?" Will not the time come in this story when Bertha will substitute another word for "baby"? And when she does so, will not the shock of realization draw all three statements into one vast catastrophe?

5. In "Bliss" Katherine Mansfield builds up an intensity of pain. Bertha is unmasked not only before the reader but before herself, and her unmasking encompasses the entire range of her existence. At the close many things will come back to Bertha and bring pain, like the repeated theme in paragraph 4. And there will be others like the following, where the irony is bitter:

a. " 'Why doth the bridegroom tarry?' "

b. " 'What she and I have shared.' "

THE OUTSTATION

BY WILLIAM SOMERSET MAUGHAM

WILLIAM SOMERSET MAUGHAM (1874–   )
is one of the most prolific and widely read
fiction writers of the twentieth century. He
was born in Paris of English parents and educated in England, Germany, and France. He
received a medical degree but never practiced. Instead he travelled widely and wrote.
His best work is his autobiographical novel,
Of Human Bondage (1915), which is a revealing portrait of an intellectually bewildered modern. Two other autobiographical
works, *The Summing Up* (1938) and *A
Writer's Notebook* (1949), describe the methods of a writer. Maugham has also written a
number of plays. His short stories have appeared in various collections, among which
are *The Trembling of a Leaf* (1921), *The
Casuarina Tree* (1926), *First Person Singular*
(1931), *The Mixture as Before* (1940), and
Creatures of Circumstance (1947).

THE new assistant arrived in the afternoon. When the Resident, Mr.
Warburton, was told that the prahu was in sight he put on his solar topee
and went down to the landing-stage. The guard, eight little Dyak soldiers,
stood to attention as he passed. He noted with satisfaction that their
bearing was martial, their uniforms neat and clean, and their guns shining.
They were a credit to him. From the landing-stage he watched the bend
of the river round which in a moment the boat would sweep. He looked

very smart in his spotless ducks and white shoes. He held under his arm
a gold-headed Malacca cane which had been given him by the Sultan of
Perak. He awaited the newcomer with mingled feelings. There was more
work in the district than one man could properly do, and during his
periodical tours of the country under his charge it had been inconvenient
to leave the station in the hands of a native clerk, but he had been so long
the only white man there that he could not face the arrival of another
without misgiving. He was accustomed to loneliness. During the war he
had not seen an English face for three years; and once when he was
instructed to put up an afforestation officer he was seized with panic, so
that when the stranger was due to arrive, having arranged everything for
his reception, he wrote a note telling him he was obliged to go up-river,
and fled; he remained away till he was informed by a messenger that his
guest had left.

Now the prahu appeared in the broad reach. It was manned by prisoners, Dyaks under various sentences, and a couple of warders were waiting on the landing-stage to take them back to jail. They were sturdy
fellows, used to the river, and they rowed with a powerful stroke. As the
boat reached the side a man got out from under the attap awning and
stepped on shore. The guard presented arms.

"Here we are at last. By God, I'm as cramped as the devil. I've brought
you your mail."

He spoke with exuberant joviality. Mr. Warburton politely held out his
hand.

"Mr. Cooper, I presume?"

"That's right. Were you expecting any one else?"

The question had a facetious intent, but the Resident did not smile.

"My name is Warburton. I'll show you your quarters. They'll bring
your kit along."

He preceded Cooper along the narrow pathway and they entered a
compound in which stood a small bungalow.

"I've had it made as habitable as I could, but of course no one has lived
in it for a good many years."

It was built on piles. It consisted of a long living-room which opened
on to a broad verandah, and behind, on each side of a passage, were two
bedrooms.

"This'll do me all right," said Cooper.

"I daresay you want to have a bath and a change. I shall be very much
pleased if you'll dine with me tonight. Will eight o'clock suit you?"

"Any old time will do for me."

The Resident gave a polite, but slightly disconcerted, smile and withdrew. He returned to the Fort where his own residence was. The impression which Allen Cooper had given him was not very favorable, but he
was a fair man, and he knew that it was unjust to form an opinion on so

brief a glimpse. Cooper seemed to be about thirty. He was a tall, thin fellow, with a sallow face in which there was not a spot of color. It was a face all in one tone. He had a large, hooked nose and blue eyes. When, entering the bungalow, he had taken off his topee and flung it to a waiting boy, Mr. Warburton noticed that his large skull, covered with short, brown hair, contrasted somewhat oddly with a weak, small chin. He was dressed in khaki shorts and a khaki shirt, but they were shabby and soiled; and his battered topee had not been cleaned for days. Mr. Warburton reflected that the young man had spent a week on a coasting steamer and had passed the last forty-eight hours lying in the bottom of a prahu.

"We'll see what he looks like when he comes in to dinner."

He went into his room where his things were as neatly laid out as if he had an English valet, undressed, and, walking down the stairs to the bath-house, sluiced himself with cool water. The only concession he made to the climate was to wear a white dinner-jacket; but otherwise, in a boiled shirt and a high collar, silk socks and patent-leather shoes, he dressed as formally as though he were dining at his club in Pall Mall. A careful host, he went into the dining-room to see that the table was properly laid. It was gay with orchids and the silver shone brightly. The napkins were folded into elaborate shapes. Shaded candles in silver candlesticks shed a soft light. Mr. Warburton smiled his approval and returned to the sitting-room to await his guest. Presently he appeared. Cooper was wearing the khaki shorts, the khaki shirt, and the ragged jacket in which he had landed. Mr. Warburton's smile of greeting froze on his face.

"Hulloa, you're all dressed up," said Cooper. "I didn't know you were going to do that. I very nearly put on a sarong."

"It doesn't matter at all. I daresay your boys were busy."

"You needn't have bothered to dress on my account, you know."

"I didn't. I always dress for dinner."

"Even when you're alone?"

"Especially when I'm alone," replied Mr. Warburton, with a frigid stare.

He saw a twinkle of amusement in Cooper's eyes, and he flushed an angry red. Mr. Warburton was a hot-tempered man; you might have guessed that from his red face with its pugnacious features and from his red hair, now growing white; his blue eyes, cold as a rule and observing, could flush with sudden wrath; but he was a man of the world and he hoped a just one. He must do his best to get on with this fellow.

"When I lived in London I moved in circles in which it would have been just as eccentric not to dress for dinner every night as not to have a bath every morning. When I came to Borneo I saw no reason to discontinue so good a habit. For three years, during the war, I never saw a white man. I never omitted to dress on a single occasion on which I was well enough to come in to dinner. You have not been very long in this country; believe me, there is no better way to maintain the proper pride which you should have in yourself. When a white man surrenders in the slightest degree to the influences that surround him he very soon loses his self-respect, and when he loses his self-respect you may be quite sure that the natives will soon cease to respect him."

"Well, if you expect me to put on a boiled shirt and a stiff collar in this heat I'm afraid you'll be disappointed."

"When you are dining in your own bungalow you will, of course, dress as you think fit, but when you do me the pleasure of dining with me, perhaps you will come to the conclusion that it is only polite to wear the costume usual in civilized society."

Two Malay boys, in sarongs and songkoks, with smart white coats and brass buttons, came in, one bearing gin pahits, and the other a tray on which were olives and anchovies. Then they went in to dinner. Mr. Warburton flattered himself that he had the best cook, a Chinese, in Borneo, and he took great trouble to have as good food as in the difficult circumstances was possible. He exercised much ingenuity in making the best of his materials.

"Would you care to look at the menu?" he said, handing it to Cooper.

It was written in French and the dishes had resounding names. They were waited on by the two boys. In opposite corners of the room two more waved immense fans, and so gave movement to the sultry air. The fare was sumptuous and the champagne excellent.

"Do you do yourself like this every day?" said Cooper.

Mr. Warburton gave the menu a careless glance.

"I have not noticed that the dinner is any different from usual," he said. "I eat very little myself, but I make a point of having a proper dinner served to me every night. It keeps the cook in practice and it's good discipline for the boys."

The conversation proceeded with effort. Mr. Warburton was elaborately courteous, and it may be that he found a slightly malicious amusement in the embarrassment which he thereby occasioned in his companion. Cooper had not been more than a few months in Sembulu, and Mr. Warburton's inquiries about friends of his in Kuala Solor were soon exhausted.

"By the way," he said presently, "did you meet a lad called Hennerley? He's come out recently, I believe."

"Oh, yes, he's in the police. A rotten bounder."

"I should hardly have expected him to be that. His uncle is my friend Lord Barraclough. I had a letter from Lady Barraclough only the other day asking me to look out for him."

"I heard he was related to somebody or other. I suppose that's how he got the job. He's been to Eton and Oxford and he doesn't forget to let you know it."

"You surprise me," said Mr. Warburton. "All his family have been at Eton and Oxford for a couple of hundred years. I should have expected him to take it as a matter of course."

"I thought him a damned prig."

"To what school did you go?"

"I was born in Barbados. I was educated there."

"Oh, I see."

Mr. Warburton managed to put so much offensiveness into his brief reply that Cooper flushed. For a moment he was silent.

"I've had two or three letters from Kuala Solor," continued Mr. Warburton, "and my impression was that young Hennerley was a great success. They say he's a first-rate sportsman."

"Oh, yes, he's very popular. He's just the sort of fellow they would like in K.S. I haven't got much use for the first-rate sportsman myself. What does it amount to in the long run that a man can play golf and tennis better than other people? And who cares if he can make a break of seventy-five at billiards? They attach a damned sight too much importance to that sort of thing in England."

"Do you think so? I was under the impression that the first-rate sportsman had come out of the war certainly no worse than any one else."

"Oh, if you're going to talk of the war then I do know what I'm talking about. I was in the same regiment as Hennerley and I can tell you that the men couldn't stick him at any price."

"How do you know?"

"Because I was one of the men."

"Oh, you hadn't got a commission."

"A fat chance I had of getting a commission. I was what was called a Colonial. I hadn't been to a public school and I had no influence. I was in the ranks the whole damned time."

Cooper frowned. He seemed to have difficulty in preventing himself from breaking into violent invective. Mr. Warburton watched him, his little blue eyes narrowed, watched him and formed his opinion. Changing the conversation, he began to speak to Cooper about the work that would be required of him, and as the clock struck ten he rose.

"Well, I won't keep you any more. I daresay you're tired by your journey."

They shook hands.

"Oh, I say, look here," said Cooper, "I wonder if you can find me a boy. The boy I had before never turned up when I was starting from K.S. He took my kit on board and all that and then disappeared. I didn't know he wasn't there till we were out of the river."

"I'll ask my head-boy. I have no doubt he can find you some one."

"All right. Just tell him to send the boy along and if I like the look of him I'll take him."

There was a moon, so that no lantern was needed. Cooper walked across from the Fort to his bungalow.

"I wonder why on earth they've sent me a fellow like that?" reflected Mr. Warburton. "If that's the kind of man they're going to get out now I don't think much of it."

He strolled down his garden. The Fort was built on the top of a little hill and the garden ran down to the river's edge; on the bank was an arbor, and hither it was his habit to come after dinner to smoke a cheroot. And often from the river that flowed below him a voice was heard, the voice of some Malay too timorous to venture into the light of day, and a complaint or an accusation was softly wafted to his ears, a piece of information was whispered to him or a useful hint, which otherwise would never have come into his official ken. He threw himself heavily into a long rattan chair. Cooper! An envious, ill-bred fellow, bumptious, self-assertive and vain. But Mr. Warburton's irritation could not withstand the silent beauty of the night. The air was scented with the sweet-smelling flowers of a tree that grew at the entrance to the arbor, and the fireflies, sparkling dimly, flew with their slow and silvery flight. The moon made a pathway on the broad river for the light feet of Siva's bride, and on the further bank a row of palm trees was delicately silhouetted against the sky. Peace stole into the soul of Mr. Warburton.

He was a queer creature and he had had a singular career. At the age of twenty-one he had inherited a considerable fortune, a hundred thousand pounds, and when he left Oxford he threw himself into the gay life which in those days (now Mr. Warburton was a man of four and fifty) offered itself to the young man of good family. He had his flat in Mount Street, his private hansom, and his hunting-box in Warwickshire. He went to all the places where the fashionable congregate. He was handsome, amusing and generous. He was a figure in the society of London in the early nineties, and society then had not lost its exclusiveness nor its brilliance. The Boer War which shook it was unthought of; the Great War which destroyed it was prophesied only by the pessimists. It was no unpleasant thing to be a rich young man in those days, and Mr. Warburton's chimney-piece during the season was packed with cards for one great function after another. Mr. Warburton displayed them with complacency. For Mr. Warburton was a snob. He was not a timid snob, a little ashamed of being impressed by his betters, nor a snob who sought the intimacy of persons who had acquired celebrity in politics or notoriety in the arts, nor the snob who was dazzled by riches; he was the naked, unadulterated common snob who dearly loved a lord. He was touchy and quick-tempered, but he would much rather have been snubbed by a person of quality than flattered by a commoner. His name figured insignificantly in *Burke's Peerage,* and it was marvelous to watch the ingenuity he used to mention his distant relationship to the noble family he

belonged to; but never a word did he say of the honest Liverpool manufacturer from whom, through his mother, a Miss Gubbins, he had come
by his fortune. It was the terror of his fashionable life that at Cowes,
maybe, or at Ascot, when he was with a duchess or even with a prince
of the blood, one of these relatives would claim acquaintance with
him.

His failing was too obvious not soon to become notorious, but its
extravagance saved it from being merely despicable. The great whom he
adored laughed at him, but in their hearts felt his adoration not unnatural.
Poor Warburton was a dreadful snob, of course, but after all he was a
good fellow. He was always ready to back a bill for an impecunious noble-
man, and if you were in a tight corner you could safely count on him for
a hundred pounds. He gave good dinners. He played whist badly, but
never minded how much he lost if the company was select. He happened
to be a gambler, an unlucky one, but he was a good loser, and it was
impossible not to admire the coolness with which he lost five hundred
pounds at a sitting. His passion for cards, almost as strong as his passion
for titles, was the cause of his undoing. The life he led was expensive and
his gambling losses were formidable. He began to plunge more heavily,
first on horses, and then on the Stock Exchange. He had a certain simplicity of character and the unscrupulous found him an ingenuous prey.
I do not know if he ever realized that his smart friends laughed at him
behind his back, but I think he had an obscure instinct that he could not
afford to appear other than careless of his money. He got into the hands
of money-lenders. At the age of thirty-four he was ruined.

He was too much imbued with the spirit of his class to hesitate in the
choice of his next step. When a man in his set had run through his money
he went out to the colonies. No one heard Mr. Warburton repine. He
made no complaint because a noble friend had advised a disastrous
speculation, he pressed nobody to whom he had lent money to repay it,
he paid his debts (if he had only known it, the despised blood of the Liverpool manufacturer came out in him there), sought help from no one, and,
never having done a stroke of work in his life, looked for a means of
livelihood. He remained cheerful, unconcerned and full of humor. He had
no wish to make any one with whom he happened to be uncomfortable
by the recital of his misfortune. Mr. Warburton was a snob, but he was
also a gentleman.

The only favor he asked of any of the great friends in whose daily
company he had lived for years was a recommendation. The able man
who was at that time Sultan of Sembulu took him into his service. The
night before he sailed he dined for the last time at his club.

"I hear you're going away, Warburton," the old Duke of Hereford
said to him.

"Yes, I'm going to Borneo."

"Good God, what are you going there for?"

"Oh, I'm broke."

"Are you? I'm sorry. Well, let us know when you come back. I hope you have a good time."

"Oh, yes. Lots of shooting, you know."

The Duke nodded and passed on. A few hours later Mr. Warburton watched the coast of England recede into the mist, and he left behind everything which to him made life worth living.

Twenty years had passed since then. He kept up a busy correspondence with various great ladies and his letters were amusing and chatty. He never lost his love for titled persons and paid careful attention to the announcements in *The Times* (which reached him six weeks after publication) of their comings and goings. He perused the column which records births, deaths, and marriages, and he was always ready with his letter of congratulation or condolence. The illustrated papers told him how people looked and on his periodical visits to England, able to take up the threads as though they had never been broken, he knew all about any new person who might have appeared on the social surface. His interest in the world of fashion was as vivid as when himself had been a figure in it. It still seemed to him the only thing that mattered.

But insensibly another interest had entered into his life. The position he found himself in flattered his vanity; he was no longer the sycophant craving the smiles of the great, he was the master whose word was law. He was gratified by the guard of Dyak soldiers who presented arms as he passed. He liked to sit in judgment on his fellow men. It pleased him to compose quarrels between rival chiefs. When the head-hunters were troublesome in the old days he set out to chastise them with a thrill of pride in his own behavior. He was too vain not to be of dauntless courage, and a pretty story was told of his coolness in adventuring single-handed into a stockaded village and demanding the surrender of a blood-thirsty pirate. He became a skilful administrator. He was strict, just and honest.

And little by little he conceived a deep love for the Malays. He interested himself in their habits and customs. He was never tired of listening to their talk. He admired their virtues, and with a smile and a shrug of the shoulders condoned their vices.

"In my day," he would say, "I have been on intimate terms with some of the greatest gentlemen in England, but I have never known finer gentlemen than some well-born Malays whom I am proud to call my friends."

He liked their courtesy and their distinguished manners, their gentleness and their sudden passions. He knew by instinct exactly how to treat them. He had a genuine tenderness for them. But he never forgot that he was an English gentleman and he had no patience with the white men who yielded to native customs. He made no surrenders. And he did not imitate so many of the white men in taking a native woman to wife, for an intrigue of this nature, however sanctified by custom, seemed to him not only shocking but undignified. A man who had been called George by Albert Edward, Prince of Wales, could hardly be expected to have any connection with a native. And when he returned to Borneo from his visits to England it was now with something like relief. His friends, like himself, were no longer young, and there was a new generation which looked upon him as a tiresome old man. It seemed to him that the England of today had lost a good deal of what he had loved in the England of his youth. But Borneo remained the same. It was home to him now. He meant to remain in the service as long as was possible, and the hope in his heart was that he would die before at last he was forced to retire. He had stated in his will that wherever he died he wished his body to be brought back to Sembulu and buried among the people he loved within sound of the softly flowing river.

But these emotions he kept hidden from the eyes of men; and no one, seeing this spruce, stout, well-set-up man, with his clean-shaven strong face and his whitening hair, would have dreamed that he cherished so profound a sentiment.

He knew how the work of the station should be done, and during the next few days he kept a suspicious eye on his assistant. He saw very soon that he was painstaking and competent. The only fault he had to find with him was that he was brusque with the natives.

"The Malays are shy and very sensitive," he said to him. "I think you will find that you will get much better results if you take care always to be polite, patient and kindly."

Cooper gave a short grating laugh.

"I was born in Barbadoes and I was in Africa in the war. I don't think there's much about niggers that I don't know."

"I know nothing," said Mr. Warburton acidly. "But we were not talking of them. We were talking of Malays."

"Aren't they niggers?"

"You are very ignorant," replied Mr. Warburton.

He said no more.

On the first Sunday after Cooper's arrival he asked him to dinner. He did everything ceremoniously, and though they had met on the previous day in the office and later, on the Fort verandah where they drank a gin and bitters together at six o'clock, he sent a polite note across to the bungalow by a boy. Cooper, however unwillingly, came in evening dress and Mr. Warburton, though gratified that his wish was respected, noticed with disdain that the young man's clothes were badly cut and his shirt ill-fitting. But Mr. Warburton was in a good temper that evening.

"By the way," he said to him, as he shook hands, "I've talked to my head-boy about finding you some one and he recommends his nephew. I've seen him and he seems a bright and willing lad. Would you like to see him?"

"I don't mind."

"He's waiting now."

Mr. Warburton called his boy and told him to send for his nephew. In a moment a tall, slender youth of twenty appeared. He had large dark eyes and a good profile. He was very neat in his sarong, a little white coat, and a fez, without a tassel, of plum-colored velvet. He answered to the name of Abas. Mr. Warburton looked on him with approval, and his manner insensibly softened as he spoke to him in fluent and idiomatic Malay. He was inclined to be sarcastic with white people, but with the Malays he had a happy mixture of condescension and kindliness. He stood in the place of the Sultan. He knew perfectly how to preserve his own dignity, and at the same time put a native at his ease.

"Will he do?" said Mr. Warburton, turning to Cooper.

"Yes, I daresay he's no more of a scoundrel than any of the rest of them."

Mr. Warburton informed the boy that he was engaged and dismissed him.

"You're very lucky to get a boy like that," he told Cooper. "He belongs to a very good family. They came over from Malacca nearly a hundred years ago."

"I don't much mind if the boy who cleans my shoes and brings me a drink when I want it has blue blood in his veins or not. All I ask is that he should do what I tell him and look sharp about it."

Mr. Warburton pursed his lips, but made no reply.

They went in to dinner. It was excellent, and the wine was good. Its influence presently had its effect on them and they talked not only without acrimony, but even with friendliness. Mr. Warburton liked to do himself well, and on Sunday night he made it a habit to do himself even a little better than usual. He began to think he was unfair to Cooper. Of course he was not a gentleman, but that was not his fault, and when you got to know him it might be that he would turn out a very good fellow. His faults, perhaps, were faults of manner. And he was certainly good at his work, quick, conscientious and thorough. When they reached the dessert Mr. Warburton was feeling kindly disposed towards all mankind.

"This is your first Sunday and I'm going to give you a very special glass of port. I've only got about two dozen of it left and I keep it for special occasions."

He gave his boy instructions and presently the bottle was brought. Mr. Warburton watched the boy open it.

"I got this port from my old friend Charles Hollington. He'd had it for forty years and I've had it for a good many. He was well known to have the best cellar in England."

"Is he a wine merchant?"

"Not exactly," smiled Mr. Warburton. "I was speaking of Lord Hollington of Castle Reagh. He's one of the richest peers in England. A very old friend of mine. I was at Eton with his brother."

This was an opportunity that Mr. Warburton could never resist and he told a little anecdote of which the only point seemed to be that he knew an earl. The port was certainly very good; he drank a glass and then a second. He lost all caution. He had not talked to a white man for months. He began to tell stories. He showed himself in the company of the great. Hearing him you would have thought that at one time ministries were formed and policies decided on his suggestion whispered into the ear of a duchess or thrown over the dinner-table to be gratefully acted on by the confidential adviser of the sovereign. The old days at Ascot, Goodwood and Cowes lived again for him. Another glass of port. There were the great house-parties in Yorkshire and in Scotland to which he went every year.

"I had a man called Foreman then, the best valet I ever had, and why do you think he gave me notice? You know in the Housekeeper's Room the ladies' maids and the gentlemen's gentlemen sit according to the precedence of their masters. He told me he was sick of going to party after party at which I was the only commoner. It meant that he always had to sit at the bottom of the table and all the best bits were taken before a dish reached him. I told the story to the old Duke of Hereford and he roared. 'By God, sir,' he said, 'if I were King of England I'd make you a viscount just to give your man a chance.' 'Take him yourself, Duke,' I said. 'He's the best valet I've ever had.' 'Well, Warburton,' he said, 'if he's good enough for you he's good enough for me. Send him along.'"

Then there was Monte Carlo, where Mr. Warburton and the Grand Duke Fyodor, playing in partnership, had broken the bank one evening; and there was Marienbad. At Marienbad Mr. Warburton had played baccarat with Edward VII.

"He was only Prince of Wales then, of course. I remember him saying to me, 'George, if you draw on a five you'll lose your shirt.' He was right; I don't think he ever said a truer word in his life. He was a wonderful man. I always said he was the greatest diplomatist in Europe. But I was a young fool in those days, I hadn't the sense to take his advice. If I had, if I'd never drawn on a five, I daresay I shouldn't be here today."

Cooper was watching him. His brown eyes, deep in their sockets, were hard and supercilious, and on his lips was a mocking smile. He had heard a good deal about Mr. Warburton in Kuala Solor. Not a bad sort, and he ran his district like clockwork, they said, but by heaven, what a snob! They laughed at him good-naturedly, for it was impossible to dislike a man who was so generous and so kindly, and Cooper had already heard the story of the Prince of Wales and the game of baccarat. But Cooper listened without indulgence. From the beginning he had re-sented the Resident's manner. He was very sensitive and he writhed under Mr. Warburton's polite sarcasms. Mr. Warburton had a knack of receiving a remark of which he disapproved with a devastating silence. Cooper had lived little in England and he had a peculiar dislike of the English. He resented especially the public-school boy since he always feared that he was going to patronize him. He was so much afraid of others putting on airs with him that, in order as it were to get in first, he put on such airs as to make every one think him insufferably con-ceited.

"Well, at all events the war has done one good thing for us," he said at last. "It's smashed up the power of the aristocracy. The Boer War started it, and 1914 put the lid on."

"The great families of England are doomed," said Mr. Warburton with the complacent melancholy of an *émigré* who remembered the court of Louis XV. "They cannot afford any longer to live in their splendid palaces and their princely hospitality will soon be nothing but a memory."

"And a damned good job too in my opinion."

"My poor Cooper, what can you know of the glory that was Greece and the grandeur that was Rome?"

Mr. Warburton made an ample gesture. His eyes for an instant grew dreamy with a vision of the past.

"Well, believe me, we're fed up with all that rot. What we want is a business government by business men. I was born in a Crown Colony and I've lived practically all my life in the colonies. I don't give a row of pins for a lord. What's wrong with England is snobbishness. And if there's anything that gets my goat it's a snob."

A snob! Mr. Warburton's face grew purple and his eyes blazed with anger. That was a word that had pursued him all his life. The great ladies whose society he had enjoyed in his youth were not inclined to look upon his appreciation of themselves as unworthy, but even great ladies are sometimes out of temper and more than once Mr. Warburton had had the dreadful word flung in his teeth. He knew, he could not help knowing, that there were odious people who called him a snob. How unfair it was! Why, there was no vice he found so detestable as snobbishness. After all, he liked to mix with people of his own class, he was only at home in their company, and how in heaven's name could any one say that was snobbish? Birds of a feather.

"I quite agree with you," he answered. "A snob is a man who admires or despises another because he is of a higher social rank than his own. It is the most vulgar failing of our English middle class."

He saw a flicker of amusement in Cooper's eyes. Cooper put up his hand to hide the broad smile that rose to his lips, and so made it more noticeable. Mr. Warburton's hands trembled a little.

Probably Cooper never knew how greatly he had offended his chief. A sensitive man himself, he was strangely insensitive to the feelings of others.

Their work forced them to see one another for a few minutes now and then during the day, and they met at six to have a drink on Mr. Warburton's verandah. This was an old-established custom of the country which Mr. Warburton would not for the world have broken. But they ate their meals separately, Cooper in his bungalow and Mr. Warburton at the Fort. After the office work was over they walked till dusk fell, but they walked apart. There were but few paths in this country, where the jungle pressed close upon the plantations of the village, and when Mr. Warburton caught sight of his assistant passing along with his loose stride, he would make a circuit in order to avoid him. Cooper, with his bad manners, his conceit in his own judgment and his intolerance, had already got on his nerves; but it was not till Cooper had been on the station for a couple of months that an incident happened which turned the Resident's dislike into bitter hatred.

Mr. Warburton was obliged to go up-country on a tour of inspection, and he left the station in Cooper's charge with more confidence, since he had definitely come to the conclusion that he was a capable fellow. The only thing he did not like was that he had no indulgence. He was honest, just and painstaking, but he had no sympathy for the natives. It bitterly amused Mr. Warburton to observe that this man, who looked upon himself as every man's equal, should look upon so many men as his own inferiors. He was hard, he had no patience with the native mind, and he was a bully. Mr. Warburton very quickly realized that the Malays disliked and feared him. He was not altogether displeased. He would not have liked it very much if his assistant had enjoyed a popularity which might rival his own. Mr. Warburton made his elaborate preparations, set out on his expedition, and in three weeks returned. Meanwhile the mail had arrived. The first thing that struck his eyes when he entered his sitting-room was a great pile of open newspapers. Cooper had met him, and they went into the room together. Mr. Warburton turned to one of the servants who had been left behind and sternly asked him what was the meaning of those open papers. Cooper hastened to explain.

"I wanted to read all about the Wolverhampton murder and so I borrowed your *Times*. I brought them back again. I knew you wouldn't mind."

Mr. Warburton turned on him, white with anger.

"But I do mind. I mind very much."

"I'm sorry," said Cooper, with composure. "The fact is, I simply couldn't wait till you came back."

"I wonder you didn't open my letters as well."

Cooper, unmoved, smiled at his chief's exasperation.

"Oh, that's not quite the same thing. After all, I couldn't imagine you'd mind my looking at your newspapers. There's nothing private in them."

"I very much object to any one reading my paper before me." He went up to the pile. There were nearly thirty numbers there. "I think it extremely impertinent of you. They're all mixed up."

"We can easily put them in order," said Cooper, joining him at the table.

"Don't touch them," cried Mr. Warburton.

"I say, it's childish to make a scene about a little thing like that."

"How dare you speak to me like that?"

"Oh, go to hell," said Cooper, and he flung out of the room.

Mr. Warburton, trembling with passion, was left contemplating his papers. His greatest pleasure in life had been destroyed by those callous, brutal hands. Most people living in out-of-the-way places when the mail comes tear open impatiently their papers and taking the last ones first glance at the latest news from home. Not so Mr. Warburton. His news-agent had instructions to write on the outside of the wrapper the date of each paper he despatched and when the great bundle arrived Mr. Warburton looked at these dates and with his blue pencil numbered them. His head-boy's orders were to place one on the table every morning in the verandah with the early cup of tea, and it was Mr. Warburton's especial delight to break the wrapper as he sipped his tea, and read the morning paper. It gave him the illusion of living at home. Every Monday morning he read the Monday *Times* of six weeks back and so went through the week. On Sunday he read *The Observer*. Like his habit of dressing for dinner it was a tie to civilization. And it was his pride that no matter how exciting the news was he had never yielded to the temptation of opening a paper before its allotted time. During the war the suspense sometimes had been intolerable, and when he read one day that a push was begun he had undergone agonies of suspense which he might have saved himself by the simple expedient of opening a later paper which lay waiting for him on a shelf. It had been the severest trial to which he had ever exposed himself, but he victoriously surmounted it. And that clumsy fool had broken open those neat tight packages because he wanted to know whether some horrid woman had murdered her odious husband.

Mr. Warburton sent for his boy and told him to bring wrappers. He folded up the papers as neatly as he could, placed a wrapper round each and numbered it. But it was a melancholy task.

"I shall never forgive him," he said. "Never."

Of course his boy had been with him on his expedition; he never traveled without him, for his boy knew exactly how he liked things, and Mr. Warburton was not the kind of jungle traveler who was prepared to dispense with his comforts; but in the interval since their arrival he had been gossiping in the servants' quarters. He had learnt that Cooper had had trouble with his boys. All but the youth Abas had left him. Abas had desired to go too, but his uncle had placed him there on the instructions of the Resident, and he was afraid to leave without his uncle's permission.

"I told him he had done well, Tuan," said the boy. "But he is unhappy. He says it is not a good house and he wishes to know if he may go as the others have gone."

"No, he must stay. The tuan must have servants. Have those who went been replaced?"

"No, Tuan, no one will go."

Mr. Warburton frowned. Cooper was an insolent fool, but he had an official position and must be suitably provided with servants. It was not seemly that his house should be improperly conducted.

"Where are the boys who ran away?"

"They are in the kampong, Tuan."

"Go and see them tonight and tell them that I expect them to be back in Tuan Cooper's house at dawn to-morrow."

"They say they will not go, Tuan."

"On my order?"

The boy had been with Mr. Warburton for fifteen years, and he knew every intonation of his master's voice. He was not afraid of him, they had gone through too much together, once in the jungle the Resident had saved his life and once, upset in some rapids, but for him the Resident would have been drowned; but he knew when the Resident must be obeyed without question.

"I will go to the kampong," he said.

Mr. Warburton expected that his subordinate would take the first opportunity to apologize for his rudeness, but Cooper had the ill-bred man's inability to express regret; and when they met next morning in the office he ignored the incident. Since Mr. Warburton had been away for three weeks it was necessary for them to have a somewhat prolonged interview. At the end of it Mr. Warburton dismissed him.

"I don't think there's anything else, thank you." Cooper turned to go, but Mr. Warburton stopped him. "I understand you've been having some trouble with your boys."

Cooper gave a harsh laugh.

"They tried to blackmail me. They had the damned cheek to run away, all except that incompetent fellow Abas—he knew when he was well off—but I just sat tight. They've all come to heel again."

"What do you mean by that?"

"This morning they were all back on their jobs, the Chinese cook and all. There they were, as cool as cucumbers; you would have thought they owned the place. I suppose they'd come to the conclusion that I wasn't such a fool as I looked."

"By no means. They came back on my express order."

Cooper flushed slightly.

"I should be obliged if you wouldn't interfere with my private concerns."

* "They're not your private concerns. When your servants run away it makes you ridiculous. You are perfectly free to make a fool of yourself, but I cannot allow you to be made a fool of. It is unseemly that your house should not be properly staffed. As soon as I heard that your boys had left you, I had them told to be back in their places at dawn. That'll do."

Mr. Warburton nodded to signify that the interview was at an end. Cooper took no notice.

"Shall I tell you what I did? I called them and gave the whole bally lot the sack. I gave them ten minutes to get out of the compound."

Mr. Warburton shrugged his shoulders.

"What makes you think you can get others?"

"I've told my own clerk to see about it."

Mr. Warburton reflected for a moment.

"I think you behaved very foolishly. You will do well to remember in future that good masters make good servants."

"Is there anything else you want to teach me?"

"I should like to teach you manners, but it would be an arduous task, and I have not the time to waste. I will see that you get boys."

"Please don't put yourself to any trouble on my account. I'm quite capable of getting them for myself."

Mr. Warburton smiled acidly. He had an inkling that Cooper disliked him as much as he disliked Cooper, and he knew that nothing is more galling than to be forced to accept the favors of a man you detest.

"Allow me to tell you that you have no more chance of getting Malay or Chinese servants here now than you have of getting an English butler or a French chef. No one will come to you except on an order from me. Would you like me to give it?"

"No."

"As you please. Good morning."

Mr. Warburton watched the development of the situation with acrid humor. Cooper's clerk was unable to persuade Malay, Dyak or Chinese to enter the house of such a master. Abas, the boy who remained faithful to him, knew how to cook only native food, and Cooper, a coarse feeder, found his gorge rise against the everlasting rice. There was no water-carrier, and in that great heat he needed several baths a day. He cursed

Abas, but Abas opposed him with sullen resistance and would not do more than he chose. It was galling to know that the lad stayed with him only because the Resident insisted. This went on for a fortnight and then, one morning, he found in his house the very servants whom he had previously dismissed. He fell into a violent rage, but he had learnt a little sense, and this time, without a word, he let them stay. He swallowed his humiliation, but the impatient contempt he had felt for Mr. Warburton's idiosyncrasies changed into a sullen hatred; the Resident with this malicious stroke had made him the laughing-stock of all the natives.   *

The two men now held no communication with one another. They broke the time-honored custom of sharing, notwithstanding personal dislike, a drink at six o'clock with any white man who happened to be at the station. Each lived in his own house as though the other did not exist. Now that Cooper had fallen into the work, it was necessary for them to have little to do with one another in the office. Mr. Warburton used his orderly to send any message he had to give his assistant, and his instructions he sent by formal letter. They saw one another constantly, that was inevitable, but did not exchange half a dozen words in a week. The fact that they could not avoid catching sight of one another got on their nerves. They brooded over their antagonism and Mr. Warburton, taking his daily walk, could think of nothing but how much he detested his assistant.

And the dreadful thing was that in all probability they would remain thus, facing each other in deadly enmity, till Mr. Warburton went on leave. It might be three years. He had no reason to send in a complaint to headquarters: Cooper did his work very well, and at that time men were hard to get. True, vague complaints reached him and hints that the natives found Cooper harsh. There was certainly a feeling of dissatisfaction among them. But when Mr. Warburton looked into specific cases, all he could say was that Cooper had shown severity where mildness would not have been misplaced and had been unfeeling when himself would have been sympathetic. He had done nothing for which he could be taken to task. But Mr. Warburton watched him. Hatred will often make a man clear-sighted, and he had a suspicion that Cooper was using the natives without consideration, yet keeping within the law, because he felt that thus he could exasperate his chief. One day perhaps he would go too far. None knew better than Mr. Warburton how irritable the incessant heat could make a man and how difficult it was to keep one's self-control after a sleepless night. He smiled softly to himself. Sooner or later Cooper would deliver himself into his hand.

When at last the opportunity came Mr. Warburton laughed aloud. Cooper had charge of the prisoners; they made roads, built sheds, rowed when it was necessary to send the prahu up- or down-stream, kept the town clean and otherwise usefully employed themselves. If well-behaved they even on occasion served as house-boys. Cooper kept them hard at it. He liked to see them work. He took pleasure in devising tasks for them; and seeing quickly enough that they were being made to do useless things the prisoners worked badly. He punished them by lengthening their hours. This was contrary to the regulations, and as soon as it was brought to the attention of Mr. Warburton, without referring the matter back to his subordinate, he gave instructions that the old hours should be kept; Cooper, going out for his walk, was astounded to see the prisoners strolling back to the jail; he had given instructions that they were not to knock off till dusk. When he asked the warder in charge why they had left off work he was told that it was the Resident's bidding.

White with rage he strode to the Fort. Mr. Warburton, in his spotless white ducks and his neat topee, with a walking-stick in his hand, followed by his dogs, was on the point of starting out on his afternoon stroll. He had watched Cooper go and knew that he had taken the road by the river. Cooper jumped up the steps and went straight up to the Resident.

"I want to know what the hell you mean by countermanding my order that the prisoners were to work till six," he burst out, beside himself with fury.

Mr. Warburton opened his cold blue eyes very wide and assumed an expression of great surprise.

"Are you out of your mind? Are you so ignorant that you do not know that that is not the way to speak to your official superior?"

"Oh, go to hell. The prisoners are my pidgin and you've got no right to interfere. You mind your business and I'll mind mine. I want to know what the devil you mean by making a damned fool of me. Every one in the place will know that you've countermanded my order."

Mr. Warburton kept very cool.

"You had no power to give the order you did. I countermanded it because it was harsh and tyrannical. Believe me, I have not made half such a damned fool of you as you have made of yourself."

"You disliked me from the first moment I came here. You've done everything you could to make the place impossible for me because I wouldn't lick your boots for you. You got your knife into me because I wouldn't flatter you."

Cooper, spluttering with rage, was nearing dangerous ground, and Mr. Warburton's eyes grew on a sudden colder and more piercing.

"You are wrong. I thought you were a cad, but I was perfectly satisfied with the way you did your work."

"You snob. You damned snob. You thought me a cad because I hadn't been to Eton. Oh, they told me in K.S. what to expect. Why, don't you know that you're the laughing-stock of the whole country? I could hardly help bursting into a roar of laughter when you told your celebrated story about the Prince of Wales. My God, how they shouted at the club when they told it. By God, I'd rather be the cad I am than the snob you are."

He got Mr. Warburton on the raw.

"If you don't get out of my house this minute I shall knock you down," he cried.

The other came a little closer to him and put his face in his.

"Touch me, touch me," he said. "By God, I'd like to see you hit me. Do you want me to say it again? Snob. Snob."

Cooper was three inches taller than Mr. Warburton, a strong, muscular young man. Mr. Warburton was fat and fifty-four. His clenched fist shot out. Cooper caught him by the arm and pushed him back.

"Don't be a damned fool. Remember I'm not a gentleman. I know how to use my hands."

He gave a sort of hoot, and, grinning all over his pale, sharp face, jumped down the verandah steps. Mr. Warburton, his heart in his anger pounding against his ribs, sank exhausted into a chair. His body tingled as though he had prickly heat. For one horrible moment he thought he was going to cry. But suddenly he was conscious that his head-boy was on the verandah and instinctively regained control of himself. The boy came forward and filled him a glass of whisky and soda. Without a word Mr. Warburton took it and drank it to the dregs.

"What do you want to say to me?" asked Mr. Warburton, trying to force a smile on to his strained lips.

"Tuan, the assistant tuan is a bad man. Abas wishes again to leave him."

"Let him wait a little. I shall write to Kuala Solor and ask that Tuan Cooper should go elsewhere."

"Tuan Cooper is not good with the Malays."

"Leave me."

The boy silently withdrew. Mr. Warburton was left alone with his thoughts. He saw the club at Kuala Solor, the men sitting round the table in the window in their flannels, when the night had driven them in from golf and tennis, drinking whiskies and gin pahits and laughing when they told the celebrated story of the Prince of Wales and himself at Marienbad. He was hot with shame and misery. A snob! They all thought him a snob. And he had always thought them very good fellows, he had always been gentleman enough to let it make no difference to him that they were of very second-rate position. He hated them now. But his hatred for them was nothing compared with his hatred for Cooper. And if it had come to blows Cooper could have thrashed him. Tears of mortification ran down his red, fat face. He sat there for a couple of hours smoking cigarette after cigarette, and he wished he were dead.

At last the boy came back and asked him if he would dress for dinner. Of course! He always dressed for dinner. He rose wearily from his chair and put on his stiff shirt and the high collar. He sat down at the prettily decorated table and was waited on as usual by the two boys while two others waved their great fans. Over there in the bungalow, two hundred yards away, Cooper was eating a filthy meal clad only in a sarong and a baju. His feet were bare and while he ate he probably read a detective story. After dinner Mr. Warburton sat down to write a letter. The Sultan was away, but he wrote, privately and confidentially, to his representative. Cooper did his work very well, he said, but the fact was that he couldn't get on with him. They were getting dreadfully on each other's nerves and he would look upon it as a very great favor if Cooper could be transferred to another post.

He despatched the letter next morning by special messenger. The answer came a fortnight later with the month's mail. It was a private note and ran as follows:

"MY DEAR WARBURTON:

"I do not want to answer your letter officially and so I am writing you a few lines myself. Of course if you insist I will put the matter up to the Sultan, but I think you would be much wiser to drop it. I know Cooper is a rough diamond, but he is capable, and he had a pretty thin time in the war, and I think he should be given every chance. I think you are a little too much inclined to attach importance to a man's social position. You must remember that times have changed. Of course it's a very good thing for a man to be a gentleman, but it's better that he should be competent and hard-working. I think if you'll exercise a little tolerance you'll get on very well with Cooper.

"Yours very sincerely,
"RICHARD TEMPLE."

The letter dropped from Mr. Warburton's hand. It was easy to read between the lines. Dick Temple, whom he had known for twenty years, Dick Temple, who came from quite a good county family, thought him a snob and for that reason had no patience with his request. Mr. Warburton felt on a sudden discouraged with life. The world of which he was a part had passed away, and the future belonged to a meaner generation. Cooper represented it and Cooper he hated with all his heart. He stretched out his hand to fill his glass and at the gesture his head-boy stepped forward.

"I didn't know you were there."

The boy picked up the official letter. Ah, that was why he was waiting.

"Does Tuan Cooper go, Tuan?"

"No."

"There will be a misfortune."

For a moment the words conveyed nothing to his lassitude. But only for a moment. He sat up in his chair and looked at the boy. He was all attention.

"What do you mean by that?"

"Tuan Cooper is not behaving rightly with Abas."

Mr. Warburton shrugged his shoulders. How should a man like Cooper know how to treat servants? Mr. Warburton knew the type: he would be grossly familiar with them at one moment and rude and inconsiderate the next.

"Let Abas go back to his family."

"Tuan Cooper holds back his wages so that he may not run away. He has paid him nothing for three months. I tell him to be patient. But he is angry, he will not listen to reason. If the tuan continues to use him ill there will be a misfortune."

"You were right to tell me."

The fool! Did he know so little of the Malays as to think he could safely injure them? It would serve him damned well right if he got a kris in his back. A kris. Mr. Warburton's heart seemed on a sudden to miss a beat. He had only to let things take their course and one fine day he would be rid of Cooper. He smiled faintly as the phrase, a masterly inactivity, crossed his mind. And now his heart beat a little quicker, for he saw the man he hated lying on his face in a pathway of the jungle with a knife in his back. A fit end for the cad and the bully. Mr. Warburton sighed. It was his duty to warn him and of course he must do it. He wrote a brief and formal note to Cooper asking him to come to the Fort at once.

In ten minutes Cooper stood before him. They had not spoken to one another since the day when Mr. Warburton had nearly struck him. He did not now ask him to sit down.

"Did you wish to see me?" Cooper asked.

He was untidy and none too clean. His face and hands were covered with little red blotches where mosquitoes had bitten him and he had scratched himself till the blood came. His long, thin face bore a sullen look.

"I understand that you are again having trouble with your servants. Abas, my head-boy's nephew, complains that you have held back his wages for three months. I consider it a most arbitrary proceeding. The lad wishes to leave you, and I certainly do not blame him. I must insist on your paying what is due to him."

"I don't choose that he should leave me. I am holding back his wages as a pledge of his good behavior."

"You do not know the Malay character. The Malays are very sensitive to injury and ridicule. They are passionate and revengeful. It is my duty to warn you that if you drive this boy beyond a certain point you run a great risk."

Cooper gave a contemptuous chuckle.

"What do you think he'll do?"

"I think he'll kill you."

"Why should you mind?"

"Oh, I wouldn't," replied Mr. Warburton, with a faint laugh. "I should bear it with the utmost fortitude. But I feel the official obligation to give you a proper warning."

"Do you think I'm afraid of a damned nigger?"

"It's a matter of entire indifference to me."

"Well, let me tell you this, I know how to take care of myself; that boy Abas is a dirty, thieving rascal, and if he tries any monkey tricks on me, by God, I'll wring his bloody neck."

"That was all I wished to say to you," said Mr. Warburton. "Good evening."

Mr. Warburton gave him a little nod of dismissal. Cooper flushed, did not for a moment know what to say or do, turned on his heel and stumbled out of the room. Mr. Warburton watched him go with an icy smile on his lips. He had done his duty. But what would he have thought had he known that when Cooper got back to his bungalow, so silent and cheerless, he threw himself down on his bed and in his bitter loneliness on a sudden lost all control of himself? Painful sobs tore his chest and heavy tears rolled down his thin cheeks.

After this Mr. Warburton seldom saw Cooper, and never spoke to him. He read his *Times* every morning, did his work at the office, took his exercise, dressed for dinner, dined and sat by the river smoking his cheroot. If by chance he ran across Cooper he cut him dead. Each, though never for a moment unconscious of the propinquity, acted as though the other did not exist. Time did nothing to assuage their animosity. They watched one another's actions and each knew what the other did. Though Mr. Warburton had been a keen shot in his youth, with age he had acquired a distaste for killing the wild things of the jungle, but on Sundays and holidays Cooper went out with his gun: if he got something it was a triumph over Mr. Warburton; if not, Mr. Warburton shrugged his shoulders and chuckled. These counter-jumpers trying to be sportsmen! Christmas was a bad time for both of them: they ate their dinners alone, each in his own quarters, and they got deliberately drunk. They were the only white men within two hundred miles and they lived within shouting distance of each other. At the beginning of the year Cooper went down with fever, and when Mr. Warburton caught sight of him again he was surprised to see how thin he had grown. He looked ill and worn. The solitude, so much more unnatural because it was due to no necessity, was getting on his nerves. It was getting on Mr. Warburton's too, and often he could not sleep at night. He lay awake brooding. Cooper was drinking heavily and surely the breaking point was near; but in his dealings with the natives he took care to do nothing that might expose him to his chief's rebuke. They fought a grim and silent battle with one another. It was a test of endurance. The months passed, and neither gave sign of weakening. They were like men dwelling in regions of eternal night, and their souls were oppressed with the knowledge that never would the day dawn for them. It looked as though their lives would continue for ever in this dull and hideous monotony of hatred.

And when at last the inevitable happened it came upon Mr. Warburton with all the shock of the unexpected. Cooper accused the boy Abas of stealing some of his clothes, and when the boy denied the theft took him by the scruff of the neck and kicked him down the steps of the bungalow. The boy demanded his wages, and Cooper flung at his head every word of abuse he knew. If he saw him in the compound in an hour he would hand him over to the police. Next morning the boy waylaid him outside the Fort when he was walking over to his office, and again demanded his wages. Cooper struck him in the face with his clenched fist. The boy fell to the ground and got up with blood streaming from his nose.

Cooper walked on and set about his work. But he could not attend to it. The blow had calmed his irritation, and he knew that he had gone too far. He was worried. He felt ill, miserable and discouraged. In the adjoining office sat Mr. Warburton, and his impulse was to go and tell him what he had done; he made a movement in his chair, but he knew with what icy scorn he would listen to the story. He could see his patronizing smile. For a moment he had an uneasy fear of what Abas might do. Warburton had warned him all right. He sighed. What a fool he had been! But he shrugged his shoulders impatiently. He did not care; a fat lot he had to live for. It was all Warburton's fault; if he hadn't put his back up nothing like this would have happened. Warburton had made life a hell for him from the start. The snob. But they were all like that: it was because he was a Colonial. It was a damned shame that he had never got his commission in the war; he was as good as any one else. They were a lot of dirty snobs. He was damned if he was going to knuckle under now. Of course Warburton would hear of what had happened; the old devil knew everything. He wasn't afraid. He wasn't afraid of any Malay in Borneo, and Warburton could go to blazes.

He was right in thinking that Mr. Warburton would know what had happened. His head-boy told him when he went in to tiffin.

"Where is your nephew now?"

"I do not know, Tuan. He has gone."

Mr. Warburton remained silent. After luncheon as a rule he slept a little, but today he found himself very wide awake. His eyes involuntarily sought the bungalow where Cooper was now resting.

The idiot! Hesitation for a little was in Mr. Warburton's mind. Did the man know in what peril he was? He supposed he ought to send for him. But each time he had tried to reason with Cooper, Cooper had insulted him. Anger, furious anger welled up suddenly in Mr. Warburton's heart, so that the veins on his temples stood out and he clenched his fists. The cad had had his warning. Now let him take what was coming to him. It was no business of his and if anything happened it was not his fault. But perhaps they would wish in Kuala Solor that they had taken his advice and transferred Cooper to another station.

He was strangely restless that night. After dinner he walked up and down the verandah. When the boy went away to his own quarters, Mr. Warburton asked him whether anything had been seen of Abas.

"No, Tuan, I think maybe he has gone to the village of his mother's brother."

Mr. Warburton gave him a sharp glance, but the boy was looking down and their eyes did not meet. Mr. Warburton went down to the river and sat in his arbor. But peace was denied him. The river flowed ominously silent. It was like a great serpent gliding with sluggish movement towards the sea. And the trees of the jungle over the water were heavy with a breathless menace. No bird sang. No breeze ruffled the leaves of the cassias. All around him it seemed as though something waited.

He walked across the garden to the road. He had Cooper's bungalow in full view from there. There was a light in his sitting-room and across the road floated the sound of rag-time. Cooper was playing his gramophone. Mr. Warburton shuddered; he had never got over his instinctive dislike of that instrument. But for that he would have gone over and spoken to Cooper. He turned and went back to his own house. He read late into the night, and at last he slept. But he did not sleep very long, he had terrible dreams, and he seemed to be awakened by a cry. Of course that was a dream too, for no cry—from the bungalow for instance—could be heard in his room. He lay awake till dawn. Then he heard hurried steps and the sound of voices, his head-boy burst into the room without his fez, and Mr. Warburton's heart stood still.

"Tuan, Tuan."

Mr. Warburton jumped out of bed.

"I'll come at once."

He put on his slippers; and in his sarong and pyjama-jacket walked across his compound and into Cooper's. Cooper was lying in bed, with his mouth open, and a kris sticking in his heart. He had been killed in his sleep. Mr. Warburton started, but not because he had not expected to see just such a sight, he started because he felt in himself a sudden glow of exultation. A great burden had been lifted from his shoulders.

Cooper was quite cold. Mr. Warburton took the kris out of the wound, it had been thrust in with such force that he had to use an effort to get it out, and looked at it. He recognized it. It was a kris that a dealer had offered him some weeks before and which he knew Cooper had bought.

"Where is Abas?" he asked sternly.

"Abas is at the village of his mother's brother."

The sergeant of the native police was standing at the foot of the bed.

"Take two men and go to the village and arrest him."

Mr. Warburton did what was immediately necessary. With set face he gave orders. His words were short and peremptory. Then he went back to the Fort. He shaved and had his bath, dressed and went into the dining-room. By the side of his plate *The Times* in its wrapper lay waiting for him. He helped himself to some fruit. The head-boy poured out his tea while the second handed him a dish of eggs. Mr. Warburton ate with a good appetite. The head-boy waited.

"What is it?" asked Mr. Warburton.

"Tuan, Abas, my nephew, was in the house of his mother's brother all night. It can be proved. His uncle will swear that he did not leave the kampong."

Mr. Warburton turned upon him with a frown.

"Tuan Cooper was killed by Abas. You know it as well as I know it. Justice must be done."

"Tuan, you would not hang him?"

Mr. Warburton hesitated an instant, and though his voice remained set and stern a change came into his eyes. It was a flicker which the Malay was quick to notice and across his own eyes flashed an answering look of understanding.

"The provocation was very great. Abas will be sentenced to a term of imprisonment." There was a pause while Mr. Warburton helped himself to marmalade. "When he has served a part of his sentence in prison I will take him into this house as a boy. You can train him in his duties. I have no doubt that in the house of Tuan Cooper he got into bad habits."

"Shall Abas give himself up, Tuan?"

"It would be wise of him."

The boy withdrew. Mr. Warburton took his *Times* and neatly slit the wrapper. He loved to unfold the heavy, rustling pages. The morning, so fresh and cool, was delicious and for a moment his eyes wandered out over his garden with a friendly glance. A great weight had been lifted from his mind. He turned to the columns in which were announced the births, deaths, and marriages. That was what he always looked at first. A name he knew caught his attention. Lady Ormskirk had had a son at last. By George, how pleased the old dowager must be! He would write her a note of congratulation by the next mail.

Abas would make a very good house-boy.

That fool Cooper!

COMMENT AND QUESTION

1. In this story, Warburton is a snob and Cooper a cad. Neither, therefore, is a gentleman. Why not? What difference would being a gentleman have made?

2. Both men have the defects of their virtues. What are the worst qualities of each? The best? Where is each man right in his attitudes? Where wrong? How each man treats the Malays is a key detail.

3. Is it possible to choose between the two men, possible to sympathize with one man to the exclusion of the other?

4. The suspense is well developed. Find the earliest sign of antagonism. Beginning with that point, find in order (1) a hidden personal quarrel, (2) an open personal quarrel, (3) a hidden professional quarrel, (4) an open professional quarrel that ends in physical violence, and finally (5) complete estrangement.

5. The story is in part a satire on the English caste system. Look for it in details about education, sports and sportsmanship, colonials, the army, and the English social life of Mr. Warburton.

6. Where there is satire, there is usually irony. What is ironical about Cooper's "democracy," the isolation of two white men in a jungle, and the statement, "Mr. Cooper, I presume?"

7. Does the setting influence the action? Is the title a good one? Would the two men have been incompatible in a large city?

8. What combination of causes brings about the final event? In the first paragraph, for example, we learn of Warburton that he "was accustomed to loneliness."

9. The point of view in this story is chiefly omniscient and emphasizes the mind and feeling of Warburton. At times the story is told dramatically. Find sections where Maugham "tells" us about a character and compare those sections with scenes where the characters are "dramatized." Is Maugham more successful with one type of narration than with the other? Could the story have been told completely from the point of view of Warburton?

FIRST CONFESSION

BY FRANK O'CONNOR

FRANK O'CONNOR (1903–   ) is the pseudo-
nym of Michael O'Donovan. He lives in Ireland and most of his writing reflects the Irish
character and the Irish setting. He was educated by the Christian Brothers in Cork, was
a director of the Abbey Theatre until 1939,
and is a member of the Irish Academy of
Letters. Among his best known volumes of
short stories are *Guests of the Nation* (1931),
Bones of Contention (1936), *Crab-Apple
Jelly* (1944), *Traveller's Samples* (1951),
and *The Stories of Frank O'Connor* (1952).
In 1956 he published *The Mirror in the Roadway*, a critical work on the technique of the
novel.

IT was a Saturday afternoon in early spring. A small boy whose face
looked as though it had been but newly scrubbed was being led by the
hand by his sister through a crowded street. The little boy showed a
marked reluctance to proceed; he affected to be very interested in the
shop-windows. Equally, his sister seemed to pay no attention to them.
She tried to hurry him; he resisted. When she dragged him he began
to bawl. The hatred with which she viewed him was almost diabolical,
but when she spoke her words and tone were full of passionate sympathy.

"Ah, sha, God help us!" she intoned into his ear in a whine of com-
miseration.

"Leave me go!" he said, digging his heels into the pavement. "I don't
want to go. I want to go home."

"But, sure, you can't go home, Jackie. You'll have to go. The parish
priest will be up to the house with a stick."

"I don't care. I won't go."

"Oh, Sacred Heart, isn't it a terrible pity you weren't a good boy?

Oh, Jackie, me heart bleeds for you! I don't know what they'll do to you at all, Jackie, me poor child. And all the trouble you caused your poor old nanny, and the way you wouldn't eat in the same room with her, and the time you kicked her on the shins, and the time you went for me with the bread knife under the table. I don't know will he ever listen to you at all, Jackie. I think meself he might sind you to the bishop. Oh, Jackie, how will you think of all your sins?"

Half stupefied with terror, Jackie allowed himself to be led through the sunny streets to the very gates of the church. It was an old one with two grim iron gates and a long, low, shapeless stone front. At the gates he stuck, but it was already too late. She dragged him behind her across the yard, and the commiserating whine with which she had tried to madden him gave place to a yelp of triumph.

"Now you're caught! Now, you're caught. And I hope he'll give you the pinitintial psalms! That'll cure you, you suppurating little caffler!"

Jackie gave himself up for lost. Within the old church there was no stained glass; it was cold and dark and desolate, and in the silence, the trees in the yard knocked hollowly at the tall windows. He allowed himself to be led through the vaulted silence, the intense and magical silence which seemed to have frozen within the ancient walls, buttressing them and shouldering the high wooden roof. In the street outside, yet seeming a million miles away, a ballad singer was drawling a ballad.

Nora sat in front of him beside the confession box. There were a few old women before her, and later a thin, sad-looking man with long hair came and sat beside Jackie. In the intense silence of the church that seemed to grow deeper from the plaintive moaning of the ballad singer, he could hear the buzz-buzz-buzz of a woman's voice in the box, and then the husky ba-ba-ba of the priest's. Lastly the soft thud of something that signalled the end of the confession, and out came the woman, head lowered, hands joined, looking neither to right nor left, and tip-toed up to the altar to say her penance.

It seemed only a matter of seconds till Nora rose and with a whispered injunction disappeared from his sight. He was all alone. Alone and next to be heard and the fear of damnation in his soul. He looked at the sad-faced man. He was gazing at the roof, his hands joined in prayer. A woman in a red blouse and black shawl had taken her place below him. She uncovered her head, fluffed her hair out roughly with her hand, brushed it sharply back, then, bowing, caught it in a knot and pinned it on her neck. Nora emerged. Jackie rose and looked at her with a hatred which was inappropriate to the occasion and the place. Her hands were joined on her stomach, her eyes modestly lowered, and her face had an expression of the most rapt and tender recollection. With death in his heart he crept into the compartment she left open and drew the door shut behind him.

He was in pitch darkness. He could see no priest nor anything else. And anything he had heard of confession got all muddled up in his mind. He knelt to the right-hand wall and said: "Bless me, father, for I have sinned. This is my first confession." Nothing happened. He repeated it louder. Still it gave no answer. He turned to the opposite wall, genu- flected first, then again went on his knees and repeated the charm. This time he was certain he would receive a reply, but none came. He repeated the process with the remaining wall without effect. He had the feeling of someone with an unfamiliar machine, of pressing buttons at random. And finally the thought struck him that God knew. God knew about the bad confession he intended to make and had made him deaf and blind so that he could neither hear nor see the priest.

Then as his eyes grew accustomed to the blackness, he perceived something he had not noticed previously: a sort of shelf at about the height of his head. The purpose of this eluded him for a moment. Then he understood. It was for kneeling on.

He had always prided himself upon his powers of climbing, but this took it out of him. There was no foothold. He slipped twice before he succeeded in getting his knee on it, and the strain of drawing the rest of his body up was almost more than he was capable of. However, he did at last get his two knees on it, there was just room for those, but his legs hung down uncomfortably and the edge of the shelf bruised his shins. He joined his hands and pressed the last remaining button. "Bless me, father, for I have sinned. This is my first confession."

At the same moment the slide was pushed back and a dim light streamed into the little box. There was an uncomfortable silence, and then an alarmed voice asked, "Who's there?" Jackie found it almost impossible to speak into the grille which was on a level with his knees, but he got a firm grip of the molding above it, bent his head down and sideways, and as though he were hanging by his feet like a monkey found himself looking almost upside down at the priest. But the priest was looking sideways at him, and Jackie, whose knees were being tortured by this new position, felt it was a queer way to hear confessions.

"'Tis me, father," he piped, and then, running all his words together in excitement, he rattled off, "Bless me, father, for I have sinned. This is my first confession."

"What?" exclaimed a deep and angry voice, and the sombre soutane figure stood bolt upright, disappearing almost entirely from Jackie's view. "What does this mean? What are you doing there? Who are you?"

And with the shock Jackie felt his hands lose their grip and his legs their balance. He discovered himself tumbling into space, and, falling, he knocked his head against the door, which shot open and permitted him to thump right into the center of the aisle. Straight on this came a small, dark-haired priest with a biretta well forward on his head. At the same time Nora came skeltering madly down the church.

"Lord God!" she cried. "The snivelling little caffler! I knew he'd do it! I knew he'd disgrace me!"

Jackie received a clout over the ear which reminded him that for some strange reason he had not yet begun to cry and that people might possibly think he wasn't hurt at all. Nora slapped him again.

"What's this? What's this?" cried the priest. "Don't attempt to beat the child, you little vixen!"

"I can't do me pinance with him," cried Nora shrilly, cocking a shocked eye on the priest. "He have me driven mad. Stop your crying, you dirty scut! Stop it now or I'll make you cry at the other side of your ugly puss!"

"Run away out of this, you little jade!" growled the priest. He suddenly began to laugh, took out a pocket handkerchief, and wiped Jackie's nose. "You're not hurt, sure you're not. Show us the ould head. . . . Ah, 'tis nothing. 'Twill be better before you're twice married. . . . So you were coming to confession?"

"I was, father."

"A big fellow like you should have terrible sins. Is it your first?"

"'Tis, father."

"Oh, my, worse and worse! Here, sit down there and wait till I get rid of these ould ones and we'll have a long chat. Never mind that sister of yours."

With a feeling of importance that glowed through his tears Jackie waited. Nora stuck out her tongue at him, but he didn't even bother to reply. A great feeling of relief was welling up in him. The sense of oppression that had been weighing him down for a week, the knowledge that he was about to make a bad confession, disappeared. Bad confession, indeed! He had made friends, made friends with the priest, and the priest expected, even demanded terrible sins. Oh, women! Women! It was all women and girls and their silly talk. They had no real knowledge of the world!

And when the time came for him to make his confession he did not beat about the bush. He may have clenched his hands and lowered his eyes, but wouldn't anyone?

"Father," he said huskily, "I made it up to kill me grandmother."

There was a moment's pause. Jackie did not dare to look up, but he could feel the priest's eyes on him. The priest's voice also seemed a trifle husky.

"Your grandmother?" he asked, but he didn't after all sound very angry.

"Yes, father."

"Does she live with you?"

"She do, father."

"And why did you want to kill her?"

"Oh, God, father, she's a horrible woman!"

"Is she now?"

"She is, father."

"What way is she horrible?"

Jackie paused to think. It was hard to explain.

"She takes snuff, father."

"Oh, my!"

"And she goes round in her bare feet, father."

"Tut-tut-tut!"

"She's a horrible woman, father," said Jackie with sudden earnestness. "She takes porter. And she ates the potatoes off the table with her hands. And me mother do be out working most days, and since that one came 'tis she gives us our dinner and I can't ate the dinner." He found himself sniffling. "And she gives pinnies to Nora and she doesn't give no pinnies to me because she knows I can't stand her. And me father sides with her, father, and he bates me, and me heart is broken and wan night in bed I made it up the way I'd kill her."

Jackie began to sob again, rubbing his nose with his sleeve, as he remembered his wrongs.

"And what way were you going to kill her?" asked the priest smoothly.

"With a hatchet, father."

"When she was in bed?"

"No, father."

"How, so?"

"When she ates the potatoes and drinks the porter she falls asleep, father."

"And you'd hit her then?"

"Yes, father."

"Wouldn't a knife be better?"

"'Twould, father, only I'd be afraid of the blood."

"Oh, of course. I never thought of the blood."

"I'd be afraid of that, father. I was near hitting Nora with the bread knife one time she came after me under the table, only I was afraid."

"You're a terrible child," said the priest with awe.

"I am, father," said Jackie noncommittally, sniffling back his tears.

"And what would you do with the body?"

"How, father?"

"Wouldn't someone see her and tell?"

"I was going to cut her up with a knife and take away the pieces and bury them. I could get an orange box for threepence and make a cart to take them away."

"My, my," said the priest. "You had it all well planned."

"Ah, I tried that," said Jackie with mounting confidence. "I borrowed a cart and practised it by meself one night after dark."

"And weren't you afraid?"

"Ah, no," said Jackie half-heartedly. "Only a bit."

"You have terrible courage," said the priest. "There's a lot of people I want to get rid of, but I'm not like you. I'd never have the courage. And hanging is an awful death."

"Is it?" asked Jackie, responding to the brightness of a new theme.

"Oh, an awful blooming death!"

"Did you ever see a fellow hanged?"

"Dozens of them, and they all died roaring."

"Jay!" said Jackie.

"They do be swinging out of them for hours and the poor fellows lepping and roaring, like bells in a belfry, and then they put lime on them to burn them up. Of course, the pretend they're dead but sure, they don't be dead at all."

"Jay!" said Jackie again.

"So if I were you I'd take my time and think about it. In my opinion 'tisn't worth it, not even to get rid of a grandmother. I asked dozens of fellows like you that killed their grandmothers about it, and they all said, no, 'twasn't worth it. . . ."

Nora was waiting in the yard. The sunlight struck down on her across the high wall and its brightness made his eyes dazzle. "Well?" she asked. "What did he give you?"

"Three Hail Marys."

"You mustn't have told him anything."

"I told him everything," said Jackie confidently.

"What did you tell him?"

"Things you don't know."

"Bah! He gave you three Hail Marys because you were a cry baby!"

Jackie didn't mind. He felt the world was very good. He began to whistle as well as the hindrance in his jaw permitted.

"What are you sucking?"

"Bull's eyes."

"Was it he gave them to you?"

"'Twas."

"Almighty God!" said Nora. "Some people have all the luck. I might as well be a sinner like you. There's no use in being good."

COMMENT AND QUESTION

1. The boy in this story is seven or eight years old. He has not yet made a confession. No more than many of the readers of this story does Jackie know what the interior of a Catholic confessional looks like.

Kneeling in the confessional, penitents usually fold their hands in prayer on a small shelf before them. This is the little shelf to which

Jackie climbs. Jackie's first exploratory movements in the confessional occur while the priest is hearing the confession of the person on the other side. The soft thud Jackie hears is that of a sliding door which the priest pushes back in order that he may hear the penitent through a grille or screen.

2. Jackie sits in the church with the fear of damnation in his soul because he is about to make a bad confession. He is about to lie to the priest and hence to God. Why has he resolved to make a bad confession?

3. The priest shows a love of children and a knowledge of child psychology. Where is he most adroit?

4. This story can be commended for its economy. How swiftly do we come to know about the priest's character?

5. Notice Jackie's first impression of the church as he is being dragged across the yard, and the brightness in his eyes at the end.

6. Humor has been defined in many ways. Consider the following definitions (enunciated by the late Professor George Pierce Baker).

    a. "Farce consists of improbable people doing improbable things."

    b. "Low comedy consists of probable people doing probable things which are obviously funny."

    c. "High comedy consists of people with some depth of characterization who are funny in a subtle, intellectual way."

These definitions of three kinds of humor can be a valuable guide to a reader. First, they pivot on a sound critical question: "How true to life is the character portrayed?" Second, they can be applied to any form of humor the reader may come upon: cartoons, comic strips, plays, stories, movies.

What kind of humor appears in the comic strips "Li'l Abner," "Blondie," or "Pogo"? Recall any amusing moving picture you have seen recently. Did it seem to depend chiefly on farce or low comedy? Remember that an intellectual element is always present in high comedy.

The reader should remember that these three terms, farce, low comedy, and high comedy are not snobbish distinctions. Farce and low comedy can be very appealing. Much of the great humor in literature is farce or low comedy. Shakespeare, for example, ranges freely in his humor. Falstaff, one of the greatest comic characters in literature is drawn now in a farcical vein, now in the vein of low comedy, now in the vein of high comedy. Falstaff's lies are probably low comedy, his actions on the field of battle at Shrewsbury are probably farce, and his elaborate story about the robbers' being robbed, a fiction which he expects no one to believe, is probably high comedy.

Can you define the quality of humor in "First Confession?" Is it subtle or broad?

Compare "First Confession" with "Zone of Quiet." Which story has better characterization? Which story has stock devices or conventional motifs?

7. READING MODERN FICTION contains a number of stories laid in various regions of the world, among various races or nationalities. We have the Irish in Joyce and O'Connor; Mexicans in "María Concepción;" Russians in "The New Villa;" American Southerners in "The Last of the Belles;" American Indians in "The Captive;" the French and the Senegalese in "They Weren't Going to Die;" hill people of Kentucky in "Fight Number Twenty-Five;" Italians in "Mario and the Magician;" an Englishman, an Australian, and Malays in "Outstation."

In all of these stories the region or race or nationality helps to explain the actions of the characters. A quality of fading Southern culture is caught in "The Last of the Belles." The character of María Concepción, and her actions are due to her peasant origin in the section of Mexico where she lives. "Fight Number Twenty-Five" has a kinship with folk tales and fairy tales. Yet the background of the Kentucky hills makes it a plausible story.

"The New Villa" is a thoroughly Russian story. But the same story with the same theme could take place in another section of the globe. Under what circumstances could the story take place elsewhere? Could the story of María Concepción take place among other peasant peoples in the world?

In "Outstation" we get a clear picture of some distinctive qualities of the Malay people. But the Englishman remains an Englishman and the Australian, an Australian.

What role does region or background or locality play in a story?

MARÍA CONCEPCIÓN

BY KATHERINE ANNE PORTER

KATHERINE ANNE PORTER (1894–   ) was
born in Texas and has lived in Mexico,
Europe, and various parts of the United
States. She received a Guggenheim award for
her collection of short stories, *Flowering
Judas* (1930). Her other collections of short
stories are *Pale Horse, Pale Rider* (1939)
and *The Leaning Tower* (1944). She now
teaches at Stanford University in California.

Mᴀʀíᴀ ᴄᴏɴᴄᴇᴘᴄɪóɴ walked carefully, keeping to the middle of the
white dusty road, where the maguey thorns and the treacherous curved
spines of organ cactus had not gathered so profusely. She would have
enjoyed resting for a moment in the dark shade by the roadside, but she
had no time to waste drawing cactus needles from her feet. Juan and his
chief would be waiting for their food in the damp trenches of the buried
city.

She carried about a dozen living fowls slung over her right shoulder,
their feet fastened together. Half of them fell upon the flat of her back,
the balance dangled uneasily over her breast. They wriggled their be-
numbed and swollen legs against her neck, they twisted their stupefied
eyes and peered into her face inquiringly. She did not see them or think
of them. Her left arm was tired with the weight of the food basket, and
she was hungry after her long morning's work.

Her straight back outlined itself strongly under her clean bright blue
cotton rebozo. Instinctive serenity softened her black eyes, shaped like
almonds, set far apart, and tilted a bit endwise. She walked with the free,

natural, guarded ease of the primitive woman carrying an unborn child. The shape of her body was easy, the swelling life was not a distortion, but the right inevitable proportions of a woman. She was entirely contented. Her husband was at work and she was on her way to market to sell her fowls.

Her small house sat half-way up a shallow hill, under a clump of pepper-trees, a wall of organ cactus enclosing it on the side nearest to the road. Now she came down into the valley, divided by the narrow spring, and crossed a bridge of loose stones near the hut where María Rosa the beekeeper lived with her old godmother, Lupe the medicine woman. María Concepción had no faith in the charred owl bones, the singed rabbit fur, the cat entrails, the messes and ointments sold by Lupe to the ailing of the village. She was a good Christian, and drank simple herb teas for headache and stomachache, or bought her remedies bottled, with printed directions that she could not read, at the drugstore near the city market, where she went almost daily. But she often bought a jar of honey from young María Rosa, a pretty, shy child only fifteen years old.

María Concepción and her husband, Juan Villegas, were each a little past their eighteenth year. She had a good reputation with the neighbors as an energetic religious woman who could drive a bargain to the end. It was commonly known that if she wished to buy a new rebozo for herself or a shirt for Juan, she could bring out a sack of hard silver coins for the purpose.

She had paid for the license, nearly a year ago, the potent bit of stamped paper which permits people to be married in the church. She had given money to the priest before she and Juan walked together up to the altar the Monday after Holy Week. It had been the adventure of the villagers to go, three Sundays one after another, to hear the banns called by the priest for Juan de Dios Villegas and María Concepción Manríquez, who were actually getting married in the church, instead of behind it, which was the usual custom, less expensive, and as binding as any other ceremony. But María Concepción was always as proud as if she owned a hacienda.

She paused on the bridge and dabbled her feet in the water, her eyes resting themselves from the sun-rays in a fixed gaze to the far-off mountains, deeply blue under their hanging drift of clouds. It came to her that she would like a fresh crust of honey. The delicious aroma of bees, their slow thrilling hum, awakened a pleasant desire for a flake of sweetness in her mouth.

"If I do not eat it now, I shall mark my child," she thought, peering through the crevices in the thick hedge of cactus that sheered up nakedly, like bared knife blades set protectingly around the small clearing. The place was so silent she doubted if María Rosa and Lupe were at home.

The leaning jacal of dried rush-withes and corn sheaves, bound to tall saplings thrust into the earth, roofed with yellow maguey leaves flattened and overlapping like shingles, hunched drowsy and fragrant in the warmth of noonday. The hives, similarly made, were scattered towards the back of the clearing, like small mounds of clean vegetable refuse. Over each mound there hung a dusty golden shimmer of bees.

A light gay scream of laughter rose from behind the hut; a man's short laugh joined in. "Ah, hahahaha!" went the voices together high and low, like a song.

"So María Rosa has a man!" María Concepción stopped short, smiling, shifted her burden slightly, and bent forward shading her eyes to see more clearly through the spaces of the hedge.

María Rosa ran, dodging between beehives, parting two stunted jasmine bushes as she came, lifting her knees in swift leaps, looking over her shoulder and laughing in a quivering, excited way. A heavy jar, swung to her wrist by the handle, knocked against her thighs as she ran. Her toes pushed up sudden spurts of dust, her half-raveled braids showered around her shoulders in long crinkled wisps.

Juan Villegas ran after her, also laughing strangely, his teeth set, both rows gleaming behind the small soft black beard growing sparsely on his lips, his chin, leaving his brown cheeks girl-smooth. When he seized her, he clenched so hard her chemise gave way and ripped from her shoulder. She stopped laughing at this, pushed him away and stood silent, trying to pull up the torn sleeve with one hand. Her pointed chin and dark red mouth moved in an uncertain way, as if she wished to laugh again; her long black lashes flickered with the quick-moving lights in her hidden eyes.

María Concepción did not stir nor breathe for some seconds. Her forehead was cold, and yet boiling water seemed to be pouring slowly along her spine. An unaccountable pain was in her knees, as if they were broken. She was afraid Juan and María Rosa would feel her eyes fixed upon them and would find her there, unable to move, spying upon them. But they did not pass beyond the enclosure, nor even glance towards the gap in the wall opening upon the road.

Juan lifted one of María Rosa's loosened braids and slapped her neck with it playfully. She smiled softly, consentingly. Together they moved back through the hives of honey-comb. María Rosa balanced her jar on one hip and swung her long full petticoats with every step. Juan flourished his wide hat back and forth, walking proudly as a game-cock.

María Concepción came out of the heavy cloud which enwrapped her head and bound her throat, and found herself walking onward, keeping the road without knowing it, feeling her way delicately, her ears strumming as if all María Rosa's bees had hived in them. Her careful sense of duty kept her moving toward the buried city where Juan's chief, the American archeologist, was taking his midday rest, waiting for his food.

Juan and María Rosa! She burned all over now, as if a layer of tiny fig-cactus bristles, as cruel as spun glass, had crawled under her skin. She wished to sit down quietly and wait for her death, but not until she had cut the throats of her man and that girl who were laughing and kissing under the cornstalks. Once when she was a young girl she had come back from market to find her jacal burned to a pile of ash and her few silver coins gone. A dark empty feeling had filled her; she kept moving about the place, not believing her eyes, expecting it all to take shape again before her. But it was gone, and though she knew an enemy had done it, she could not find out who it was, and could only curse and threaten the air. Now here was a worse thing, but she knew her enemy. María Rosa, that sinful girl, shameless! She heard herself saying a harsh, true word about María Rosa, saying it aloud as if she expected someone to agree with her: "Yes, she is a whore! She has no right to live."

At this moment the gray untidy head of Givens appeared over the edges of the newest trench he had caused to be dug in his field of excavations. The long deep crevasses, in which a man might stand without being seen, lay crisscrossed like orderly gashes of a giant scalpel. Nearly all of the men of the community worked for Givens, helping him to uncover the lost city of their ancestors. They worked all the year through and prospered, digging every day for those small clay heads and bits of pottery and fragments of painted walls for which there was no good use on earth, being all broken and encrusted with clay. They themselves could make better ones, perfectly stout and new, which they took to town and peddled to foreigners for real money. But the unearthly delight of the chief in finding these worn-out things was an endless puzzle. He would fairly roar for joy at times, waving a shattered pot or a human skull above his head, shouting for his photographer to come and make a picture of this!

Now he emerged, and his young enthusiast's eyes welcomed María Concepción from his old-man face, covered with hard wrinkles and burned to the color of red earth. "I hope you've brought me a nice fat one." He selected a fowl from the bunch dangling nearest him as María Concepción, wordless, leaned over the trench. "Dress it for me, there's a good girl. I'll broil it."

María Concepción took the fowl by the head, and silently, swiftly drew her knife across its throat, twisting the head off with the casual firmness she might use with the top of a beet.

"Good God, woman, you do have nerve," said Givens, watching her. "I can't do that. It gives me the creeps."

"My home country is Guadalajara," exclaimed María Concepción, without bravado, as she picked and gutted the fowl.

She stood and regarded Givens condescendingly, that diverting white man who had no woman of his own to cook for him, and moreover appeared not to feel any loss of dignity in preparing his own food. He squatted now, eyes squinted, nose wrinkled to avoid the smoke, turning the roasting fowl busily on a stick. A mysterious man, undoubtedly rich, and Juan's chief, therefore to be respected, to be placated.

"The tortillas are fresh and hot, señor," she murmured gently. "With your permission I will now go to market."

"Yes, yes, run along; bring me another of these tomorrow." Givens turned his head to look at her again. Her grand manner sometimes reminded him of royalty in exile. He noticed her unnatural paleness. "The sun is too hot, eh?" he asked.

"Yes, sir. Pardon me, but Juan will be here soon?"

"He ought to be here now. Leave his food. The others will eat it."

She moved away; the blue of her rebozo became a dancing spot in the heat waves that rose from the gray-red soil. Givens liked his Indians best when he could feel a fatherly indulgence for their primitive childish ways. He told comic stories of Juan's escapades, of how often he had saved him, in the past five years, from going to jail, and even from being shot, for his varied and always unexpected misdeeds.

"I am never a minute too soon to get him out of one pickle or another," he would say. "Well, he's a good worker, and I know how to manage him."

After Juan was married, he used to twit him, with exactly the right shade of condescension, on his many infidelities to María Concepción. "She'll catch you yet, and God help you!" he was fond of saying, and Juan would laugh with immense pleasure.

It did not occur to María Concepción to tell Juan she had found him out. During the day her anger against him died, and her anger against María Rosa grew. She kept saying to herself, "When I was a young girl like María Rosa, if a man had caught hold of me so, I would have broken my jar over his head." She forgot completely that she had not resisted even so much as María Rosa, on the day that Juan had first taken hold of her. Besides she had married him afterwards in the church, and that was a very different thing.

Juan did not come home that night, but went away to war and María Rosa went with him. Juan had a rifle at his shoulder and two pistols at his belt. María Rosa wore a rifle also, slung on her back along with the blankets and the cooking pots. They joined the nearest detachment of troops in the field, and María Rosa marched ahead with the battalion of experienced women of war, which went over the crops like locusts, gathering provisions for the army. She cooked with them, and ate with them what was left after the men had eaten. After battles she went out on the field with the others to salvage clothing and ammunition and guns from the slain before they should begin to swell in the heat. Sometimes they would encounter the women from the other army, and a second battle as grim as the first would take place.

There was no particular scandal in the village. People shrugged, grinned. It was far better that they were gone. The neighbors went around saying that María Rosa was safer in the army than she would be in the same village with María Concepción.

María Concepción did not weep when Juan left her; and when the baby was born, and died within four days, she did not weep. "She is mere stone," said old Lupe, who went over and offered charms to preserve the baby.

"May you rot in hell with your charms," said María Concepción.

If she had not gone so regularly to church, lighting candles before the saints, kneeling with her arms spread in the form of a cross for hours at a time, and receiving holy communion every month, there might have been talk of her being devil-possessed, her face was so changed and blind-looking. But this was impossible when, after all, she had been married by the priest. It must be, they reasoned, that she was being punished for her pride. They decided that this was the true cause for everything: she was altogether too proud. So they pitied her.

During the year that Juan and María Rosa were gone María Concepción sold her fowls and looked after her garden and her sack of hard coins grew. Lupe had no talent for bees, and the hives did not prosper. She began to blame María Rosa for running away, and to praise María Concepción for her behavior. She used to see María Concepción at the market or at church, and she always said that no one could tell by looking at her now that she was a woman who had such a heavy grief.

"I pray God everything goes well with María Concepción from this out," she would say, "for she has had her share of trouble."

When some idle person repeated this to the deserted woman, she went down to Lupe's house and stood within the clearing and called to the medicine woman, who sat in her doorway stirring a mess of her infallible cure for sores: "Keep your prayers to yourself, Lupe, or offer them for others who need them. I will ask God for what I want in this world."

"And will you get it, you think, María Concepción?" asked Lupe, tittering cruelly and smelling the wooden mixing spoon. "Did you pray for what you have now?"

Afterward everyone noticed that María Concepción went oftener to church, and even seldomer to the village to talk with the other women as they sat along the curb, nursing their babies and eating fruit, at the end of the market-day.

"She is wrong to take us for enemies," said old Soledad, who was a thinker and a peace-maker. "All women have these troubles. Well, we should suffer together."

But María Concepción lived alone. She was gaunt, as if something were gnawing her away inside, her eyes were sunken, and she would not speak a word if she could help it. She worked harder than ever, and her butchering knife was scarcely ever out of her hand.

Juan and María Rosa, disgusted with military life, came home one day without asking permission of anyone. The field of war had unrolled itself, a long scroll of vexations, until the end had frayed out within twenty miles of Juan's village. So he and María Rosa, now lean as a wolf, burdened with a child daily expected, set out with no farewells to the regiment and walked home.

They arrived one morning about daybreak. Juan was picked up on sight by a group of military police from the small barracks on the edge of town, and taken to prison, where the officer in charge told him with impersonal cheerfulness that he would add one to a catch of ten waiting to be shot as deserters the next morning.

María Rosa, screaming and falling on her face in the road, was taken under the armpits by two guards and helped briskly to her jacal, now sadly run down. She was received with professional importance by Lupe, who helped the baby to be born at once.

Limping with foot soreness, a layer of dust concealing his fine new clothes got mysteriously from somewhere, Juan appeared before the captain at the barracks. The captain recognized him as head digger for his good friend Givens, and dispatched a note to Givens saying: "I am holding the person of Juan Villegas awaiting your further disposition."

When Givens showed up Juan was delivered to him with the urgent request that nothing be made public about so humane and sensible an operation on the part of military authority.

Juan walked out of the rather stifling atmosphere of the drumhead court, a definite air of swagger about him. His hat, of unreasonable dimensions and embroidered with silver thread, hung over one eyebrow, secured at the back by a cord of silver dripping with bright blue tassels. His shirt was of a checkerboard pattern in green and black, his white cotton trousers were bound by a belt of yellow leather tooled in red. His feet were bare, full of stone bruises, and sadly ragged as to toenails. He removed his cigarette from the corner of his full-lipped wide mouth. He removed the splendid hat. His black dusty hair, pressed moistly to his forehead, sprang up suddenly in a cloudy thatch on his crown. He bowed to the officer, who appeared to be gazing at a vacuum. He swung his arm wide in a free circle upsoaring towards the prison window, where forlorn heads poked over the window sill, hot eyes following after the lucky departing one. Two or three of the heads nodded, and a half dozen hands were flipped at him in an effort to imitate his own casual and heady manner.

Juan kept up this insufferable pantomime until they rounded the first clump of fig-cactus. Then he seized Givens' hand and burst into oratory. "Blessed be the day your servant Juan Villegas first came under your eyes. From this day my life is yours without condition, ten thousand thanks with all my heart!"

"For God's sake stop playing the fool," said Givens irritably. "Some day I'm going to be five minutes too late."

"Well, it is nothing much to be shot, my chief—certainly you know I was not afraid—but to be shot in a drove of deserters, against a cold wall, just in the moment of my home-coming, by order of that . . ."

Glittering epithets tumbled over one another like explosions of a rocket. All the scandalous analogies from the animal and vegetable worlds were applied in a vivid, unique and personal way to the life, loves, and family history of the officer who had just set him free. When he had quite cursed himself dry, and his nerves were soothed, he added: "With your permission, my chief!"

"What will María Concepción say to all this?" asked Givens. "You are very informal, Juan, for a man who was married in the church."

Juan put on his hat.

"Oh, María Concepción! That's nothing. Look, my chief, to be married in the church is a great misfortune for a man. After that he is not himself any more. How can that woman complain when I do not drink even at fiestas enough to be really drunk? I do not beat her; never, never. We were always at peace. I say to her, Come here, and she comes straight. I say, Go there, and she goes quickly. Yet sometimes I looked at her and thought, Now I am married to that woman in the church, and I felt a sinking inside, as if something were lying heavy on my stomach. With María Rosa it is all different. She is not silent; she talks. When she talks too much, I slap her and say, Silence, thou simpleton! and she weeps. She is just a girl with whom I do as I please. You know how she used to keep those clean little bees in their hives? She is like their honey to me. I swear it. I would not harm María Concepción because I am married to her in the church; but also, my chief, I will not leave María Rosa, because she pleases me more than any other woman."

"Let me tell you, Juan, things haven't been going as well as you think. You be careful. Some day María Concepción will just take your head off with that carving knife of hers. You keep that in mind."

Juan's expression was the proper blend of masculine triumph and sentimental melancholy. It was pleasant to see himself in the role of hero to two such desirable women. He had just escaped from the threat of a disagreeable end. His clothes were new and handsome, and they had cost him just nothing. María Rosa had collected them for him here and there after battles. He was walking in the early sunshine, smelling the good smells of ripening cactus-figs, peaches, and melons, of pungent berries dangling from the pepper-trees, and the smoke of his cigarette under his nose. He was on his way to civilian life with his patient chief. His situation was ineffably perfect, and he swallowed it whole.

"My chief," he addressed Givens handsomely, as one man of the world to another, "women are good things, but not at this moment. With your permission, I will now go to the village and eat. My God, *how* I shall eat! Tomorrow morning very early I will come to the buried city and work like seven men. Let us forget María Concepción and María Rosa. Each one in her place. I will manage them when the time comes."

News of Juan's adventure soon got abroad, and Juan found many friends about him during the morning. They frankly commended his way of leaving the army. It was in itself the act of a hero. The new hero ate a great deal and drank somewhat, the occasion being better than a feast-day. It was almost noon before he returned to visit María Rosa.

He found her sitting on a clean straw mat, rubbing fat on her three-hour-old son. Before this felicitous vision Juan's emotions so twisted him that he returned to the village and invited every man in the "Death and Resurrection" pulque shop to drink with him.

Having thus taken leave of his balance, he started back to María Rosa, and found himself unaccountably in his own house, attempting to beat María Concepción by way of re-establishing himself in his legal household.

María Concepción, knowing all the events of that unhappy day, was not in a yielding mood, and refused to be beaten. She did not scream nor implore; she stood her ground and resisted; she even struck at him. Juan, amazed, hardly knowing what he did, stepped back and gazed at her inquiringly through a leisurely whirling film which seemed to have lodged behind his eyes. Certainly he had not even thought of touching her. Oh, well, no harm done. He gave up, turned away, half-asleep on his feet. He dropped amiably in a shadowed corner and began to snore.

María Concepción, seeing that he was quiet, began to bind the legs of her fowls. It was market-day and she was late. She fumbled and tangled the bits of cord in her haste, and set off across the plowed fields instead of taking the accustomed road. She ran with a crazy panic in her head, her stumbling legs. Now and then she would stop and look about her, trying to place herself, then go on a few steps, until she realized that she was not going towards the market.

At once she came to her senses completely, recognized the thing that troubled her so terribly, was certain of what she wanted. She sat down quietly under a sheltering thorny bush and gave herself over to her long devouring sorrow. The thing which had for so long squeezed her whole body into a tight dumb knot of suffering suddenly broke with shocking violence. She jerked with the involuntary recoil of one who receives a blow, and the sweat poured from her skin as if the wounds of her whole life were shedding their salt ichor. Drawing her rebozo over her head, she bowed her forehead on her updrawn knees, and sat there in deadly silence and immobility. From time to time she lifted her head where the sweat formed steadily and poured down her face, drenching the front of her chemise, and her mouth had the shape of crying, but there were no tears and no sound. All her being was a dark confused memory of grief burning in her at night, of deadly baffled anger eating at her by day, until her very tongue tasted bitter, and her feet were as heavy as if she were mired in the muddy roads during the time of rains.

After a great while she stood up and threw the rebozo off her face, and set out walking again.

Juan awakened slowly, with long yawns and grumblings, alternated with short relapses into sleep full of visions and clamors. A blur of orange light seared his eyeballs when he tried to unseal his lids. There came from somewhere a low voice weeping without tears, saying meaningless phrases over and over. He began to listen. He tugged at the leash of his stupor, he strained to grasp those words which terrified him even though he could not quite hear them. Then he came awake with frightening suddenness, sitting up and staring at the long sharpened streak of light piercing the corn-husk walls from the level disappearing sun.

María Concepción stood in the doorway, looming colossally tall to his betrayed eyes. She was talking quickly, and calling his name. Then he saw her clearly.

"God's name!" said Juan, frozen to the marrow, "here I am facing my death!" for the long knife she wore habitually at her belt was in her hand. But instead, she threw it away, clear from her, and got down on her knees, crawling toward him as he had seen her crawl many times toward the shrine at Guadalupe Villa. He watched her approach with such horror that the hair of his head seemed to be lifting itself away from him. Falling forward upon her face, she huddled over him, lips moving in a ghostly whisper. Her words became clear, and Juan understood them all.

For a second he could not move nor speak. Then he took her head between both his hands, and supported her in this way, saying swiftly, anxiously reassuring, almost in a babble:

"Oh, thou poor creature! Oh, madwoman! Oh, my María Concepción, unfortunate! Listen. . . . Don't be afraid. Listen to me! I will hide thee away, I thy own man will protect thee! Quiet! Not a sound!"

Trying to collect himself, he held her and cursed under his breath for a few moments in the gathering darkness. María Concepción bent over, face almost on the ground, her feet folded under her, as if she would hide behind him. For the first time in his life Juan was aware of danger. This was danger. María Concepción would be dragged away between two gendarmes, with him following helpless and unarmed, to spend the rest of her days in Belén Prison, maybe. Danger! The night swarmed with threats. He stood up and dragged her up with him. She was silent and perfectly rigid, holding to him with resistless strength, her hands stiffened on his arms.

"Get me the knife," he told her in a whisper. She obeyed, her feet slipping along the hard earth floor, her shoulders straight, her arms close to her side. He lighted a candle. María Concepción held the knife out to him. It was stained and dark even to the handle with drying blood.

He frowned at her harshly, noting the same stains on her chemise and hands.

"Take off thy clothes and wash thy hands," he ordered. He washed the knife carefully, and threw the water wide of the doorway. She watched him and did likewise with the bowl in which she had bathed.

"Light the brasero and cook food for me," he told her in the same peremptory tone. He took her garments and went out. When he returned, she was wearing an old soiled dress, and was fanning the fire in the charcoal burner. Seating himself cross-legged near her, he stared at her as at a creature unknown to him, who bewildered him utterly, for whom there was no possible explanation. She did not turn her head, but kept silent and still, except for the movements of her strong hands fanning the blaze which cast sparks and small jets of white smoke, flaring and dying rhythmically with the motion of the fan lighting her face and darkening it by turns.

Juan's voice barely disturbed the silence: "Listen to me carefully, and tell me the truth, and when the gendarmes come here for us, thou shalt have nothing to fear. But there will be something for us to settle between us afterward."

The light from the charcoal burner shone in her eyes; a yellow phosphorescence glimmered behind the dark iris.

"For me everything is settled now," she answered, in a tone so tender, so grave, so heavy with suffering, that Juan felt his vitals contract. He wished to repent openly, not as a man, but as a very small child. He could not fathom her, nor himself, nor the mysterious fortunes of life grown so instantly confused where all had seemed so gay and simple. He felt too that she had become invaluable, a woman without equal among a million women, and he could not tell why. He drew an enormous sigh that rattled in his chest.

"Yes, yes, it is all settled. I shall not go away again. We must stay here together."

Whispering, he questioned her and she answered whispering, and he instructed her over and over until she had her lesson by heart. The hostile darkness of the night encroached upon them, flowing over the narrow threshold, invading their hearts. It brought with it sighs and murmurs, the pad of secretive feet in the near-by road, the sharp staccato whimper of wind through the cactus leaves. All these familiar, once friendly cadences were now invested with sinister terrors; a dread, form-less and uncontrollable, took hold of them both.

"Light another candle," said Juan, loudly, in too resolute, too sharp a tone. "Let us eat now."

They sat facing each other and ate from the same dish, after their old habit. Neither tasted what they ate. With food half-way to his mouth, Juan listened. The sound of voices rose, spread, widened at the turn of the road along the cactus wall. A spray of lantern light shot through the hedge, a single voice slashed the blackness, ripped the fragile layer of silence suspended above the hut.

"Juan Villegas!"

"Pass, friends!" Juan roared back cheerfully.

They stood in the doorway, simple cautious gendarmes from the vil-lage, mixed-bloods themselves with Indian sympathies, well known to all the community. They flashed their lanterns almost apologetically upon the pleasant, harmless scene of a man eating supper with his wife.

"Pardon, brother," said the leader. "Someone has killed the woman María Rosa, and we must question her neighbors and friends." He paused, and added with an attempt at severity, "Naturally!"

"Naturally," agreed Juan. "You know that I was a good friend of María Rosa. This is bad news."

They all went away together, the men walking in a group, María Concepción following a few steps in the rear, near Juan. No one spoke.

The two points of candlelight at María Rosa's head fluttered uneasily; the shadows shifted and dodged on the stained darkened walls. To María Concepción everything in the smothering enclosing room shared an evil restlessness. The watchful faces of those called as witnesses, the faces of old friends, were made alien by the look of speculation in their eyes. The ridges of the rose-colored rebozo thrown over the body varied con-tinually, as though the thing it covered was not perfectly in repose. Her eyes swerved over the body in the open painted coffin, from the candle tips at the head to the feet, jutting up thinly, the small scarred soles protruding, freshly washed, a mass of crooked, half-healed wounds, thorn-pricks and cuts of sharp stones. Her gaze went back to the candle flame, to Juan's eyes warning her, to the gendarmes talking among themselves. Her eyes would not be controlled.

With a leap that shook her her gaze settled upon the face of María Rosa. Instantly her blood ran smoothly again: there was nothing to fear. Even the restless light could not give a look of life to that fixed coun-tenance. She was dead. María Concepción felt her muscles give way softly; her heart began beating steadily without effort. She knew no more rancor against that pitiable thing, lying indifferently in its blue coffin under the fine silk rebozo. The mouth drooped sharply at the corners in a grimace of weeping arrested half-way. The brows were distressed; the dead flesh could not cast off the shape of its last terror. It was all finished. María Rosa had eaten too much honey and had had too much love. Now she must sit in hell, crying over her sins and her hard death forever and ever.

Old Lupe's cackling voice arose. She had spent the morning helping María Rosa, and it had been hard work. The child had spat blood the moment it was born, a bad sign. She thought then that bad luck would come to the house. Well, about sunset she was in the yard at the back of the house grinding tomatoes and peppers. She had left mother and babe asleep. She heard a strange noise in the house, a choking and smothered calling, like someone wailing in sleep. Well, such a thing is only natural. But there followed a light, quick, thudding sound—

"Like the blows of a fist?" interrupted an officer.

"No, not at all like such a thing."

"How do you know?"

"I am well acquainted with that sound, friends," retorted Lupe. "This was something else."

She was at a loss to describe it exactly. A moment later, there came the sound of pebbles rolling and slipping under feet; then she knew someone had been there and was running away.

"Why did you wait so long before going to see?"

"I am old and hard in the joints," said Lupe. "I cannot run after people. I walked as fast as I could to the cactus hedge, for it is only by this way that anyone can enter. There was no one in the road, sir, no one. Three cows, with a dog driving them; nothing else. When I got to María Rosa, she was lying all tangled up, and from her neck to her middle she was full of knife-holes. It was a sight to move the Blessed Image Himself! Her eyes were—"

"Never mind. Who came oftenest to her house before she went away? Did you know her enemies?"

Lupe's face congealed, closed. Her spongy skin drew into a network of secretive wrinkles. She turned withdrawn and expressionless eyes upon the gendarmes.

"I am an old woman. I do not see well. I cannot hurry on my feet. I know no enemy of María Rosa. I did not see anyone leave the clearing."

"You did not hear splashing in the spring near the bridge?"

"No, sir."

"Why, then, do our dogs follow a scent there and lose it?"

"God only knows, my friend. I am an old wo—"

"Yes. How did the footfalls sound?"

"Like the tread of an evil spirit!" Lupe broke forth in a swelling oracular tone that startled them. The Indians stirred uneasily, glanced at the dead, then at Lupe. They half expected her to produce the evil spirit among them at once.

The gendarme began to lose his temper.

"No, poor unfortunate; I mean, were they heavy or light? The footsteps of a man or of a woman? Was the person shod or barefoot?"

A glance at the listening circle assured Lupe of their thrilled attention. She enjoyed the dangerous importance of her situation. She could have ruined that María Concepción with a word, but it was even sweeter to make fools of these gendarmes who went about spying on honest people. She raised her voice again. What she had not seen she could not describe, thank God! No one could harm her because her knees were stiff and she could not run even to seize a murderer. As for knowing the difference between footfalls, shod or bare, man or woman, nay, between devil and human, who ever heard of such madness?

"My eyes are not ears, gentlemen," she ended grandly, "but upon my heart I swear those footsteps fell as the tread of the spirit of evil!"

"Imbecile!" yapped the leader in a shrill voice. "Take her away, one of you! Now, Juan Villegas, tell me—"

Juan told his story patiently, several times over. He had returned to his wife that day. She had gone to market as usual. He had helped her prepare her fowls. She had returned about mid-afternoon, they had talked, she had cooked, they had eaten, nothing was amiss. Then the gendarmes came with the news about María Rosa. That was all. Yes, María Rosa had run away with him, but there had been no bad blood between him and his wife on this account, nor between his wife and María Rosa. Everybody knew that his wife was a quiet woman.

María Concepción heard her own voice answering without a break. It was true at first she was troubled when her husband went away, but after that she had not worried about him. It was the way of men, she believed. She was a church-married woman and knew her place. Well, he had come home at last. She had gone to market, but had come back early, because now she had her man to cook for. That was all.

Other voices broke in. A toothless old man said: "She is a woman of good reputation among us, and María Rosa was not." A smiling young mother, Anita, baby at breast, said: "If no one thinks so, how can you accuse her? It was the loss of her child and not of her husband that changed her so." Another: "María Rosa had a strange life, apart from us. How do we know who might have come from another place to do her evil?" And old Soledad spoke up boldly: "When I saw María Concepción in the market today, I said, 'Good luck to you, María Concepción, this is a happy day for you!'" and she gave María Concepción a long easy stare, and the smile of a born wise-woman.

María Concepción suddenly felt herself guarded, surrounded, upborne by her faithful friends. They were around her, speaking for her, defending her, the forces of life were ranged invincibly with her against the beaten dead. María Rosa had thrown away her share of strength in them, she lay forfeited among them. María Concepción looked from one to the other of the circling, intent faces. Their eyes gave back reassurance, understanding, a secret and mighty sympathy.

The gendarmes were at a loss. They, too, felt that sheltering wall cast impenetrably around her. They were certain she had done it, and yet they could not accuse her. Nobody could be accused; there was not a shred of true evidence. They shrugged their shoulders and snapped their fingers and shuffled their feet. Well, then, good night to everybody. Many pardons for having intruded. Good health!

A small bundle lying against the wall at the head of the coffin squirmed like an eel. A wail, a mere sliver of sound, issued. María Concepción took the son of María Rosa in her arms.

"He is mine," she said clearly, "I will take him with me."

No one assented in words, but an approving nod, a bare breath of complete agreement, stirred among them as they made way for her.

María Concepción, carrying the child, followed Juan from the clearing. The hut was left with its lighted candles and a crowd of old women who would sit up all night, drinking coffee and smoking and telling ghost stories.

Juan's exaltation had burned out. There was not an ember of excitement left in him. He was tired. The perilous adventure was over. María Rosa had vanished, to come no more forever. Their days of marching, of eating, of quarreling and making love between battles, were all over. Tomorrow he would go back to dull and endless labor, he must descend into the trenches of the buried city as María Rosa must go into her grave. He felt his veins fill up with bitterness, with black unendurable melancholy. Oh, Jesus! what bad luck overtakes a man!

Well, there was no way out of it now. For the moment he craved only to sleep. He was so drowsy he could scarcely guide his feet. The occasional light touch of the woman at his elbow was as unreal, as ghostly as the brushing of a leaf against his face. He did not know why he had fought to save her, and now he forgot her. There was nothing in him except a vast blind hurt like a covered wound.

He entered the jacal, and without waiting to light a candle, threw off his clothing, sitting just within the door. He moved with lagging, half-awake hands, to strip his body of its heavy finery. With a long groaning sigh of relief he fell straight back on the floor, almost instantly asleep, his arms flung up and outward.

María Concepción, a small clay jar in her hand, approached the gentle little mother goat tethered to a sapling, which gave and yielded as she pulled at the rope's end after the farthest reaches of grass about her. The kid, tied up a few feet away, rose bleating, its feathery fleece shivering in the fresh wind. Sitting on her heels, holding his tether, she allowed him to suckle a few moments. Afterward—all her movements very deliberate and even—she drew a supply of milk for the child.

She sat against the wall of her house, near the doorway. The child, fed and asleep, was cradled in the hollow of her crossed legs. The silence overfilled the world, the skies flowed down evenly to the rim of the valley, the stealthy moon crept slantwise to the shelter of the mountains. She felt soft and warm all over; she dreamed that the newly born child was her own, and she was resting deliciously.

María Concepción could hear Juan's breathing. The sound vapored from the low doorway, calmly; the house seemed to be resting after a burdensome day. She breathed, too, very slowly and quietly, each inspiration saturating her with repose. The child's light, faint breath was a mere shadowy moth of sound in the silver air. The night, the earth under her, seemed to swell and recede together with a limitless, unhurried, benign breathing. She drooped and closed her eyes, feeling the slow rise and fall within her own body. She did not know what it was, but it eased her all through. Even as she was falling asleep, head bowed over the child, she was still aware of a strange, wakeful happiness.

COMMENT AND QUESTION

1. "María Concepción" is a study of primitive people glimpsed in their response to basic human experiences like birth, death, marriage. What actions in this story would astonish "civilized" people? What lies behind the profound distrust of law?

2. Primitive people do not lack a sense of humor. In spite of the violence, a strong comic feeling pervades "María Concepción." Find examples of it. The story has some fine passages describing mental and emotional states, and some of these passages are comic.

3. Can you explain the psychology of the following episodes?

a. Juan's attitude when his wife awakens him and tells him of her danger. Why is he proud? What other emotions move him? Notice the sudden use of "thou." What does this form indicate?

b. The neighbors' support of María Concepción.

c. The final scene with the child.

4. One object is associated always with María Concepción and only with her. What is this object? Similarly, one object is always associated with María Rosa. What function do such details perform in a story?

5. The character of Givens seems to emphasize the gulf between a primitive culture and a "civilized" culture. Consider the statement: "Givens liked his Indians best when he could feel a fatherly indulgence for their primitive childish ways." Do "primitive childish ways" describe the violence and passion in this story? How much does Givens know of what happens?

THE VALIANT WOMAN

BY J. F. POWERS

JAMES F. POWERS (1917–   ) was born in
Jacksonville, Illinois, and lived for a time in
Chicago. He has also lived in Minnesota; in
Wisconsin, where he taught writing courses
at Marquette University in Milwaukee; and
in Ireland, where he worked on a novel. He
received a Guggenheim Fellowship in 1948.
He has appeared in the *O. Henry Memorial
Award Prize Stories* and also in *Best American Short Stories*. His two volumes of short
stories, *Prince of Darkness and Other Stories*
(1947) and *The Presence of Grace* (1956),
have won great praise.

T HEY had come to the dessert in a dinner that was a shambles. "Well,
John," Father Nulty said, turning away from Mrs. Stoner and to Father
Firman, long gone silent at his own table. "You've got the bishop coming
for confirmations next week."

"Yes," Mrs. Stoner cut in, "and for dinner. And if he don't eat any
more than he did last year—"

Father Firman, in a rare moment, faced it. "Mrs. Stoner, the bishop is
not well. You know that."

"And after I fixed that fine dinner and all." Mrs. Stoner pouted in
Father Nulty's direction.

"I wouldn't feel bad about it, Mrs. Stoner," Father Nulty said. "He
never eats much anywhere."

"It's funny. And that new Mrs. Allers said he ate just fine when he

---

was there," Mrs. Stoner argued, and then spit out, "but she's a damned liar!"

Father Nulty, unsettled but trying not to show it, said, "Who's Mrs. Allers?"

"She's at Holy Cross," Mrs. Stoner said.

"She's the housekeeper," Father Firman added, thinking Mrs. Stoner made it sound as though Mrs. Allers were the pastor there.

"I swear I don't know what to do about the dinner this year," Mrs. Stoner said.

Father Firman moaned. "Just do as you've always done, Mrs. Stoner."

"Huh! And have it all to throw out! Is that any way to do?"

"Is there any dessert?" Father Firman asked coldly.

Mrs. Stoner leaped up from the table and bolted into the kitchen, mumbling. She came back with a birthday cake. She plunged it in the center of the table. She found a big wooden match in her apron pocket and thrust it at Father Firman.

"I don't like this bishop," she said. "I never did. And the way he went and cut poor Ellen Kennedy out of Father Doolin's will!"

She went back into the kitchen.

"Didn't they talk a lot of filth about Doolin and the housekeeper?" Father Nulty asked.

"I should think they did," Father Firman said. "All because he took her to the movies on Sunday night. After he died and the bishop cut her out of the will, though I hear he gives her a pension privately, they talked about the bishop."

"I don't like this bishop at all," Mrs. Stoner said, appearing with a cake knife. "Bishop Doran—there was the man!"

"We know," Father Firman said. "All man and all priest."

"He did know real estate," Father Nulty said.

Father Firman struck the match.

"Not on the chair!" Mrs. Stoner cried, too late.

Father Firman set the candle burning—it was suspiciously large and yellow, like a blessed one, but he could not be sure. They watched the fluttering flame.

"I'm forgetting the lights!" Mrs. Stoner said, and got up to turn them off. She went into the kitchen again.

The priests had a moment of silence in the candlelight.

"Happy birthday, John," Father Nulty said softly. "Is it fifty-nine you are?"

"As if you didn't know, Frank," Father Firman said, "and you the same but one."

Father Nulty smiled, the old gold of his incisors shining in the flickering light, his collar whiter in the dark, and raised his glass of water,

which would have been wine or better in the bygone days, and toasted
Father Firman.

"Many of 'em, John."

"Blow it out," Mrs. Stoner said, returning to the room. She waited by
the light switch for Father Firman to blow out the candle.

Mrs. Stoner, who ate no desserts, began to clear the dishes into the
kitchen, and the priests, finishing their cake and coffee in a hurry, went
to sit in the study.

Father Nulty offered a cigar.

"John?"

"My ulcers, Frank."

"Ah, well, you're better off." Father Nulty lit the cigar and crossed
his long black legs. "Fish Frawley has got him a Filipino, John. Did you
hear?"

Father Firman leaned forward, interested. "He got rid of the woman
he had?"

"He did. It seems she snooped."

"Snooped, eh?"

"She did. And gossiped. Fish introduced two town boys to her, said,
'Would you think these boys were my nephews?' That's all, and the
next week the paper had it that his two nephews were visiting him from
Erie. After that, he let her believe he was going East to see his parents,
though both are dead. The paper carried the story. Fish returned and
made a sermon out of it. Then he got the Filipino."

Father Firman squirmed with pleasure in his chair. "That's like Fish,
Frank. He can do that." He stared at the tips of his fingers bleakly. "You
could never get a Filipino to come to a place like this."

"Probably not," Father Nulty said. "Fish is pretty close to Minneapolis.
Ah, say, do you remember the trick he played on us all in Marmion Hall!"

"That I'll not forget!" Father Firman's eyes remembered. "Getting up
New Year's morning and finding the toilet seats all painted!"

"*Happy Circumcision!* Hah!" Father Nulty had a coughing fit.

When he had got himself together again, a mosquito came and sat on
his wrist. He watched it a moment before bringing his heavy hand down.
He raised his hand slowly, viewed the dead mosquito, and sent it spinning
with a plunk of his middle finger.

"Only the female bites," he said.

"I didn't know that," Father Firman said.

"Ah, yes . . ."

Mrs. Stoner entered the study and sat down with some sewing—
Father Firman's black socks.

She smiled pleasantly at Father Nulty. "And what do you think of the
atom bomb, Father?"

"Not much," Father Nulty said.

Mrs. Stoner had stopped smiling. Father Firman yawned.

Mrs. Stoner served up another: "Did you read about this communist convert, Father?"

"He's been in the Church before," Father Nulty said, "and so it's not a conversion, Mrs. Stoner."

"No? Well, I already got him down on my list of Monsignor's converts."

"It's better than a conversion, Mrs. Stoner, for there is more rejoicing in heaven over the return of . . . uh, he that was lost, Mrs. Stoner, is found."

"And that congresswoman, Father?"

"Yes. A convert—she."

"And Henry Ford's grandson, Father. I got him down."

"Yes, to be sure."

Father Firman yawned, this time audibly, and held his jaw.

"But he's one only by marriage, Father," Mrs. Stoner said. "I always say you got to watch those kind."

"Indeed you do, but a convert nonetheless, Mrs. Stoner. Remember, Cardinal Newman himself was one."

Mrs. Stoner was unimpressed. "I see where Henry Ford's making steering wheels out of soybeans, Father."

"I didn't see that."

"I read it in the *Reader's Digest* or some place."

"Yes, well . . ." Father Nulty rose and held his hand out to Father Firman. "John," he said. "It's been good."

"I heard Hirohito's next," Mrs. Stoner said, returning to converts.

"Let's wait and see, Mrs. Stoner," Father Nulty said.

The priests walked to the door.

"You know where I live, John."

"Yes. Come again Frank. Good night."

Father Firman watched Father Nulty go down the walk to his car at the curb. He hooked the screen door and turned off the porch light. He hesitated at the foot of the stairs, suddenly moved to go to bed. But he went back into his study.

"Phew!" Mrs. Stoner said. "I thought he'd never go. Here it is after eight o'clock."

Father Firman sat down in his rocking chair. "I don't see him often," he said.

"I give up!" Mrs. Stoner exclaimed, flinging the holey socks upon the horsehair sofa. "I'd swear you had a nail in your shoe."

"I told you I looked."

"Well, you ought to look again. And cut your toenails, why don't you? Haven't I got enough to do?"

Father Firman scratched in his coat pocket for a pill, found one, swallowed it. He let his head sink back against the chair and closed his eyes. He could hear her moving about the room, making the preparations; and how he knew them—the fumbling in the drawer for a pencil with a point, the rip of the page from his daily calendar, and finally the leg of the card table sliding up against his leg.

He opened his eyes. She yanked the floor lamp alongside the table, setting the bead bringe tinkling on the shade, and pulled up her chair on the other side. She sat down and smiled at him for the first time that day. Now she was happy.

She swept up the cards and began to shuffle with the abandoned virtuosity of an old river-boat gambler, standing them on end, fanning them out, whirling them through her fingers, dancing them halfway up her arms, cracking the whip over them. At last they lay before him tamed into a neat deck.

"Cut?"

"Go ahead," he said. She liked to go first.

She gave him her faint, avenging smile and drew a card, cast it aside for another which he thought must be an ace from the way she clutched it face down.

She was getting all the cards, as usual, and would have been invincible if she had possessed his restraint and if her cunning had been of a higher order. He knew a few things about leading and lying back that she would never learn. Her strategy was attack, forever attack, with one baffling departure: she might sacrifice certain tricks as expendable if only she could have the last ones, the heartbreaking ones, if she could slap them down one after another, shatteringly.

She played for blood, no bones about it, but for her there was no other way; it was her nature, as it was the lion's, and for this reason he found her ferocity pardonable, more a defect of the flesh, venial, while his own trouble was all in the will, mortal. He did not sweat and pray over each card as she must, but he did keep an eye out for reneging and demanded a cut now and then just to aggravate her, and he was always secretly hoping for aces.

With one card left in her hand, the telltale trick coming next, she delayed playing it, showing him first the smile, the preview of defeat. She laid it on the table—so! She held one more trump than he had reasoned possible. Had she palmed it from somewhere? No, she would not go that far; that would not be fair, was worse than reneging, which so easily and often happened accidentally, and she believed in being fair. Besides he had been watching her.

God smote the vines with hail, the sycamore trees with frost, and offered up the flocks to the lightning—but Mrs. Stoner! What a cross Father Firman had from God in Mrs. Stoner! There were other housekeepers as bad, no doubt, walking the rectories of the world, yes, but . . . yes. He could name one and maybe two priests who were worse off. One, maybe two. Cronin. His scraggly blonde of sixty—take her, with her everlasting banging on the grand piano, the gift of the pastor; her proud talk about the goiter operation at the Mayo Brothers', also a gift; her honking the parish Buick at passing strange priests because they were all in the game together. She was worse. She was something to keep the home fires burning. Yes sir. And Cronin said she was not a bad person really, but what was he? He was quite a freak himself.

For that matter, could anyone say that Mrs. Stoner was a bad person? No. He could not say it himself, and he was no freak. She had her points, Mrs. Stoner. She was clean. And though she cooked poorly, could not play the organ, would not take up the collection in an emergency, and went to card parties, and told all—even so, she was clean. She washed everything. Sometimes her underwear hung down beneath her dress like a paratrooper's pants, but it and everything she touched was clean. She washed constantly. She was clean.

She had her other points, to be sure—her faults, you might say. She snooped—no mistake about it—but it was not snooping for snooping's sake; she had a reason. She did other things, always with a reason. She overcharged on rosaries and prayer books, but that was for the sake of the poor. She censored the pamphlet rack, but that was to prevent scandal. She pried into the baptismal and matrimonial records, but there was no other way if Father was out, and in this way she had uncovered a bastard and flushed him out of the rectory, but that was the perverted decency of the times. She held her nose over bad marriages in the presence of the victims, but that was her sorrow and came from having her husband buried in a mine. And he had caught her telling a bewildered young couple that there was only one good reason for their wanting to enter into a mixed marriage—the child had to have a name, and that—that was what?

She hid his books, kept him from smoking, picked his friends (usually the pastors of her colleagues), bawled out people for calling after dark, had no humor, except at cards, and then it was grim, very grim, and sat hatchet-faced every morning at Mass. But she went to Mass, which was all that kept the church from being empty some mornings. She did annoying things all day long. She said annoying things into the night. She said she had given him the best years of her life. Had she? Perhaps—for the miner had her only a year. It was too bad, sinfully bad, when he thought of it like that. But all talk of best years and life was nonsense. He had to consider the heart of the matter, the essence. The essence was that housekeepers were hard to get, harder to get than ushers, than willing workers, than organists, than secretaries—yes, harder to get than assistants or vocations.

And she was a *saver*—saved money, saved electricity, saved string, bags, sugar, saved—him. That's what she did. That's what she said she did, and she was right, in a way. In a way, she was usually right. In fact, she was always right—in a way. And you could never get a Filipino

to come way out here and live. Not a young one anyway, and he had
never seen an old one. Not a Filipino. They liked to dress up and live.

Should he let it drop about Fish having one, just to throw a scare
into her, let her know he was doing some thinking? No. It would be a
perfect cue for the one about a man needing a woman to look after him.
He was not up to that again, not tonight.

Now she was doing what she liked most of all. She was making a grand
slam, playing it out card for card, though it was in the bag, prolonging
what would have been cut short out of mercy in gentle company. Father
Firman knew the agony of losing.

She slashed down the last card, a miserable deuce trump, and did in
the hapless king of hearts he had been saving.

"Skunked you!"

She was awful in victory. Here was the bitter end of their long day
together, the final murderous hour in which all they wanted to say—all
he wouldn't and all she couldn't—came out in the cards. Whoever won
at honeymoon won the day, slept on the other's scalp, and God alone
had to help the loser.

"We've been at it long enough, Mrs. Stoner," he said, seeing her
assembling the cards for another round.

"Had enough, huh!"

Father Firman grumbled something.

"No?"

"Yes."

She pulled the table away and left it against the wall for the next
time. She went out of the study carrying the socks, content and clucking.
He closed his eyes after her and began to get under way in the rocking
chair, the nightly trip to nowhere. He could hear her brewing a cup of
tea in the kitchen and conversing with the cat. She made her way up
the stairs, carrying the tea, followed by the cat, purring.

He waited, rocking out to sea, until she would be sure to be through
in the bathroom. Then he got up and locked the front door (she looked
after the back door) and loosened his collar going upstairs.

In the bathroom he mixed a glass of antiseptic, always afraid of
pyorrhea, and gargled to ward off pharyngitis.

When he turned on the light in his room, the moths and beetles began
to batter against the screens, the lighter insects humming. . . .

Yes, and she had the guest room. How did she come to get that? Why
wasn't she in the back room, in her proper place? He knew, if he cared
to remember. The screen in the back room—it let in mosquitoes, and if
it didn't do that she'd love to sleep back there, Father, looking out at
the steeple and the blessed cross on top, Father, if it just weren't for the
screen, Father. Very well, Mrs. Stoner, I'll get it fixed or fix it myself.
Oh, could you now, Father? I could, Mrs. Stoner, and I will. In the

meantime you take the guest room. Yes, Father, and thank you, Father, the house ringing with amenities then. Years ago, all that. She was a pie-faced girl then, not really a girl perhaps, but not too old to marry again. But she never had. In fact, he could not remember that she had even tried for a husband since coming to the rectory, but, of course, he could be wrong, not knowing how they went about it. God! God save us! Had she got her wires crossed and mistaken him all these years for *that? That!* Him! Suffering God! No. That was going too far. That was getting morbid. No. He must not think of that again, ever. No.

But just the same she had got the guest room and she had it yet. Well, did it matter? Nobody ever came to see him any more, nobody to stay overnight anyway, nobody to stay very long . . . not any more. He knew how they laughed at him. He had heard Frank humming all right— before he saw how serious and sad the situation was and took pity— humming, "Wedding Bells Are Breaking Up That Old Gang of Mine." But then they'd always laughed at him for something—for not being an athlete, for wearing glasses, for having kidney trouble . . . and mail coming addressed to Rev. and Mrs. Stoner.

Removing his shirt, he bent over the table to read the volume left open from last night. He read, translating easily, "Eisdem licet cum illis . . . Clerics are allowed to reside only with women about whom there can be no suspicion, either because of a natural bond (as mother, sister, aunt) or of advanced age, combined in both cases with good repute."

Last night he had read it, and many nights before, each time as though this time to find what was missing, to find what obviously was not in the paragraph, his problem considered, a way out. She was neither mother, sister, nor aunt, and *advanced age* was a relative term (why, she was younger than he was) and so, eureka, she did not meet the letter of the law—but, alas, how she fulfilled the spirit! And besides it would be a slimy way of handling it after all her years of service. He could not afford to pension her off, either.

He slammed the book shut. He slapped himself fiercely on the back, missing the wily mosquito, and whirled to find it. He took a magazine and folded it into a swatter. Then he saw it—oh, the preternatural cunning of it!—poised in the beard of St. Joseph on the bookcase. He could not hit it there. He teased it away, wanting it to light on the wall, but it knew his thoughts and flew high away. He swung wildly, hoping to stun it, missed, swung back, catching St. Joseph across the neck. The statue fell to the floor and broke.

Mrs. Stoner was panting in the hall outside his door.

"What is it!"

"Mosquitoes!"

"What is it, Father? Are you hurt?"

"Mosquitoes—damn it! And only the female bites!"

Mrs. Stoner, after a moment, said, "Shame on you, Father. She needs the blood for her eggs."

He dropped the magazine and lunged at the mosquito with his bare hand.

She went back to her room, saying, "Pshaw, I thought it was burglars murdering you in your bed."

He lunged again.

COMMENT AND QUESTION

1. *The title of the story.* The title of the story is Biblical. It comes from a passage in Proverbs 31:10-28. The entire passage is given so that the reader may compare the "valiant woman" of the Bible with Mrs. Stoner of Powers' story.

"10. Who shall find a valiant woman? Far and from the uttermost coasts is the price of her.

11. The heart of her husband trusteth in her: and he shall have no need of spoils.

12. She will render him good, and not evil, all the days of her life.

13. She hath sought wool and flax, and hath wrought by the counsel of her hands.

14. She is like the merchant's ship: she bringeth her bread from afar.

15. And she hath risen in the night, and given a prey to her household, and victuals to her maidens.

16. She hath considered a field, and bought it: with the fruit of her hands she hath planted a vineyard.

17. She hath girded her loins with strength, and hath strengthened her arm.

18. She hath tasted and seen that her traffic is good: her lamp shall not be put out in the night.

19. She hath put out her hand to strong things: and her fingers have taken hold of the spindle.

20. She hath opened her hand to the needy, and stretched out her hands to the poor.

21. She shall not fear for her house in the cold of snow: for all her domestics are clothed with double garments.

22. She hath made for herself clothing of tapestry: fine linen, and purple is her covering.

23. Her husband is honourable in the gates, when he sitteth among the senators of the land.

24. She made fine linen, and sold it, and delivered a girdle to the Chanaanite.

25. Strength and beauty are her clothing: and she shall laugh in the latter day.

26. She hath opened her mouth to wisdom: and the law of clemency is on her tongue.

27. She hath looked well to the paths of her house, and hath not eaten her bread idle.

28. Her children rose up, and called her blessed: her husband, and he praised her."

This justly famous passage praises a woman who is a wife, mother, and head of a household. What ironical implications does the author intend by referring to this passage?

2. *The purpose of the author.* J. F. Powers, who is a Catholic, almost always uses a Catholic background in his stories. He often presents priests, nuns, and bishops in their commonplace activities, not in moments of religious exaltation. He finds his transgressors and their sins, large and small, in everyday life and everyday actions. In "The Valiant Woman," Powers depicts a simple situation showing the tensions of day to day living. Father Firman is not the only priest in the story whose life is burdened by the presence of a housekeeper more likely to be incompatible than not. By virtue of his Holy Orders, a gulf lies—or should lie— between a priest and his housekeeper. But how does Mrs. Stoner destroy the dignity of Father Firman?

3. *The character of Mrs. Stoner.* Toward the close of the story, Father Firman in his reflections gives the final touches to the portrait of Mrs. Stoner, a portrait whose lines are clearly etched in the opening passages of the story. Mrs. Stoner is said to have one virtue. What are her many defects? Are her defects passive? Or is she actively hostile and malignant? One of the best descriptions of Mrs. Stoner occurs in the comment," . . . she did not meet the letter of the law—but, alas, how she fulfilled the spirit!"

4. *The problem of Mrs. Stoner.* Many people in "The Valiant Woman," jocosely or seriously, consciously or unconsciously, feel that the position of Father Firman is similar to that of a husband chained to and nagged by an incompatible wife. Mrs. Stoner's tactics are those of infiltration. Will there ever be an end to her tactics? Has Father Firman any defense against her? Is the problem of Mrs. Stoner light or grave? Consider the implications of the following passage: "Here was the bitter end of their long day together, the final murderous hour in which all they wanted to say—all he wouldn't and all she couldn't—came out in the cards."

5. *Symbols.*

    a. Notice the mosquitoes.

    b. Notice the shuffling of the cards by Mrs. Stoner and the phrases, "cracking the whip over them," and "tamed into a neat deck."

    c. Is Mrs. Stoner well named? What of Father Firman's name?

THE PASSION OF
LANCE CORPORAL HAWKINS

BY IRWIN SHAW

IRWIN SHAW (1913–   ) was born in Brook-
lyn. When he was twenty-three, he wrote a
successful play, *Bury the Dead*, with an anti-
war theme. Later he served in the second
World War, enlisting as a private. His war
novel, *The Young Lions* (1948), was well received. He has published several collections
of short stories: *Sailor Off the Bremen* (1939),
Welcome to the City (1942), *Act of Faith*
(1947), and *Mixed Company* (1950). He has
appeared in the *Best American Short Stories*
annual and also in the *O. Henry Memorial
Award Prize Stories* collection.

LANCE CORPORAL ALFRED HAWKINS stood on the Haifa dock, his fingers
wet on the long nightstick in his hands, the unaccustomed helmet heavy on
his head, watching a naval launch slowly bring in the two-masted
schooner *Hope,* its decks and tattered rigging swarming with people, who
looked like clustered dark bees, so far away, and not like people at all.
Please, Lord, Hawkins prayed to himself, standing at ease with his
platoon, warm in the yellow Mediterranean sun, please, Lord, keep me
from hitting any of them.

"Don't take any nonsense from the buggers," Lieutenant Madox said,
standing in front of the platoon. "Whack 'em a couple of times and they'll
behave like bloody gentlemen." He turned and peered at the shabby
schooner slowly approaching the dock, and Hawkins was sure that the look
on the Lieutenant's thick red face was one of pleasurable anticipation.

THE PASSION OF LANCE CORPORAL HAWKINS   From *Mixed Company* by Irwin
Shaw. Reprinted by permission of Random House, Inc. Copyright, 1947, by
Irwin Shaw.

Hawkins looked at the other men of the platoon. Except for Hogan, you couldn't tell anything from their faces. In London once, during the war, Hawkins had overheard an American Air Force major saying, "The British would watch Hitler hanging or their daughters marrying into the Royal Family or their own legs being chopped off at the knee and not change expression by one twitch of the eyebrow. You can't beat an army like that." The American had been drunk, of course, but, looking around him now, and remembering other times, too—like the day outside Caen and the day on the Rhine and the day his company went into the concentration camp at Belsen—Hawkins could understand what the American had been talking about. In ten or fifteen minutes, the men around him might be in the middle of a very mean fight on board the schooner, against clubs and knives, perhaps, and maybe even home-made bombs, and except for Hogan, again, all of them looked as though they were merely lined up for a routine roll call outside their barracks in the morning. And Hogan, of course, was an Irishman, and not the same thing at all. He was a small, thin boy, with a tough, broken-nosed, handsome face, and now he was fidgeting uneasily, his jaw rigid with excitement, pushing his helmet back and forth on his head, shifting his nightstick, breathing loudly enough to be heard over all the small noises of the harbor and the platoon around him.

They were singing now on the schooner. The rising and falling, chanting, foreign melody came thinly and defiantly across the oily green water. Hawkins could understand several words of Hebrew, but he could not make out what the song was about. It sounded wild and somehow menacing, as though it should not be sung in sunshine and in the morning or by women's voices but late at night, in the desert, by lawless and desperate men. Esther had translated two or three Hebrew songs for Hawkins in the last few weeks, and he had noticed that the words "freedom" and "justice" figured in them prominently, but those words did not seem to fit with the flat, dangerous, hoarse music hammering across the harbor from the slowly moving old boat.

Hawkins wished they wouldn't sing. It made it harder if they sang and you knew they were singing about freedom or justice. After all, they were singing to him, and to the other men around him, and what did they expect him to do?

Hawkins closed his eyes, as though by shutting out the sight of the dark-clustered boat inexorably being pushed to the dock, and the clubs, and the transport waiting to take them to the stockade on Cyprus, he could somehow also shut out the sound of the rough, challenging voices of the Jews.

He closed his eyes, his youthful, almost childish face, sweating under the hot helmet, painfully composed, painfully disclosing nothing to the Lieutenant or the men around him or to the eyes of the fugitives he was expected to punish. He closed his eyes. He was uncomfortable in his wool battle dress and the tight canvas belting, and was sorry he was in Palestine, sorry he was in the Army, sorry he was an Englishman, sorry he was alive. This was not what he had expected when he had reënlisted, six months after the war was over. He didn't know exactly what he had expected. He had just known he did not want to live in Southampton, in the foggy weather, among the ruined docks and the torn buildings; in the same house with his father, who had had his arm torn off during a raid in 1941; in the same house with his sister, whose husband had been killed at Bari in 1943; in the same house in which he had lived for such a short while with Nancy, who had later divorced him and married an American sergeant in the port battalion—and that was a soft job for a soldier, wasn't it, during a war. He had just known that after four years in the Army, ever since he was seventeen, he did not want to start looking for a job as a longshoreman on the wrecked wharves, he did not want to stand in a queue collecting the unemployment dole, he did not want the bitter weather of unheated winter England after glimpses of Africa and summer France. And the only thing he had known was soldiering. They had made it a little more attractive—they had raised the pay and promised many rather vague benefits—and, if the truth must be told, the only time anyone had ever really taken care of him was in the Army. It was certain no one was really going to take care of you as a civilian, Socialist government or no Socialist government. Though he had voted for them, of course. He had read all the pamphlets and he knew what he was doing, a common soldier in the Army of the King, the son of a workingman, the grandson of a workingman, the great-grandson of a workingman. That was another thing about the Army. It had given him the chance to read for the first time in his life. Especially the two periods he'd been in the hospital, first with the bullet in his hip and then with the piece of shrapnel he'd picked up twelve days before the end of the war. The hospital library had had a complete set of H. G. Wells, and he had slowly and studiously gone through it all, soberly agreeing with the energetic arguments of the old man. By the time he'd got out of the hospital, he had become a confirmed Socialist, believing that education could change the world, and that violence was a hangover from primitive times, and that year by year the human race was certain to improve. He opened his eyes for a moment and looked at the schooner. It was much closer now, and he could smell it, too. There were perhaps three hundred people jammed onto it, men and women, and they had obviously not had the most complete sanitation facilities. He wished H. G. Wells were on the dock in the uniform of an infantry lance corporal today; it would be interesting to see what he would do.

It had been so much simpler during the war. There were the Germans across the fields, or up on a hill two miles away, and you shot them and they shot you. They had bombed your home and torn the arm off your father's shoulder and killed your brother-in-law, and there were no further decisions to be made about them. And all the men around you felt exactly as you did, no matter who they were. But now . . . There was Lieutenant Madox, who hated all Jews and was delighted with this duty on the dock this morning. Of course, Lieutenant Madox hated everybody, except Englishmen, and if he had been in India or Malaya or France, he would have looked forward to cracking Indian or Malayan or French skulls with equal pleasure. But he happened to be in Palestine, and he happened to be looking forward to hitting Jews. Then there was Private Fleming, a quiet, capable man of thirty-five. Private Fleming was a Communist. Communists, Hawkins knew, did not think much of Zionism, but certainly they didn't believe in braining Jews, and yet there was Private Fleming, an excellent soldier, standing quietly at ease, ready to do his duty, gripping his nightstick like all the others. And there was Hogan, who was one of Hawkins' best friends, with whom he drank beer in Jerusalem and Tel Aviv, and who was a Catholic, like Hawkins, and went to Mass on Sunday morning with him, and whose father had been killed by the British in the trouble in Dublin in 1916. Hogan often went out with him and Esther, too. Esther would bring a friend and they would swim on the beach at Tel Aviv and go to the movies at night when they played musical pictures. Hogan hated the Jews, though, because his second cousin, who was in the Sixth Airborne, had got his foot blown off by a Jewish mine on the Rehovoth Road two months before. What would H. G. Wells have made of the Dublin orphan on the sunny dock this morning, tense with pent-up fury as he glared at the naval launch slowly pushing the tattered, dark, chanting refugees toward him?

And, supposing H. G. Wells had been a Jew, and were standing on the deck of the *Hope* this morning, after the years of murder in Germany, after the displaced persons' camps, after the illegal journey across Europe and the crooked voyage down the Mediterranean, what clever, hopeful statement would he make then, waiting there like an old bull in the knacker's yard, waiting for the clubs and the Cyprian wire?

An Arab laborer walked by, rolling a wheelbarrow. He put the wheelbarrow down in front of the platoon, his long, skinny arms dark mahogany, dangling out of his tattered shirt. He had a little black scraggly beard, and he didn't smell so good, either. He grinned at the soldiers. His teeth were not all there, but when he smiled, he looked childlike and ingratiating, and some of the men smiled back at him. The Arab looked over his shoulder at the approaching boat, grinned more widely, and moved his finger across his Adam's apple in the gesture of throat slitting.

"Get out of here, you filthy old rascal," Lieutenant Madox said, smiling broadly. "Go ahead. Out of the way. We'll have no international incidents on this dock."

The Arab bobbed his head, the grin fixed on his face, and made the throat-cutting gesture again, like a child who repeats a trick that he sees has pleased his elders. Then he bent and picked up the handles of the wheelbarrow again and trundled it off, giggling to himself.

Hawkins didn't remember what H. G. Wells had had to say about the Arabs. He was sure there must have been something on the subject, because there was something on every subject in the old man's books, but he couldn't remember. The Arabs, Hawkins had to admit, were much more pleasant to have around than the Jews. For one thing, they did what you told them. For another thing, they weren't likely to get you off in a corner and engage you in a loud political argument. Esther lived in the same house with a family by the name of Freedman, who were German refugees and whose two sons had been in the Jewish Brigade during the war. The two boys lay in wait for Hawkins when he came to call for Esther and battered him with questions like "Why doesn't Britain live up to the Balfour Declaration?" and "Why does Britain allow the Grand Mufti of Jerusalem, who worked with the Nazis during the war, to come back to lead the Arabs from Cairo?" It was very queer, sitting in the small white living room of the apartment house, with your rifle leaning against the wall (from time to time, Division Headquarters ordered that all troops be armed when they left the barracks), drinking tea and eating little sweet cookies that Mrs. Freedman kept pressing on you, debating politely with the two fierce young veterans, who were probably members of the Jewish underground and had probably blown up a sergeant major in the morning.

"It's not fair," he had said to Esther after one such session, when he had finally managed to get her away from the house. "They talk as though I was personally responsible."

Esther had glanced at him obliquely, then looked away. "Maybe," she said softly, "maybe that's what they think about every British soldier."

"Is that what you think?"

Esther had shaken her head and gripped his arm more firmly. "No," she had said gravely, her low, soft voice solemn and warm. "No, I do not think of you as a British soldier." They had been walking along the quiet, white street, in the clear, foreign evening air—his boots making a hob-nailed clatter on the pavement and his rifle sling pulling at his shoulder and the girl beside him in a thin white dress with a blue sweater over it, her hair blowing gently, soft and pale brown, in the stirring wind.

"Listen to them sing," Hogan said, his voice nervous and angry. "The murderin' heathen! They'll sing a different tune an hour from now, they will!"

Hawkins opened his eyes. The ship was much closer now, and the songs clamored across the water from the packed ship, with the soprano of the women shrill and glittering over the menacing bass of the men's voices.

Hogan, Hawkins remembered, also sang songs in another language—in Gaelic—and the words "freedom" and "justice" figured prominently in them, too. They were songs Hogan's grandfather had taught him in memory of his dead father, shot through the throat on a Dublin pavement by men in the same uniform that Hogan was wearing now so far away, seventy-five miles north of Jerusalem.

Hawkins closed his eyes again. It would do no good to watch the boat come nearer, foot by foot. There would be time enough to look, later. He thought of Esther. He had arranged to meet her that night in Tel Aviv and take her to a movie if he got off duty early. He had not known what the duty would be, though, and he doubted if he would tell her later on. Matters were complicated enough with Esther as it was. She looked so cheerful and agreeable, so pretty and young, like the very nicest kind of girl you might meet by a lucky accident at home, but there had been the terrible times when she had suddenly broken down, for no apparent reason, and wept in his arms, wildly and inconsolably, clutching him as though to make certain again and again that he was there and alive. She was a German girl, whose mother and father had been killed in Munich, and whose husband had been caught by the British near Haifa unloading illegal immigrants in 1939. He had been put into a camp, where he had caught typhus and died. The authorities had permitted Esther to visit her husband the day he died, and once Esther had told Hawkins about it, although most of the time they avoided talking about things like that. The husband, who was twenty-four years old and had been a robust, laughing young man (Hawkins had seen his picture), had been wasted by the disease to ninety pounds and was screaming in his delirium when Esther finally saw him. He did not recognize his wife at all when she came into the room, and that, somehow, was Esther's bitterest memory—the screaming, skeleton-like boy turning his head senselessly to the wall in the bare, barred room. Then, after that, all through the war, Esther had been kept under house arrest and had not been permitted to go out into the streets from sunset to dawn. When Hawkins had first known her, she had been quiet, almost fearful, and perhaps it was because she had matched his own shyness and fearfulness so well that he had begun to love her.

For the past several months, whenever Hawkins was waiting somewhere, and closed his eyes, as he was doing now, he had had a recurrent daydream. It was winter in the dream, a cold, windy night, and he and Esther were sitting before a warm fire in their own house. He could never decide whether the house was in England, in a quiet village, or on a farm in Palestine, cupped in the small, old hills, among the orange orchards. They were reading, and occasionally they looked up from their books and smiled at each other, not having to talk, in the firelight. After a time, there was a knock on the door and guests began to come in; not many of them, just good friends. Hogan, with his wild hair plastered down politely.

Fleming, with the schoolteacher wife from Leeds he talked about so often. Robinson, who had been in Hawkins' platoon in Africa—it was always hard to remember, especially in a daydream, that Robinson was dead, buried in the small, windy cemetery near Constantine. They talked quietly in the warm room, and Hawkins opened up the tall bottles of heavy beer, and after a while Hogan sang, in his hoarse, accurate boy's voice, the sad, thrilling songs his grandfather had taught him in his father's honor, songs whose words no one understood but whose melodies made you somehow melancholy and proud.

Hawkins blinked and refused himself the pleasure of taking the daydream through to its quiet ending. It was ridiculous to allow himself to moon like that, and it only made it worse when he finally opened his eyes and looked around him. There he was, on the dock, in the hot, bare sun, with the nightstick, waiting for Lieutenant Madox to order him to fight. And in the hills behind him, among the orange groves, people were hiding rifles and knives and machine guns to murder each other in the long winter nights. And in England, from all the letters he got from his family, they were preparing to starve and freeze to celebrate their victory in the war. He was sorry he was not older. Perhaps if he were thirty or forty or fifty, he could understand it better. During the war they had been warm, during the war they had been fed, during the war the Russians had loved them, the Americans had admired them, the French had kissed them when they came into a town; wherever they had gone, they had been heroes and saviors. He remembered the day that the election returns came out. He was still in Germany, in Hamburg, and an American sergeant had come over to him and said, very solemnly, "Soldier, my name is McCarthy. I'm a paid-up C.I.O. member from Indianapolis. I decided I wanted to tell some Englishman how wonderful I think they are, and you're the first one I've come across since I made the decision. You've shown the whole world how civilized human beings should behave." The American had been drunk, of course (was it possible that Americans appreciated other people only when they had ten drinks under their belts?), but he had shaken Hawkins' hand sternly and clapped him on the back, and Hawkins had walked away grinning and feeling proud because he had voted for Attlee and the others who were going to prove that a country could be run for the benefit of the workingman without violence or disaster. He was glad the American wasn't around to see him standing on the dock today with helmet and nightstick, in this land of widows and orphans, in this land where there were no whole families, only survivors, in this land where everyone—every girl on the street, every child in a schoolroom, every farmer plowing a furrow—had a story like Esther's, memories like Esther's, nightmares like Esther's, where the memory of the furnace flickered across every face, the knocking of the midnight arrest broke into every dream, where agony was so commonplace that no one even remarked it. What a puzzling, sad thing it was to be an Englishman today, Hawkins thought, staring at the boat, which was so close now. If he was in England, he was caught between cold and hunger, in Palestine between Jew and Arab, in Indian between Hindu and Moslem, in the East Indies between Dutchman and Javanese, and no friends anywhere, no approval anywhere, just the helmet and the nightstick, the barbed wire and the Lieutenant, the songs in the strange languages hurled at your head like hand grenades. You could read all the pamphlets, vote all the elections, pray all the Sundays, and each day it became worse, each day made you more of a villain, each day your uniform was cursed on the streets of more cities, in more languages. He closed his eyes.

"Hawkins!"

Hawkins jumped and straightened up. Lieutenant Madox was standing in front of him. "Damn you, Hawkins!" Madox was saying. "Will you keep your bloody eyes open! Get over here!"

"Yes, sir," said Hawkins. He gripped his club and moved to where two sailors were swinging a gangplank up to the railing of the boat. The boat was tied to the dock now, and a terrible stillness had settled over the people on it.

"Spread out, spread out," Madox was shouting to the platoon. "Don't let anyone jump onto the dock. Make 'em all come down the gangplank."

The smell was awful now, and in the silence the Jews stared down at the Lieutenant and the men of the platoon with cold, devouring hatred. Over a loudspeaker came a cool, pleasant voice.

"Ladies and gentlemen," the voice said, and it sounded like at least a colonel in the Guards, "we wish to do this in as orderly a fashion as possible. You will please come down the gangplank in twos and march to your right and go aboard the vessel moored directly behind your boat. You are going to be transferred to Cyprus, where you will be taken care of in British Army camps. Your sick will be treated and you will be given every consideration possible. Now, if you please, start leaving your vessel."

The voice halted in a mechanical crackle. No one moved.

"All right," Madox said. "Let's get on board."

Slowly and deliberately, the men of the platoon started up the gangplank. Hawkins was right behind the Lieutenant, with Hogan at his side. For a moment, at the top of the gangplank, he stopped. He looked down at the deck of the schooner. There was a blur of eyes, dark, staring, wild; a confusion of gaunt, ravaged faces; a wavering mass of tattered clothing such as might have been recovered from the corpses of a dug-up graveyard. Hawkins tottered momentarily, feeling, dizzily, this had happened to me before. Then he remembered. Belsen, he thought—wherever you turn, it is Belsen. In Belsen, he remembered, there had been the smell, too, and the same eyes, the same clothes, and there had been the old man (although later Hawkins had found out the man was only thirty) who had opened a door of one of the huts and come slowly out, holding his hands in front of him, his hands like claws, his face twisted skull-like and horrible in what Hawkins had later realized the man had meant as a glorious smile of greeting but which at the moment had seemed weird and threatening. Then, just as he had reached Hawkins, he had dropped to the ground, and when Hawkins had bent over him, he had died. But no one here approached Hawkins; there was no expression here that might later be deciphered into a smile. On the other side of the deck, there were the women, and standing, facing the gangplank, were the young men, and then Hawkins knew there was going to be a fight. Crazily, he thought: I'll bet there are some of these people here who will recognize me from Belsen. What will they think of me?

"Come on!" Madox was shouting furiously. "Come on, Hawkins, get in there!"

Slowly, with dreamy obedience, Hawkins moved toward the first line of men. I am not going to hit them, he thought as he walked through the stinking, unreal silence. No matter what, I am not going to hit them. Then he saw Hogan swing and there was the flat, awful noise of the stick hitting a shoulder. Then the screams began, and the shouting, which closed around you in a savage, wild, echoing vault of sound, and the bodies slamming into you, and the spurt of someone's blood, hot and slippery, in your face, and the confused flailing of arms and the black gleam of wood flashing against the yellow sky and a form dropping with a scream out of the rigging. Hawkins tried to keep his arms over his head, so that he wouldn't be pinned in helplessly, but hands grabbed at his club, and stabbed into his face, and he had to move his arms furiously to keep the club from being torn away. Then, suddenly, there was a pair of hands at his throat and he was staring into a dark, grimacing face, the eyes, just six inches from his, pitiless, mad, as the powerful fingers pressed and pressed. Hawkins tried to pull away, but there was no escaping the hands. Oh, God, Hawkins thought, feeling the blood pounding in his head, oh, God, he is going to kill me. No, he wanted to say, you don't understand. I am not doing anything. I was at Belsen. I was one of the people at Belsen. But the hands gripped firmer and firmer, the eyes stared coldly and triumphantly close to his own, as though the man who was choking him were finally taking vengeance for the ghetto in Poland, the death of his children, the locked cars, the whips, the furnaces, the graves of Europe. Hawkins felt his eyes clouding, his throat being torn, his knees slowly crumpling, as he pressed back and back, with the screams and the wet smashing of blows all around him. With his waning strength, he wrenched away. Then he hit the man. The man did not let go. Hawkins hit him again, across the face, and the man's face disappeared in a fuzz of blood, but still the fingers gripped, as strong as ever. Then, again and again, with all the desperate strength in his arms and body, Hawkins lashed out at the man who was trying to strangle him. The man's face seemed to crumble in a red, dissolving tissue, his jaw hanging queer and sidewise in a broken leer, only his eyes, steadfast and full of hatred, still glaring into Hawkins' own. There was a last, convulsive spasm of the fingers at Hawkins' throat; then the man slowly and silently slid down and away. Hawkins stared at him, then fell on top of him, and something crashed across his head, and when he opened his eyes again, he was lying on the dock and everything was very quiet, except for the weeping of women, soft and far away.

Hawkins sat up. The fight was over. Now they were taking the women down the gangplank, and that was where the weeping was coming from— from the raddled bundles of living rags being carried by troopers onto the soil of Palestine and back onto the other ship, thirty-five feet away. Hawkins felt his throat. It was terribly sore, and blood was still oozing from a cut under his ear. He felt sick and lightheaded. He turned his head away from the women. He did not want to look at them. Lying next to him on the dock, very quiet, face downward, was a man. He had on an American Army shirt and a pair of Royal Air Force pants. He was barefooted and his feet were terribly cut and swollen, black with blood. Slowly, Hawkins took the man's shoulder and rolled him over. The eyes were still open. The face was smashed, the jaw leering and dislocated, the teeth broken and red at the roots. But the eyes were open and they were the eyes of the man who had tried to kill Hawkins on board the schooner *Hope*.

Hawkins stood up. It was hard to walk, but he moved slowly over to the gate in the barbed wire at the other end of the dock. Madox was there, sweating but looking pleased.

"Very well done, Hawkins," Madox said. "I watched you. Are you hurt?"

"A little, sir," Hawkins said, surprised at the croaking, strange noise that came from his throat. "Not too bad."

"Good," said Madox. "It's just about finished here. We'll be going back to camp in a minute." He looked solicitously at Hawkins' torn throat. "You're in rather bad shape. You'd better not go with the others in the lorry. I'll take you with me in my jeep."

"Yes, sir," said Hawkins flatly. He walked slowly over to where the jeep was parked and laboriously climbed into the back. He leaned against the canvas. He closed his eyes, thinking of nothing.

Ten minutes later, Madox and his driver got into the jeep, and the jeep rolled slowly through the gate. Hawkins did not look back purposely, but he could not help seeing the dock, the two boats, the old, silent, broken, deserted schooner, and the full transport, beginning to work up steam for the voyage to Cyprus. They were singing again on board the transport, but softer now, and wearily, and Hawkins thought, I must get Esther to translate that song for me. And on the dock, with the Arab laborer, still holding his wheelbarrow, standing curiously over him, lay the dead man, flat and alone. Hawkins closed his eyes as the jeep spurted away from the waterfront.

I wonder, he was thinking, slowly and painfully, because his head did not seem familiar or normal to him any more, I wonder if I can get off tonight to go into Tel Aviv to take Esther to the movies. Then there was the explosion, and even as he felt himself slamming through the air, Hawkins thought, They must have got hold of some Army mines. Then he hit. He moved with crawling, broken slowness, feeling everything slippery and sliding all around him, thinking with dull persistence, I must tell them, they mustn't do this to me, they don't understand, I was at Belsen. Then he lay still.

COMMENT AND QUESTION

1. Diplomats would call the background of this story an "international incident." At the end of the second World War, thousands of Jews who were Displaced Persons in Europe sought a home in Palestine. (Even before the War, the Zionist Movement had worked for the setting up of an independent majority Jewish state.) This mass immigration movement was accompanied by a campaign of terrorism by Jewish extremists against the British administration in Palestine and by warfare between Jews and Arabs, who tried to block the admission of Jewish immigrants. In the summer of 1946, illegal Jewish immigrants became a flood, and the British began to send all new arrivals to camps in Cyprus. Finally, in 1949, the new state of Israel was formed, comprising the greater part of Palestine. This story takes place about 1946.

2. The passion of Christ is universally known. What, then, does the title mean?

3. The lives of Hawkins, Esther, and Hogan reflect a disordered world. What are the nationalities of these three people?

4. What is ironical in the statement of Lieutenant Madox to the Arab: "We'll have no international incidents on this dock"?

5. What is the connection between the man who met Hawkins at the Nazi concentration camp of Belsen and the man who attacks Hawkins on the ship?

6. This is a *tendenz* story, a dramatized argument. What part do the songs of "freedom" and "justice" sung by Jews and by Irish play in this argument?

7. What is significant about Hawkins' statement: "They talk as though I was personally responsible."?

FIGHT NUMBER TWENTY-FIVE

BY JESSE STUART

JESSE STUART (1907–   ) was born in Kentucky and educated in the South. He served in the Navy in the second World War. He has taught school, lectured, and was for a time the superintendent of city schools in Greenup, Kentucky. He received a Guggenheim Fellowship in 1937. He has written poetry, novels, and short stories. He is a regional writer and has explored the mountain dwellers, the hill people of Kentucky. His best known novel is *Taps for Private Tussie* (1943). His volumes of short stories include *H o' W-Hollow* (1936), *Men of the Mountains* (1941), *Tales from the Plum Grove Hills* (1946), and *Clearing in the Sky* (1950).

I'D just taken my first shipment of hides to the Greenwood express office when Hade Stableton saw me.

"Eddie—hey, you Eddie Battlestrife—just a minute," Hade hollered at me. "I want to see you!"

"Make it snappy," I yelled. "I want to get this batch of hides on Number Three."

I didn't want to fool with Hade. For every time he'd ever stopped me in his life, he wanted to borrow something from me or he wanted me to do something for him.

"Eddie, I had bad luck last night," Hade grunted soon as he reached me.

"What happened?" I asked.

"Lost my good tree dog, old Rags, and a hundred dollars to boot," he sighed. "You caused it, Eddie!"

"How did I cause it?" I asked him.

"Remember that big wildcat you catched out on Seaton Ridge?" he asked me.

"But what does that have to do with your losin' your best tree dog and a hundred dollars?" I asked. "That wildcat went to West Virginia."

"West Virginia, hell," Hade said. "That wildcat's right up here at Auckland in a cage. I wish that wildcat's hide was among this batch of fur you're expressin'. I'd be a lot better off."

"How'd that wildcat get to Auckland?" I said. "I sold 'im to Elmer Pratt."

"You know who's got the wildcat now?"

"No, I don't."

"Jason Radnor's got 'im," Hade told me.

"Jason Radnor?" I said.

"Yep, Jason Radnor's got 'im," Hade said, shaking his head sadly. "He's got 'im in a big cage. And you pay a dollar to get in to see the cat fight a dog. If you fight a dog against the cat, you pay five dollars! And there's plenty of betting a-goin' on. Old Jason will cover any bet that the cat will whip a dog. Now he's even giving odds. Last night bets went up to five hundred dollars. Jason covered everything that the men bet against his cat!"

"I sold that wildcat to Elmer Pratt for fifty dollars," I said. "I don't need a cat. I didn't want to keep 'im. I could get more for 'im that way than I could for his pelt."

"I know it's bad, Eddie," Hade said. "But I thought I'd tell you! I thought you ought to know about it."

"Yes, I'm glad you told me," I said, as I began thinking about what the wildcat had done to Hade's dog. "I need to know about it. Where do they have that cage?"

"Over the hill from the slaughterhouse where we used to fight our game roosters. But listen, Eddie," Hade went on to warn me, "if you're thinkin' about a-takin' old Buck up there and fightin' that cat you'd better be keerful! I'm a-tellin' you, Eddie! It looked like easy money to me. And I went atter it. Old Scout kilt many a wildcat too. But he never fit one like this cat! He'll never fight another cat! Scout was the nineteenth dog the wildcat's kilt. Boys told me up there last night that old Jason was a-feedin' the wildcat beef blood to make 'im mean. Never saw a meaner cat in my life! Didn't hardly get old Scout in the cage until the cat sprang on him and laid open his side until you could see a whole panel of his ribs!"

"But that didn't kill 'im?" I said.

"Nope, but the old cat spat 'im with the other paw," Hade said. "That finished the best dog I ever had! Had to give a man five dollars to take Scout out behind the house and shoot 'im to put 'im outen his misery. Guns barked all the time I was there. Had to take the dogs that fit the cat out behind the house and polish 'em off."

"I'd fight that wildcat myself," I said, as I thought about the poor dogs the cat had mangled. "I'll go in the cage with it!"

"Somebody'd haf to polish you off, too," Hade said. "Now don't get riled. Don't get worked up and lose your head. If I'd a-knowed it would've upset you like this I wouldn't have told you!"

I stood a minute looking down at the toe of my shoe. I thought about the October night when old Buck put the cat up a tree and the way he ran it, full speed like he's after a fox. That was the way Buck had put many a coon up a tree. And just as soon as he treed, I hurried to the tree, thinking he'd got me a coon. But when I reached the place where he was barkin' up a great saw-timber-sized oak with branches big enough for crossties sprangled out from its bushy top, I knew it wasn't any coon. I hardly had to use my lamp, for the big wagon wheel of an October moon was as bright as day and flooded the fields and woods with light. And the wind had whipped enough of the rich wine-colored leaves from the tree so that I could about see over every limb. I walked around the tree looking up and spied the old cat, stretched out, his belly against a big flat limb. He didn't look worried to me. He looked like a cat that was full of confidence. He was a pretty thing a-layin' up there on the limb with his head a-stickin' over and his eyes shining like wind-whipped embers on a pitch-black night.

"Buck, you won't fight 'im," I said to myself. "I'll take care of him, myself." So I went up the tree with my lasso rope. The old cat didn't mind my climbing up there. He laid perfectly still. He was a-takin' himself a good rest. Buck had crowded him pretty hard in the chase. He didn't let him get to the Artner rock cliffs. That was where the wildcats denned. I climbed up at about the right distance and hung my lamp on a twig. I looked for the right opening to throw my rope so I wouldn't hit a limb and scare the cat and make him jump from the tree. I didn't want Buck to fight this cat; I wanted to take 'im alive. I found the right opening. I steadied myself and I threw my lasso.

Guess I was lucky. It went around his neck and I jerked the slack as the cat jumped. But I had him. The more he jumped the tighter the rope drew around his neck. And when his long red tongue popped outen his mouth, I drew him up to me, some weight at the end of the rope. I took him from the tree and released the lasso enough to give him enough breath to keep him alive. I tied his feet with the cords, good and tight. I kept the lasso tight enough not to give him too much wind. I put the wildcat under my arm and carried him to Blakesburg.

Old Buck wasn't satisfied because he didn't get to fight the cat, and he trailed along at my heels a little disappointed. But I knew this was a good catch for one night. It was more than a coffee sack full of dead possums, coons, polecats, minks, weasels, and foxes. If you hunt in these woods, fifty dollars for one night is not to be sneezed at. And it made me the most respected hunter in Blake County, for I was the only man that had ever gone up a tree and took a wildcat with my hands and carried him home in my arms. People knew that I did it, for I'd done it many times before. Older hunters than I was had seen me do it. I took the wildcat home, put him in a cage, and when people passed along the street, they'd come to look at him. And it pleased me when they walked over to see what kind of a looking man I was, just a little, slender, beanpole-sized man with a scraggly beard, that could go up a tree and catch a wildcat.

"Eddie, I'm a-tellin' you not to fight old Buck against that cat," Hade said. "If you'd see that thing cut a dog all to pieces once, you'd never go up in the tree and take him down any more. You'd lose your nerve. The way my poor old Scout run to the side of the cage, looked at me, and cried like a baby," Hade's voice changed until I thought he was crying, "I'll never be able to forget."

I couldn't stand to see that, I thought. I love dogs too well. But I didn't say another word to Hade. Thoughts were running through my mind. I walked into the express office and left Hade standing.

"Remember, Eddie, that my dog was the nineteenth dog that cat had kilt," Hade warned me. "Remember, Radnor'll take your money and——"

I didn't hear the rest of his words. I knew what I was going to do. I knew Buck or I, one, would fight the cat. I didn't want it a-killin' any more dogs. And I knew that I'd like to fight Jason Radnor to even up an old score. I didn't care if he did weigh two hundred and ninety. I hardly knew what I was doin' when I expressed my batch of hides. I went to the First and Peoples Bank and drew out every dollar I'd ever saved. When I got home, I went over to the corner of the house where I had old Buck tied.

"Buck, one of us has to kill a wildcat tonight," I said. "Do you think you can do it?"

Old Buck looked up at me with his big, soft, brown eyes. Then I unsnapped his chain and started across the yard. I was on my way.

"You're not a-goin' a-huntin' this early," Mollie said when she saw me leading Buck across the yard.

"Yep, I am." I said. "There's a wildcat that's a-killin' a lot of dogs and we want to get 'im."

"Do be careful, Eddie," Mollie warned me. "If it's that dangerous and old Buck trees it, don't you go up and take it from the tree."

"I'll promise you I won't take it from a tree," I said.

I wonder if old Jason will remember me, I thought, as I walked toward Auckland, a distance of twelve miles.

When I reached the shack down the hill from the slaughterhouse there was a man ahead of me with a big English bull.

"There's the dog that'll kill that damned wildcat," a beardy-faced man said, pointing to the big broad bulldog.

The beardy-faced man looked at old Buck, then he looked at me. Buck wasn't a big dog. And he looked pinched in two, for I hadn't fed him anything. I didn't want to feed 'im anything before a fight. Buck smelled blood and trouble. He held his tail down as if he were about to spring at something. Then I heard a pistol go off behind the house and I knew another dog was finished. Buck was on his mettle, for he didn't know exactly what was taking place. I pulled my hat down low and got my six-hundred-odd dollars ready.

Soon as the big red-faced man ahead of me had paid the five dollars to fight his bulldog, I stepped up to the entrance.

"Say, feller," said the tall, hatched-faced man at the door, "you don't aim to fight that old dog against this wildcat, do you? He's not as big as the wildcat!"

"I want to fight the dog or fight the wildcat myself," I said, and then I gave a wild laugh.

The man looked at me with his black, beady eyes like he thought I was crazy. But he let me inside the shack.

It was a big room filled with men and a few dogs. Over at the far end of the room was a big wire cage. And inside the cage lay the same old wildcat that I had taken from the oak tree on Seaton Ridge. He was a-layin' there as peaceful-like, just like any cat, with his head across his paws, as if he wanted to sleep and the men and dogs wouldn't let him. He looked just as mean as he did the night I carried him back to Blakesburg. His big tushes hung out over his lips. And his whiskers looked like old Davey Burton's handle-bar mustache. Beardy-faced men, with meanlooking eyes, stood back and looked at the cat. I led Buck up to the cage where he could get a whiff of the cat. I looked down to see what Buck thought. All he did was jerk his tail. He never even growled.

When the big, clean-shaven, well-dressed man led his bulldog up to the cage, the bull tried to break through to the cat. He trembled all over, growled, and scratched the floor. When he barked, the slobbers flew from his big mouth.

"I'm a-puttin' up a hundred dollars on that dog," a man said. "What odds you givin'?"

And then the bets started. I looked over against the wall and there sat big Jason Radnor behind a table, counting out money to cover the bet. Since the cat belonged to Jason, no one but him was allowed to bet on the cat. Jason covered all the money that was bet on the dog, giving three-to-two odds. It was a funny way to bet, and we'd never bet that way at rooster fighting. And I guess that's why everybody wanted to see the cat killed. Jason was raking in the money. But I wanted to see the cat killed because it was killin' the dogs.

"Jason's got a gold mine with that cat," said a tall lantern-jawed man who was standing beside me.

And while the greenbacks were shelled out on top of the table, for the bulldog was a good bet, Jason pulled money from a drawer and covered each bet. I watched Jason to see if he was looking at me and if he recognized me. But he was too busy betting and making money to recognize anybody. He was sitting there with all that money around him, and I knew this kind of betting was better than playing poker on Sundays or spitting at cracks. Jason was in the money.

"Say, mister, what have you been a-feedin' that bulldog?" asked a short, dark-complexioned man.

"Beef blood and beef bones," the owner said. "I've been a-feedin' 'im that and getting 'im ready for this fight ever since Radnor first brought the cat here!"

"I'll bet a hundred then," the man said.

Jason covered his hundred while the bulldog charged at the chain.

"All bets in?" Jason asked.

There wasn't any answer.

"Let 'im in the gate, Little Man," Jason said.

A little man with a scattered, heavy beard on his weather-beaten face unlocked the cage door. And the big man patted his dog on the back.

He's a good-lookin' bull to be slaughtered by that cat, I thought.

"Take 'im, Buck, and good luck!" the man spoke with a trembling voice as he unsnapped the collar and the bulldog charged full force toward the cat. As the bulldog charged at its throat, the cat leaped high in the air, and when it came down on the dog's back, it raked a paw around his slats, his big claws, longer than a tack hammer, sinking deeper and deeper as the bulldog groaned.

"There goes my money," a man shouted.

"There goes all our money," the tall man said. "Damn, I wish we'd get a dog that could kill that hellcat. I've lost over a thousand dollars in this dang hole."

I didn't listen to all the men said. I looked down at my Buck. He was moving his tail like a cat does when it sees a mouse and gets ready for the crouch. When the poor bulldog got the cat's claws from his ribs, he came over to the wire and cried like a baby. I never heard more pitiful crying. It hurt me through and through to hear it.

"He's through," a man said. "When they do that, they've had enough. Take him from the cage."

He didn't look like he was clawed up too badly until he came from the cage.

"Mister, you'll have to have Sherman to polish 'im off," Little Man said. "He's through. If you don't have 'im finished, he'll die by degrees."

When the well-dressed man led his bulldog out behind the house to have Sherman polish him off, another tall lanky man from Culp Creek came up with a big mountain cur. He was a long dog with a mean black eye.

You might not get to fight the cat, Buck, I thought. If I were betting, I'd bet on this dog.

"What have you been a-feedin' this dog, mister?" a little stooped-shouldered man asked.

"Corndodger," the cur's owner said. "Just what you feed a good dog."

"I was raised on it, mister," another man said. "I'm bettin' fifty on your dog!"

"Looks like a good bet to me," a tall lanky man with fuzzy chin whiskers said. "I like his build. Listen to his growlin' at that cat! Sounds like low thunder!"

But the bets didn't go as high as they did on the English bull. I looked over at Jason's table and I didn't see the stacks of greenbacks like I'd seen there a few minutes before. And just as the last money was in and Jason was covering it, we heard a pistol fire twice. The English bull had been polished off. And the big mountain cur, with his bristles raised on his back like jutted rocks along the top of a winter-bleak mountain, charged against the chain to get to the cat.

"Ready to go, Little Man," Jason said. "Turn 'im in."

The beard-scant, weathered-looking little man who tended to the cage unlocked the door, and the tall man let the big cur inside and unsnapped the collar. When the cat saw this big black mountain cur, he never rose to his feet but laid flat on his back as the dog charged, and just as the dog started over for the cat's throat, he ripped into him from beneath with both hind feet. The cur whined, fell over, got up again, and whined as pitifully as a small baby crying. He walked slowly to a corner of the cage—I couldn't bear to look at him. I wanted to get into that cage so bad I could hardly stand it.

"It's a shame," one of the men said, "to fight good dogs against that murdering wildcat. You can feed 'em beef, beef's blood, corndodger, and anything you want to feed 'em, but that doesn't make any difference when it comes to a fight. Not one dog has stayed with that cat three minutes!"

"Lost again," another man said, not paying any attention to the poor cur that had lost his life. "Lost another fifty bucks."

Sighs went up from among the mean-eyed men when Little Man pulled the cur through the door. He was awful to look at, and to think of him now makes me mad. Old Buck looked at the poor cut-to-pieces cur disgustedly.

"Get 'im to Sherman quick," Little Man said. "Let 'im polish 'im off soon as he can, to put 'im outen his misery."

We saw two more fights. We saw the cat lay on his back and cut a pretty shepherd to pieces. There wasn't much betting on this fight, although the shepherd came the nearest getting to the cat's throat of any of the dogs. And there was a big brindle bulldog that the cat seemed to hate more than any dog that had been turned in. That bull never even got close to the wildcat. He had him cut to pieces before he got halfway across the cage. What was left of him was dragged outside by his master, a well-dressed city man from Auckland.

"I'm glad it's over," said a big fat man with a handle-bar mustache. "I'd rather see cockfighting, a boxing bout, or a wrestling match any old time as to see these good-looking dogs go in there and get ripped up."

"Yep, I'd rather go with my wife to the movies as to slip out here to this unlawful place and see this," said the tall man who had bet heavily on every fight against the cat.

"It's a wonder this place ain't raided by the law!"

"But it's not over yet," I said loud enough so the men could hear me.

They were mixing around and intermingling in the crowded room, getting ready to leave. And I couldn't blame them for that. I'd smelled enough and I'd seen enough for one evening. The smell in the shack was awful. The crowd was awful, too.

I couldn't understand how anybody could enjoy seein' dogs cut to pieces by a wildcat.

"But that dog can't do anything," one man said. "That cat'd kill 'im before Little Man got 'im inside."

"Little Man ain't a-puttin' this dog in," I said. "I'm goin' in the cage with 'im myself."

"What's that I hear?" Jason said from over in the corner, as he stacked his money away.

"I'm going to take old Buck in myself," I said.

"Are you crazy, feller?" Jason said. "Don't you know if a man gets ripped up here, we can't have Sherman to polish 'im off, and this place will be raided shore enough."

"I wouldn't be afraid to fight that cat," I said. "Give me a piece of rope fourteen feet long and I'll fight 'im."

"Don't be foolish," Jason said. "You don't seem to know much about the power of a wildcat!"

Then I heard a lot of whispers in the crowd. I heard men saying that I was off in the head.

"How much are you willing to bet that my wildcat won't kill your dog?" Jason said. "You'll be the only one to bet on your dog. No one else will!"

"I think I got about six hundred and fifty-three dollars," I said. "It's my life savings and I don't want to bet it all."

"Well, I've got ten times that," Jason said. "I'll put my pile against yours!"

Then the men who'd been moving toward the door stopped. They were surprised at the money I had. And they were surprised when Jason said he'd put up all he had against what I had. They knew he had a pile, for he had taken their money on twenty-four fights. My dog was Number Twenty-five for the cat to fight. And I knew all the men except Sherman, Little Man, Jason, and the fellow who took our money at the door would be for me. They'd want to see my dog win.

"Mister Radnor, I hate to bet all my money," I said. "If I lose, I won't have a dollar in the world left and my dog will be gone."

"Well, that's what you come here for, to fight that old mongrel, wasn't it?" Jason said gruffly as he put the last roll of bills back in the table drawer. "And I'd as soon have your money as anybody else's."

"Yes, but I didn't know you had sich a big wildcat," I said. "And I can't stand to see it a-killin' all these fine-looking dogs."

"Come on or get out," Jason said. "After all, we bet here. This isn't a playhouse. It's a fightin' house."

"Will you let me take my dog inside? If you will, I'll put my pile up against yours!"

"I'm afraid of it," Jason said.

"Let 'im learn," one of the men shouted. "We've seen about everything now. Let's see something new!"

"I'm willin' to run the risk," Jason said thoughtfully, as he arose from the table and looked me over.

Then I went over to the table and counted out my money. Jason brought his from the drawer and I made him let me look inside to see that the drawer was clean.

"You watch the money, men," I said to the fellows gathered around me. "I want this to be square and honest."

"We'll see to that," said the fellow that had lost the big English bull.

"Sure we will," said the one that had lost the cur.

"Then open the door, Little Man," I said.

Old Buck didn't growl and he didn't charge against the chain. He just looked at the cat and jerked his tail.

"He's a funny dog," said one of the men behind me.

But I didn't look back to see who had said it. I had my eye on the cat. Buck had his eye on the cat. Then I reached down and rubbed his back. I patted his head as I reached midway of the cage. The cat laid perfectly still. He planned to work on Buck like he did the big mountain cur. Then I unsnapped Buck's chain. Buck crouched halfway. But he didn't take his eye off the cat. And he never growled, but he crept slowly toward the cat as I stepped to one side. Men rushed up and stood on their toes around the cage, like something was going to happen.

Buck went close. But he wouldn't go farther.

"Watch 'im, Buck," I said. "Let 'im make the first move."

Buck held like an Irish setter—he didn't go a step. The cat looked at him with his shiny green eyes, and Buck looked back at the cat. Then all at once the cat began to crouch. Buck held his position. Then the cat made a flying charge and Buck flattened on the cage floor. As the cat went over, Buck whirled and sprang from behind like April lightning. He caught the cat across the skull and the sound went plunk. It was a light crash but the cat sprawled senseless on the floor, its legs quivering and drawing up to its body then out again, each time a little weaker.

"What did that dog do?" a man asked me.

"What about that?" another man said.

"Leave that money or there'll be another death," I heard a voice growl.

"That dog knows how to tree wildcats," I said. "And he knows how to kill them. It's been suicide on the dogs to put them in here, dogs that never fought a wildcat. Buck knows that a wildcat's skull is as easy to crush as a rabbit's. It's a little bit easier—a wildcat's skull is thinner."

"Good boy, Buck," I patted his head.

I snapped the chain into his collar and we left the cage. The wildcat had breathed his last.

"There's your cat, Jason Radnor," I said. "He'll never kill another dog. And the money you made by clawin' dogs to pieces won't do you any good."

"Who are you, anyway?" Jason said, his voice trembling. He was shaking all over.

"Jason, I'm the man that caught that wildcat," I said. "My dog treed it and I went up in the tree and brought it down with my hands. I'm Eddie Battlestrife. You remember my dad, don't you—remember, you tried to kill him? Shot 'im not four feet away between the eyes but you didn't kill him. The bullet parted his hair. He was taking a few quarters from you in a poker game that Sunday afternoon. Now don't shake, Jason, I'm not a-goin' to hurt you. I just want all that money. It's good money and I like money and I like to see old Buck kill a wildcat that's kilt twenty-four dogs."

"Easy, Radnor," said the tall man that owned the cur. "Don't move. Keep your hands up! He took your money and he took it fair."

"Fairer than the way you got it from us," the bulldog's owner said.

"Nice bank account now," I said as I picked up the rolls of greenbacks and put them back in my hunting coat.

"It's a fraud," Jason wept. "It's a stick-up!"

"Easy, Mr. Radnor," the tall man said, as I walked from the shack with old Buck. "Keep your hands up!"

"You won't have to polish this dog off, Sherman," I said as I went through the door. "You can bury your cat."

COMMENT AND QUESTION

1. "Fight Number Twenty-Five" is a folk tale with parallels reaching back to stories of dragons or other monsters holding a countryside in terror. It is also a regional story of Kentucky mountain men.

2. The "champion" in this story performs extraordinary feats. What realistic details make them seem believable?

3. Do the men in this story have any depth of characterization? Do they need it? How would you classify men like Jason, Little Man, and Eddie?

4. What kind of dog is Buck? How does he differ from the English Bull and the mountain cur?

5. Does a primitive and satisfying justice finally prevail in the shack?

6. Stuart seems to "gild the lily" in handling the plot. Does the underlying motive of revenge detract from the interest in the main plot? Do the sums of money mentioned seem incredible, considering the locality? Would not the simplicity of the main plot have made a better story?

7. Notice that the point of view differs from that in Clark's "Hook." Could "Fight Number Twenty-Five" be effectively told from the point of view used in "Hook"? If not, why not?

FIRST LOVE

BY EUDORA WELTY

EUDORA WELTY (1909–   ) was born in
Jackson, Mississippi. She was educated in the
North at the University of Wisconsin and
Columbia University, but has continued to
reside in the South and to write about the
South. She won a Guggenheim Fellowship in
1942. She has appeared consistently in the
O. Henry Memorial Award volume and in *The
Best American Short Stories* annual. She has
published two volumes of short stories, *A
Curtain of Green* (1941) and *The Wide Net*
(1943), and three short novels, *The Robber
Bridegroom* (1942), *Delta Wedding* (1946),
and *Golden Apples* (1949).

WHATEVER happened, it happened in extraordinary times, in a season
of dreams, and in Natchez it was the bitterest winter of them all. The
north wind struck one January night in 1807 with an insistent penetration,
as if it followed the settlers down by their own course, screaming down
the river bends to drive them further still. Afterwards there was the
strange drugged fall of snow. When the sun rose the air broke into a
thousand prisms as close as the flash-and-turn of gulls' wings. For a long
time afterwards it was so clear that in the evening the little companion-
star to Sirius could be seen plainly in the heavens by travelers who took
their way by night, and Venus shone in the daytime in all its course
through the new transparency of the sky.

The Mississippi shuddered and lifted from its bed, reaching like a
somnambulist driven to go in new places; the ice stretched far out over

the waves. Flatboats and rafts continued to float downstream, but with unsignalling passengers submissive and huddled, mere bundles of sticks; bets were laid on shore as to whether they were alive or dead, but it was impossible to prove it either way.

The coated moss hung in blue and shining garlands over the trees along the changed streets in the morning. The town of little galleries was all laden roofs and silence. In the fastness of Natchez it began to seem then that the whole world, like itself, must be in a transfiguration. The only clamor came from the animals that suffered in their stalls, or from the wildcats that howled in closer rings each night from the frozen cane. The Indians could be heard from greater distances and in greater numbers than had been guessed, sending up placating but proud messages to the sun in continual ceremonies of dancing. The red percussion of their fires could be seen night and day by those waiting in the dark trance of the frozen town. Men were caught by the cold, they dropped in its snare-like silence. Bands of travelers moved closer together, with intenser caution, through the glassy tunnels of the Trace, for all proportion went away, and they followed one another like insects going at dawn through the heavy grass. Natchez people turned silently to look when a solitary man that no one had ever seen before was found and carried in through the streets, frozen the way he had crouched in a hollow tree, gray and huddled like a squirrel, with a little bundle of goods clasped to him.

Joel Mayes, a deaf boy twelve years old, saw the man brought in and knew it was a dead man, but his eyes were for something else, something wonderful. He saw the breaths coming out of people's mouths, and his dark face, losing just now a little of its softness, showed its secret desire. It was marvelous to him when the infinite designs of speech became visible in formations on the air, and he watched with awe that changed to tenderness whenever people met and passed in the road with an exchange of words. He walked alone, slowly through the silence, with the sturdy and yet dreamlike walk of the orphan, and let his own breath out through his lips, pushed it into the air, and whatever word it was it took the shape of a tower. He was as pleased as if he had had a little conversation with someone. At the end of the street, where he turned into the Inn, he always bent his head and walked faster, as if all frivolity were done, for he was boot-boy there.

He had come to Natchez some time in the summer. That was through great worlds of leaves, and the whole journey from Virginia had been to him a kind of childhood wandering in oblivion. He had remained to himself: always to himself at first, and afterwards too—with the company of Old Man McCaleb who took him along when his parents vanished in the forest, were cut off from him, and in spite of his last backward look, dropped behind. Arms bent on destination dragged him forward

through the sharp bushes, and leaves came toward his face which he
finally put his hands out to stop. Now that he was a boot-boy, he had
thought little, frugally, almost stonily, of that long time . . . until lately
Old Man McCaleb had reappeared at the Inn, bound for no telling where,
his tangled beard like the beards of old men in dreams; and in the act
of cleaning his boots, which were uncommonly heavy and burdensome
with mud, Joel came upon a little part of the old adventure, for there
it was, dark and crusted . . . came back to it, and went over it
again. . . .

He rubbed, and remembered the day after his parents had left him,
the day when it was necessary to hide from the Indians. Old Man
McCaleb, his stern face lighting in the most unexpected way, had herded
them, the whole party alike, into the dense cane brake, deep down off
the Trace—the densest part, where it grew as thick and locked as some
kind of wild teeth. There they crouched, and each one of them, man,
woman, and child, had looked at all the others from a hiding place that
seemed the least safe of all, watching in an eager wild instinct for any
movement or betrayal. Crouched by his bush, Joel had cried; all his
understanding would desert him suddenly and because he could not
hear he could not see or touch or find a familiar thing in the world.
He wept, and Old Man McCaleb first felled the excited dog with the
blunt end of his axe, and then he turned a fierce face toward him and
lifted the blade in the air, in a kind of ecstasy of protecting the silence
they were keeping. Joel had made a sound. . . . He gasped and put his
mouth quicker than thought against the earth. He took the leaves in his
mouth. . . . In that long time of lying motionless with the men and
women in the cane brake he had learned what silence meant to other
people. Through the danger he had felt acutely, even with horror, the
nearness of his companions, a speechless embrace of which he had had no
warning, a powerful, crushing unity. The Indians had then gone by,
followed by an old woman—in solemn, single file, careless of the inflaming
arrows they carried in their quivers, dangling in their hands a few strings
of catfish. They passed in the length of the old woman's yawn. Then one
by one McCaleb's charges had to rise up and come out of the hiding
place. There was little talking together, but a kind of shame and shuffling.
As soon as the party reached Natchez, their little cluster dissolved completely. The old man had given each of them one long, rather forlorn
look for a farewell, and had gone away, no less preoccupied than he
had ever been. To the man who had saved his life Joel lifted the gentle,
almost indifferent face of the child who has asked for nothing. Now he
remembered the white gulls flying across the sky behind the old man's
head.

Joel had been deposited at the Inn, and there was nowhere else for
him to go, for it stood there and marked the foot of the long Trace,

with the river back of it. So he remained. It was a noncommittal arrangement: he never paid them anything for his keep, and they never paid
him anything for his work. Yet time passed, and he became a little part
of the place where it passed over him. A small private room became his
own; it was on the ground floor behind the saloon, a dark little room
paved with stones with its ceiling rafters curved not higher than a man's
head. There was a fireplace and one window, which opened on the
courtyard filled always with the tremor of horses. He curled up every
night on a highbacked bench, when the weather turned cold he was
given a collection of old coats to sleep under, and the room was almost
excessively his own, as it would have been a stray kitten's that came to
the same spot every night. He began to keep his candlestick carefully
polished, he set it in the center of the puncheon table, and at night when
it was lighted all the messages of love carved into it with a knife in
Spanish words, with a deep Spanish gouging, came out in black relief,
for anyone to read who came knowing the language.

Late at night, nearer morning, after the travelers had all certainly
pulled off their boots to fall into bed, he waked by habit and passed with
the candle shielded up the stairs and through the halls and rooms, and
gathered up the boots. When he had brought them all down to his table
he would sit and take his own time cleaning them, while the firelight
would come gently across the paving stones. It seemed then that his
whole life was safely alighted, in the sleep of everyone else, like a bird
on a bough, and he was alone in the way he liked to be. He did not
despise boots at all—he had learned boots; under his hand they stood
up and took a good shape. This was not a slave's work, or a child's either.
It had dignity: it was dangerous to walk about among sleeping men.
More than once he had been seized and the life half shaken out of him
by a man waking up in a sweat of suspicion or nightmare, but he dealt
nimbly as an animal with the violence and quick frenzy of dreamers. It
might seem to him that the whole world was sleeping in the lightest of
trances, which the least movement would surely wake; but he only
walked softly, stepping around and over, and got back to his room. Once
a rattlesnake had shoved its head from a boot as he stretched out his
hand; but that was not likely to happen again in a thousand years.

It was in his own room, on the night of the first snowfall, that a new
adventure began for him. Very late in the night, toward morning, Joel
sat bolt upright in bed and opened his eyes to see the whole room
shining brightly, like a brimming lake in the sun. Boots went completely
out of his head, and he was left motionless. The candle was lighted in
its stick, the fire was high in the grate, and from the window a wild
tossing illumination came, which he did not even identify at first as the
falling of snow. Joel was left in the shadow of the room, and there before

him, in the center of the strange multiplied light, were two men in black capes sitting at his table. They sat in profile to him, tall under the little arch of the rafters, facing each other across the good table he used for everything, and talking together. They were not of Natchez, and their names were not in the book. Each of them had a white glitter upon his boots—it was the snow; their capes were drawn together in front, and in the blackness of the folds, snowflakes were just beginning to melt.

Joel had never been able to hear the knocking at a door, and still he knew what that would be; and he surmised that these men had never knocked even lightly to enter his room. When he found that at some moment outside his knowledge or consent two men had seemingly fallen from the clouds onto the two stools at his table and had taken everything over for themselves, he did not keep the calm heart with which he had stood and regarded all men up to Old Man McCaleb, who snored upstairs.

He did not at once betray the violation that he felt. Instead, he simply sat, still bolt upright, and looked with the feasting the eyes do in secret— at their faces, the one eye of each that he could see, the cheeks, the half-hidden mouths—the faces each firelit, and strange with a common reminiscence or speculation. . . . Perhaps he was saved from giving a cry by knowing it could be heard. Then the gesture one of the men made in the air transfixed him where he waited.

One of the two men lifted his right arm—a tense, yet gentle and easy motion—and made the dark wet cloak fall back. To Joel it was like the first movement he had ever seen, as if the world had been up to that night inanimate. It was like the signal to open some heavy gate or paddock, and it did open to his complete astonishment upon a panorama in his own head, about which he knew first of all that he would never be able to speak—it was nothing but brightness, as full as the brightness on which he had opened his eyes. Inside his room was still another interior, this meeting upon which all the light was turned, and within that was one more mystery, all that was being said. The men's heads were inclined together against the blaze, their hair seemed light and floating. Their elbows rested on the boards, stirring the crumbs where Joel had eaten his biscuit. He had no idea of how long they had stayed when they got up and stretched their arms and walked out through the door, after blowing the candle out.

When Joel woke up again at daylight, his first thought was of Indians, his next of ghosts, and then the vision of what had happened came back into his head. He took a light beating for forgetting to clean the boots, but then he forgot the beating. He wondered for how long a time the men had been meeting in his room while he was asleep, and whether they had ever seen him, and what they might be going to do to him, whether they would take him each by the arm and drag him on further, through the leaves. He tried to remember everything of the night before, and he could, and then of the day before, and he rubbed belatedly at a boot in a long and deepening dream. His memory could work like the slinging of a noose to catch a wild pony. It reached back and hung trembling over the very moment of terror in which he had become separated from his parents, and then it turned and started in the opposite direction, and it would have discerned some shape, but he would not let it, of the future. In the meanwhile, all day long, everything in the passing moment and each little deed assumed the gravest importance. He divined every change in the house, in the angle of the doors, in the height of the fires, and whether the logs had been stirred by a boot or had only fallen in an empty room. He was seized and possessed by mystery. He waited for night. In his own room the candlestick now stood on the table covered with the wonder of having been touched by unknown hands in his absence and seen in his sleep.

It was while he was cleaning boots again that the identity of the men came to him all at once. Like part of his meditations, the names came into his mind. He ran out into the street with this knowledge rocking in his head, remembering then the tremor of a great arrival which had shaken Natchez, caught fast in the grip of the cold, and shaken it through the lethargy of the snow, and it was clear now why the floors swayed with running feet and unsteady hands shoved him aside at the bar. There was no one to inform him that the men were Aaron Burr and Harman Blennerhassett, but he knew. No one had pointed out to him any way that he might know which was which, but he knew that: it was Burr who had made the gesture.

They came to his room every night, and indeed Joel had not expected that the one visit would be the end. It never occurred to him that the first meeting did not mark a beginning. It took a little time always for the snow to melt from their capes—for it continued all this time to snow. Joel sat up with his eyes wide open in the shadows and looked out like the lone watcher of a conflagration. The room grew warm, burning with the heat from the little grate, but there was something of fire in all that happened. It was from Aaron Burr that the flame was springing, and it seemed to pass across the table with certain words and through the sudden nobleness of the gesture, and touch Blennerhassett. Yet the breath of their speech was no simple thing like the candle's gleam between them. Joel saw them still only in profile, but he could see that the secret was endlessly complex, for in two nights it was apparent that it could never be all told. All that they said never finished their conversation. They would always have to meet again. The ring Burr wore caught the firelight repeatedly and started it up again in the intricate whirlpool of a signet. Quicker and fuller still was his eye, darting its look about, but never at Joel. Their eyes had never really seen his room . . . the fine polish he had given the candlestick, the clean boards from which he had scraped the crumbs, the wooden bench where he was himself, from which he put outward—just a little, carelessly—his hand. . . . Everything in the room was conquest, all was a dream of delights and powers beyond its walls. . . . The light-filled hair fell over Burr's sharp forehead, his cheek grew taut, his smile was sudden, his lips drove the breath through. The other man's face, with its quiet mouth, for he was the listener, changed from ardor to gloom and back to ardor. . . . Joel sat still and looked from one man to the other.

At first he believed that he had not been discovered. Then he knew that they had learned somehow of his presence, and that it had not stopped them. Somehow that appalled him. . . . They were aware that if it were only before him, they could talk forever in his room. Then he put it that they accepted him. One night, in his first realization of this, his defect seemed to him a kind of hospitality. A joy came over him, he was moved to gaiety, he felt wit stirring in his mind, and he came out of his hiding place and took a few steps toward them. Finally, it was too much: he broke in upon the circle of their talk, and set food and drink from the kitchen on the table between them. His hands were shaking, and they looked at him as if from great distances, but they were not surprised, and he could smell the familiar black wetness of travelers' clothes steaming up from them in the firelight. Afterwards he sat on the floor perfectly still, with Burr's cloak hanging just beside his own shoulder. At such moments he felt a dizziness as if the cape swung him about in a great arc of wonder, but Aaron Burr turned his full face and looked down at him only with gravity, the high margin of his brows lifted above tireless eyes.

There was a kind of dominion promised in his gentlest glance. When he first would come and throw himself down to talk and the fire would flame up and the reflections of the snowy world grew bright, even the clumsy table seemed to change its substance and to become a part of a ceremony. He might have talked in another language, in which there was nothing but evocation. When he was seen so plainly, all his movements and his looks seemed part of a devotion that was curiously patient and had the illusion of wisdom all about it. Lights shone in his eyes like travelers' fires seen far out on the river. Always he talked, his talking was his appearance, as if there were no eyes, nose, or mouth to remember; in his face there was every subtlety and eloquence, and no features, no kindness, for there was no awareness whatever of the present. Looking up from the floor at his speaking face, Joel knew all at once some secret of temptation and an anguish that would reach out after it like a closing hand. He would allow Burr to take him with him wherever it was that he meant to go.

Sometimes in the nights Joel would feel himself surely under their eyes, and think they must have come; but that would be a dream, and when he sat up on his bench he often saw nothing more than the dormant firelight stretched on the empty floor, and he would have a strange feeling of having been deserted and lost, not quite like anything he had ever felt in his life. It was likely to be early dawn before they came.

When they were there, he sat restored, though they paid no more attention to him than they paid the presence of the firelight. He brought all the food he could manage to give them; he saved a little out of his own suppers, and one night he stole a turkey pie. He might have been their safety, for the way he sat up so still and looked at them at moments like a father at his playing children. He never for an instant wished for them to leave, though he would so long for sleep that he would stare at them finally in bewilderment and without a single flicker of the eyelid. Often they would talk all night. Blennerhassett's wide vague face would grow out of devotion into exhaustion. But Burr's hand would always reach across and take him by the shoulder as if to rouse him from a dull sleep, and the radiance of his own face would heighten always with the passing of time. Joel sat quietly, waiting for the full revelation of the meetings. All his love went out to the talkers. He would not have known how to hold it back.

In the idle mornings, in some morning need to go looking at the world, he wandered down to the Esplanade and stood under the trees which bent heavily over his head. He frowned out across the ice-covered race-track and out upon the river. There was one hour when the river was the color of smoke, as if it were more a thing of the woods than an element and a power in itself. It seemed to belong to the woods, to be gentle and watched over, a tethered and grazing pet of the forest, and then when the light spread higher and color stained the world, the river would leap suddenly out of the shining ice around, into its full-grown torrent of life, and its strength and its churning passage held Joel watching over it like the spell unfolding by night in his room. If he could not speak to the river, and he could not, still he would try to read in the river's blue and violet skeins a working of the momentous event. It was hard to understand. Was any scheme a man had, however secret and intact, always broken upon by the very current of its work-ing? One day, in anguish, he saw a raft torn apart in midstream and the men scattered from it. Then all that he felt move in his heart at the sight of the inscrutable river went out in hope for the two men and their genius that he sheltered.

It was when he returned to the Inn that he was given a notice to paste on the saloon mirror saying that the trial of Aaron Burr for treason would be held at the end of the month at Washington, capitol of Mississippi Territory, on the campus of Jefferson College, where the crowds might be amply accommodated. In the meanwhile, the arrival of the full, armed flotilla was being awaited, and the price of whisky would not be advanced in this tavern, but there would be a slight increase in the tariff on a bed upstairs, depending on how many slept in it.

The month wore on, and now it was full moonlight. Late at night the whole sky was lunar, like the surface of the moon brought as close as a cheek. The luminous ranges of all the clouds stretched one beyond the other in heavenly order. They seemed to be the streets where Joel was walking through the town. People now lighted their houses in entertainments as if they copied after the sky, with Burr in the center of them always, dancing with the women, talking with the men. They followed and formed cotillion figures about the one who threatened or lured them, and their minuets skimmed across the nights like a pebble expertly skipped across water. Joel would watch them take sides, and watch the arguments, all the frilled motions and the toasts, and he thought they were to decide whether Burr was good or evil. But all the time, Joel believed, when he saw Burr go dancing by, that did not touch him at all. Joel knew his eyes saw nothing there and went always beyond the room, although usually the most beautiful woman there was somehow in his arms when the set was over. Sometimes they drove him in their carriages down to the Esplanade and pointed out the moon to him, to end the evening. There they sat showing everything to Aaron Burr, nodding with a magnificence that approached fatigue toward the reaches of the ice that stretched over the river like an impossible bridge, some extension to the West of the Natchez Trace; and a radiance as soft and near as rain fell on their hands and faces, and on the plumes of the breaths from the horses' nostrils, and they were as gracious and as grand as Burr.

Each day that drew the trial closer, men talked more hotly on the corners and the saloon at the Inn shook with debate; every night Burr was invited to a finer and later ball; and Joel waited. He knew that Burr was being allotted, by an almost specific consent, this free and unmolested time till dawn, to meet in conspiracy, for the sake of continuing and perfecting the secret. This knowledge Joel gathered to himself by being, himself, everywhere; it decreed his own suffering and made it secret and filled with private omens.

One day he was driven to know everything. It was the morning he was given a little fur cap, and he set it on his head and started out. He walked through the dark trodden snow all the way up the Trace to the Bayou Pierre. The great trees began to break that day. The pounding of their explosions filled the subdued air; to Joel it was as if a great foot had stamped on the ground. And at first he thought he saw the fulfillment of all the rumor and promise—the flotilla coming around the bend, and he did not know whether he felt terror or pride. But then he saw that what covered the river over was a chain of great perfect trees floating down, lying on their sides in postures like slain giants and heroes of battle, black cedars and stone-white sycamores, magnolias with their leavy leaves shining as if they were in bloom, a long procession. Then it was terror that he felt.

He went on. He was not the only one who had made the pilgrimage to see what the original flotilla was like, that had been taken from Burr. There were many others: there was Old Man McCaleb, at a little distance. . . . In care not to show any excitement of expectation, Joel made his way through successive little groups that seemed to meditate there above the encampment of militia on the snowy bluff, and looked down at the water.

There was no galley there. There were nine small flatboats tied to the shore. They seemed so small and delicate that he was shocked and distressed, and looked around at the faces of the others, who looked coolly back at him. There was no sign of weapon about the boats or anywhere, except in the hands of the men on guard. There were barrels of molasses and whisky, rolling and knocking each other like drowned men, and stowed to one side of one of the boats, in a dark place, a strange little collection of blankets, a silver bridle with bells, a book swollen with water, and a little flute with a narrow ridge of snow along it. Where Joel stood looking down upon them, the boats floated in clusters of three, as small as water-lilies on a still bayou. A canoe filled with crazily wrapped-up Indians passed at a little distance, and with severe open mouths the Indians all laughed.

But the soldiers were sullen with cold, and very grave or angry, and Old Man McCaleb was there with his beard flying and his finger pointing prophetically in the direction of upstream. Some of the soldiers and all the women nodded their heads, as though they were the easiest believers, and one woman drew her child tightly to her. Joel shivered. Two of the young men hanging over the edge of the bluff flung their arms in sudden exhilaration about each other's shoulders, and a look of wildness came over their faces.

Back in the streets of Natchez, Joel met part of the militia marching and stood with his heart racing, back out of the way of the line coming with bright guns tilted up in the sharp air. Behind them, two of the soldiers dragged along a young dandy whose eyes glared at everything. There where they held him he was trying over and over again to make Aaron Burr's gesture, and he never convinced anybody.

Joel went in all three times to the militia's encampment on the Bayou Pierre, the last time on the day before the trial was to begin. Then out beyond a willow point a rowboat with one soldier in it kept laconic watch upon the north.

Joel returned on the frozen path to the Inn, and stumbled into his room, and waited for Burr and Blennerhassett to come and talk together. His head ached. . . . All his walking about was no use. Where did people learn things? Where did they go to find them? How far?

Burr and Blennerhassett talked across the table, and it was growing late on the last night. Then there in the doorway with a fiddle in her hand stood Blennerhassett's wife, wearing breeches, come to fetch him home. The fiddle she had simply picked up in the Inn parlor as she came through, and Joel did not think she bothered now to speak at all. But she waited there before the fire, still a child and so clearly related to her husband that their sudden movements at the encounter were alike and made at the same time. They stood looking at each other there in the firelight like creatures balancing together on a raft, and then she lifted the bow and began to play.

Joel gazed at the girl, not much older than himself. She leaned her cheek against the fiddle. He had never examined a fiddle at all, and when she began to play it she frightened and dismayed him by her almost insect-like motions, the pensive antennae of her arms, her mask of a countenance. When she played she never blinked her eye. Her legs, fantastic in breeches, were separated slightly, and from her bent knees she swayed back and forth as if she were weaving the tunes with her body. The sharp odor of whisky moved with her. The slits of her eyes were milky. The songs she played seemed to him to have no beginnings and no endings, but to be about many hills and valleys, and chains of lakes. She, like the men, knew of a place. . . . All of them spoke of a country.

And quite clearly, and altogether to his surprise, Joel saw a sight that he had nearly forgotten. Instead of the fire on the hearth, there was a mimosa tree in flower. It was in the little back field at his home in Virginia and his mother was leading him by the hand. Fragile, delicate, cloudlike it rose on its pale trunk and spread its long level arms. His mother pointed to it. Among the trembling leaves the feathery puffs of sweet bloom filled the tree like thousands of paradisical birds all alighted at an instant. He had known then the story of the Princess Labam, for his mother had told it to him, how she was so radiant that she sat on the roof-top at night and lighted the city. It seemed to be the mimosa tree that lighted the garden, for its brightness and fragrance overlaid all the rest. Out of its graciousness this tree suffered their presence and shed its splendor upon him and his mother. His mother pointed again, and its scent swayed like the Asiatic princess moving up and down the pink steps of its branches. Then the vision was gone. Aaron Burr sat in front of the fire, Blennerhassett faced him, and Blennerhassett's wife played on the violin.

There was no compassion in what this woman was doing, he knew that—there was only a frightening thing, a stern allurement. Try as he might, he could not comprehend it, though it was so calculated. He had instead a sensation of pain, the ends of his fingers were stinging. At first he did not realize that he had heard the sounds of her song, the only thing he had ever heard. Then all at once as she held the lifted bow still for a moment he gasped for breath at the interruption, and he did not care to learn her purpose or to wonder any longer, but bent his head and listened for the note that she would fling down upon them. And it was so gentle then, it touched him with surprise; it made him think of animals sleeping on their cushioned paws.

For a moment his love went like sound into a myriad life and was divided among all the people in his room. While they listened, Burr's radiance was somehow quenched, or theirs was raised to equal it, and they were all alike. There was one thing that shone in all their faces, and that was how far they were from home, how far from everywhere that they knew. Joel put his hand to his own face, and hid his pity from them while they listened to the endless tunes.

But she ended them. Sleep all at once seemed to overcome her whole body. She put down the fiddle and took Blennerhassett by both hands. He seemed tired too, more tired than talking could ever make him. He went out when she led him. They went wrapped under one cloak, his arm about her.

Burr did not go away immediately. First he walked up and down before the fire. He turned each time with diminishing violence, and light and shadow seemed to stream more softly with his turning cloak. Then he stood still. The firelight threw its changes over his face. He had no one to talk to. His boots smelled of the fire's closeness. Of course he had forgotten Joel, he seemed quite alone. At last with a strange natural- ness, almost with a limp, he went to the table and stretched himself full length upon it.

He lay on his back. Joel was astonished. That was the way they laid out the men killed in duels in the Inn yard; and that was the table they laid them on.

Burr fell asleep instantly, so quickly that Joel felt he should never be left alone. He looked at the sleeping face of Burr, and the time and the place left him, and all that Burr had said that he had tried to guess left him too—he knew nothing in the world except the sleeping face. It was quiet. The eyes were almost closed, only dark slits lay beneath the lids. There was a small scar on the cheek. The lips were parted. Joel thought, I could speak if I would, or I could hear. Once I did each thing. . . . Still he listened . . . and it seemed that all that would speak, in this world, was listening. Burr was silent; he demanded noth- ing, nothing. . . . A boy or a man could be so alone in his heart that he could not even ask a question. In such silence as falls over a lonely man there is childlike supplication, and all arms might wish to open to him, but there is no speech. This was Burr's last night: Joel knew that. This was the moment before he would ride away. Why would the heart break so at absence? Joel knew that it was because nothing had been told. The heart is secret even when the moment it dreamed of has come, a moment when there might have been a revelation. . . . Joel stood motionless; he lifted his gaze from Burr's face and stared at nothing. . . . If love does a secret thing always, it is to reach backward, to a time that could not be known—for it makes a history of the sorrow and the dream it has contemplated in some instant of recognition. What Joel saw before him he had a terrible wish to speak out loud, but he would have had to find names for the places of the heart and the times for its shadowy and tragic events, and they seemed of great magnitude, heroic and terrible and splendid, like the legends of the mind. But for lack of a way to tell how much was known, the boundaries would lie between him and the others, all the others, until he died.

Presently Burr began to toss his head and to cry out. He talked, his face drew into a dreadful set of grimaces, which it followed over and over. He could never stop talking. Joel was afraid of these words, and afraid that eavesdroppers might listen to them. Whatever words they were, they were being taken by some force out of his dream. In horror, Joel put out his hand. He could never in his life have laid it across the mouth of Aaron Burr, but he thrust it into Burr's spread-out fingers. The fingers closed and did not yield; the clasp grew so fierce that it hurt his hand, but he saw that the words had stopped.

As if a silent love had shown him whatever new thing he would ever be able to learn, Joel had some wisdom in his fingers now which only this long month could have brought. He knew with what gentleness to hold the burning hand. With the gravity of his very soul he received the furious pressure of this man's dream. At last Burr drew his arm back beside his quiet head, and his hand hung like a child's in sleep, released in oblivion.

The next morning, Joel was given a notice to paste on the saloon mirror that conveyances might be rented at the Inn daily for the excursion to Washington for the trial of Mr. Burr, payment to be made in advance. Joel went out and stood on a corner, and joined with a group of young boys walking behind the militia.

It was warm—a "false spring" day. The little procession from Natchez, decorated and smiling in all they owned or whatever they borrowed or chartered or rented, moved grandly through the streets and on up the Trace. To Joel, somewhere in the line, the blue air that seemed to lie between the high banks held it all in a mist, softly colored, the fringe waving from a carriage top, a few flags waving, a sword shining when some gentleman made a flourish. High up on their horses a number of the men were wearing their Revolutionary War uniforms, as if to re-iterate that Aaron Burr fought once at their sides as a hero.

Under the spreading live-oaks at Washington, the trial opened like a festival. There was a theatre of benches, and a promenade; stalls were set out under the trees and glasses of whisky, and colored ribbons, were sold. Joel sat somewhere among the crowds. Breezes touched the yellow and violet of dresses and stirred them, horses pawed the ground, and the people pressed upon him and seemed more real than those in dreams, and yet their pantomime was like those choruses and companies whose movements are like the waves running together. A hammer was then pounded, there was sudden attention from all the spectators, and Joel felt the great solidifying of their silence.

He had dreaded the sight of Burr. He had thought there might be some mark or disfigurement that would come from his panic. But all his grace was back upon him, and he was smiling to greet the studious faces which regarded him. Before their bright façade others rose first, declaim-ing men in turn, and then Burr.

In a moment he was walking up and down with his shadow on the grass and the patches of snow. He was talking again, talking now in great courtesy to everybody. There was a flickering light of sun and shadow on his face.

Then Joel understood. Burr was explaining away, smoothing over all that he had held great enough to have dreaded once. He walked back and forth elegantly in the sun, turning his wrist ever so airily in its frill, making light of his dream that had terrified him. And it was the deed they had all come to see. All around Joel they gasped, smiled, pressed one another's arms, nodded their heads; there were tender smiles on the women's faces. They were at Aaron Burr's feet at last, learning their superiority. They loved him now, in their condescension. They leaned forward in delight at the parading spectacle he was making. And when it was over for the day, they shook each other's hands, and Old Man McCaleb could be seen spitting on the ground, in the anticipation of another day as good as this one.

Blennerhassett did not come that night.

Burr came very late. He walked in the door, looked down at Joel where he sat among his boots, and suddenly stooped and took the dirty cloth out of his hand. He put his face quickly into it and pressed and rubbed it against his skin. Joel saw that all his clothes were dirty and ragged. The last thing he did was to set a little cap of turkey feathers on his head. Then he went out.

Joel followed him along behind the dark houses and through a ravine.

Burr turned toward the Halfway Hill. Joel turned too, and he saw Burr walk slowly up and open the great heavy gate.

He saw him stop beside a tall camellia bush as solid as a tower and pick up one of the frozen buds which were shed all around it on the ground. For a moment he held it in the palm of his hand, and then he went on. Joel, following behind, did the same. He held the bud, and studied the burned edges of its folds by the pale half-light of the East. The bud came apart in his hand, its layers like small velvet shells, still iridescent, the shriveled flower inside. He held it tenderly and yet timidly, in a kind of shame, as though all disaster lay pitifully disclosed now to the eyes.

He knew the girl Burr had often danced with under the rings of tapers when she came out in a cloak across the shadowy hill. Burr stood, quiet and graceful as he had always been as her partner at the balls. Joel felt a pain like a sting while she first merged with the dark figure and then drew back. The moon, late-risen and waning, came out of the clouds. Aaron Burr made the gesture there in the distance, toward the West, where the clouds hung still and red, and when Joel looked at him in the light he saw as she must have seen the absurdity he was dressed in, the feathers on his head. With a curious feeling of revenge upon her, he watched her turn, draw smaller within her own cape, and go away.

Burr came walking down the hill, and passed close to the camellia bush where Joel was standing. He walked stiffly in his mock Indian dress with the boot polish on his face. The youngest child in Natchez would have known that this was a remarkable and wonderful figure that had humiliated itself by disguise.

Pausing in an open space, Burr lifted his hand once more and a slave led out from the shadows a majestic horse with silver trappings shining in the light of the moon. Burr mounted from the slave's hand in all the clarity of his true elegance, and sat for a moment motionless in the saddle. Then he cut his whip through the air, and rode away.

Joel followed him on foot toward the Liberty Road. As he walked through the streets of Natchez he felt a strange mourning to know that Burr would never come again by that way. If he had left in disguise, the thirst that was in his face was the same as it had ever been. He had eluded judgment, that was all he had done, and Joel was glad while he still trembled. Joel would never know now the true course, or the true outcome of any dream: this was all he felt. But he walked on, in the frozen path into the wilderness, on and on. He did not see how he could ever go back and still be the boot-boy at the Inn.

He did not know how far he had gone on the Liberty Road when the posse came riding up behind and passed him. He walked on. He saw that the bodies of the frozen birds had fallen out of the trees, and he fell down and wept for his father and mother, to whom he had not said goodbye.

COMMENT AND QUESTION

1. *The background.* "First Love" takes place at the climax of the conspiracy of Aaron Burr, who reached for an empire in the West, an empire including Mexico and vaguely, perhaps, western America. But the story is more than a study of a man, Burr; a city, Natchez; and a conspiracy. It is primarily the story of a dream, the dream of empire.

The story is laid in Natchez, Mississippi, itself an outpost of empire in 1807. Across the Mississippi from Natchez lay the great Southwest. Joel's encounter with the Indians occurs on the Natchez Trace, the trail running for five hundred miles through the wilderness between Nashville and Natchez. Much of the story takes place in the King's Inn, a tavern which stood (and still stands) at the end of the Natchez Trace.

2. *The dream-like atmosphere.* The opening sentence of the story begins to create the dream-like atmosphere which is to envelope the action: "Whatever happened, it happened in extraordinary times, in a season of dreams." Notice the details in the first two pages which develop this atmosphere: the "drugged fall of snow"; the Mississippi "reaching like a somnambulist"; the whole world in a "transfiguration"; the "dark trance" of the frozen town. Here and throughout the story the characters seem to move in a dream. Joel awakens from sleep to the sensations of a dream when he sees the two men for the first time against "a wild tossing illumination." What is the author's purpose in creating this dream-like atmosphere?

3. *The dream of empire.* The dream of empire is a living thing in this story. Burr and the dream merge. What describes one describes the other. What, then, are Burr and the dream like? Most of the time the author dramatizes the qualities of Burr and the dream. She does not *tell*; she *shows*.

A key detail is Burr's gesture, which occurs first on p. 472. How does it affect Joel? This gesture occurs again on p. 473. Finally, on p. 482 it encompasses the West, "where the clouds hung still and red." What is the author showing in these passages? One other person in the story tries to make the gesture. What happens to him? Why? At the trial, what has become of Burr's gesture?

Burr's gesture opens up a panorama of "brightness." This is another quality of the dream of empire. The student should heed all references to light, fire, flame in relation to Burr. Joel sees Burr first in a "strange multiplied light." What is the source of this light? But what effect is the author creating? Again the author writes of Burr: "Lights shone in his eyes like travelers' fires seen far out on the river." The references to light, fire, or flame are many. What effect do they achieve?

The details which develop Burr and his dream are almost inexhaustible. They build up the idea of a magnificent conquest in the making and what this conquest required of Burr and his followers. They demand reflection and discussion. What do the following references mean?

 a. Burr's face holds "no kindness" because there is "no awareness whatever of the present."

 b. Joel catches from Burr "some secret of temptation and an anguish. . . ."

 c. When Burr leaves, "the thirst that was in his face was the same as it had ever been."

4. *The plot.* In a story which moves on poetic and symbolic levels, the reader may come to feel that the plot itself is elusive and shadowy, all "poetry," too. But the action here is strong, vivid, and historically true. The student should fit all the incidents of the plot together—the severe cold, the shabby "invasion" flotilla, the balls, the withdrawal of Blennerhassett, the flight of Burr. These and all the other incidents make a coherent story of conspiracy and flight. The posse at the end, for example, suggests that Burr was caught.

5. *Symbols.* Although this story as a whole is symbolic in the widest sense, it also contains a number of discrete symbols which illumine the author's meaning. The episode of the camellia bud on p. 482 is a revelation of Burr and his dream as well as of Joel and his dream. What was the "disaster" for Joel? Notice the following specific episodes for their symbolism: Burr asleep on a table; Joel watching the Mississippi destroy a raft; Joel staring at trees floating down the river.

Another symbolic episode concerns Blennerhassett's wife. The music of her violin seems to quench "Burr's radiance" or to create an equal radiance in the three of them, Blennerhassett, his wife, and Burr. What is this radiance? What is the theme of the music? How does it affect Joel? Burr? Blennerhassett? Blennerhassett's home was on the Ohio river. Where does the violin describe that home? The violin evokes for Joel a symbol in opposition to the symbols of the dream of empire—the mimosa tree.

6. *Joel and the meaning of the title.* Burr, Joel, and the dream of empire run the same course. The title, therefore, refers to all three. But it refers most clearly to Joel.

Human experience seems to show that first love—in its very essence— is innocent and comes to no fulfillment. Joel is a child, and innocent. But he is also deaf. He can hear no treason, if, indeed, there was great treason in this complicated and still unexplained episode of American history. (The opening words of the story are important here: "Whatever happened. . . .") In his response to Burr, Joel experiences a pure emotion, which may be what first love is. If Burr and the dream of empire are synonymous, did the boy, then, fall in love with both simultaneously? And is the dream of empire also a pure emotion here?

Because of his deafness Joel acquires a knowledge different from the knowledge of any other human being associated with Burr. The scene where Burr talks in his sleep is significant. Joel could not put his hands across Burr's lips. Why not? True, no one in Burr's life had been able to do so. As the author comments, Burr's "talking was his appearance, as if there were no eyes, nose, or mouth to remember." But that is not the whole explanation here, for Joel quiets Burr by holding his hand.

If Joel's first love is innocent because of his deafness, it also comes to no fulfillment because of his deafness. On p. 480, the reasons for Joel's sorrow are made quite explicit. Why does Joel's heart break? He alone knows some things, yet he cannot speak of them. What are these things? What do they have to do with Burr and the dream of empire? The end of the story is revealing. Joel weeps not for his parents, but for whom? And why? As we watch the departure of Burr at the end, the ideas and feelings in this story become double-edged because we are experiencing them through Joel.

7. *Joel on the Natchez Trace.* Joel's experience with the Indians early in the story sets a tone of silence, secrecy, and danger. It also serves as exposition in presenting the background and qualities of Joel. It is, however, more than exposition. It becomes part of the action because it explains Joel's response to the two men who invade his room. He wonders if Burr and Blennerhassett will "drag him on further through the leaves." The reader, like Joel, must associate this response with the "arms bent on destination" of the travelers on the Natchez Trace. Most important for the action, however, is the fact that Joel had learned early "what silence meant to other people."